SAE
Ground Vehicle Lighting
Standards Manual

1997 Edition

SAE HS-34

Published by:
Society of Automotive Engineers, Inc.
400 Commonwealth Drive
Warrendale, PA 15096-0001
U.S.A.
Phone: (412) 776-4841; Fax: (412) 776-5760
http://www.sae.org

#37265788

2-98

Table of Contents

2.4 Switches and Flashers

2.5 Test Procedures and Materials

2.6 Warning Lamps and Devices

2.7 Agricultural Machinery

2.8 Construction and Industrial Machinery

2.9 Motorcycles

Introduction

The 1997 SAE Ground Vehicle Lighting Standards Manual provides a comprehensive compilation of SAE Technical Reports relating to the design, engineering, testing, inspection and installation of motor vehicle lighting and signalling equipment. The basic Standards and Recommended Practices in the Manual are those developed under the auspices of the SAE Lighting Committee. The Manual also includes related reports which were developed by other SAE Technical Committees, and Technical Committees of the Organization for International Standardization (ISO). The SAE Lighting Committee has actively cooperated with these committees. As an informational guide and background for the values, procedures, etc. in the SAE Technical Reports, the Manual also includes a bibliography of papers presented at SAE meetings and conferences on related subjects.

A Key Word Index is provided to assist users of the Manual in locating information in the reports. It is a simplified alphabetical listing of basic terms and phrases found in the titles of the reports.

SAE also produces Standards, Recommended Practices and Information Reports for the Aerospace industry. SAE Aerospace Committee A-20 - Aircraft Lighting has developed many technical documents dealing with various aspects of aerospace lighting. These are listed in the Bibliography of Related SAE Aerospace Lighting Documents.

Requests for information on this Manual or other SAE documents should be directed to:

Customer Sales and Satisfaction
SAE
400 Commonwealth Dr.
Warrendale, PA 15096-0001
Phone: (412) 776-4841
Fax: (412) 776-4970
Telex: 866-355
http://www.sae.org

SAE Lighting
Technical Reports

Report of the Lighting Committee approved March 1969 and completely revised October 1988. Rationale statement available. Completely revised by the SAE Signaling and Marking Devices Standards Committee and the SAE Lighting Coordinating Committee September 1995. Rationale statement available.

1. Scope—This SAE Recommended Practice provides definitions of common terms used in SAE Technical Reports pertaining to motor vehicle lighting. It covers not only basic lighting terms but also terms which identify major segments of technical reports.

2. References—There are no referenced publications specified herein.

3. Definitions

3.1 Light—Visible radiant energy.

3.2 Light Source—An emitter of visible radiant energy.

3.2.1 LIGHT SOURCE UNIT, BULB—A functionally indivisible assembly which contains a light source and which is normally used in a lamp. An example is an incandescent bulb or a light-emitting diode.

3.2.2 FILAMENT BULB—FILAMENT LAMP—Device in which light is produced by means of one or more filaments heated to incandescence by the passage of an electric current.

3.2.3 DISCHARGE BULB—DISCHARGE LAMP—Device in which light is produced by an electric discharge through a gas, a metal vapor, or a mixture of gases and vapors.

3.2.4 LIGHT-EMITTING DIODE—An indivisible, discrete light source unit containing a semiconductor junction in which visible light is non-thermally produced when a forward current flows as a result of an applied voltage.

3.2.5 SEASONED LIGHT SOURCE UNIT, BULB—A light source unit energized at design voltage for 1% of its average rated lab life or 10 h maximum, whichever is shorter.

3.2.6 ACCURATE RATED LIGHT SOURCE UNIT, BULB—A seasoned light source unit operated at design mean spherical luminous intensity and having its light source(s) positioned within strict tolerances as specified in the applicable standard.

3.3 Lamp—A divisible assembly which contains a light source unit(s) and generally an optical system such as a lens, a reflector, or both and which provides a lighting function.

3.3.1 MULTIPLE COMPARTMENT LAMP—A lamp which provides its lighting function using two or more separately lighted areas which are joined by one or more common parts, such as a housing or lens.

3.3.2 MULTIPLE LAMP ARRANGEMENT—An array of two or more separate lamps on each side of the vehicle which operate together for a particular lighting function.

3.3.3 OPTICALLY COMBINED—A lamp shall be deemed to be "optically combined" if both of the following conditions exist:

a. It has a single or two filament light source or two or more separate light sources that operate in different ways.

b. Its optically functional lens area is wholly or partially common on two or more lamp functions.

3.3.4 LIGHT-EMITTING SURFACE—"Light-Emitting Surface" means all or part of the exterior surface of the transparent or translucent lens that encloses the light source or signaling device and allows conformance with photometric and colorimetric requirements.

3.3.5 EFFECTIVE PROJECTED LUMINOUS AREA—"Effective Projected Luminous Area" is that area of the light-emitting surface projected on a plane at right angles to the axis of a lamp, excluding reflex reflectors (but including congruent reflexes), which is not obstructed by opaque objects such as mounting screws, mounting rings, bezel or trim, or similar ornamental feature areas. Areas of optical or other configurations, for example, molded optical rings or markings, shall be considered part of the total "effective projected luminous area". The axis of the lamp corresponds to the H-V axis used for photometric requirements.

3.3.6 CENTROID OF A LENS AREA—The geometric centroid of a plane area which is perpendicular to the axis of reference of the vehicle and upon which the projection of the light-emitting lens area falls. An example: The axis of reference for lamps mounted on the front and rear of a vehicle is the longitudinal axis of the vehicle.

3.4 Device—Any piece of equipment or mechanism designed to serve a specific purpose or perform a specific function.

3.5 Unit—An indivisible assembly which provides a mechanical, electrical, or lighting function, for example, sealed beam unit or flasher.

4. Technical Report Content

4.1 Guidelines—Advisory, informational, or instructional statements to assist designers, installers, laboratory personnel, or manufacturers in meeting the requirements in the evaluation and use of a device or component.

4.2 Requirements—Objectives to be attained in the evaluation and use of new and unused devices, manufactured using production tooling and assembled by production processes.

4.2.1 PERFORMANCE REQUIREMENTS—Characteristics of a device which are essential for its proper functioning, for example: color, luminous intensity, and ability to withstand vibration.

4.2.2 DESIGN REQUIREMENTS—Dimensional or physical characteristics to be attained.

Report of the Lighting Division, approved January 1937, last revised by the Lighting Committee December 1974, editorial change May 1981. Rationale statement available.

This code is intended only for the inspection and maintenance of lighting equipment on motor vehicles that are in use.

The original SAE code, adopted in 1937, was drafted for use in preparing Interstate Commerce Commission regulations for trucks and buses in interstate operation under the 1935 Motor-Carrier Act. Subsequently, the SAE code served as a basis for Section 2, Lighting Systems, of the American National Standard Code for Inspection Requirements for Motor Vehicles, ANSI D7-1939. The ANSI inspection requirements for lighting systems were adopted by the Society as the SAE Recommended Practice in January 1940.

1. Definitions

1.1 Sealed Beam Unit—An integral and indivisible optical assembly with the name "Sealed Beam" molded in the lens.

1.2 Upper Beam—A beam intended primarily for distant illumination and for use on the open highway when not meeting other vehicles.

1.3 Lower Beam—A beam intended to illuminate the road ahead of the vehicle without causing undue glare to other drivers.

1.4 7 in. (178 mm) Sealed Beam System—A system employing two 7 in. (178 mm) Sealed Beam units.

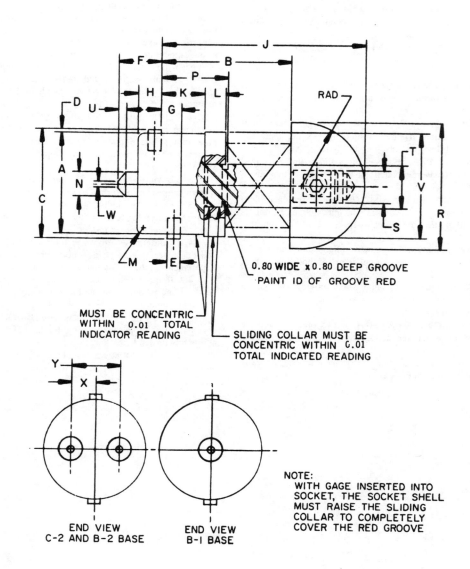

0.80 WIDE x 0.80 DEEP GROOVE
PAINT ID OF GROOVE RED

MUST BE CONCENTRIC
WITHIN 0.01 TOTAL
INDICATOR READING

SLIDING COLLAR MUST BE
CONCENTRIC WITHIN 0.01
TOTAL INDICATED READING

END VIEW
C-2 AND B-2 BASE

END VIEW
B-1 BASE

NOTE:
WITH GAGE INSERTED INTO
SOCKET, THE SOCKET SHELL
MUST RAISE THE SLIDING
COLLAR TO COMPLETELY
COVER THE RED GROOVE

FIG. 3—BULB SUPPORT GAGE

4

1.5 7 in. (178 mm) Type 2 Sealed Beam Unit—A 7 in. (178 mm) diameter unit (with a numeral 2 molded in the lens), which provides an upper and a lower beam. These units are mechanically aimable. NOTE: Original 7 in. (178 mm) Sealed Beam units which can be identified by the absence of "2" on the lens shall be aimed visually on the upper beam.

1.6 5¾ in. (146 mm) Sealed Beam System—A system employing four 5¾ in. (146 mm) Sealed Beam units: two Type 1 and two Type 2.

1.7 5¾ in. (146 mm) Type 1 Sealed Beam Unit—A 5¾ in. (146 mm) diameter unit having a single filament and used in a four-lamp system to provide the principal portion of the upper beam.

1.8 5¾ in. (146 mm) Type 2 Sealed Beam Unit—A 5¾ in. (146 mm) diameter unit having two filaments and used in a four-lamp system to provide the lower beam and a secondary portion of the upper beam.

1.9 4 x 6½ in. (100 x 165 mm) Sealed Beam System—A system employing four 4 x 6½ in. (100 x 165 mm) sealed beam units: two Type 1A and two Type 2A.

1.10 4 x 6½ in. (100 x 165 mm) Type 1A Sealed Beam Unit—A 4 x 6½ in. (100 x 165 mm) rectangular unit having a single filament and used in a four-lamp system to provide the principal portion of the upper beam.

1.11 4 x 6½ in. (100 x 165 mm) Type 2A Sealed Beam Unit—A 4 x 6½ in. (100 x 165 mm) rectangular unit having two filaments and used in a four-lamp system to provide the lower beam and a secondary portion of the upper beam.

1.12 Mechanically Aimable Sealed Beam Unit—A unit having three pads on the face of the lens forming a plane which is intended to be used to adjust and inspect the aim of the unit when installed on the vehicle.

1.13 Symmetrical Beam—A beam in which both sides are symmetrical with respect to the median vertical plane of the beam.

1.14 Asymmetrical Beam—A beam in which both sides are not symmetrical with respect to the median vertical plane of the beam. All lower beams are asymmetrical. NOTE: The inspector should see that the driver understands how to use multiple beam headlamps so as to obtain the best road lighting with minimum glare to other users of the highway.

2. Equipment—It is recommended that mechanically aimable headlamps be aimed and inspected for aim by mechanical aimers. Another aiming and inspection method is by visual means on a screen at a distance of 25 ft (7.6 m) ahead of the headlamps or on the screen of a headlamp testing machine.

2.1 The mechanical aimer used shall conform to the requirements of SAE J602. The device shall be in good repair, calibrated and used according to the manufacturer's instructions.

2.2 If a screen is used, it should be of adequate size with a matte-white surface well shaded from extraneous light and properly adjusted to the floor area on which the vehicle stands. Provision should be made for moving the screen or its vertical centerline so that it can be aligned with the vehicle axis. In addition to the vertical centerline, the screen should be provided with four laterally adjustable vertical tapes and two vertically adjustable horizontal tapes. The four movable vertical tapes should be located on the screen at the left and right limits called for in the specification with reference to centerlines ahead of each headlamp unit. The headlamp centerlines shall be spaced either side of the fixed centerline on the screen by the amount the headlamp units are to the left and right. The horizontal tapes should be located on the screen at the upper and lower limits called for in the specifications with reference to the height of lamp centers and the plane on which the vehicle rests, not the floor on which the screen rests. See Fig. 1.

2.3 The Headlamp Testing Machine used shall conform to the requirements of SAE J600. The device shall be in good repair, calibrated and used according to the manufacturer's instructions.

3. Preparation for Headlamp Aim or Inspection—Before checking beam aim, the inspector shall:

  3.1 Remove ice or mud from under fenders.
  3.2 See that no tire is noticeably deflated.
  3.3 Check car springs for sag or broken leaves.
  3.4 See that there is no load in the vehicle other than the driver.
  3.5 Check functioning of any "level-ride" control.
  3.6 Clean lenses and aiming pads.
  3.7 Check for bulb burnout, broken mechanical aiming pads, and proper beam switching.
  3.8 Stabilize suspension by rocking vehicle sideways.

4. Headlamp Aim Adjustment for Service Facilities

4.1 The following aim adjustment requirements should apply to dealers, service stations, and others who do headlamp adjusting.

4.2 It is recommended that mechanically aimable headlamps be aimed using mechanical aimers (paragraph 2.1). The aimers shall be calibrated for accuracy and shall be compensated for the level of the floor in the aiming area.

4.3 Mechanical Aiming

4.3.1 The correct mechanical aim for both Type 1 and Type 2 units is 0-0.

4.3.2 If a headlamp being serviced is not so aimed, the aim shall be corrected to 0-0.

4.4 Visual Aiming

4.4.1 The correct visual aim for Type 1 units is with the center of the high intensity zone at horizontal and straight ahead vertically. (See Fig. 2.)

4.4.2 The correct visual aim for Type 2 units is with the top edge of the high intensity zone of the lower beam horizontal and the left edge at vertical. (See Fig. 3.)

4.4.3 If the headlamp being serviced is not so aimed, it should be corrected to the above aim.

5. Headlamp Aim Inspection Limits for Vehicle Inspection Facilities

5.1 The following inspection limits should apply to stations that conduct mandatory inspection of vehicles.

5.2 It is recommended that mechanically aimable lamps be inspected using mechanical aimers (paragraph 2.1). The aimers shall be calibrated for accuracy and shall be compensated for the level of the floor in the inspection area.

5.3 Mechanical Aim Inspection

5.3.1 The mechanical inspection limits for both Type 1 and Type 2 units shall be 4 (100 mm) up to 4 (100 mm) down and 4 (100 mm) left to 4 (100 mm) right.

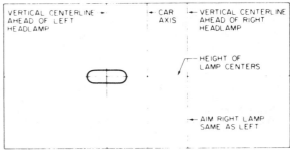

FIG. 2—HOW PROPERLY AIMED UPPER BEAM OF 5¾ IN (146 MM) TYPE 1 AND 7 IN (178 MM) SEALED BEAM (NOT MARKED "2" ON LENS) WILL APPEAR ON THE AIMING SCREEN 25 FT (7.6 M) IN FRONT OF VEHICLE. (SHADED AREA INDICATES HIGH INTENSITY ZONE)

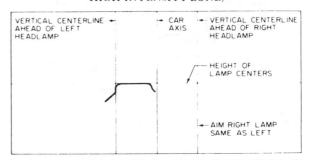

FIG. 3—HOW PROPERLY AIMED LOWER BEAM OF 5¾ IN (146 MM) AND 7 IN (178 MM) TYPE 2 SEALED BEAM WILL APPEAR ON THE AIMING SCREEN 25 FT (7.6 M) IN FRONT OF THE VEHICLE. (SHADED AREA INDICATES HIGH INTENSITY ZONE)

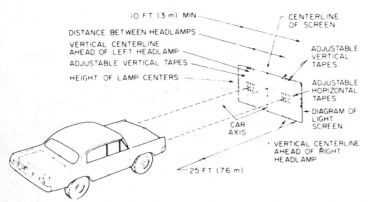

FIG. 1—ALIGNMENT OF HEADLAMP AIMING SCREEN

5.3.2 Failure to meet these limits shall be cause for rejection.

5.4 Visual Aiming

5.4.1 The visual inspection limits for Type 1 units shall be with the center of the high intensity zone from 4 (100 mm) up to 4 (100 mm) down and from 4 (100 mm) left to 4 (100 mm) right based in inches (millimeters) on a screen at 25 ft (7.6 m). (See Fig. 4.)

5.4.2 The visual inspection limits for Type 2 units shall be with the top edge of the high intensity zone from 4 (100 mm) up to 4 (100 mm) down and the left edge of the high intensity zone from 4 (100 mm) left to 4 (100 mm) right based in inches (millimeters) on a screen at 25 ft (7.6 m). (See Fig. 5.)

5.4.3 Failure to meet these limits shall be cause for rejection.

6. Fog Lamps (Symmetrical Beams) Aim Adjustment for Service Facilities

6.1 The following aim adjustment requirements should apply to dealers, service stations, and others who do headlamp adjusting.

6.2 The correct visual aim for fog lamps (symmetrical beams) is with the top edge of the high intensity zone 4 (100) below horizontal and the center of the high intensity zone straight ahead vertically based in inches (millimeters) on a screen at 25 ft (7.6m) (See Fig. 6.)

7. Fog Lamps (Symmetrical Beam) Aim Inspection Limits for Vehicle Inspection Facilities

7.1 The following inspection limits should apply to stations that conduct mandatory inspection of vehicles.

ed. 7.2 The visual inspection limits for fog lamps (symmetrical beam), which are installed with universal mounting applications so as to fit many different vehicle models, shall be with the top edge of the high intensity zone at horizontal or below and with the center of the high intensity zone from 4 (100) left to 4 (100) right based in inches (millimeters) on a screen at 25 ft (7.6m) (See Fig. 7.)

ed. 7.3 The visual inspection limits for fog lamps (symmetrical beam), which are designed to be integrated into one specific vehicle, shall be with the top edge of the high intensity zone at horizontal or below on a screen at 25 ft (7.6m). (See Fig. 8.)

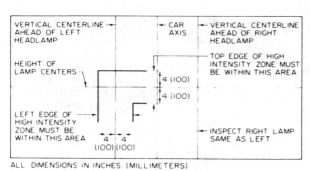

FIG. 4—AIM INSPECTION LIMITS FOR UPPER BEAM OF 5¾ IN (146 MM) TYPE 1 SEALED BEAM AND 7 IN (178 MM) SEALED BEAM UNITS NOT MARKED "2" AT THE TOP OF THE LENS. ALSO, TWO-BEAM LAMPS NOT MARKED SEALED BEAM ON THE LENS

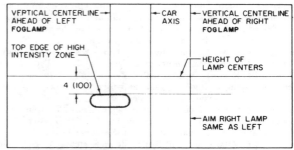

FIG. 5—AIM INSPECTION LIMITS FOR LOWER BEAM OF 5¾ IN (146 MM) TYPE 2 SEALED BEAM AND 7 IN (178 MM) TYPE 2 SEALED BEAM AND FOR AUXILIARY PASSING LAMP

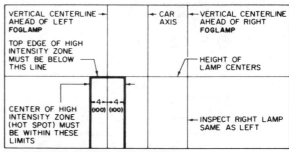

ed. FIG. 6—HOW PROPERLY AIMED FOG LAMP (SYMMETRICAL BEAM) WILL APPEAR ON THE AIMING SCREEN 25 FT (7.6 M) IN FRONT OF VEHICLE. (SHADED AREA INDICATES HIGH INTENSITY ZONE)

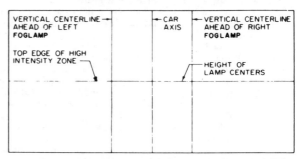

ed. FIG. 7—AIM INSPECTION LIMITS FOR FOG LAMPS (SYMMETRICAL BEAM) (UNIVERSAL APPLICATION)

ed. FIG. 8—AIM INSPECTION LIMITS FOR FOG LAMPS (SYMMETRICAL BEAM) (INTEGRATED TYPE)

8. Fog Lamps (Asymmetrical Beam) and Passing Lamps Aim Adjustment and Inspection Limits

8.1 Lamp aim adjustment and inspection is the same as for Type 2 Sealed Beam headlamp units. See paragraph 4.4.2 for adjustment and 5.4.2 for inspection.

9. General Lamp Inspection Other Than Headlamp Aim Inspection—This includes the following types of lamps: head, tail, stop, license, clearance, signal, marker, reflex reflector, and fog. Any of the following defects shall be cause for rejection.

9.1 Any bulb in any lamp which fails to function properly.

9.2 An improperly connected circuit which does not light the proper filaments for the different switch positions.

9.3 A cracked, broken, or missing lens.

9.4 A lens that is rotated, upside down, wrongside out, or is otherwise incorrectly installed. A lens marked "left" or "right", not appropriately installed.

9.5 A separate type lens, the name of which does not correspond with the name stamped on the lamp body, unless it is specifically approved for use with that lamp body.

Report of Electrical Equipment Division approved August 1915 and revised by the Lighting Committee November 1987. Rationale statement available.

1. Scope—This SAE Standard covers the performance and functional requirements of the lamp bulb retention system applicable for use in motor vehicles.

2. Definition—The lamp bulb retention system is a device which retains a lamp bulb in its intended application and provides electrical continuity.

3. Requirements

3.1 The lamp bulb retention system shall accept and provide for the retention and removal of the maximum and minimum bulb gages. See Table 1 for bulb gages.

3.2 The bulb retention system shall provide required electrical connections.

3.3 Bulb retention systems employing multiple contacts shall have them spaced so that they will not contact (electrically insulated from) each other or short to ground.

3.4 When the bulb retention system is assembled in its intended application, the insertion and rotational forces required to lock the maximum bulb gage in its final seating position shall not exceed the values shown below:

Maximum Insertion Force
B and C base sockets—60 N
A base sockets—40 N

Maximum Torque
C base sockets—0.6 N·m
B base sockets—0.6 N·m
A base sockets—0.3 N·m

NOTE: Bulb retention systems designed to be removed from their intended application for bulb service may be checked while removed.

3.5 When the bulb retention system is assembled in its intended application, the B and C base bulb retention systems shall provide a minimum bulb support as measured with the bulb support gage. (See Table 2 for bulb support gages and Fig. 3 for gage.)

NOTES:

1. Bulb retention systems designed to be removed from their intended application for bulb service may be checked while removed.

2. Bulb retention systems which provide alternative equivalent bulb supporting means may be used and need not be checked with the bulb support gage.

ΦTABLE 1—MAXIMUM AND MINIMUM BULB RETENTION SYSTEM GAGES (mm)

Dimension[a]	C-2 Base				B-2 Base				B-1 Base			
	Max Gage		Min Gage		Max Gage		Min Gage		Max Gage		Min Gage	
A	15.30	+0.01 −0.00	15.05	+0.00 −0.01	15.30	+0.01 −0.00	15.05	+0.00 −0.01	15.30	+0.01 −0.00	15.05	+0.00 −0.01
C	16.97	+0.01 −0.00	16.32	+0.00 −0.01	16.97	+0.01 −0.00	16.32	+0.00 −0.01	16.97	+0.01 −0.00	16.32	+0.00 −0.01
D	—		0.64	+0.00 −0.01	—		0.64	+0.00 −0.01	—		0.64	+0.00 −0.01
E	2.03	+0.01 −0.00	1.88	+0.00 −0.01	2.03	+0.01 −0.00	1.88	+0.00 −0.01	2.03	+0.01 −0.00	1.88	+0.00 −0.01
F	8.03	+0.01 −0.00	6.32	+0.00 −0.01	8.03	+0.01 −0.00	6.32	+0.00 −0.01	8.03	+0.01 −0.00	6.32	+0.00 −0.01
G	1.27	+0.00 −0.13	0.38	+0.00 −0.01	1.27	+0.00 −0.13	0.38	+0.00 −0.01	1.27	+0.00 −0.13	0.38	+0.00 −0.01
H	4.32	+0.03 −0.00	3.51	+0.00 −0.03	4.32	+0.03 −0.00	3.51	+0.00 −0.03	4.32	+0.03 −0.00	3.51	+0.00 −0.03
K	—		8.89	+0.00 −0.01	—		8.89	+0.00 −0.01	—		8.89	+0.00 −0.01
L	16.38	+0.01 −0.00	—		16.38	+0.01 −0.00	—		16.38	+0.01 −0.00	—	
N	5.21	+0.03 −0.00	4.50	+0.00 −0.03	5.21	+0.03 −0.00	4.50	+0.00 −0.03	5.21	+0.03 −0.00	4.50	+0.00 −0.03
P	3.38	+0.03 −0.00	2.97	+0.00 −0.05	0.00	+0.03 −0.03	0.00	+0.00 −0.03	0.00	+0.03 −0.03	0.00	+0.00 −0.03
S	6.78	+0.01 −0.00	6.78	+0.00 −0.01	6.78	+0.01 −0.00	6.78	+0.00 −0.01	NA		NA	
T	1.52	+0.13 −0.00	1.52	+0.13 −0.00	1.52	+0.13 −0.00	1.52	+0.13 −0.00	1.52	+0.13 −0.00	1.52	+0.13 −0.00
U	—		—		—		—		—		—	

Dimension*	A-1 Base		Wedge Base	
	Max Gage	Min Gage	Max Gage	Min Gage
A	9.30 +0.01/-0.00	9.07 +0.00/-0.01	4.45 +0.01/-0.00	3.68 +0.00/-0.01
C	10.97 +0.01/-0.00	10.26 +0.00/-0.01	6.10 +0.01/-0.00	3.68 +0.00/-0.01
D	NA	0.64 +0.00/-0.01	—	—
E	1.70 +0.01/-0.00	1.55 +0.00/-0.01	9.50 +0.01/-0.00	9.50 +0.00/-0.01
F	6.48 +0.01/-0.00	4.57 +0.00/-0.01	3.05 +0.01/-0.00	NA
G	1.27 +0.00/-0.13	0.38 +0.00/-0.01	4.06 +0.01/-0.00	3.30 +0.00/-0.01
H	3.33 +0.01/-0.00	2.41 +0.00/-0.03	—	—
K	—	4.57 +0.00/-0.01	—	—
L	10.41 +0.01/-0.00	—	—	—
N	4.32 +0.03/-0.00	3.73 +0.00/-0.03	1.65 +0.00/-0.01	—
P	0.00 +0.03/-0.03	0.00 +0.03/-0.03	2.41 +0.01/-0.00	1.91 +0.00/-0.01
S	NA	NA	—	—
T	1.52 +0.13/-0.00	1.52 +0.13/-0.00	—	—
U	6.40 +0.03/-0.00	—	—	—

*See Figs. 1 and 2.

ΦTABLE 2—BULB SUPPORT GAGE (SEE FIG. 3)

Dimension	B-1 and B-2 Base Bulb Support Gage	C-2 Base Bulb Support Gage	Dimension	B-1 and B-2 Base Bulb Support Gage	C-2 Base Bulb Support Gage
A	15.05 +0.01/-0.00	15.05 +0.01/-0.00	N	4.85 +0.13/-0.00	4.85 +0.13/-0.00
B	19.05 +0.25/-0.25	19.05 +0.25/-0.25	P	10.36 +0.01/-0.00	10.36 +0.01/-0.00
C	16.32 +0.01/-0.00	16.32 +0.01/-0.00	R	18.90 +0.00/-0.25	26.44 +0.00/-0.25
D	0.64 +0.01/-0.00	0.64 +0.01/-0.00	S	4.75D S/F	4.75D S/F
E	1.88 +0.01/-0.00	1.88 +0.01/-0.00	T	6.35D S/F	6.35D S/F
F	6.32 +0.01/-0.00	6.58 +0.01/-0.00	U	0.89 +0.00/-0.13	0.89 +0.00/-0.13
G	0.00 +0.03/-0.03	2.97 +0.05/-0.00	V	15.48 +0.01/-0.00	15.48 +0.01/-0.00
H	3.51 +0.01/-0.00	3.51 +0.01/-0.00	W	1.52 +0.13/-0.00	1.52 +0.13/-0.00
J	30.18 +0.13/-0.00	44.45 +0.13/-0.00	X	B-1 0.00 / B-2 3.45 +0.00/-0.08	— / 3.45 +0.00/-0.08
K	6.86 +0.00/-0.13	6.86 +0.00/-0.13	Y	B-1 0.00 / B-2 6.78 +0.13/-0.00	— / 6.78 +0.13/-0.00
L	3.18 +0.01/-0.00	3.18 +0.01/-0.00			
M	0.76R +0.03/-0.03	0.76R +0.03/-0.03			

NOTE: Dim. P − L = 7.19 mm Dim.

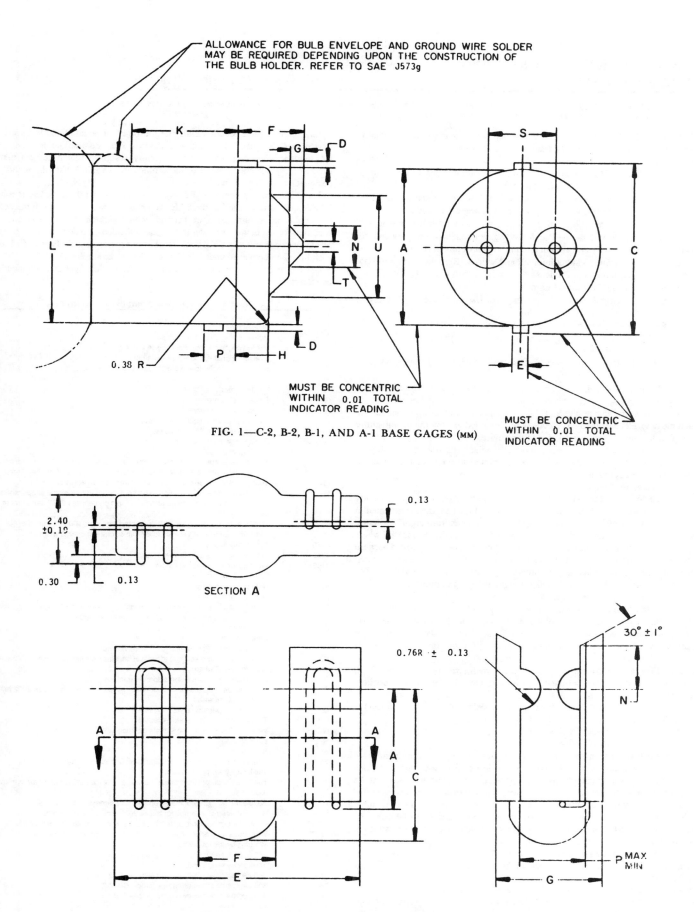

ALLOWANCE FOR BULB ENVELOPE AND GROUND WIRE SOLDER MAY BE REQUIRED DEPENDING UPON THE CONSTRUCTION OF THE BULB HOLDER. REFER TO SAE J573g

0.38 R

MUST BE CONCENTRIC WITHIN 0.01 TOTAL INDICATOR READING

MUST BE CONCENTRIC WITHIN 0.01 TOTAL INDICATOR READING

FIG. 1—C-2, B-2, B-1, AND A-1 BASE GAGES (MM)

2.40 ±0.19

0.30   0.13

0.13

SECTION A

0.76R ± 0.13

30° ± 1°

N

P MAX. MIN

FIG. 2—WEDGE BASE GAGES (MM)

9

Report of the Lighting Committee, approved November 1960, and revised December, 1987. Completely revised by the SAE Lighting Coordinating Committee June 1991. Revised by the SAE Lighting Coordinating Committee January 1995. Rationale statement available.

1. Scope—This SAE Recommended Practice provides the lighting function identification codes for use on all passenger cars and trucks.

2. References

2.1 Applicable Documents—The following publications form a part of this specification to the extent specified herein.

2.1.1 GOVERNMENT PUBLICATION—Available from the Superintendent of Documents, U.S. Government Printing Office, Washington, DC 20402.

FMVSS 108—Lamps, Reflective Devices, and Associated Equipment

(R) **2.2 Related Publication**—The following publications are provided for information purposes only and are not a required part of this document.

SAE J587—License Plate Illumination Devices (Rear Registration Plate Illumination Devices)

SAE J914—Side Turn Signal Lamps

SAE J1432—High Mounted Stop Lamps for Use on Vehicles 2032 mm or More in Overall Width

SAE J2009—Discharge Forward Lighting System

SAE J2039—Side Turn Signal Lamp for Large Vehicles or Trains of Vehicles

SAE J2041—Reflex Reflectors for Use on Vehicles 2032 mm or More in Overall Width

2.3 Definition—A lighting identification code is a series of standardized markings for lighting devices which a manufacturer or a supplier may use to mark his product to indicate the SAE Lighting Specification or Specifications to which the device is designed. The code is not intended to limit the manufacturer or supplier in applying other markings to the devices.

NOTE—SAE does not approve products; hence, the use of markings in accordance with this code should not be interpreted to mean that a device so marked has SAE approval.

3. Requirements

3.1 Code Location—The identification code should be permanently marked on the lens or body where it can be observed with the device mounted in its normal position on the vehicle, except that headlamps, turn signal switches, hazard warning switches, and flashers may have the markings located where they can be observed by removing other parts. This exception is granted because many of these devices are not visible as installed on the vehicle. However, when these same devices are externally mounted, the markings must be visible. The manufacturer's identification and model designation (or part number) is required on both the housing and lens of separable devices.

3.2 Size of Markings—Identification numerals and letters shall be at least 3 mm high, except that raised molded markings 2 mm high may be used on lenses containing less than 12.5 cm^2 of area. The smaller markings are permitted when they are raised, molded markings (not stamped, etched, or lettered in indelible ink).

3.3 Flashers—Flashers, because of their small size, may use 2 mm high markings and these may be permanently stamped, etched, or lettered in indelible ink. The markings required on flashers are:

a. The manufacturer's identification and model number (or part number).

b. The appropriate SAE Specification.

EXAMPLE: Flasher Co. 200
SAE J590e

3.4 Multicompartment and Multiple Lamp Arrangements—Multicompartment lamps or individual lamps designed to use more than one compartment or lamp to comply with the appropriate SAE requirements shall be marked to indicate the number of compartments or lamps that are to be operated together to meet this requirement. Lamps which do not carry a number within a circle or parentheses to indicate that more than one lamp is to be used are intended to be used alone unless exceptions are noted in the appropriate SAE Specification. See example in Section 4.

3.5 Content of Identification Code—The identification code should consist of a series of letters and numbers in the following sequence:

3.5.1 SAE.

3.5.2 A number within a circle or parentheses indicating the number of compartments in a multicompartment device or the number of separate lamps when more than one compartment or one lamp is needed to satisfy the requirements of the applicable SAE Specification. No number is required for a single compartment device.

3.5.3 One or more letters identifying the function or functions for which the device was designed. Multipurpose devices shall be marked to cover each function for which the device was originally designed. Such devices may be used to carry out one or more of these functions. Table 1 lists the identifying designations for SAE Specifications.

3.5.4 The last two numbers of a year which means that the code letters refer to SAE Specifications listed in the SAE Handbook current in the year indicated, or the applicable requirements of Federal Motor Vehicle Safety Standard 108 specified for the device function in the year indicated. To denote that a function meets the requirements of FMVSS 108, but not the current SAE Specification, a dash line shall be placed under the function letter. Example: AI RST 75.

Devices marked prior to the adoption of this SAE Specification need not be remarked.

(R) TABLE 1—LETTERS INDICATING DEVICE FUNCTIONS

A	Reflex reflectors
A2	Wide angle reflex reflectors
C	Motorcycle auxiliary front lamps
D	Motorcycle and motor-driven cycle turn signal lamps
E	Side turn signal lamps—vehicles 12 m or more in length
E2	Side turn signal lamps—vehicles less than 12 m in length
F	Front fog lamps
F2	Fog tail lamps
G	Truck cargo lamp
H	Sealed beam headlamp
HG	Discharge forward lighting (headlamp)
HH	Sealed beam headlamp housing
HR	Replaceable bulb headlamp
I	Turn signal lamps
I3	Turn signal lamps spaced from 75 mm to less than 100 mm from headlamp
I4	Turn signal lamps spaced from 60 mm to less than 75 mm from headlamp
I5	Turn signal lamps spaced less than 60 mm from headlamp
I6	Rear mounted turn signal lamps and front mounted turn signal lamps mounted 100 mm or more from the headlamp, for use on vehicles 2032 mm or more in overall width
I7	Front mounted turn signal lamps mounted less than 100 mm from the headlamp, for use on vehicles 2032 mm or more in overall width
J590	Turn signal flasher
J945	Hazard warning signal flasher
J1054	Warning lamp alternating flasher
K	Front cornering lamps
K2	Rear cornering lamps
L	License plate lamps
M	Motorcycle and motor-driven cycle headlamps—motorcycle type
N	Motorcycle and motor-driven cycle headlamps—motor driven cycle type
O	Spot lamps
P	Parking lamps
P2	Clearance, sidemarker, and identification lamps
P3	Clearance, sidemarker, and identification lamps for use on vehicles 2032 mm or more in overall width
PC	Combination clearance and sidemarker lamps
PC2	Combination clearance and sidemarker lamps for use on vehicles 2032 mm or more in overall width
Q	Turn signal operating units—Class A
QB	Turn signal operating units—Class B
QC	Vehicular hazard warning signal operating unit
R	Backup lamps
S	Stop lamps
S2	Stop lamp for use on vehicles 2032 mm or more in overall width
T	Tail lamps (rear position lamps)
T2	Tail lamps (rear position lamps) for use on vehicles 2032 mm or more in overall width
U	Supplemental high-mounted stop and turn signal lamps
U2	High-mounted stop lamps for trucks 2032 mm or more in overall width
U3	Center high-mounted stop lamp for passenger cars, light trucks, and MPVs
W	Warning lamps for emergency, maintenance, and service vehicles
W2	Warning lamps for school buses
W3	360 degree emergency warning lamps
W4	Emergency warning device
W5-1	360 degree gaseous discharge lamp—Class 1
W5-2	360 degree gaseous discharge lamp—Class 2
W5-3	360 degree gaseous discharge lamp—Class 3
Y	Driving lamps
Y2	Daytime running lamps
Z	Auxiliary low beam lamps

3.6 Content of Manufacturer's Identification—The manufacturer's lettered identification and model designation (or part number). Pictorial trademarks are permitted but they must be in addition to the required lettered identification. The lettered identification must be reproducible on a typewriter or computer. The manufacturer's identification does not have to be located in sequence with the identification code markings but may be located on a different area of the lens or body.

4. Examples—Examples of code and manufacturer's identification markings:

SAE AIST 75

XYZ Corp. 400

Translated, this means SAE Specifications current in 1975 for stop lamps, tail lamps, turn signals, and reflectors. The manufacturer is the XYZ Corp. (the word corporation is shown for example only, since this is generally not used) and their model number is Model 400.

SAE A (2) I (2) S (3) T 75

Translated, this means a three-compartment or three-lamp arrangement with two of the compartments needed to meet optically the stop and turn signal requirements, and all three of the compartments needed to meet the tail lamp requirements. If, for example, each of the compartments fully complied with the tail lamp requirements, the 3 preceding the letter T would be omitted. This would signify that all of the compartments were not necessary to meet the tail lamp requirement and that each individual compartment met it as a separate single function. If the SAE Specifications referenced in the examples were not revised and would still be current in the year 1976, for example, the manufacturer could change the marking on this device to 76, if he so desired. This coding change regarding the year might also be made if the SAE Specifications have been revised in the interim and the device meets the new requirements.

Report of the Lighting Committee approved March 1979 and completely revised by the Lighting Coordinating Committee June 1989. Rationale statement available. Revised by the Road Illuminating Devices Standards Committee of the SAE Lighting Coordinating Committee January 1995. Rationale statement available.

1. Scope—This SAE Standard provides test procedures, performance requirements and guidelines for auxiliary driving lamps.

(R)   *2. References*

2.1 Applicable Documents—The following publications form a part of this specification to the extent specified herein. Unless otherwise specified, the latest issue of SAE publications shall apply.

2.1.1 SAE PUBLICATIONS—Available from SAE, 400 Commonwealth Drive, Warrendale, PA 15096-0001.

SAE J575—Tests for Motor Vehicle Lighting Devices and Components

SAE J576—Plastic materials for Use in Optical Parts Such as Lenses and Reflectors of Motor Vehicle Lighting Devices

SAE J578—Color Specification

SAE J599—Lighting Inspection Code

SAE J759—Lighting Identification Code

2.2 Definition

2.2.1 AUXILIARY DRIVING LAMP—A lighting device mounted to provide illumination forward of the vehicle and intended to supplement the upper beam of a standard headlamp system. It is not intended for use alone or with the lower beam of a standard headlamp system.

3. Lighting Identification Code—The auxiliary driving lamps may be identified by the code "Y," in accordance with SAE J759.

4. Tests

4.1 SAE J575—The following test procedures in SAE J575 are a part of this report with the modifications indicated:

4.1.1 VIBRATION TEST

4.1.2 MOISTURE TEST

4.1.3 DUST TEST—(Dust test shall not be required for sealed units.)

4.1.4 CORROSION TEST

4.1.5 WARPAGE TEST—(Devices produced from plastic components.)

4.1.6 A PHOTOMETRIC TEST

4.1.6.1 The photometric tests for bulb replaceable units shall be made at a distance of at least 18.3 m (60 ft) from the photometer to the lamp.

4.1.6.2 Lamp Aim—A lamp or sealed beam unit, which is designed to be aimed mechanically, shall be centered on the photometric axis with the aiming planes normal to that axis. A lamp or sealed unit, not designed to be aimed mechanically, shall be photoelectrically aimed so that the test points in Figure 1 designated by the squares have equal intensity and those designated by triangles have equal intensity.

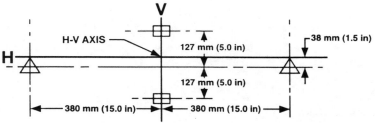

FIGURE 1—TEST POINTS ON A SCREEN AT 7.6 m

4.2 Color Test—SAE J578 is a part of this report.

5. Requirements

5.1 Performance Requirements

5.1.1 SAE J575—A device when tested in accordance with the test procedures in Section 4, shall meet the following requirements in SAE J575, with the modifications indicated:

5.1.1.1 Vibration

5.1.1.2 Moisture

5.1.1.3 Dust

5.1.1.4 Corrosion

5.1.1.5 Warpage Test on Devices with Plastic Components

5.1.1.6 Photometry—The lamp under test shall meet the photometric requirements contained in Table 1.

TABLE 1—PHOTOMETRIC REQUIREMENTS

Test Point Degrees[1]	Candela, cd
2U — 3R and 3L	1600 min
1U — 3R and 3L	4000 min
H — V	20 000 min and 60 000 max
H — 3R and 3L	8000 min
1D — 6R and 6L	2960 min
2D — 6R and 6L	1600 min
4D — V	6000 max

[1] A tolerance of ±1/4 degree in location may be allowed at any test point.

5.2 Color—The color of the emitted light shall be white as defined in SAE J578.

5.3 Plastic Materials—The plastic materials used in optical parts shall meet the requirements in SAE J576.

6. Guidelines

6.1 The photometric design guidelines for auxiliary driving lamps, when tested in accordance with 4.1.6 of this document, are contained in Table 2.

TABLE 2—PHOTOMETRIC DESIGN GUIDELINES

Test Point Degrees[1]	Candela, cd
2U — 3R and 3L	2000 min
1U — 3R and 3L	5000 min
H — V	25 000 min and 50 000 max
H — 3R and 3L	10 000 min
1D — 6R and 6L	3700 min
2D — 6R and 6L	2000 min
4D V	5000 max

[1] A tolerance of ±1/4 degree in location may be allowed at any test point.

6.2 These guidelines apply to the device as used on the vehicle and are not a part of the laboratory test procedures and requirements.

6.3 Lamp Aim—The lamp aim adjustments on the vehicle should be with mechanical aimers, if possible. Set the mechanical aim to 0-0, reference SAE J599.

(R)   **6.4 Other Aiming Procedures**—If the vehicle mounting or lamp design precludes mechanical aiming, the lamp shall be aimed photometrically (see 4.1.6.2), or visually aimed. The correct visual aim is with the high intensity zone of the beam symmetric about and 38 mm (1.5 in) below the H-V axis of the lamp on an aiming screen at 7.6 m (25 ft).

AUXILIARY LOW BEAM LAMPS
—SAE J582 MAR95

SAE Recommended Practice

Report of the Lighting Division approved January 1941. Completely revised by the Lighting Committee September 1984. Rationale statement available. Completely revised by the Road Illuminating Devices Committee and the Lighting Coordinating Committee March 1995. Rationale statement available.

1. Scope—This SAE Recommended Practice provides general design and performance requirements, test procedures, and installation guidelines for auxiliary low beam lamps.

2. References

2.1 Applicable Documents—The following publications form a part of this specification to the extent specified herein. The latest issue of SAE publications shall apply.

2.1.1 SAE PUBLICATIONS—Available from SAE, 400 Commonwealth Drive, Warrendale, PA 15096-0001.

SAE J575—Test Methods and Equipment for Lighting Devices and Components for Use on Vehicles Less Than 2032 mm in Overall Width

SAE J576—Plastic Materials for Use in Optical Parts Such as Lenses and Reflectors of Motor Vehicle Lighting Devices

SAE J578—Color Specification

SAE J602—Headlamp Aiming Device for Mechanically Aimable Sealed Beam Headlamp Units

SAE J759—Lighting Inspection Code

SAE J1383—Sealed Beam Headlamps for Motor Vehicles

3. Definitions

3.1 Auxiliary Low Beam Lamps—A lamp which supplements the lower beam of a standard headlamp system.

4. Lighting Tests Identification Code—Auxiliary low beam lamps may be identified by the code "Z," in accordance with SAE J759.

5. Tests

5.1 SAE J575 is a part of this document. The following tests are applicable with modifications as indicated.

5.1.1 VIBRATION TEST

5.1.2 MOISTURE TEST

5.1.3 DUST TEST

5.1.4 CORROSION

5.1.5 PHOTOMETRY TESTS

5.1.5.1 Photometric tests shall be made with the photometer at a distance of at least 18.3 m (60 ft) from the headlamp. The lamp shall be aimed mechanically by centering the lamp on the photometer axis with the aiming plane on the lens normal to the photometer axis.

5.1.5.2 A lamp designed not to be aimed mechanically shall be centered on the photometer axis with the beam aimed downward so that 1000 cd is directed at some point on the horizontal between 6.0 degrees left and 6.0 degrees right.

5.1.6 WARPAGE TEST FOR DEVICES WITH PLASTIC COMPONENTS

5.1.7 COLOR TEST—SAE J578 is a part of this document.

6. Requirements

6.1 Performance Requirements—A lamp, when tested in accordance with the test procedure specified in Section 5, shall meet the following requirements.

6.1.1 VIBRATION—SAE J575

6.1.2 MOISTURE—SAE J575

6.1.3 DUST—SAE J575

6.1.4 CORROSION—SAE J575

6.1.5 PHOTOMETRY—SAE J575

6.1.5.1 The lamp under test shall meet the photometric performance requirements contained in Table 1 and its footnotes.

6.1.5.2 Unless otherwise specified, bulbs used in the tests shall be supplied by the laboratory and be representative of standard bulbs in regular production. The rated bulbs shall be operated at their designed luminous intensity (MSCP); sealed units shall be seasoned and operated at their design voltage.

6.1.6 WARPAGE—SAE J575

6.1.7 COLOR—The color of light from the auxiliary low beam lamp shall be white as specified in SAE J578.

6.1.8 OUT-OF-FOCUS—The auxiliary low beam lamp shall meet the photometric requirements of Table 2 for each of the out-of-focus positions.

6.2 Material Requirements—Plastic materials used in the optical parts shall meet the requirements of SAE J576.

TABLE 1—PHOTOMETRIC DESIGN GUIDELINES

Test Point Deg.[1]	Candela-Max.	Candela-Min.
10U - 90U[2]	75	—
1.5U - 1L to L	300	—
1.5U - 1R to R	300	—
.5U - 1L to L	400	—
.5U - 1R to 3R	400	—
.5D - 1R to 3R	25000	2000
.5D - 1L to L	10000	—
5D - 4R	—	3000
5D - 4L	—	3000
1D - 1R	—	10000
3D - 3R	5000	—
4D - V	3000	—
2.5D - 15L	—	1500
2.5D - 15R	—	1500

[1] A tolerance of +0.25 degrees in location is allowed at any test point.

[2] From the normally exposed surface of the lens.

TABLE 2—PHOTOMETRIC PERFORMANCE REQUIREMENTS

Test Point Deg.[1]	Requirements, cd Max	Requirements, cd Min
1.5U - 1R	300	—
.5U - 1L to L	400	—
.5U - 1R	400	—
.5D - 1.5R to 3R	—	3000
1D - 3R	—	15000

[1] A tolerance of 0.25 degrees in location is allowed at any test point.

7. Guidelines

7.1 Photometric Design Guidelines

7.1.1 The photometric design guidelines for auxiliary low beam lamps, when tested in accordance with 5.1.5 of this document, are contained in Table 1.

7.2 Lamp Aim—Mechanical lamp aim adjustment and inspection may be performed in accordance with SAE J602.

7.2.1 If vehicle mounting precludes mechanical aiming, the lamp may be visually aimed. The correct visual aim is with the top edge of the high intensity zone 25 mm (1 in) below horizontal at 7.6 m (25 ft).

7.3 Means shall be provided to turn off the auxiliary low beam lamp independently of the lower beam lamps of the standard headlights system.

7.4 Lamp Mounting

7.4.1 A single lamp shall be mounted at the front and to the left side (driver's side) of the center of the vehicle. If two lamps are used, they shall be mounted at the same mounting height, and no higher than the standard headlamps (reference lens center).

(R) FRONT FOG LAMPS
—SAE J583 JUN93

SAE Standard

Report of the Lighting Division, approved May 1937. Completely revised by the Lighting Committee July 1977, editorial change May 1981. Rationale statement available. Completely revised by the SAE Road Illumination Devices Standards Committee June 1993. Rationale statement available.

1. Scope—This SAE Standard provides performance requirements, test procedures, and design and installation guidelines for front fog lamps.

2. References

2.1 Applicable Documents—The following publications form a part of this specification to the extent specified herein. The latest issue of SAE publications shall apply.

2.1.1 SAE PUBLICATIONS—Available from SAE, 400 Commonwealth Drive, Warrendale, PA 15096-0001.

SAE J575—Tests for Motor Vehicle Lighting Devices and Components

SAE J576—Plastic Materials for Use in Optical Parts Such as Lenses and Reflectors of Motor Vehicle Lighting Devices

SAE J578—Color Specification

SAE J599—Lighting Inspection Code

SAE J759—Lighting Identification Code

2.2 Definition

2.2.1 A FRONT FOG LAMP is a lighting device providing illumination forward of the vehicle under conditions of fog, rain, snow, or dust. Principally, the front fog lamp supplements the lower beam of a standard headlamp system.

3. Lighting Identification Code—Front fog lamps may be identified by the code "F" in accordance with SAE J759.

4. Tests

4.1 Test Voltage—In conducting tests on front fog lamps, the test voltage shall be 12.8 V ± 20 mV, DC as measured at the terminals of the lamp.

4.2 SAE J575—SAE J575 is a part of this report. The following test procedures are applicable with modifications indicated:

4.2.1 TESTS

4.2.1.1 Vibration Test

4.2.1.2 Moisture Test

4.2.1.3 Dust Test

4.2.1.4 Corrosion Test

4.2.1.5 Photometry Test

4.2.1.5.1 Photometric tests shall be made with the photometer at a distance of at least 18.3 m (60 ft) from the fog lamp. A front fog lamp designed to be aimed mechanically shall be centered on the photometer axis with the aiming plane on the lens normal to the photometer axis.

4.2.1.5.2 A front fog lamp not intended to be aimed mechanically shall be centered on the photometer axis with the beam aimed downward so that 500 cd is directed at some point on the horizontal between 6L and 6R, whereby the horizontal beam distribution is being kept symmetrical with respect to the photometer axis. This can also be accomplished by balancing the beam.

4.2.1.5.3 A front fog lamp that has no provisions for mechanical lateral aim, shall be mounted in the design position of the goniometer, as it is prescribed to be mounted on the vehicle. The beam is aimed downward so that 500 cd is directed at some point on the horizontal between 6L and 6R.

4.2.1.6 Warpage Test (on devices with plastic components)

4.3 Color Test—SAE J578 is a part of this report.

4.4 Plastic Materials—Plastic materials used in optical parts shall be tested in accordance with the procedures in SAE J576.

4.5 Sealed Beam Unit Tests—Sealed beam units designed for use as front fog lamps, when tested without other parts of the lamp assembly, are not subject to moisture, dust, and corrosion tests.

5. Requirements

5.1 Performance Requirements

5.1.1 SAE J575 REQUIREMENTS—A device, when tested in accordance with the test procedures specified in Section 4, shall meet the following requirements in SAE J575:

5.1.1.1 Vibration

5.1.1.2 Moisture

5.1.1.3 Dust

5.1.1.4 Corrosion

5.1.1.5 Warpage (This is a requirement only for devices with plastic components.)

5.1.2 COLOR—The color of the light from a front fog lamp shall be white to yellow within the limits specified in SAE J578.

5.1.3 PHOTOMETRY—The beam of the front fog lamp shall be designed to conform to the light intensity distribution (candela) values as shown in Table 2. The lamp shall meet the photometric performance requirements contained in Table 1.

TABLE 1—PHOTOMETRIC REQUIREMENTS

Test Point[1] Degree	Candela (Cd) Max	Candela (Cd) Min
8U - 90U[2]	90	—
4U - 6L and 6R	150	—
2U - 6L and 6R	300	—
1U - 6L and 6R	420	—
H - 6L and 6R	600	—
1-1/2D - 3L and 3R	12 000	1600
1-1/2D - 9L and 9R	—	800
3D - 15L and 15R	—	800

[1] A tolerance of ±1/4 degree in location is allowed at any test point.
[2] From the normally exposed surface of the lens.

5.1.4 PLASTIC MATERIALS—The plastic materials used in optical parts shall meet the material performance requirements as listed in SAE J576.

6. Guidelines

6.1 Photometric Design Guidelines—The photometric design guidelines for front fog lamps when tested in accordance with 4.2.5 of this document are contained in Table 2.

TABLE 2—PHOTOMETRIC DESIGN GUIDELINES

Test Point[1] Degree	Candela (Cd) Max	Candela (Cd) Min
8U - 90U[2]	75	—
4U - 6L and 6R	125	—
2U - 6L and 6R	250	—
1U - 6L and 6R	350	—
H - 6L and 6R	500	—
1-1/2D - 3L and 3R	10 000	2000
1-1/2D - 9L and 9R	—	1000
3D - 15L and 15R	—	1000

[1] A tolerance of ±1/4 degree in location is allowed at any test point.
[2] From the normally exposed surface of the lens.

6.2 Installation Guidelines—These guidelines apply to the device as used on the vehicle and are not part of the design guidelines, performance requirements, or the test procedures.

6.2.1 LAMP AIM ON THE VEHICLE

6.2.1.1 Lamp aim adjustments and inspection should be made with mechanical aimers. The correct mechanical aim is 0-0 based on SAE J599.

6.2.1.2 If vehicle mounting or lamp design preclude mechanical aim, the lamp should be aimed visually. The correct visual aim is made with the top of the beam 100 mm (4 in) below the lamp center at 7.6 m (25 ft). The beam should be centered laterally about a vertical line directly ahead of the lamp.

6.2.1.3 Fog lamps designed for universal mounting applications to fit various vehicle makes and models should be provided with means for vertical and horizontal aim adjustment. Lamps and composite units, which are designed to be integrated into one specific vehicle, need only have means for vertical adjustment.

Report of Lighting Committee approved March 1961 and last revised December 1974.

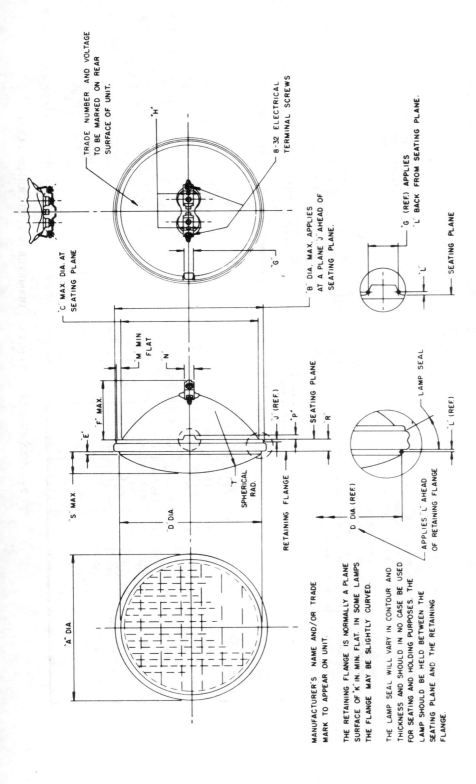

MANUFACTURER'S NAME AND/OR TRADE MARK TO APPEAR ON UNIT.

THE RETAINING FLANGE IS NORMALLY A PLANE SURFACE OF "K" IN. MIN. FLAT. IN SOME LAMPS THE FLANGE MAY BE SLIGHTLY CURVED.

THE LAMP SEAL WILL VARY IN CONTOUR AND THICKNESS AND SHOULD IN NO CASE BE USED FOR SEATING AND HOLDING PURPOSES. THE LAMP SHOULD BE HELD BETWEEN THE SEATING PLANE AND THE RETAINING FLANGE.

LETTER	INCH	MM
A	5.70 +.00 -.10	144.8 +0.0 -2.5
B	5.475	139.06
C	5.100	129.54
D	5.265 +.000 -.030	133.7 +0.00 -0.76
E	.078 +.062 -.000	2.00 +1.50 -0.00
F	2.50	63.5
G	.440 +.000 -.025	11.17 +0.00 -0.63
H	.125 ± .010	3.17 ± 0.25
J	.110	2.79
K	.062	1.57
L	.030	0.76
M	.125	3.18

LETTER	INCH	MM
N	.375 ± .010	9.52 ± 0.25
P	.135 +.030 -.000	3.43 +0.76 -0.00
R	.53 ± .04	13.5 ± 1.0
S	.92	23.36
T	5.00 ± .12	127.0 ± 3.0

FIG. 1—DIMENSIONS OF 5¾ IN (146 mm) DIAMETER SEALED LIGHTING UNIT

15

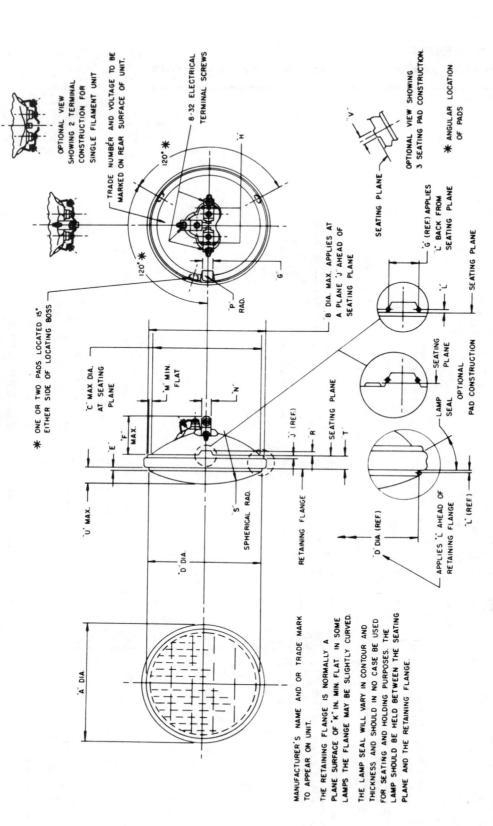

* ONE OR TWO PADS LOCATED 15°
EITHER SIDE OF LOCATING BOSS

MANUFACTURER'S NAME AND OR TRADE MARK
TO APPEAR ON UNIT.

THE RETAINING FLANGE IS NORMALLY A
PLANE SURFACE OF 'K' IN. MIN. FLAT. IN SOME
LAMPS THE FLANGE MAY BE SLIGHTLY CURVED.

THE LAMP SEAL WILL VARY IN CONTOUR AND
THICKNESS AND SHOULD IN NO CASE BE USED
FOR SEATING AND HOLDING PURPOSES. THE
LAMP SHOULD BE HELD BETWEEN THE SEATING
PLANE AND THE RETAINING FLANGE.

OPTIONAL VIEW
SHOWING 2 TERMINAL
CONSTRUCTION FOR
SINGLE FILAMENT UNIT

TRADE NUMBER AND VOLTAGE TO BE
MARKED ON REAR SURFACE OF UNIT.

8-32 ELECTRICAL
TERMINAL SCREWS

OPTIONAL VIEW SHOWING
3 SEATING PAD CONSTRUCTION.

* ANGULAR LOCATION
OF PADS

LETTER	INCH	MM
A	4.460 +.000 -.100	113.28 +0.00 -2.50
B	4.215	107.06
C	3.850	97.79
D	4.050 +.000 -.030	102.87 +0.00 -0.76
E	.078 +.062 -.000	1.98 +1.60 -0.00
F	1.625	41.27
G	.440 +.000 -.025	11.17 +0.00 -0.63
H	.125 ±.010	3.17 ±0.25
J	.110	2.79
K	.062	1.57
L	.030	0.76

LETTER	INCH	MM
M	.125	3.18
N	.375 ±.010	9.52 ± 0.25
P	.06	1.5
R	.135 +.030 -.000	3.43 +0.76 -0.00
S	4.50 ± .12	114.3 ± 3.0
T	.525 ±.040	13.33 ± 1.00
U	.59	14.98
V	.31 ±.12	7.9 ±3.0

FIG. 2—DIMENSIONS OF 4½ IN (114 mm) DIAMETER SEALED LIGHTING UNIT

16

FRONT CORNERING LAMPS FOR USE ON MOTOR VEHICLES—SAE J852 DEC93

SAE Recommended Practice

Report of the Lighting Committee approved April 1963 and completely revised November 1987. Rationale statement available. Reaffirmed by the SAE Road Illumination Devices Standards Committee December 1993. Rationale statement available.

Foreword—This reaffirmed document has been changed only to reflect the new SAE Technical Standards Board format.

1. Scope—This SAE Recommended Practice provides test procedures, requirements, and guidelines for front cornering lamps that are mounted on the exterior of a vehicle.

2. References

2.1 Applicable Documents—The following publications form a part of this specification to the extent specified herein. The latest issue of SAE publications shall apply.

2.1.1 SAE PUBLICATIONS—Available from SAE, 400 Commonwealth Drive, Warrendale, PA 15096-0001.

SAE J567—Lamp Bulb Retention System

SAE J575—Tests for Motor Vehicle Lighting Devices and Components

SAE J576—Plastic Material for Use in Optical Parts Such as Lenses and Reflectors of Motor Vehicle Lighting Devices

SAE J578—Color Specifications for Electric Signal Lighting Devices

SAE J759—Lighting Identification Code

2.2 Definition

2.2.1 FRONT CORNERING LAMPS—Steady burning lamps used in conjunction with the turn signal system to supplement the headlamps by providing additional illumination in the direction of turn.

3. Lighting Identification Code—Front cornering lamps meeting the performance requirements of Section 5 of this document may be identified by the code K in accordance with SAE J759.

4. Tests

4.1 SAE J575 is a part of this document. The following tests are applicable with the modifications as indicated.

4.1.1 VIBRATION TEST

4.1.2 MOISTURE TEST

4.1.3 DUST TEST

4.1.4 CORROSION TEST

4.1.5 PHOTOMETRY—In addition to the test procedures in SAE J575, the following apply:

4.1.5.1 Photometric measurements shall be made with the light source of the lamp at least 3 m from the photometer. The H-V axis shall be taken as the horizontal line through the light source and perpendicular to the longitudinal axis of the vehicle.

4.1.6 WARPAGE TEST ON DEVICE WITH PLASTIC COMPONENTS

4.2 Color Test—SAE J578 is a part of this document.

5. Requirements

5.1 Performance Requirements—A device when tested in accordance with the test procedure specified in Section 4 shall meet the following requirements:

5.1.1 VIBRATION—SAE J575

5.1.2 MOISTURE—SAE J575

5.1.3 DUST—SAE J575

5.1.4 CORROSION—SAE J575

5.1.5 PHOTOMETRY—SAE J575—The lamp under test shall meet the photometric requirements contained in Table 1. Test points shown are for a lamp mounted on the left side of the vehicle—left-hand angles should be substituted for right-hand angles for a lamp mounted on the right side of the vehicle.

TABLE 1—PHOTOMETRIC REQUIREMENTS

Test Position		Candlepower
8°U to 90°U- 90°L to 90°R		150 max
4°U- 90°L to 90°R		240 max
2°U- 90°L to 90°R		360 max
1°U- 90°L to 90°R		480 max
H- 90°L to 90°R		600 max
2.5°D	-30°R	240 min
2.5°D	-45°R	400 min
2.5°D	-60°R	240 min

5.1.6 WARPAGE—SAE J575

5.1.7 COLOR—SAE J578—The color of the light from a front cornering lamp shall be white or amber, as specified in SAE J578.

5.2 Material Requirements—Plastic materials used in optical parts shall meet the requirements of SAE J576.

6. Guidelines

6.1 Photometric Design Guidelines for front cornering lamps, when tested in accordance with 4.1.5 of this document, are contained in Table 2. Test points shown are for a lamp mounted on the left side of the vehicle—left-hand angles should be substituted for right-hand angles for a lamp mounted on the right side of the vehicle.

TABLE 2—PHOTOMETRIC DESIGN GUIDELINES

Test Position		Candlepower
8°U to 90°U- 90°L to 90°R		125 max
4°U- 90°L to 90°R		200 max
2°U- 90°L to 90°R		300 max
1°U- 90°L to 90°R		400 max
H- 90°L to 90°R		500 max
2.5°D	-30°R	300 min
2.5°D	-45°R	500 min
2.5°D	-60°R	300 min

6.2 Operating Guidelines—The following guidelines apply to front cornering lamps as used on the vehicle and shall not be considered part of the requirements.

6.2.1 The front cornering lamps are primarily intended to be used during the times that headlamps are required.

6.2.2 Means should be provided to turn on the front cornering lamps with the turn signal lamps and they should turn off when the turn signal lamps are turned off. If the front cornering lamps are not turned off automatically, a visual or audible means should be provided to indicate to the driver when the lamps are on.

7. Notes

7.1 As a matter of additional information, attention is called to SAE J567 for requirements and gages used in socket design.

Report of the Lighting Committee, approved April 1985. Rationale statement available. Completely revised by the Road Illumination Devices Standards Committee June 1990. Rationale statement available.

TABLE OF CONTENTS

1. Scope—This SAE Recommended Practice is intended as a guide toward standard practice and is subject to change to keep pace with experience and technical advances. This document establishes performance requirements, material requirements, design requirements, and design guidelines for headlamps and replaceable bulbs for headlamps.

2. References

2.1 Applicable Documents

2.1.1 SAE PUBLICATIONS—Available from SAE, 400 Commonwealth Drive, Warrendale, PA 15096-0001.

SAE J575—Tests for Motor Vehicle Lighting Devices and Components

SAE J759—Lighting Identification Code

2.2 Definitions

2.2.1 HEADLAMP—A lighting device providing an upper and/or a lower beam used for providing illumination forward of the vehicle.

2.2.2 SEALED BEAM HEADLAMP ASSEMBLY—A major lighting assembly which includes one or more indivisible optical assemblies used to provide general illumination ahead of the vehicle.

2.2.3 REPLACEABLE BULB (BULB)—A light source with related envelope and mounting base which is removable from the headlamp for the purpose of replacement.

2.2.4 MECHANICALLY AIMABLE HEADLAMP—A headlamp having three pads on the lens, forming an aiming plane used for laboratory photometric testing and for adjusting and inspecting the aim of the headlamp when installed on the vehicle.

2.2.5 AIMING PLANE—A plane defined by the surface of the three aiming pads on the lens.

2.2.6 HEADLAMP MECHANICAL AXIS—The line formed by the intersection of a horizontal and a vertical plane through the light source parallel to the longitudinal axis of the vehicle. If the mechanical axis of the headlamp is not at the geometric center of the lens, then the location will be indicated by the manufacturer on the headlamp.

2.2.7 H-V AXIS—A line from the center of the principal filament (low beam filament of two filament bulbs) to the intersection of the horizontal (H) and vertical (V) lines on the screen (see Figure 1).

2.2.8 SEASONING—Process of energizing the filament of a bulb at design voltage for a period of time equal to 1% of design life or 10 h maximum, whichever is shorter.

TABLE 1—REPLACEABLE HEADLAMP BULBS

Design Designation	Number of Filaments	Luminous Wattage (Watts) at 12.8 V U.B./L.B.	Flux (Lumens) at 12.8 V U.B./L.B.	Design Life (Hours) Æ 14 V U.B./L.B.[2]	Filament Type
9004 (ANSI)	2	65/45	1200/700[1]	150/320	C6/C6
9005 (ANSI)	1	65	1700	150	C8
9006 (ANSI)	1	55	1000[1]	320	C8
9007 (ANSI)	2	65/55	1350/1000[1]	150/320	C8/C8
H1	1	60.5	1410	320	C8
H3	1	60.5	1310	320	C6
H4	2	67/60.5	1500/910[1]	150/320	C8/C8

[1] With opaque coating
[2] Guideline

TABLE 2—REPLACEABLE BULBS AND RELATED DIMENSIONAL FIGURES

Bulb Identification	Figures Relative To: Dimensional Specifications Standard Bulb	Figures Relative To: Specifications For Bulb Holders	Figures Relative To: Measurement Method — Bulb Filament Dimension and Tolerance	Figures Relative To: Dimensional Specifications for Accurate Rated Bulb
9004	Figures 33 to 36	37	Sections 7, 8, 9	38
9005	Figures 39 to 43	44	Sections 10, 11, 12, 13	Sections 10, 11, 12, 13, and Figure 46
9006	Figures 47 to 51	52	53	Sections 10, 11, 12, 13, and Figure 53
9007	Figures 54 to 57	58	Sections 14, 15, 16	59
H1	Figures 60 to 61	62	63	64
H3	Figures 65 to 66	67	68	69
H4	Figures 70 to 72	73	Sections 17, 18, 19, 20, 21 and Figure 74	71
HB2	Figures 70 to 72	73	Sections 17, 18, 19, 20, 21 and Figure 74	71

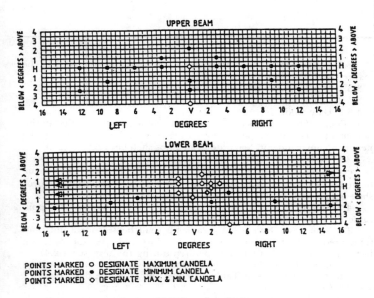

POINTS MARKED ○ DESIGNATE MAXIMUM CANDELA
POINTS MARKED ● DESIGNATE MINIMUM CANDELA
POINTS MARKED ◇ DESIGNATE MAX. & MIN. CANDELA

FIGURE 1—PHOTOMETRIC TABLES

2.2.9 DESIGN VOLTAGE—The voltage used for design purposes.

2.2.10 TEST VOLTAGE—The specified voltage and tolerance to be used when conducting a test.

2.2.11 RATED VOLTAGE—The nominal circuit or vehicle electrical system voltage classification. (Example: 12 V Headlamp)

2.2.12 HEADLAMP TEST FIXTURE—Device specifically designed to support a headlamp in the test position during laboratory testing. Mounting hardware and components shall be representative of those necessary to operate the headlamp in its normal manner.

2.2.13 MOUNTING RING—The adjustable ring upon which the sealed beam bulb is mounted and which forces the sealed beam bulb to seat against the aiming ring when assembled into a sealed beam headlamp assembly.

2.2.14 RETAINING RING—The clamping ring that holds the sealed beam bulb against the mounting ring.

2.2.15 AIMING RING—The clamping ring that retains the sealed beam bulb against the mounting ring, and that provides an interface between the bulb's aiming/seating pads and the headlamp aimer adapter (locating plate). It also describes and is coincident with the aiming plane.

2.2.16 AIMING SCREWS—Horizontal and vertical adjusting screws with self-locking features used to aim and retain the headlamp unit in the proper position.

2.2.17 INTEGRAL AIM—A vertical aiming system which is mounted to the headlamp and does not require a separate vertical mechanical aiming device.

2.2.18 ACCURATE RATED BULB—A seasoned bulb operated at design luminous flux shown in Table 1 and having its filaments located within the tolerances indicated in figures specified in Table 2. Separate bulbs may be used for high and low beams.

2.2.19 HIGH BEAM—A beam intended primarily for distant illumination and for use when not meeting or following other vehicles.

2.2.20 LOW BEAM—A beam intended to illuminate the road ahead of the vehicle when meeting or following another vehicle.

2.2.21 HIGH BEAM FILAMENT—Filament coil designed to provide high beam function.

2.2.22 LOW BEAM FILAMENT—Filament coil designed to provide low beam function.

2.2.23 FILAMENT ROTATION—Any nonparallelism of either coil with respect to the centerline of the design nominal filament location or any additional width of the end view of the filament in excess of the outside diameter of the first full turn.

2.2.24 RATED AVERAGE LAB LIFE—An average life in hours which is obtained by laboratory life testing of bulbs at the specified test voltage over a long period of production time. It is meant to partially describe a manufactured product recognizing that individual lifetimes vary greatly. It is not the same as service life which is generally shorter due to environmental conditions such as vibration, voltage fluctuations, and temperature.

2.2.25 DESIGN LIFE—An operational time objective in hours of a headlamp filament at the test voltage.

2.2.26 GAGING STANDARD—A gage produced for each bulb type with all critical tolerances affecting filament location one-tenth the stated tolerances in the design requirements.

3. Identification Code Designation

3.1 SAE J759 Lighting Identification Code

3.2 Headlamp Marking Requirements—Headlamps shall be marked with the following markings:

3.2.1 Manufacturer's name and/or trademark shall appear on the lens.

3.2.2 Voltage and part number or trade number shall appear on the headlamp.

3.2.3 The face of letters, numbers, or other symbols molded on the surface of the lens shall not be raised more than 0.5 mm (0.020 in).

3.2.4 HEADLAMP TYPE IDENTIFICATION CODE

3.2.4.1 Headlamp lenses shall be marked with a two or three character code.

3.2.4.2 The marking shall be molded in the lens and shall be 6.35 mm (0.25 in) or greater in size.

3.2.4.3 The first character (a number) of the three character identification code indicates the number of beams in the headlamp. All headlamps marked with a "1" are aimed on the high beam and all headlamps marked with a "2" are aimed on the low beam.

3.2.4.4 The second character (a letter) stands for the size and number of headlamps used on the vehicle.

A — 100 × 165 mm rectangular, four lamp system
B — 142 × 200 mm rectangular, two lamp system
C — 146 mm round, four lamp system
D — 178 mm round, two lamp system
E — 100 × 165 mm rectangular, two lamp system
F — 92 × 150 mm rectangular, four lamp system
G — 100 × 165 mm rectangular, four lamp system
H — 100 × 165 mm rectangular, two lamp system
J — 56 × 75 mm rectangular, eight lamp system
K — 55 × 135 mm rectangular, four lamp system

3.2.4.5 The third character (a number) indicates the photometric specification which applies to the headlamp. Headlamps designed to Table 3 have "1" as the third character.

TABLE 3—PHOTOMETRY

	Low Beam Min	Low Beam Max
10U to 90U, 45R to 45L		125 cd
8L to 8R, H to 4U	64 cd	
4L to 4R, H to 2U	135	
1U—1-1/2L to L		700
1/2U—1-1/2L to L		1 000
1/2D—1-1/2L to L		3 000
1-1/2U—1R to R		1 400
1/2U—1R, 2R, 3R		2 700
1/2D—1-1/2R	8 000	20 000
1D—6L	750	
1-1/2D—2R	15 000	
1-1/2D—9L & 9R	750	
2D—15L & 15R	700	
4D—4R		8 000
H—2R	4 000	10 000
1D—V	6 000	15 000

TABLE 3—PHOTOMETRY (CONTINUED)

	High Beam Min	High Beam Max
2U—V	1 500 cd	
1U—3R & 3L	5 000	
H—V	20 000	75 000 cd
H—3R & 3L	10 000	
H—6R & 6L	3 250	
H—9R & 9L	2 000	
H—12R & 12L	500	
1-1/2D—V	5 000	
1-1/2D—9R & 9L	1 500	
2-1/2D—V	2 000	
2-1/2D—12R & 12L	750	
4D—V		12 500
Maximum Beam Candela [1]—30 000 cd Min		

[1] The highest candela reading found in the beam pattern.

3.2.4.6 Headlamps designed to UF, UK, LF, and LK specifications shall meet the following criteria:

3.2.4.6.1 The first character indicates the upper (high) or low beam function.

3.2.4.6.2 The second character indicates the size and number of headlamps used on the vehicle.

3.2.4.7 *Headlamp Type Identification*—See Table 4.

TABLE 4—HEADLAMP TYPE IDENTIFICATION

Size	Type	Number of Headlamps
100 × 165 mm (4 × 6.5 in)	1A1	2
	2A1	2
	1G1	2
	2G1	2
142 × 200 mm	2B1	2
146 mm (5.75 in)	1C1	2
	2C1	2
178 mm (7.0 in)	2D1	2
100 × 165 mm (4 × 6.5 in)	2E1	2
	2H1	2
92 × 150 mm	UF	2
	LF	2
56 × 75 mm	UJ	4
	LJ	4
55 × 135 mm	UK	2
	LK	2

3.3 Replaceable Bulb Marking Requirements—Bulbs shall be marked with the following information.

3.3.1 Manufacturer's name and/or trademark

3.3.2 Trade number (ANSI)

3.3.3 Date Code

4. *Tests*—The test procedures and test requirements specified in this document were developed emphasizing extreme conditions in the headlamp environment. Separate headlamps shall be used for each test.

4.1 Bulbs—Unless otherwise specified, bulbs used in the tests shall be representative of bulbs in regular production. Testing shall be conducted on lot sizes established by the manufacturer. The manufacturer shall obtain and be able to supply the data.

4.2 SAE J575 is a part of this report. The following tests are applicable with the modifications as indicated.

4.2.1 Vibration Test—The headlamp shall be seasoned and photometered to the test points in Table 3 before and after the vibration test. The filament shall not be operated during the test (see 4.2.4).

4.2.2 Dust Test—The headlamp shall be seasoned and photometered to the test points in Table 3 before and after the dust test.

4.2.3 Corrosion Test

4.2.3.1 The headlamp shall be seasoned and photometered to the test points in Table 3 before and after the corrosion test.

4.2.3.2 The test period shall be 240 h consisting of 10 cycles of 23 h exposure followed by 1 h drying.

4.2.4 Photometry

4.2.4.1 Test samples shall be new, unused headlamps manufactured from production tooling and assembled by production processes.

4.2.4.2 The headlamp shall be seasoned and photometered at the appropriate test points as listed in Table 3. The headlamp shall be in operation a minimum of 5 min prior to photometry.

4.2.4.3 Photometric test shall be made with the photometer sensor at a distance of at least 18.3 m from the headlamp.

4.2.4.4 The headlamp shall be aimed mechanically with the aiming plane at the design angle(s) to the photometer axis and the mechanical axis of the headlamp on the photometer axis.

4.2.4.5 *Test Voltage*—The voltage for the photometric test shall be 12.8 V ± 20 mV, DC as measured at the terminals of the headlamp.

4.3 Color Test—SAE J578 is a part of this report.

4.4 Plastic Materials—SAE J576 is a part of this report except 4.2.1, Luminous Transmittance.

4.5 Beam Pattern Location Test

4.5.1 Headlamps designed to be aimed on high beam, shall be seasoned and photometered to find the location of maximum intensity (see 4.2.4).

4.5.2 Headlamps designed to be aimed on low beam, shall be seasoned and photometered (see 4.2.4) at the test points H-2R and 1D-V.

4.6 Wattage Test

4.6.1 The wattage of each filament shall be determined at 12.8 V ± 20 mV DC.

4.6.2 Filaments shall be seasoned prior to wattage measurement.

4.7 Luminous Flux Test

4.7.1 Each filament shall be seasoned and photometered at 12.8 V ± 20 mV DC to determine luminous flux.

4.7.2 The tests shall be conducted in accordance with IES Approved Method for Electrical and Photometric Measurements of General Service Incandescent Filament Lamps, IES Lighting Handbook, Reference Volume, Illuminating Engineering Society, New York, NY, Procedure LM-45.

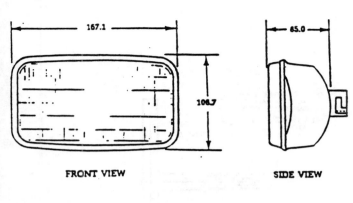

FRONT VIEW · SIDE VIEW

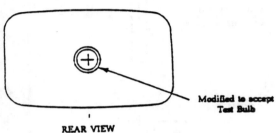

Modified to accept
Test Bulb

REAR VIEW

FIGURE 2—TEST ENCLOSURE DIMENSIONS

4.8 Luminous Flux Maintenance Test

4.8.1 The luminous flux for each filament shall be determined in accordance with 4.7.

4.8.2 The bulb shall then be energized in a horizontal or its normal burning position in the test enclosure shown in Figure 2.

4.8.3 The test voltage shall be 14.0 V ± 0.1 V DC. Two-filament bulbs shall be tested by cycle burning the high beam filament 12 min for each hour of testing.

4.8.4 The luminous flux of a single filament bulb shall be measured after burning for 70% of the design life.

4.8.5 The luminous flux of each filament of two-filament bulbs shall be measured in accordance with 4.7 after the low beam filament on-time equals 70% of the design life when tested according to 4.8.3.

4.9 Out-of-Focus Test

4.9.1 This test shall be conducted on headlamps with replaceable bulbs.

4.9.2 The headlamp shall be mounted in the goniometer with the mechanical axis coincident with the photometer axis.

4.9.3 The test voltage for the headlamp shall be 12.8 V ± 20 mV DC.

4.9.4 The headlamp shall be photometered at the appropriate test points as listed in Table 3.

4.9.5 Intensity measurements shall be made at six out-of-focus positions with the filament located at 2/3 of the tolerance value specified for the filament tolerance specifications referenced in Table 2.

4.10 Impact Test

4.10.1 The headlamp shall be rigidly mounted in a test fixture on the seating plane with the lens facing up.

4.10.2 The seating plane of the test fixture shall consist of 13 mm thick oak wood. The test fixture shall rest on an oak wood base.

4.10.3 One impact shall be delivered to the headlamp lens along the mechanical axis using a 23 mm diameter steel sphere (approximately 50 g) dropped freely, without side forces, from a distance of 40 cm above the lens.

4.11 Aiming Adjustment Test

4.11.1 When making the aiming adjustment test, an accurate measurement technique shall be used. This may consist of: (a) Attaching a device such as a spot projector to the headlamp, or (b) replacing the headlamp with a mirror along with a separate light source, or (c) other equally accurate means.

4.11.2 When conducting the test, the headlamp shall be mounted in the design position with the unit at nominal aim (0,0).

4.12 Inward Force Test—The mechanism, including the aiming adjusters, shall be subjected to an inward force of 222 N directed normal to the headlamp aiming plane and symmetrically about the center of the sealed beam unit face (see Figure 3).

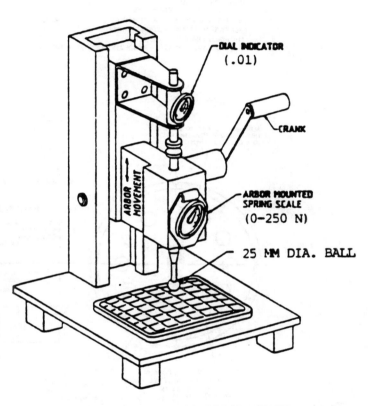

FIGURE 3—INWARD FORCE TESTER

4.13 Torque Deflection Test—Applies to headlamps which do not incorporate on-board headlamp aiming system.

4.13.1 The headlamp assembly to be tested shall be mounted in design vehicle position and set at nominal aim (0,0).

4.13.2 Sealed beam headlamps shall be replaced by the appropriate deflectometer (Figures 4 to 8).

4.13.3 Replaceable bulb headlamps shall be equipped with an appropriate fixture on the face of the lens with the applied load acting parallel to the aiming reference plane and in a downward direction. The force shall be applied through the aiming pads.

4.13.4 A torque of 2.25 Nm shall be applied to the headlamp assembly through the deflectometer and a reading on the thumbwheel shall be taken. The torque shall then be removed and a second reading on the thumbwheel shall be taken.

4.14 Deflection Test—Applies to replaceable headlamp bulbs.

4.14.1 The bulb shall be rigidly mounted in a fixture in a manner indicated in Figure 9.

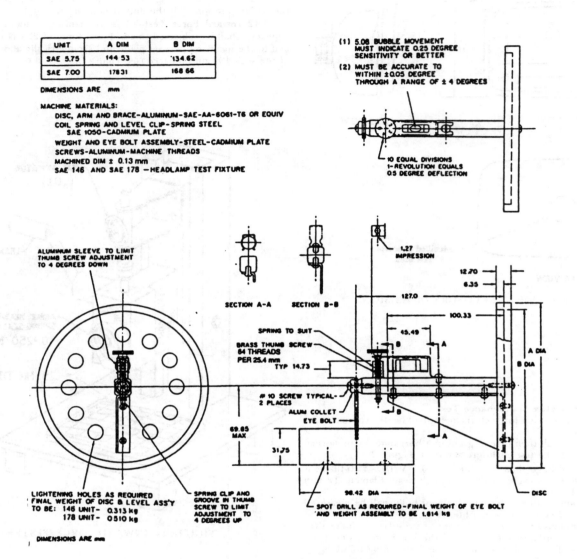

UNIT	A DIM	B DIM
SAE 5.75	144 53	134.62
SAE 7.00	178 31	168 66

DIMENSIONS ARE mm

MACHINE MATERIALS:
 DISC, ARM AND BRACE—ALUMINUM—SAE-AA-6061-T6 OR EQUIV
 COIL SPRING AND LEVEL CLIP—SPRING STEEL
  SAE 1050—CADMIUM PLATE
 WEIGHT AND EYE BOLT ASSEMBLY—STEEL—CADMIUM PLATE
 SCREWS—ALUMINUM—MACHINE THREADS
 MACHINED DIM ± 0.13 mm
 SAE 146 AND SAE 178—HEADLAMP TEST FIXTURE

(1) 5.08 BUBBLE MOVEMENT
 MUST INDICATE 0.25 DEGREE
 SENSITIVITY OR BETTER
(2) MUST BE ACCURATE TO
 WITHIN ±0.05 DEGREE
 THROUGH A RANGE OF ± 4 DEGREES

10 EQUAL DIVISIONS
1-REVOLUTION EQUALS
0.5 DEGREE DEFLECTION

ALUMINUM SLEEVE TO LIMIT
THUMB SCREW ADJUSTMENT
TO 4 DEGREES DOWN

SECTION A-A   SECTION B-B

1.27
IMPRESSION

12.70
6.35
127.0
100.33
45.49

SPRING TO SUIT

BRASS THUMB SCREW
64 THREADS
PER 25.4 mm
TYP 14.73

A DIA
B DIA

10 SCREW TYPICAL-
2 PLACES

ALUM COLLET
EYE BOLT

69.85
MAX

31.75

98.42 DIA

DISC

LIGHTENING HOLES AS REQUIRED
FINAL WEIGHT OF DISC & LEVEL ASS'Y
TO BE: 146 UNIT- 0.313 kg
    178 UNIT- 0.510 kg

SPRING CLIP AND
GROOVE IN THUMB
SCREW TO LIMIT
ADJUSTMENT TO
4 DEGREES UP

SPOT DRILL AS REQUIRED-FINAL WEIGHT OF EYE BOLT
AND WEIGHT ASSEMBLY TO BE 1.814 kg

DIMENSIONS ARE mm

FIGURE 4—DEFLECTOMETER

22

SAE HEADLAMP TEST FIXTURE
100 X 165MM

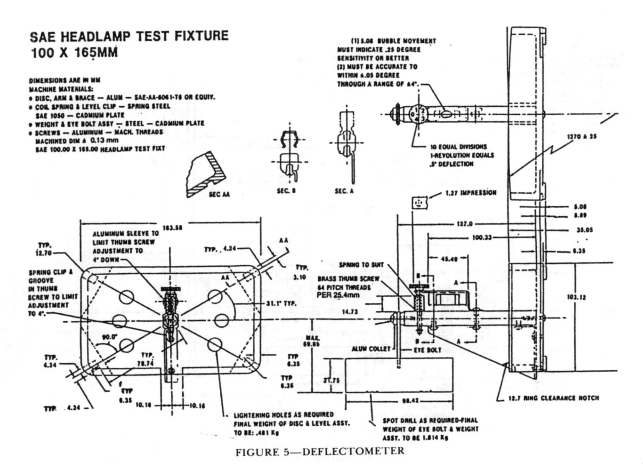

FIGURE 5—DEFLECTOMETER

SAE HEADLAMP TEST FIXTURE
142 X 200MM

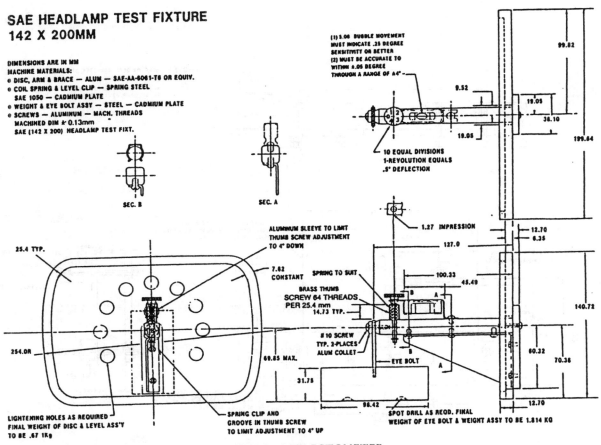

FIGURE 6—DEFLECTOMETER

HEADLAMP TEST FIXTURE
92 X 150 MM

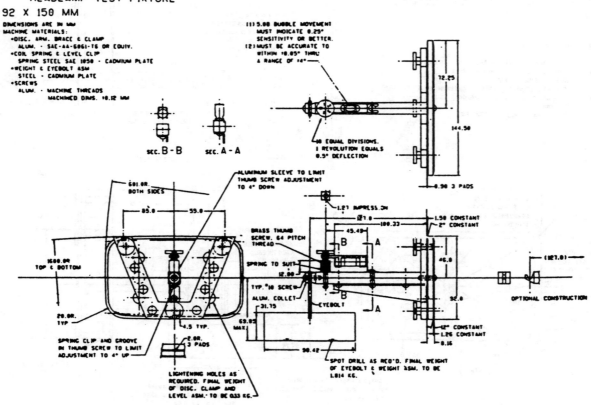

FIGURE 7—DEFLECTOMETER

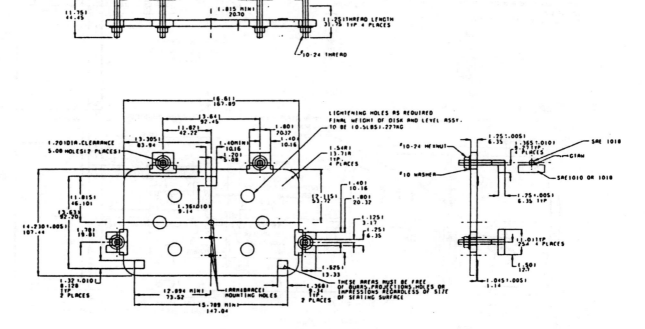

FIGURE 8—DEFLECTOMETER

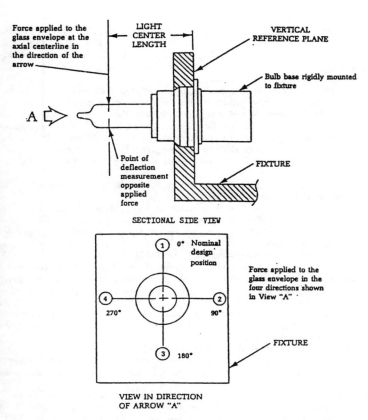

FIGURE 9—BULB DEFLECTION TEST

4.14.2 A force of 18.0 N ± 0.4 shall be applied for a maximum of 5.0 s at the locations shown in Figure 9 using a rod with a hard rubber tip with a minimum radius of 1.0 mm.

4.14.3 A separated bulb shall be used for each load application at 0, 90, 180, and 270 degrees.

4.15 Sealing Test—Applies to bulbs designed for an airtight fit to the headlamp.

4.15.1 The bulb shall be inserted into a fixture as shown in Figure 10 and retained by the same method intended for application, or equivalent.

4.15.2 The chamber shall be gradually pressurized to 70.0 kPa ± 1.0 gage while the fixture and terminal end of the bulb is completely submerged in water. The 70 kPa gage pressure shall be held for 60 s.

4.15.3 The bulb shall be observed for the presence of air bubbles during the 60 s time period.

4.16 Chemical Resistance Test

4.16.1 The test shall be conducted with the headlamps and the test fluids at an ambient temperature of 23 °C ± 4.

4.16.2 The test headlamps shall be seasoned and photometered to the test points in Table 3 before and after the chemical resistance test (see 4.2.4).

4.16.3 A separated headlamp shall be used for each of the test fluids.

4.16.4 The test fluids are:

  a. Windshield washer fluid (50% concentration by volume of methanol/ detergent base, 0.16% ethanolamine)

  b. Antifreeze (50% concentration by volume of ethylene glycol in water)

  c. Simulated unleaded gasoline (test fluid ASTM D 471-79 Reference fuel "D")

4.16.5 An unfixtured headlamp in its design operating position and condition shall be used for the test.

4.16.6 A 6 in square cotton cloth shall be folded twice to form a 3 in square and placed onto the bottom of a beaker.

4.16.7 Meter 3 mL of the test fluid onto the folded cloth.

4.16.8 Remove the cloth from the beaker (5 s after completion of test fluid metering for Reference Fuel D and windshield washer fluid, and 60 s after completion of test fluid metering for antifreeze).

4.16.9 Within 5 s after removal of the cloth from the beaker, wipe the lens with that cloth surface which was uppermost in the beaker. The entire exterior optical surface of the lens of the fixtured headlamp shall be wiped in three horizontal cycles (one cycle consists of one back and forth motion). The first cycle shall apply the test fluid to the upper segment of the lens, the second cycle shall apply it to the center segment, and the third cycle shall apply it to the lower segment.

4.16.10 After applying the test fluid, the test headlamp shall be set aside for a period of 48 h where upon the headlamp shall be wiped clean with a soft, dry, cotton cloth.

4.17 Abrasion Test of Plastic Headlamp Lens Material

4.17.1 A 100 × 165 mm flat test specimen shall be measured for luminous transmittance before and after wiping clean after the abrasion test.

4.17.2 The test specimen shall be mounted in the abrasion test machine as indicated in Figure 11.

4.17.3 The size of the abrading pad shall be 25 × 100 mm constructed of 0000 steel wool and firmly attached to a pad support of equal size such that the "grain" of the pad is perpendicular to the direction of motion.

4.17.4 The abrading pad shall be loaded such that an average pad pressure of 14 kPa ± 1 exists normal to the surface of the test specimen.

4.17.5 The density of the abrading pad shall be such that when the abrading pad mounted to the pad support is resting unloaded on the test specimen, the pad support shall be no closer than 3.1 mm to the surface of the test specimen.

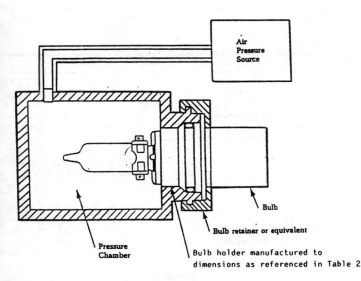

FIGURE 10—TEST FOR AIRTIGHT SEAL

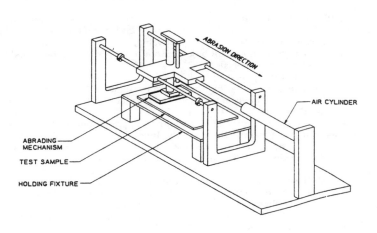

FIGURE 11—ABRASION TEST MACHINE

4.17.6 An abrasion cycle is one forward stroke 10 cm ± 2 and one rearward stroke of the same distance. The velocity of the abrading pad shall be 10 cm/s ± 2.

4.17.7 The test specimen shall be subjected to 20 abrasion cycles.

4.18 Thermal Cycle Test

4.18.1 The headlamp shall be seasoned and photometered to the test points in Table 3 before and after the thermal cycle test (see 4.2.4).

4.18.2 The headlamp shall be rigidly mounted in a test fixture on its seating plane in its design operating condition and design mounting position.

4.18.3 The headlamp shall be exposed to the thermal cycle profile shown in Figure 12.

4.18.4 Separate or single test chambers may be used to generate the temperature environment described by the thermal cycle.

AMBIENT TEMPERATURE TRANSITION RATES:
MINIMUM 0.6°C (1°F) PER MINUTE
MAXIMUM 4°C (8°F) PER MINUTE

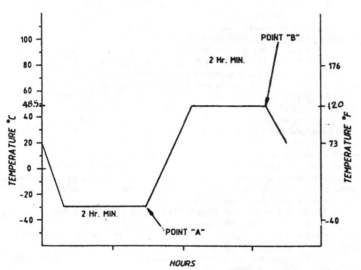

FIGURE 12—THERMAL CYCLE PROFILE

4.18.5 The headlamp shall be energized at 12.8 V ± 20 mV, its highest wattage mode commencing at point "A" of Figure 12 and de-energized at point "B" of each cycle.

4.18.6 The test period shall be 10 cycles of 8 h per cycle.

4.19 Internal Heat Test

4.19.1 The headlamp shall be seasoned and photometered to the test points in Table 3 before and after the internal heat test (see 4.2.4).

4.19.2 The headlamp shall be rigidly mounted in a test fixture on its seating plane in its design operating condition and design mounting position.

4.19.3 A dirt mixture, soluble in water, shall be sprayed uniformly on the face of the lens and allowed to dry until the light intensity at H-V is reduced by 50% of its original value.

4.19.4 The headlamp shall be energized in its highest wattage mode and placed in a chamber at 35 °C ± 3.

4.19.5 The test cycle shall be 30 min.

4.19.6 The test voltage for the headlamp shall be 12.8 V ± 0.1.

4.19.7 After the internal heat test, the lens face shall be wiped clean.

4.20 Humidity Test

4.20.1 The headlamp shall be seasoned and photometered to the test points in Table 3 before and after the humidity test (see 4.2.4).

4.20.2 The headlamp shall be rigidly mounted in a test fixture on its seating plane, in its design operating condition and design mounting position.

4.20.3 The headlamp shall be placed in a controlled environment of 95% ± 5 relative humidity at 38 °C (100 °F). There may be airflow within the test chamber not to exceed 16.5 km/h.

4.20.4 The headlamp shall be energized in its highest wattage mode for a test cycle of 1 h "on" and 5 h "off".

4.20.5 The test voltage for the headlamp shall be 12.8 V ± 0.1.

4.20.6 TEST DURATION—EIGHT COMPLETE CYCLES—The test is to end in the "off" cycle mode.

4.20.7 After completion of the eighth test cycle, the humidity shall be reduced in the test chamber to 30% ± 10 for 1 h. The headlamp shall be turned off during this period. During this period there may be a maximum air flow within the test chamber of 16.5 km/h when measured at the center of the chamber.

4.20.8 After a 1 h soak period, the headlamp shall be removed from the humidity chamber and photometered within 10 min ± 1.

4.21 Filament Rated Average Lab Life Test

4.21.1 The filament shall be energized at 14 V ± 0.1 V DC in a horizontal burning position in the standard enclosure shown in Figure 2.

4.21.2 The filament shall be unenergized 15 min for each 24 h of testing. The off time is not part of the test time of the filament being tested.

4.21.3 Each filament shall be tested separately and a different bulb shall be used for each filament.

4.21.4 The test may be terminated at 150% of design life.

5. Performance Requirements—A headlamp, when tested in accordance with the test procedures specified in Section 4, shall meet the following requirements.

5.1 Vibration Requirement (SAE J575)

5.1.1 The photometric values measured after the vibration test shall not vary more than ±10% from the values measured before the test.

5.1.2 There shall be no evidence of loose or broken parts, or intermittent electrical circuit.

5.2 Dust Requirement (SAE J575)—The photometric values measured after the dust test shall not vary by more than ±10% from the values measured before the test.

5.3 Corrosion Requirement (SAE J575)

5.3.1 The test headlamp shall show no evidence of exterior or internal corrosion or edge corrosion beyond 2 mm (0.08 in) from a sheared or cut edge.

5.3.2 The headlamp shall show no evidence of surface deterioration, fractures, color bleeding, or deterioration of bonding materials.

5.3.3 The photometric values measured after the corrosion test shall not vary more than ±10% from the values measured before the test.

5.4 Photometric Performance Requirement—Headlamps designed to meet the specifications of Table 3 shall meet the photometric requirements of Table 5.

TABLE 5—HEADLAMP PHOTOMETRIC PERFORMANCE REQUIREMENTS

Test Point[1]	Requirement, cd
Low Beam	
Type 2A1, 2B1, 2C1, 2D1, 2E1, or Equivalent	
10U-90U, 45R-45L	438 cd max permissible within 2 degree conical angle
1/2U—1-1/2L	1 100 max
1/2U—1R	3 240 max
1/2D—1-1/2R	6 400 min/24 000 max
1D—6L	600 min
High Beam	
Type 1A1 and 1C1, or Equivalent	
2U-V	800 min
H-3R and 3L	9 600 min
H-V	16 000 min
2-1/2D-V	1 600 min

[1] A tolerance of ±1/2 degree in location may be allowed at any test point.

5.5 Color—The color of the emanating light produced by a headlamp shall be white as specified in SAE J578.

5.6 Material Requirements—Headlamps shall meet the material requirements of SAE J576, except 4.2.1 Luminous Transmittance.

5.7 Beam Pattern Location Requirement

5.7.1 HEADLAMPS DESIGNED TO BE AIMED ON HIGH BEAM—The beam pattern is properly oriented to the aiming plane if the location of the maximum beam intensity point does not deviate from the H-V axis more than ±0.5 degree vertically and ±0.8 degree horizontally (rectangular box).

5.7.2 HEADLAMPS DESIGNED TO BE AIMED ON LOW BEAM—The beam pattern is properly oriented to the aiming plane if the intensity requirements listed in Table 3 for the test points H-2R and 1D-V are met.

5.8 Wattage Requirement—Measured wattage for each filament shall not exceed the design wattage listed in Tables 1 and 6 by more than 7.5%.

5.9 Luminous Flux Requirement—Applies to replaceable headlamp bulbs.

TABLE 6—TYPICAL HEADLAMPS

Headlamp Type and Identification Code[1]	Trade No.[2]	Design Watts at 12.8 V U.B.	Design Watts at 12.8 V L.B.	Design Life at 14 V[3] U.B.	Design Life at 14 V[3] L.B.	Max. Amps at 12.8 V U.B.	Max. Amps at 12.8 V L.B.	Size, mm	Dimensional Specs	Terminals No.
2C1	4000	37.5	60	200	320	3.14	5.02	146 Dia	Figure 24	3
2C1	4040[2]	37.5	60	200	320	3.14	5.02	146 Dia	Figure 24	3
2C1	H5006	35	35	200	320	2.94	2.94	146 Dia	Figure 24	3
1C1	4001	37.5		200		3.14		146 Dia	Figure 23	2
1C1	H4001	37.5		200		3.14		146 Dia	Figure 23	2
1C1	5001	50		200		4.20		146 Dia	Figure 23	2
1C1	H5001	50		200		4.20		146 Dia	Figure 23	2
2D1	6014	50	50	200	320	5.02	4.20	178 Dia	Figure 25	3
2D1	H6014	60	50	200	320	5.02	4.20	178 Dia	Figure 25	3
2D1	6015[2]	60	50	320	320	5.02	4.20	178 Dia	Figure 25	3
2D1	6016[2]	60	50	300	500	5.02	4.20	178 Dia	Figure 25	3
2D1	H6017	60	35	200	320	5.02	2.94	178 Dia	Figure 25	3
1A1	4651	50		200		4.20		100 X 165	Figure 20	2
1A1	H4651	50		200		4.20		100 X 165	Figure 20	2
2A1	4652	40	60	200	320	3.36	5.02	100 X 165	Figure 21	3
2A1	H4656	35	35	200	320	2.94	2.94	100 X 165	Figure 21	3
2A1	H4662	40	45	200	320	3.36	3.78	100 X 165	Figure 21	3
2A1	H4739	40	50	500	2000	3.36	4.20	100 X 165	Figure 21	3
2B1	6052	65	55	150	320	5.46	4.62	142 X 200	Figure 22	3
2B1	H6052	65	55	150	320	5.46	4.62	142 X 200	Figure 22	3
2B1	H6054	65	35	150	320	5.46	2.94	142 X 200	Figure 22	3
2E1	H4666	65	45	150	320	5.46	3.78	100 X 165	Figure 26	3
UF	H4701	65		150		5.46		92 X 150	Figure 27	2
LF	H4703		55		320		4.62	92 X 150	Figure 27	2
1G1		50		200		4.20		100 X 165	Figure 28	3
2G1		35	35	200	320	2.94	2.94	100 X 165	Figure 28	3
2H1		65	45	150	320	5.46	3.78	100 X 165	Figure 28	3
UJ		25		150		2.10		56 X 75	Figure 29	2
LJ			20		500		1.68	56 X 75	Figure 30	2
UK[4]	H4352	65		150		5.46		55 X 135	Figure 31	2
LK	H4351		55		500		4.62	55 X 135	Figure 32	2

[1]Headlamp identification codes are explained in 5.25.
[2]Heavy duty headlamps.
[3]All headlamps designs for 12.8 V usage are life tested at 14 V. In general, the life at vehicle voltage is longer.
[4]UK and LK photometric beam patterns are combined for high beam.

27

5.9.1 For bulbs with no opaque coating, the measured luminous flux shall be within ±12% of the design luminous flux listed in Table 1.

5.9.2 For bulbs with opaque coating, the measured luminous flux shall be within ±15% of the design luminous flux listed in Table 1.

5.10 Maintenance of Luminous Flux Requirement—When tested in accordance with 4.7—For samples from each lot tested, the average luminous flux value for single filament bulbs for each filament of two-filament bulbs after burning for 70% of design life shall be no less than 90% of the initial average luminous flux value.

5.11 Out-of-Focus Requirement—The headlamp shall meet the requirements of Table 5 for each of the out-of-focus test positions.

5.12 Impact Requirement—The headlamp shall show no evidence of broken, cracked, or chipped pieces of the headlamp, coating adhesion failure, or delamination of material, or visible loosening or breaking apart of headlamp parts.

5.13 Aiming Adjustment Requirement—When tested in accordance with 4.11, the headlamp shall meet the following requirements:

5.13.1 For headlamps with individual horizontal and vertical aim adjustments, tested in the laboratory, a minimum aiming adjustment of ±4.0 degrees shall be provided in the vertical plane and ±2.5 degrees in the horizontal plane.

5.13.2 On headlamp assemblies with independent vertical and horizontal aiming provision, the adjustments shall be such that when tested in the laboratory, neither the vertical nor horizontal aim shall deviate more than 100 mm from horizontal or vertical planes, respectively, at a distance of 7.6 m through an angle of ±4.0 degrees vertically and ±2.5 degrees horizontally.

5.13.3 On headlamps with integral aim tested in the laboratory, the headlamp shall be able to indicate variations in vertical aim within a range extending from 1.2 degrees above to at least 1.2 degrees below a longitudinal horizontal plane through the center of the headlamp system.

5.13.4 On headlamps with integral aim, photometric tests shall be performed with the vertical aiming system set to its specified design vertical aim, and with the headlamp assembly mounted to the test fixture in the same attitude as its design mounting position in the vehicle.

5.13.5 The self-locking devices used to hold aiming screws in position shall continue to operate satisfactorily for a minimum of 20 adjustments on each screw, over a length of screw thread of not less than 3 mm.

NOTE: 5.13.2 and 5.13.3 are not applicable to headlamps with ball and socket or equivalent adjusting means.

5.14 Inward Force Requirements—When subjected to the tests in 4.12, the headlamp shall meet the following requirements:

5.14.1 The headlamp shall not permanently recede by more than 2.5 mm.

5.14.2 The aim of the headlamp shall not permanently deviate by more than 3.2 mm at a distance of 7.6 m.

5.15 Torque Deflection Requirement—When subjected to the tests in 4.13, the difference between the two readings shall not exceed 0.30 degree.

5.16 Deflection Requirement—After the load application, the permanent deflection of the glass envelope of the bulb shall not exceed 0.13 mm.

5.17 Sealing Requirement—While the fixture and terminal end is submerged, no bubble(s) shall develop outside the test fixture.

5.18 Chemical Resistance Requirement

5.18.1 The exposed headlamp, when compared to an unexposed headlamp, shall not show surface deterioration, delamination, fractures, deterioration of bonding materials, color bleeding, or color pickup as a result of exposure to the test fluids.

5.18.2 The photometric values measured after the chemical resistance test shall not vary more than ±10% from the values measured before the test.

5.19 Abrasion of Plastic Headlamp Lens Material Requirements—The luminous transmittance of the abraded test specimen using CIE Illuminant A (2856D), shall show a maximum of 3% deterioration from the luminous transmittance of the unabraded control sample.

5.20 Thermal Cycle Requirement

5.20.1 The headlamp shall show no evidence of delamination, fractures, seal fractures, deterioration of bonding material, color bleeding, warp, or deforming.

5.20.2 The photometric values measured after the temperature cycle test shall not vary by more than ±10% from values measured before the test.

5.21 Internal Heat Requirement—The photometric values measured after the internal heat test shall not vary by more than ±10% from the values measured before the test.

5.22 Humidity Requirement

5.22.1 At the end of the 10 min test period (see 4.22), the headlamp shall be inspected immediately and show no evidence of condensed moisture or droplets inside the headlamp.

5.22.2 The headlamp shall show no evidence of delamination, bonding, material deterioration, or seal failure.

5.22.3 The photometric values measured after the humidity test shall not vary by more than ±10% from the values measured before the test.

5.23 Retaining Ring Requirements

5.23.1 Positive means shall be provided for holding the headlamp to the mounting ring.

5.23.2 The fastening means shall be capable of holding the headlamp securely in its proper position at the end of 20 replacements.

5.23.3 When a headlamp having a flange thickness (as shown in Table 7) is secured between the retaining ring and mounting ring, there shall be no evidence of looseness:

TABLE 7—FLANGE THICKNESS

Headlamp Type	Flange Thickness
146 mm	11.7 mm
178 mm	11.7 mm
100 × 165 mm	33.9 mm
142 × 200 mm	10.1 mm
92 × 150 mm	9.6 mm
55 × 135 mm	9.6 mm
56 × 75	3.6 mm

5.24 Design Requirements

5.24.1 Dimensions of sealed beam headlamp mounting-sealed beam headlamp mounting rings and retaining rings shall meet the dimensions marked "I" in the following figures to assure compatibility with the corresponding types of units.

5.24.2 DIMENSIONS OF SEALED BEAM HEADLAMPS—Sealed beam headlamps shall meet the dimensions marked "I" in the following figures to assure interchangeability with other sealed beam headlamps of the same type.

5.24.3 Dimensions for Mechanical Aiming of Headlamps—Headlamps shall meet the following requirements to assure compatibility with mechanical aimers.

5.24.3.1 Type 1C1, 2C1, and 2D1 headlamps shall have no raised letters or embossing on the outside surface of the lens between the diameters of 40 and 90 mm about the lens center.

5.24.3.2 Type 1A1, 2A1, 2B1, 2E1, UF, LF, 1G1, 2G1, and 2H1 headlamps shall have no raised letters or embossing on the outside surface of the lens within a diameter of 70 mm about the lens center.

5.24.3.3 Aiming pad design may vary, but shall meet limiting dimensions as shown on the figures specified in 5.24.1 and 5.24.2.

5.24.4 Headlamp Mounting Assembly—The headlamp mounting assembly shall meet the requirements of Figure 13, Dimensions of Sealed Beam Headlamp Mounting.

5.24.5 Aimer Compatibility—Headlamps which do not incorporate integral headlamp aim shall be designed and installed so that they may be inspected and aimed by mechanical aimers as specified in SAE J602 without the removal of any ornamental trim rings or other parts.

5.24.6 Bulbs and bulb holders shall meet the requirements referenced in Table 2 to ensure interchangeability.

5.24.7 Accurate rated bulbs shall meet the dimensional requirements shown in each applicable figure of Table 2.

5.24.8 Typical replaceable headlamp bulbs are listed in Table 1.

6. Guidelines

6.1 When in use, a headlamp shall not have any styling ornament or other feature, such as a glass cover or grille, in front of the lens.

6.2 **Photometric Design Guidelines**—Guidelines for the photometric design of headlamps are shown in Table 3.

6.3 **Dimensional Guidelines**—Guidelines for dimensions are shown in the following figures:

6.3.1 Mounting and Retaining Rings—Figures 13 to 18

6.3.2 Sealed Beam Headlamps—See Table 6 and Figures 20 to 32

6.3.3 Replaceable Bulbs—See Table 2 and Figures 33 to 70

6.3.4 Reflector Bulb Mounting Hole for Replaceable Bulbs—See Table 2.

6.4 **Filament Rated Average Lab Life Guideline**—Rated average lab life shall approximate design life. The design life for the filament(s) of each bulb type is shown in Table 1 or 5.

6.5 **Replaceable Bulb Filament End Coil Definition**—Shown in Figure 19.

6.6 **Summary of Requirements and Guidelines**—Table 8 summarizes the classification of the various sections of this report into requirements and guidelines.

6.7 **Fixed Horizontal Aim Guideline**—When horizontal aim adjusting screws are provided on fixed horizontal aim headlamps, they shall be of a tamperproof design or shall be difficult to access.

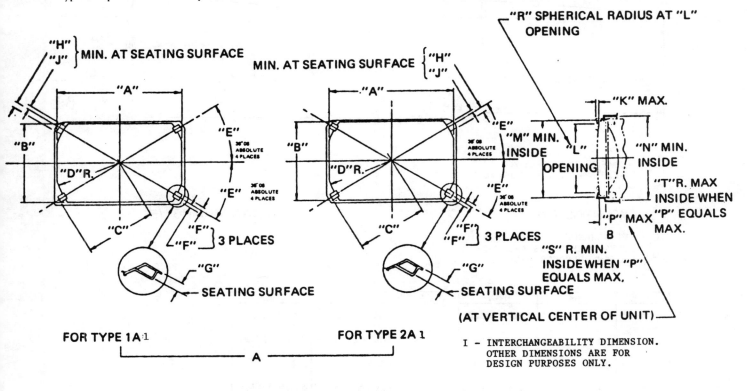

FOR TYPE 1A1   FOR TYPE 2A1

I — INTERCHANGEABILITY DIMENSION. OTHER DIMENSIONS ARE FOR DESIGN PURPOSES ONLY.

	Letter	in	mm		Letter	in	mm
	A	6.518 ± 0.020	165.56 ± 0.50	L	L	3.660 ± 0.059 × 6.040 ± 0.059	92.96 ± 1.50 × 153.42 ± 1.50
	B	4.140 ± 0.020	105.16 ± 0.50				
I	C	3.670 +0.015 −0.000	93.218 +0.37 0.00	I	M	4.080 × 0.46	103.64 × 164.10
	D	3.408 ± 0.020	87.00 ± 0.50	I	N	4.25 × 6.63	107.95 × 168.40
	E	31.10° ± 0.08°			P	0.418	10.62
I	F	0.178 +0.020 −0.000	4.52 +0.51 −0.00		R	50.0 +0.50 −2.00	1270.0 +13.0 −50.8
I	G	0.170 +0.000 −0.030	4.318 +0.00 −0.76		S	0.075	1.91
I	H	0.334	8.48		T	0.060	1.52
I	J	0.120	3.05				
	K	0.060	1.52				

FIGURE 13—(A) FRONT VIEW OF SLOTS OR NOTCHES FOR 100 × 165 mm
RECTANGULAR HEADLAMP MOUNTING RING OR LAMP BODY;
(B) RECTANGULAR HEADLAMP RETAINING RING

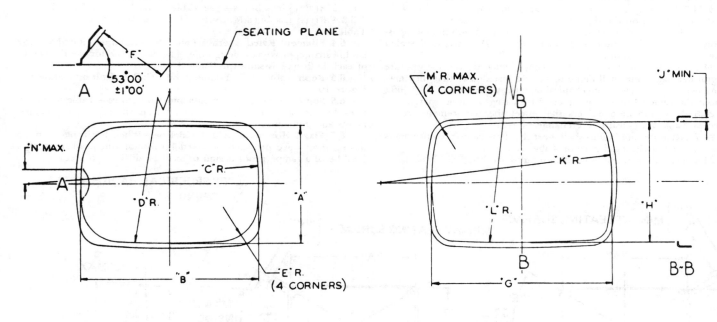

DIMENSIONS APPLY AT
SEATING PLANE SURFACE

MOUNTING RING (A)   RETAINING RING (B)

I - INTERCHANGEABILITY DIMENSION.
OTHER DIMENSIONS ARE FOR
DESIGN PURPOSES ONLY.

LETTER	MM	INCH		LETTER	MM	INCH
A	132.9 ± 0.5	5.232 ± 0.020	I	G	190.42 ± 0.30	7.497 ± 0.012
B	191.0 ± 0.5	7.520 ± 0.020	I	H	132.42 ± 0.30	5.213 ± 0.012
C	250.0 ± 5.0	9.843 ± 0.197	I	J	5.34	0.210
D	2400.0 ± 50.0	94.488 ± 1.969	I	K	250.0 $^{+30.0}_{-0}$	9.843 $^{+1.181}_{-0.000}$
E	41.0 ± 2.0	1.614 ± 0.079	I	L	2402.0 $^{+2250.0}_{-0}$	94.567 $^{+88.583}_{-0.000}$
F	79.90 ± 0.40	3.146 ± 0.016	I	M	20.4	0.803
				N	19.0	0.748

FIGURE 14—(A) FRONT VIEW OF MOUNTING RING OR LAMP BODY FOR
142 × 200 mm RECTANGULAR HEADLAMP; (B) RETAINING RING

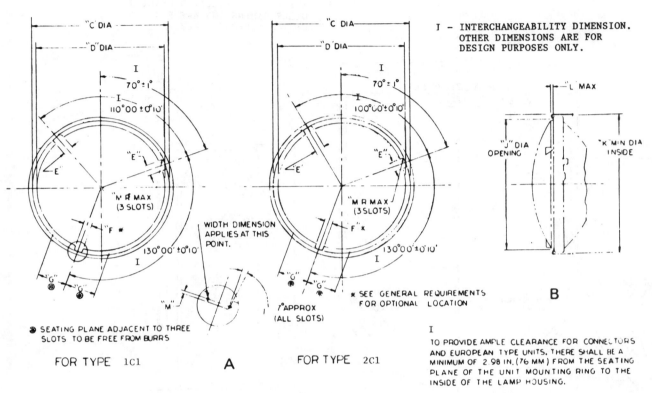

I - INTERCHANGEABILITY DIMENSION.
OTHER DIMENSIONS ARE FOR
DESIGN PURPOSES ONLY.

FOR TYPE 1C1

A

FOR TYPE 2C1

B

WIDTH DIMENSION
APPLIES AT THIS
POINT.

1° APPROX
(ALL SLOTS)

✱ SEE GENERAL REQUIREMENTS
FOR OPTIONAL LOCATION

⊛ SEATING PLANE ADJACENT TO THREE
SLOTS TO BE FREE FROM BURRS

I

TO PROVIDE AMPLE CLEARANCE FOR CONNECTORS
AND EUROPEAN TYPE UNITS, THERE SHALL BE A
MINIMUM OF 2.98 IN. (76 MM) FROM THE SEATING
PLANE OF THE UNIT MOUNTING RING TO THE
INSIDE OF THE LAMP HOUSING.

DIMENSIONS

Letter	in	mm	Letter	in	mm
I C	$5.450 \begin{smallmatrix}+0.010\\-0.000\end{smallmatrix}$	$138.43 \begin{smallmatrix}+0.25\\-0\end{smallmatrix}$	G	1.20	30.48
I D	5.250 – 5.140	133.35 – 130.55	I J	5.400 – 5.360	137.16 – 136.14
I E	$0.410 \begin{smallmatrix}+0.010\\-0.000\end{smallmatrix}$	$10.41 \begin{smallmatrix}+0.25\\-0\end{smallmatrix}$	I K	5.710	145.03
I F	$0.330 \begin{smallmatrix}+0.005\\-0.000\end{smallmatrix}$	$8.38 \begin{smallmatrix}+0.12\\-0\end{smallmatrix}$	L	0.100	2.54
			M	0.06	1.52

FIGURE 15—(A) FRONT VIEW OF SLOTS OR NOTCHES FOR 146 mm DIAMETER HEADLAMP
MOUNTING RING OR LAMP BODY; (B) 146 mm HEADLAMP RETAINING RING

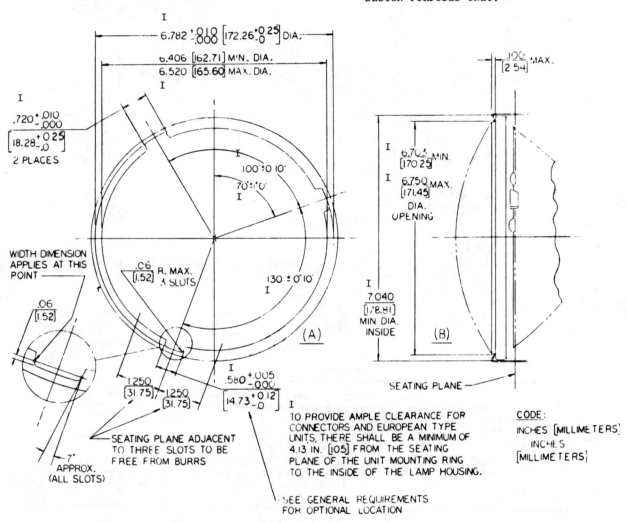

FIGURE 16—(A) FRONT VIEW OF SLOT OR NOTCHES FOR 178 mm DIAMETER HEADLAMP
MOUNTING RING OR LAMP BODY; (B) 178 mm HEADLAMP RETAINING RING

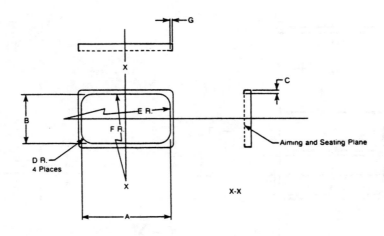

Aiming Ring

X-X

Aiming and Seating Plane

LETTER	INCH	MM
A	5.721 ± .006	145.30 ± 0.30
B	3.284 ± .006	83.40 ± 0.30
C	.213 MIN.	5.40 MIN.
D	.670 MAX.	17.00 MAX.
E	23.7 ± 2.0	602.2 ± 50.0
F	63.0 ± 3.93	1600.0 ± 100.5
G	134 MIN.	3.40 MIN.

FIGURE 17—AIMING/SEATING RING FOR TYPE LF AND UF
RECTANGULAR SEALED BEAM HEADLAMP UNITS

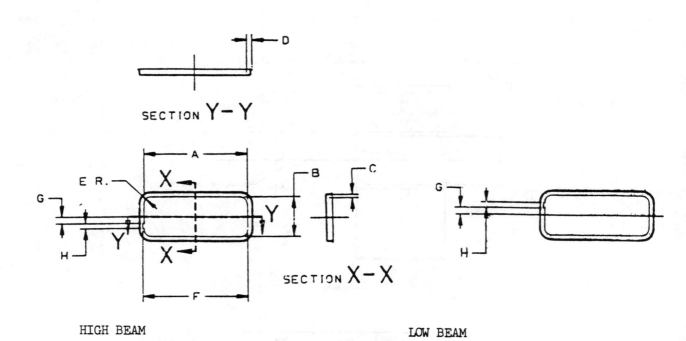

SECTION Y-Y

SECTION X-X

HIGH BEAM		
LETTER	INCH	MM
A	5.38 ±.010	136.7 ±0.30
B	2.25 ±.010	57.0 ±0.30
C	.154 MIN	3.9 MIN
D	.197 MIN	5.0 MIN
E	.26 ±.010	6.5 ±0.30
F	5.47 ±.02	139.0 ±0.30
G	.33 ±.02	8.5 ±0.5
H	.39 ±.02	10.0 ±0.5

LOW BEAM		
LETTER	INCH	MM
NOTE: SAME AS HIGH BEAM EXCEPT AS SHOWN		
G	.33 ±.02	8.5 ±0.5
H	.39 ±.02	10.0 ±0.5

FIGURE 18—AIMING RING—55 × 135 UK/LK

The following guideline is intended to depict the current methods which are being used by the lighting industry for identifying the end of filaments. It is not possible to predict every filament leg configuration. When the filament legs are in some other configuration than those shown below, a guideline is: The end turns of the filament are defined as being the first luminous turn and the last luminous turn that are substantially at the correct helix angle. The ends of the filament would then be the beginning of the first turn and conclusion of the last turn that are substantially at the correct helix angle.

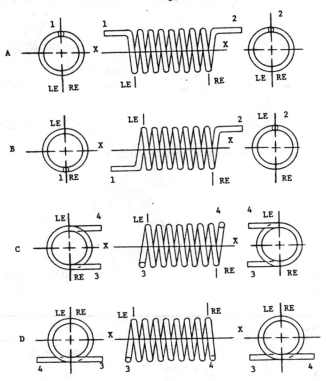

X-X axis of the filament
    LE - Left end of filament
    RE - Right end of filament

Filament configuration A and B:
    LE - is 180 degrees around circumference on the first turn from (1) leg of the filament, when looking parallel to X-X

    RE - is 180 degrees around circumference on the first turn from (2) leg of the filament, when looking parallel to X-X

Filament configuration C and D:

    LE - is 180 degrees around circumference on the first turn from (3) centerline of filament leg, when looking parallel to X-X

    RE - is 180 degrees around circumference on the first turn from (4) centerline of filament leg, when looking parallel to X-X

FIGURE 19—GUIDELINE REPLACEABLE BULB FILAMENT END COIL DEFINITION

35

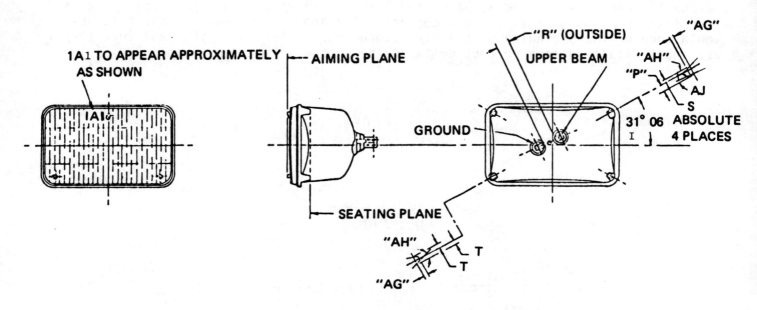

1A1 TO APPEAR APPROXIMATELY AS SHOWN

AIMING PLANE

SEATING PLANE

"R" (OUTSIDE)
UPPER BEAM
GROUND
"AG"
"AH"
"P"
AJ
S
31° 06 ABSOLUTE
I ↕ 4 PLACES

"AH"
"AG"
T
T

I – INTERCHANGEABILITY DIMENSION. OTHER DIMENSIONS ARE FOR DESIGN PURPOSES ONLY.

NOTE: SAME AS TYPE 2A1 EXCEPT AS SHOWN

	Letter	in	mm
	A G	0.160 ± 0.010	4.064 ± 0.25
I	R	0.669 $+0.035 / -0.000$	17.0 $+0.9 / -0$
	AH	15°00' ± 3°00'	
I	T	0.167 ± 0.0100	4.24 ± 0.25
	AJ	4°20' ± 1°00'	
I	P	0.313 $+0.015 / -0.010$	7.95 $+0.38 / -0.25$
I	S	0.122 $+0.015 / -0.010$	3.10 $+0.38 / -0.25$

FIGURE 20—TYPE 1A1 HEADLAMP 100 × 165 mm RECTANGULAR

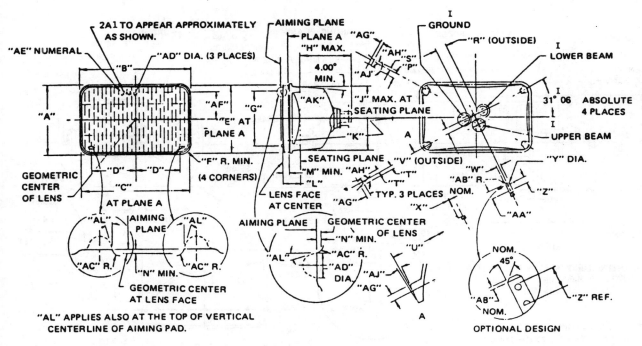

Letter	in	mm	Letter	in	mm	Letter	in	mm
I A	4.200 +0.030 −0.170	106.68 +0.76 −4.32	I P	0.313 +0.015 −0.010	7.95 +0.38 −0.25	AA	0.535 +0.000 −0.071	13.58 +0 −1.80
I B	6.580 +0.030 −0.170	167.13 +0.76 −4.32	I R	0.669 +0.035 −0.000	17.02 +0.88 −0.00	AB	0.060 ± 0.020	1.5 ± 0.5
I C	6.440 ± 0.030	163.58 ± 0.76	I S	0.122 ± 0.015	3.10 +0.38 −0.25	AC	0.060 ± 0.020	1.5 ± 0.5
D	2.700 ± 0.020	68.58 ± 0.51				AD	0.200 ± 0.010	5.08 ± 0.25
I E	4.060 ± 0.030	103.12 ± 0.76	I T	0.167 ± 0.010	4.24 ± 0.25	AE	0.250 ± 0.030	6.35 ± 0.76
I F	0.540	13.71	I U	3.640 ± 0.010	92.47 ± 0.25	AF	1.660 ± 0.010	42.16 ± 0.25
G	3.320 ± 0.030	84.33 ± 0.76	I V	0.335 +0.020 −0.000	8.5 +0.5 −0	AG	0.160 ± 0.010	4.06 ± 0.25
I H	3.350	85.09				AH	15° max	
I J	4.01	101.85	I W	0.304 +0.016 −0.000	7.72 +0.40 −0.00	AJ	3.33° min	
K	50.000 +0.500 −2.00	1270.0 +13.0 −50.8	I X	0.030 ± 0.002	0.76 ± 0.05	AK	1.56° max	39.6 max
			Y	0.120 +0.010 −0.000	3.05 +0.25 −0	AL	16° max	
I L	1.375 ± 0.040	34.93 ± 1.02						
I M	0.420	10.68	Z	0.345 +0.059 −0.000	8.76 +1.50 −0			
N	0.020	0.51						

I − INTERCHANGEABILITY DIMENSION.
OTHER DIMENSIONS ARE FOR
DESIGN PURPOSES ONLY.

FIGURE 21—TYPE 2A1 HEADLAMP 100 × 165 mm RECTANGULAR

37

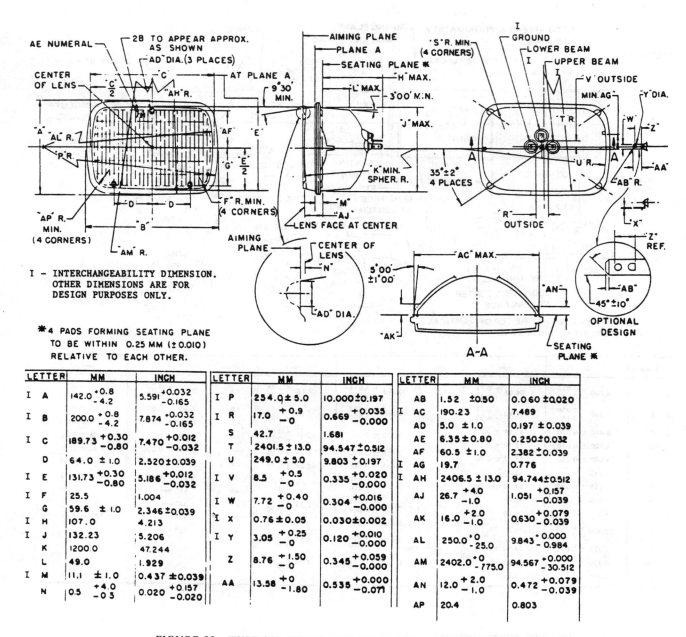

I - INTERCHANGEABILITY DIMENSION.
OTHER DIMENSIONS ARE FOR
DESIGN PURPOSES ONLY.

✱ 4 PADS FORMING SEATING PLANE
TO BE WITHIN 0.25 MM (±0.010)
RELATIVE TO EACH OTHER.

LETTER		MM	INCH	LETTER		MM	INCH	LETTER	MM	INCH
I	A	142.0 +0.8/-4.2	5.591 +0.032/-0.165	I	P	254.0±5.0	10.000±0.197	AB	1.52 ±0.50	0.060 ±0.020
I	B	200.0 +0.8/-4.2	7.874 +0.032/-0.165	I	R	17.0 +0.9/-0	0.669 +0.035/-0.000	I AC	190.23	7.489
I	C	189.73 +0.30/-0.80	7.470 +0.012/-0.032		S	42.7	1.681	AD	5.0 ±1.0	0.197 ±0.039
	D	64.0 ±1.0	2.520±0.039		T	2401.5 ±13.0	94.547±0.512	AE	6.35±0.80	0.250±0.032
I	E	131.73 +0.30/-0.80	5.186 +0.012/-0.032		U	249.0 ±5.0	9.803 ±0.197	AF	60.5 ±1.0	2.382±0.039
I	F	25.5	1.004	I	V	8.5 +0.5/-0	0.335 +0.020/-0.000	I AG	19.7	0.776
	G	59.6 ±1.0	2.346±0.039	I	W	7.72 +0.40/-0	0.304 +0.016/-0.000	I AH	2406.5 ±13.0	94.744±0.512
I	H	107.0	4.213		X	0.76±0.05	0.030±0.002	AJ	26.7 +4.0/-1.0	1.051 +0.157/-0.039
I	J	132.23	5.206	I	Y	3.05 +0.25/-0	0.120 +0.010/-0.000	AK	16.0 +2.0/-1.0	0.630 +0.079/-0.039
	K	1200.0	47.244		Z	8.76 +1.50/-0	0.345 +0.059/-0.000	AL	250.0 +0.000/-25.0	9.843 +0.000/-0.984
	L	49.0	1.929		AA	13.58 +0/-1.80	0.535 +0.000/-0.071	AM	2402.0 +0/-775.0	94.567 +0.000/-30.512
I	M	11.1 ±1.0	0.437±0.039					AN	12.0 +2.0/-1.0	0.472 +0.079/-0.039
	N	0.5 +4.0/-0.5	0.020 +0.157/-0.020					AP	20.4	0.803

FIGURE 22—TYPE 2B1 HEADLAMP 142 × 200 mm RECTANGULAR

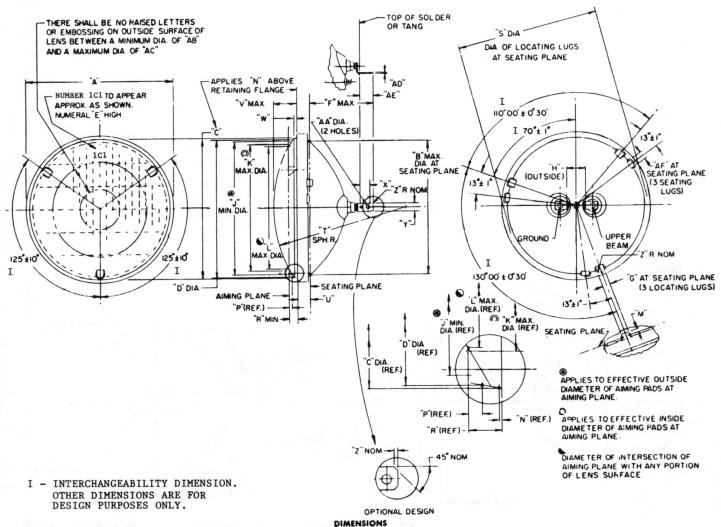

I - INTERCHANGEABILITY DIMENSION.
OTHER DIMENSIONS ARE FOR
DESIGN PURPOSES ONLY.

OPTIONAL DESIGN

DIMENSIONS

Letter	in	mm		Letter	in	mm
I A	$5.700^{+0.000}_{-0.100}$	$144.78^{+0}_{-2.54}$		T	$5.06\ \pm0.12$	128.52 ± 3.04
I B	5.120	130.04		I U	0.500 ± 0.040	12.70 ± 1.01
I C	$5.355^{+0.000}_{-0.030}$	$136.01^{+0}_{-0.76}$		V	0.92	23.36
D	5.280 – 5.340	134.11 – 135.63		W	$0.078^{+0.062}_{-0.000}$	$1.98^{+1.57}_{-0}$
E	1/4 ±1/32	6.35 ±0.79		I X	$0.345^{+0.060}_{-0.000}$	$8.76^{+1.52}_{-0}$
I F	2.60	66.04		I Y	$0.304^{+0.016}_{-0.000}$	$7.72^{+0.40}_{-0}$
I G	0.312 ± 0.010	7.92 ± 0.25		Z	0.06	1.52
I H	$0.670^{+0.035}_{-0.000}$	$17.01^{+0.88}_{-0}$		I AA	$0.120^{+0.010}_{-0.000}$	$3.04^{+0.25}_{-0}$
I J	5.060	128.52		AB	1.50	38.10
K	4.57	116.07		AC	3.60	91.44
L	4.53	115.06		I AD	0.030 ± 0.002	0.76 ± 0.05
I M	$0.100^{+0.050}_{-0.000}$	$2.54^{+1.27}_{-0}$		AE	$0.535^{+0.000}_{-0.070}$	$13.58^{+0}_{-1.77}$
N	0.030	0.76		AF	$0.31\ \pm0.12$	7.87 ± 3.04
P	0.165	4.19				
I R	0.320	8.12				
I S	$5.440^{+0.000}_{-0.040}$	$138.17^{+0}_{-1.01}$				

FIGURE 23—TYPE 1C1 HEADLAMP 146 mm DIAMETER

39

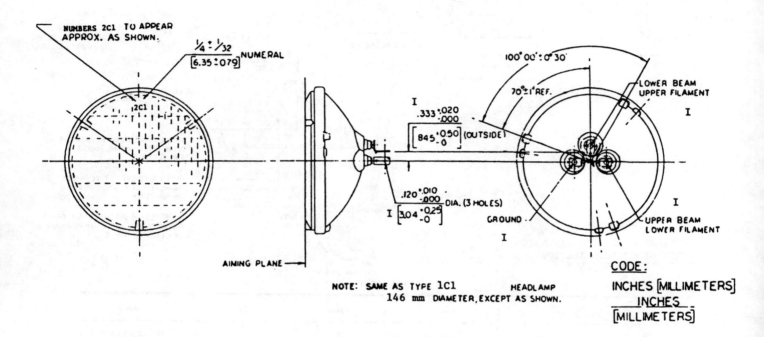

NUMBERS 2C1 TO APPEAR APPROX. AS SHOWN.

¼ ± ¹⁄₃₂ NUMERAL
[6.35 ± .079]

2C1

100° 00' ± 0° 30'

70° ± 1° REF.

LOWER BEAM
UPPER FILAMENT

I

.333 ⁺·⁰²⁰ ₋·⁰⁰⁰

[845 ⁺·⁰⁵⁰ ₋·⁰] (OUTSIDE)

I

I

.120 ⁺·⁰¹⁰ ₋·⁰⁰⁰ DIA. (3 HOLES)

I [3.04 ⁺·⁰²⁵ ₋·⁰]

GROUND

UPPER BEAM
LOWER FILAMENT

AIMING PLANE

CODE:

INCHES [MILLIMETERS]

INCHES

[MILLIMETERS]

NOTE: SAME AS TYPE 1C1 HEADLAMP
146 mm DIAMETER, EXCEPT AS SHOWN.

FIGURE 24—TYPE 2C1 HEADLAMP 146 mm DIAMETER

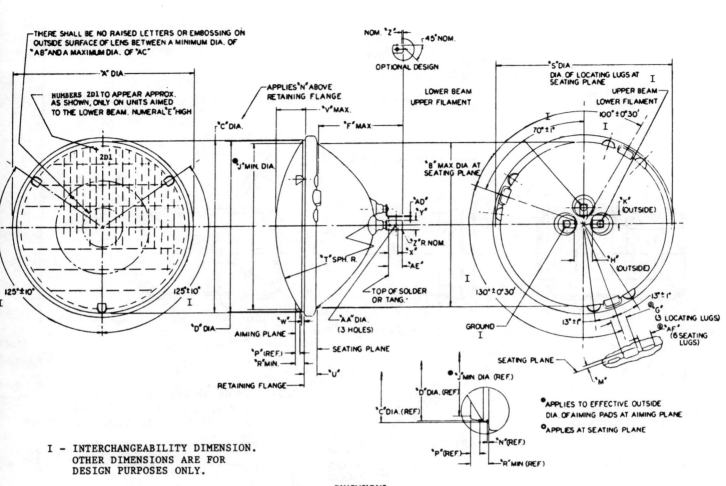

I – INTERCHANGEABILITY DIMENSION.
OTHER DIMENSIONS ARE FOR
DESIGN PURPOSES ONLY.

DIMENSIONS

Letter	In	mm	Letter	In	mm
I A	$7.031^{+0.000}_{-0.109}$	$178.58^{+0}_{-2.76}$	I S	$6.770^{+0.000}_{-0.040}$	$171.95^{+0}_{-1.01}$
I B	6.380	162.05	T	$6.000^{+0.250}_{-0.000}$	$152.40^{+6.35}_{-0}$
I C	$6.687^{+0.000}_{-0.030}$	$169.84^{+0}_{-0.76}$	I U	0.500 ± 0.040	12.70 ± 1.01
D	6.595 – 6.675	167.52 – 169.54	V	1.150	29.21
E	3/8 ± 1/32	9.52 ± 0.79	W	$0.078^{+0.062}_{-0.000}$	$1.98^{+1.57}_{-0}$
I F	3.500	88.90	I X	$0.345^{+0.060}_{-0.000}$	$8.76^{+1.52}_{-0}$
I G	$0.575^{+0.000}_{-0.025}$	$14.60^{+0}_{-0.63}$	I Y	$0.304^{+0.016}_{-0.000}$	$7.72^{+0.40}_{-0}$
I H	$0.670^{+0.035}_{-0.000}$	$17.01^{+0.88}_{-0}$	Z	0.06	1.52
I J	6.450	163.83	I AA	$0.120^{+0.010}_{-0.000}$	$3.04^{+0.25}_{-0}$
I K	$0.333^{+0.020}_{-0.000}$	$8.45^{+0.50}_{-0}$	AB	1.50	38.10
			AC	3.60	91.44
I M	$0.106^{+0.100}_{-0.000}$	$2.69^{+2.54}_{-0}$	I AD	0.030 ± 0.002	0.76 ± 0.05
N	0.030	0.76	AE	$0.535^{+0.000}_{-0.070}$	$13.58^{+0}_{-1.77}$
P	0.180	4.57	AF	0.50 ± 0.25	12.70 ± 6.35
I R	0.350	8.89			

FIGURE 25—TYPE 2D1 HEADLAMP 178 mm DIAMETER

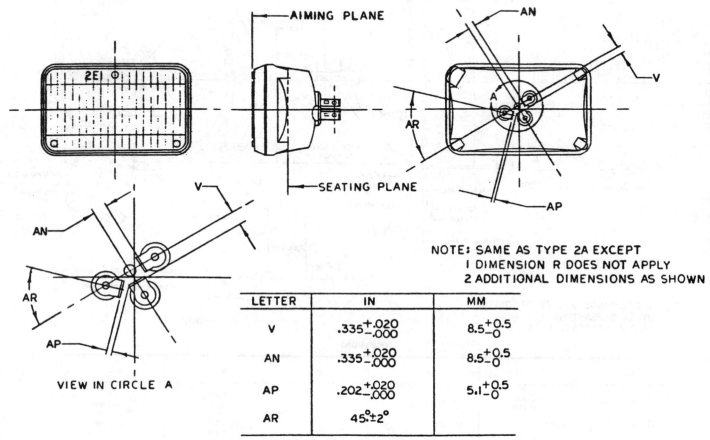

NOTE: SAME AS TYPE 2A EXCEPT
1 DIMENSION R DOES NOT APPLY
2 ADDITIONAL DIMENSIONS AS SHOWN

VIEW IN CIRCLE A

LETTER	IN	MM
V	$.335^{+.020}_{-.000}$	$8.5^{+0.5}_{-0}$
AN	$.335^{+.020}_{-.000}$	$8.5^{+0.5}_{-0}$
AP	$.202^{+.020}_{-.000}$	$5.1^{+0.5}_{-0}$
AR	$45°.±2°$	

TYPE 2EI SEALED BEAM HEADLAMP UNIT
4 X 6 1/2 IN (100 X 165 MM) RECTANGULAR UNIT

FIGURE 26—TYPE 2E1 HEADLAMP 100 × 165 mm RECTANGULAR

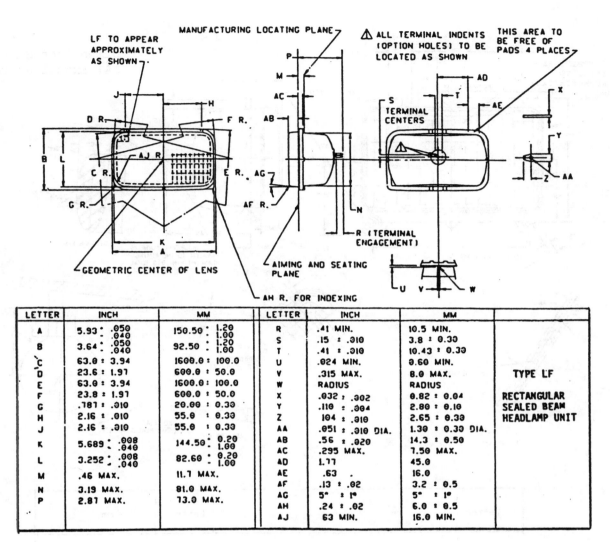

LETTER	INCH	MM	LETTER	INCH	MM	
A	5.93 +.050/-.040	150.50 +1.20/-1.00	R	.41 MIN.	10.5 MIN.	
B	3.64 +.050/-.040	92.50 +1.20/-1.00	S	.15 ± .010	3.8 ± 0.30	
C	63.0 ± 3.94	1600.0 ± 100.0	T	.41 ± .010	10.43 ± 0.30	
D	23.6 ± 1.97	600.0 ± 50.0	U	.024 MIN.	0.60 MIN.	TYPE LF
E	63.0 ± 3.94	1600.0 ± 100.0	V	.315 MAX.	8.0 MAX.	
F	23.8 ± 1.97	600.0 ± 50.0	W	RADIUS	RADIUS	RECTANGULAR
G	.787 ± .010	20.00 ± 0.30	X	.032 ± .002	0.82 ± 0.04	SEALED BEAM
H	2.16 ± .010	55.0 ± 0.30	Y	.110 ± .004	2.80 ± 0.10	HEADLAMP UNIT
J	2.16 ± .010	55.0 ± 0.30	Z	104 ± .010	2.65 ± 0.30	
K	5.689 +.008/-.040	144.50 +0.20/-1.00	AA	.051 ± .010 DIA.	1.30 ± 0.30 DIA.	
L	3.252 +.008/-.040	82.60 +0.20/-1.00	AB	.56 ± .020	14.3 ± 0.50	
M	.46 MAX.	11.7 MAX.	AC	.295 MAX.	7.50 MAX.	
N	3.19 MAX.	81.0 MAX.	AD	1.77	45.0	
P	2.87 MAX.	73.0 MAX.	AE	.63	16.0	
			AF	.13 ± .02	3.2 ± 0.5	
			AG	5° ± 1°	5° ± 1°	
			AH	.24 ± .02	6.0 ± 0.5	
			AJ	63 MIN.	16.0 MIN.	

TYPE UF
RECTANGULAR SEALED BEAM HEADLAMP UNIT

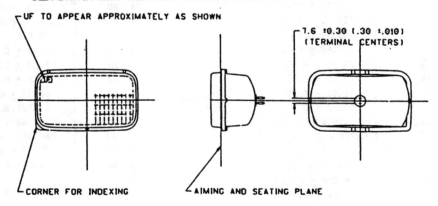

Note: Same as Type LF except as shown (.XX) Inch Dim.

FIGURE 27—TYPE "UF" AND "LF" HEADLAMPS 92 × 150 mm RECTANGULAR

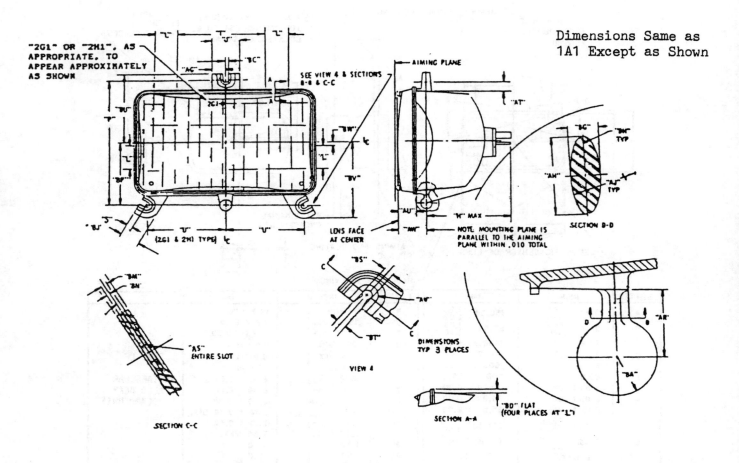

Dimensions Same as
1A1 Except as Shown

Letter	mm	Letter	mm.
H MAX	88.87 ± 0.38 I	BA	5.59 SPHER.R I
J	25.40 ± 0.38	BC	5.00 ± 0.13 I
L	31.75 MIN.	BD	1.02 MIN. I
P	121.92 ± 0.66 I	BG	3.81 ± 0.25 I
S	6.35 ± 0.13 I	BH	0.81R
T	97.40 ± 0.25	BJ	18.29 ± 0.38
U	71.63 ± 0.38 I	BM	1.62 ± 0.10 I
AG	12.70 ± 0.25	BN	0.81 ± 0.10 I
AH	10.41 ± 0.25 I	BP	62.23 ± 0.38
AJ	10.67 ± 0.25	BS	4.52/4.60 DIA I
AR	9.40 MIN. I	BT	4.42/4.47 I
AS	0.76R + 0.0.- 0.76 I	BU	69.34 ± 0.38
AT	5.84 MIN. I	BV	75.69 ± 0.38
AU	16.76 ± 1.02 I	BW	4.06 ± 0.25
AV	5.08R ± 0.25 I		
AW	27.94 ± 1.02 I		

FIGURE 28—TYPES 1G1, 2G1, AND 2H1 HEADLAMPS 100 × 165 mm RECTANGULAR

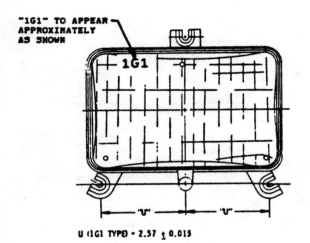

"1G1" TO APPEAR
APPROXIMATELY
AS SHOWN

U (1G1 TYPE) = 2.57 ± 0.015

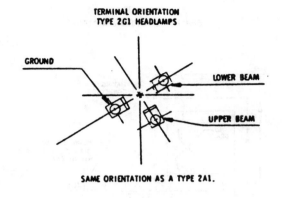

TERMINAL ORIENTATION
TYPE 2G1 HEADLAMPS

GROUND

LOWER BEAM

UPPER BEAM

SAME ORIENTATION AS A TYPE 2A1.

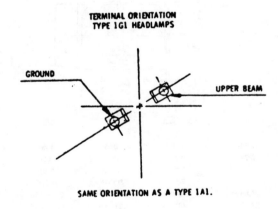

TERMINAL ORIENTATION
TYPE 1G1 HEADLAMPS

GROUND

UPPER BEAM

SAME ORIENTATION AS A TYPE 1A1.

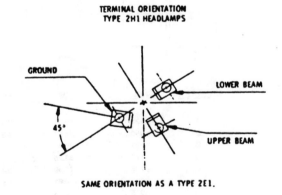

TERMINAL ORIENTATION
TYPE 2H1 HEADLAMPS

GROUND

LOWER BEAM

45°

UPPER BEAM

SAME ORIENTATION AS A TYPE 2E1.

Noninterchangeability Configurations for Integral Mount Sealed Beam Headlamps, Type G and H

FIGURE 28 (CONTINUED)

45

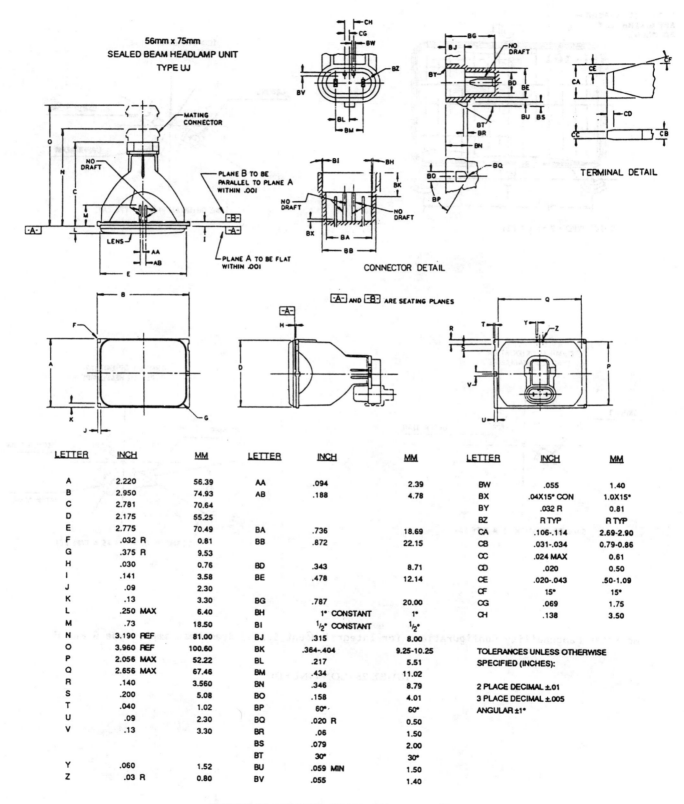

56mm x 75mm
SEALED BEAM HEADLAMP UNIT
TYPE UJ

MATING CONNECTOR

NO DRAFT

PLANE B TO BE PARALLEL TO PLANE A WITHIN .001

LENS

PLANE A TO BE FLAT WITHIN .001

TERMINAL DETAIL

CONNECTOR DETAIL

-A- AND -B- ARE SEATING PLANES

LETTER	INCH	MM	LETTER	INCH	MM	LETTER	INCH	MM
A	2.220	56.39	AA	.094	2.39	BW	.055	1.40
B	2.950	74.93	AB	.188	4.78	BX	.04X15° CON	1.0X15°
C	2.781	70.64				BY	.032 R	0.81
D	2.175	55.25				BZ	R TYP	R TYP
E	2.775	70.49	BA	.736	18.69	CA	.106-.114	2.69-2.90
F	.032 R	0.81	BB	.872	22.15	CB	.031-.034	0.79-0.86
G	.375 R	9.53				CC	.024 MAX	0.61
H	.030	0.76	BD	.343	8.71	CD	.020	0.50
I	.141	3.58	BE	.478	12.14	CE	.020-.043	.50-1.09
J	.09	2.30				CF	15°	15°
K	.13	3.30	BG	.787	20.00	CG	.069	1.75
L	.250 MAX	6.40	BH	1° CONSTANT	1°	CH	.138	3.50
M	.73	18.50	BI	1/2° CONSTANT	1/2°			
N	3.190 REF	81.00	BJ	.315	8.00			
O	3.960 REF	100.60	BK	.364-.404	9.25-10.25			
P	2.056 MAX	52.22	BL	.217	5.51	TOLERANCES UNLESS OTHERWISE		
Q	2.656 MAX	67.46	BM	.434	11.02	SPECIFIED (INCHES):		
R	.140	3.560	BN	.346	8.79			
S	.200	5.08	BO	.158	4.01	2 PLACE DECIMAL ±.01		
T	.040	1.02	BP	60°	60°	3 PLACE DECIMAL ±.005		
U	.09	2.30	BQ	.020 R	0.50	ANGULAR ±1°		
V	.13	3.30	BR	.06	1.50			
			BS	.079	2.00			
			BT	30°	30°			
Y	.060	1.52	BU	.059 MIN	1.50			
Z	.03 R	0.80	BV	.055	1.40			

FIGURE 29—SEALED BEAM HEADLAMP UNIT
TYPE UJ

46

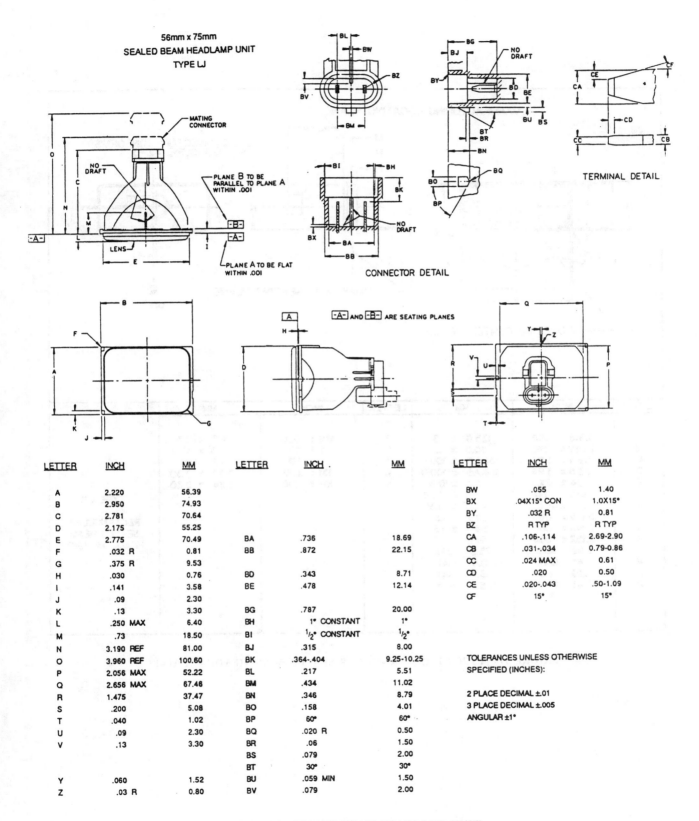

56mm x 75mm
SEALED BEAM HEADLAMP UNIT
TYPE LJ

TERMINAL DETAIL

CONNECTOR DETAIL

-A- AND -B- ARE SEATING PLANES

LETTER	INCH	MM	LETTER	INCH	MM	LETTER	INCH	MM
A	2.220	56.39				BW	.055	1.40
B	2.950	74.93				BX	.04X15° CON	1.0X15°
C	2.781	70.64				BY	.032 R	0.81
D	2.175	55.25				BZ	R TYP	R TYP
E	2.775	70.49	BA	.736	18.69	CA	.106-.114	2.69-2.90
F	.032 R	0.81	BB	.872	22.15	CB	.031-.034	0.79-0.86
G	.375 R	9.53				CC	.024 MAX	0.61
H	.030	0.76	BD	.343	8.71	CD	.020	0.50
I	.141	3.58	BE	.478	12.14	CE	.020-.043	.50-1.09
J	.09	2.30				CF	15°	15°
K	.13	3.30	BG	.787	20.00			
L	.250 MAX	6.40	BH	1° CONSTANT	1°			
M	.73	18.50	BI	1/2° CONSTANT	1/2°			
N	3.190 REF	81.00	BJ	.315	8.00			
O	3.960 REF	100.60	BK	.364-.404	9.25-10.25	TOLERANCES UNLESS OTHERWISE		
P	2.056 MAX	52.22	BL	.217	5.51	SPECIFIED (INCHES):		
Q	2.656 MAX	67.46	BM	.434	11.02			
R	1.475	37.47	BN	.346	8.79	2 PLACE DECIMAL ±.01		
S	.200	5.08	BO	.158	4.01	3 PLACE DECIMAL ±.005		
T	.040	1.02	BP	60°	60°	ANGULAR ±1°		
U	.09	2.30	BQ	.020 R	0.50			
V	.13	3.30	BR	.06	1.50			
			BS	.079	2.00			
			BT	30°	30°			
Y	.060	1.52	BU	.059 MIN	1.50			
Z	.03 R	0.80	BV	.079	2.00			

FIGURE 30—SEALED BEAM HEADLAMP UNIT
TYPE LJ

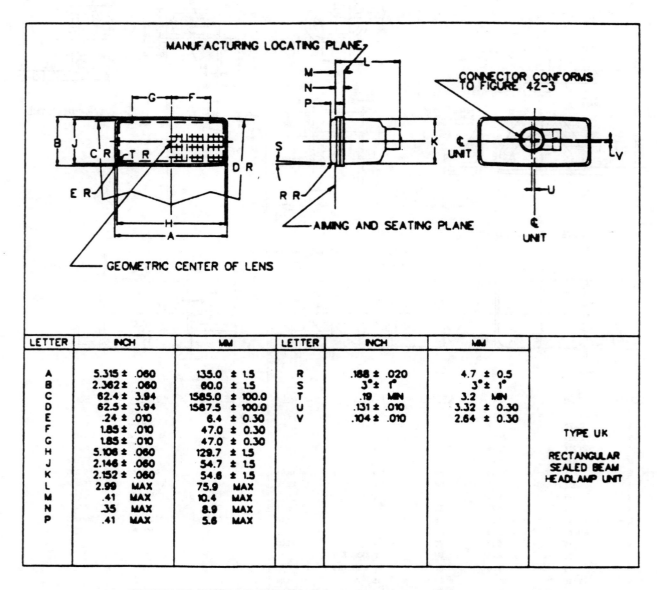

LETTER	INCH	MM	LETTER	INCH	MM	
A	5.315 ± .060	135.0 ± 1.5	R	.188 ± .020	4.7 ± 0.5	
B	2.362 ± .060	60.0 ± 1.5	S	3° ± 1°	3° ± 1°	
C	62.4 ± 3.94	1585.0 ± 100.0	T	.19 MIN	3.2 MIN	
D	62.5 ± 3.94	1587.5 ± 100.0	U	.131 ± .010	3.32 ± 0.30	
E	.24 ± .010	6.4 ± 0.30	V	.104 ± .010	2.64 ± 0.30	
F	1.85 ± .010	47.0 ± 0.30				
G	1.85 ± .010	47.0 ± 0.30				TYPE UK
H	5.106 ± .060	129.7 ± 1.5				
J	2.146 ± .060	54.7 ± 1.5				RECTANGULAR
K	2.152 ± .060	54.6 ± 1.5				SEALED BEAM
L	2.99 MAX	75.9 MAX				HEADLAMP UNIT
M	.41 MAX	10.4 MAX				
N	.35 MAX	8.9 MAX				
P	.41 MAX	5.6 MAX				

FIGURE 31—TYPE UK RECTANGULAR SEALED BEAM HEADLAMP UNIT

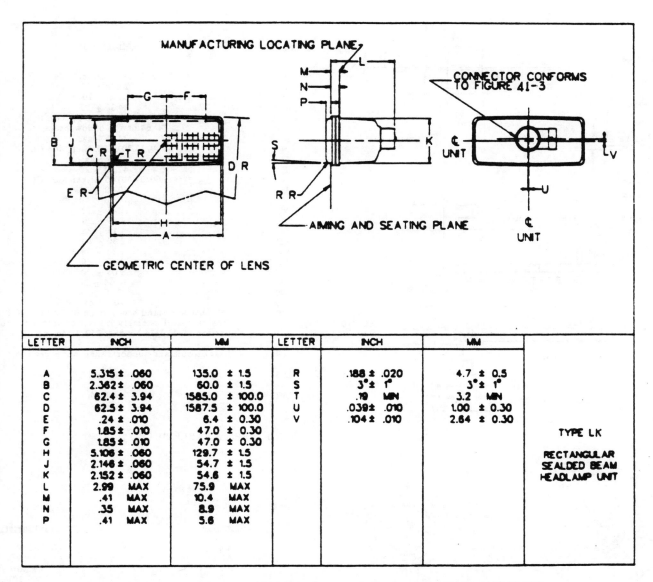

LETTER	INCH	MM	LETTER	INCH	MM	
A	5.315 ± .060	135.0 ± 1.5	R	.188 ± .020	4.7 ± 0.5	
B	2.362 ± .060	60.0 ± 1.5	S	3° ± 1°	3° ± 1°	
C	62.4 ± 3.94	1585.0 ± 100.0	T	.19 MIN	3.2 MIN	
D	62.5 ± 3.94	1587.5 ± 100.0	U	.039 ± .010	1.00 ± 0.30	
E	.24 ± .010	6.4 ± 0.30	V	.104 ± .010	2.64 ± 0.30	
F	1.85 ± .010	47.0 ± 0.30				
G	1.85 ± .010	47.0 ± 0.30				TYPE LK
H	5.106 ± .060	129.7 ± 1.5				
J	2.148 ± .060	54.7 ± 1.5				RECTANGULAR
K	2.152 ± .060	54.6 ± 1.5				SEALED BEAM
L	2.99 MAX	75.9 MAX				HEADLAMP UNIT
M	.41 MAX	10.4 MAX				
N	.35 MAX	8.9 MAX				
P	.41 MAX	5.6 MAX				

FIGURE 32—TYPE LK RECTANGULAR SEALED BEAM HEADLAMP UNIT

7. Bulb Filament Dimension and Location Test for the 9004 Replaceable Bulb—Filament locations relative to the bulb base (with O-ring removed) shall be determined for both production and accurate rated bulbs, as outlined below. For the actual conduct of these measurements, gaging standards shall be used for equipment calibration purposes.

7.1 Low Beam Filament Location Test—The location shall be determined by measuring from the midpoint of the smallest rectangle which encloses the filament image to the axial centerline of the base (see Figure 38):

    a. Axially—in the right side view
    b. Vertically—in the right side view
    c. Transversely—in the plan view

7.2 High Beam Filament Location Test—The location shall be determined as indicated in 7.1.

8. Low Beam Filament Location—Production bulbs (refer to Figure 38).

8.1 Axial—The low beam filament axial or fore/aft location shall be measured in the right side view from the reference plane of the base to the center of the smallest rectangle which encloses the low beam filament image.

8.2 Vertical—The low beam filament vertical or side view from a horizontal plane through the base centerline to the center of the smallest rectangle which encloses the low beam filament image.

8.3 Transverse—The low beam filament transverse or left/right location shall be measured in the plan view from the vertical plane through the center of the base to the midpoint of the smallest rectangle which encloses the low beam filament image.

9. High Beam Filament Location—Production bulbs (refer to Figure 38).

9.1 Axial—The high beam filament axial location shall be measured in the right side view of the high beam filament from the centerline of the low beam filament to the centerline of the smallest rectangle which encloses the high beam filament image.

9.2 Vertical—The high beam filament vertical location shall be measured in the right side view of the high beam filament from the centerline of the low beam filament to the centerline of the smallest rectangle which encloses the high beam filament image.

9.3 Transverse—The high beam filament horizontal location shall be measured in the plan view of the high beam filament from the midpoint of the low beam filament to the midpoint of the smallest rectangle which encloses the high beam filament image.

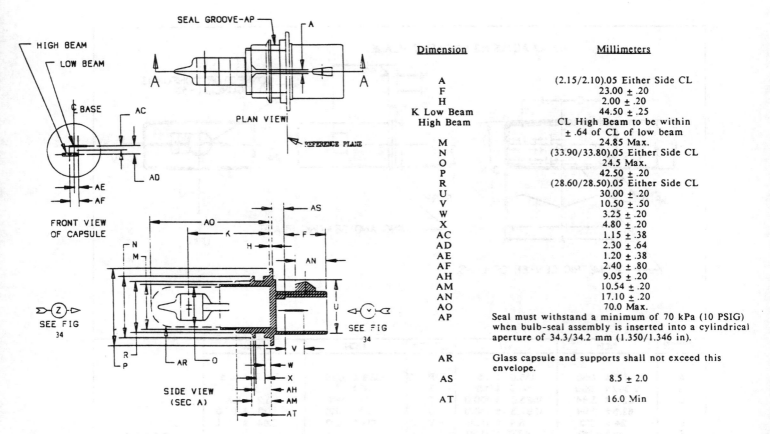

Dimension	Millimeters
A	(2.15/2.10).05 Either Side CL
F	23.00 ± .20
H	2.00 ± .20
K Low Beam	44.50 ± .25
High Beam	CL High Beam to be within ± .64 of CL of low beam
M	24.85 Max.
N	(33.90/33.80).05 Either Side CL
O	24.5 Max.
P	42.50 ± .20
R	(28.60/28.50).05 Either Side CL
U	30.00 ± .20
V	10.50 ± .50
W	3.25 ± .20
X	4.80 ± .20
AC	1.15 ± .38
AD	2.30 ± .64
AE	1.20 ± .38
AF	2.40 ± .80
AH	9.05 ± .20
AM	10.54 ± .20
AN	17.10 ± .20
AO	70.0 Max.
AP	Seal must withstand a minimum of 70 kPa (10 PSIG) when bulb-seal assembly is inserted into a cylindrical aperture of 34.3/34.2 mm (1.350/1.346 in).
AR	Glass capsule and supports shall not exceed this envelope.
AS	8.5 ± 2.0
AT	16.0 Min

FIGURE 33—SPECIFICATION FOR THE 9004 REPLACEABLE BULB

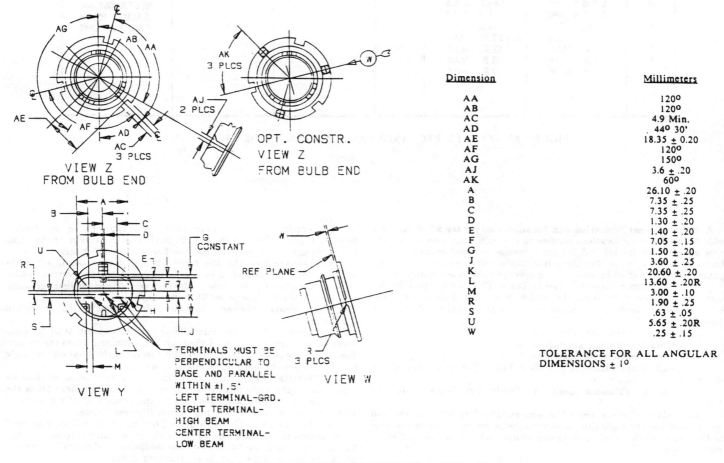

Dimension	Millimeters
AA	120°
AB	120°
AC	4.9 Min.
AD	44° 30'
AE	18.35 ± 0.20
AF	120°
AG	150°
AJ	3.6 ± .20
AK	60°
A	26.10 ± .20
B	7.35 ± .25
C	7.35 ± .25
D	1.30 ± .20
E	1.40 ± .20
F	7.05 ± .15
G	1.50 ± .20
J	3.60 ± .25
K	20.60 ± .20
L	13.60 ± .20R
M	3.00 ± .10
R	1.90 ± .25
S	.63 ± .05
U	5.65 ± .20R
W	.25 ± .15

TOLERANCE FOR ALL ANGULAR DIMENSIONS ± 1°

FIGURE 34—SPECIFICATION FOR THE 9004 REPLACEABLE BULB

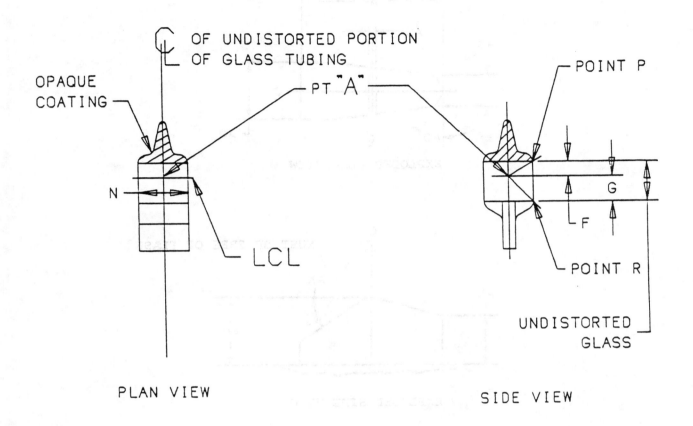

OF UNDISTORTED PORTION
OF GLASS TUBING

OPAQUE COATING

PT "A"

POINT P

N

LCL

POINT R

UNDISTORTED GLASS

G

F

PLAN VIEW

SIDE VIEW

Dimensional Specifications
Figure 35

Dimension	Specification
F	$(N/2)\tan 38° \pm 1.0$mm
G	$(N/2)\tan 43°$ MIN
N	Actual Capsule Dia. (To Be Established By Manufacturer)
P	Entire Radius and Distorted Glass Shall Be Covered to the Plane Passing Through Point "P", Perpendicular to the Glass Capsule Centerline.

FIGURE 35—SPECIFICATION FOR THE 9004 REPLACEABLE BULB

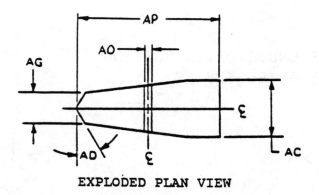

EXPLODED PLAN VIEW

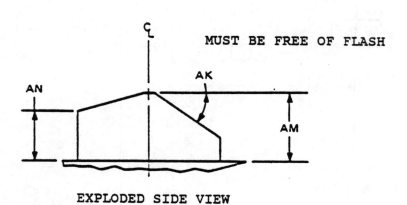

MUST BE FREE OF FLASH

EXPLODED SIDE VIEW

Dimension	Millimeters
AC	4.55 ± .20
AD	30° ± 3°
AG	2.50 ± .20
AK	35° ± 3°
AM	5.50 ± .20
AN	4.00 ± .20
AO	.5 ± .20
AP	11.4 ± .20

FIGURE 36—SPECIFICATION FOR THE 9004 REPLACEABLE BULB
LOCKING FEATURE

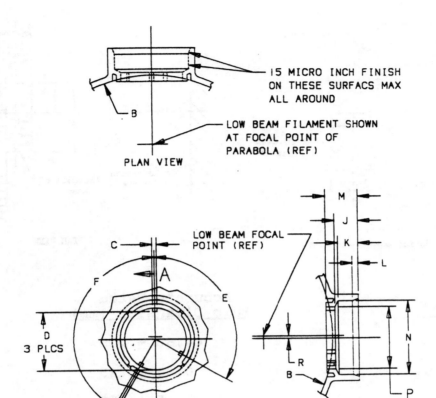

15 MICRO INCH FINISH
ON THESE SURFACS MAX
ALL AROUND

LOW BEAM FILAMENT SHOWN
AT FOCAL POINT OF
PARABOLA (REF)

PLAN VIEW

LOW BEAM FOCAL
POINT (REF)

3 PLCS

2 PLCS

FRONT VIEW

SIDE VIEW
(SECTION A)

Dimension	Millimeters
B	Ref Line
	Lamp Parabola
C	2.00 ± .05
	.05 Either Side of CL
D	27.10 ± .20
E	120°
F	150°
G	2.00 ± .20
H	15.15 ± .20
J	11.10 ± .20
K	9.50 ± .20
L	2.75 ± .20
N	34.24 +.08/-.05
P	28.70 +.10/-.05
	Diameter P shall be concentric to
	diameter N within ± .05
R	1.15 ± .10

TOLERANCE FOR ALL ANGULAR
DIMENSIONS ± 1°

FIGURE 37—SPECIFICATION FOR THE 9004 REPLACEABLE BULB

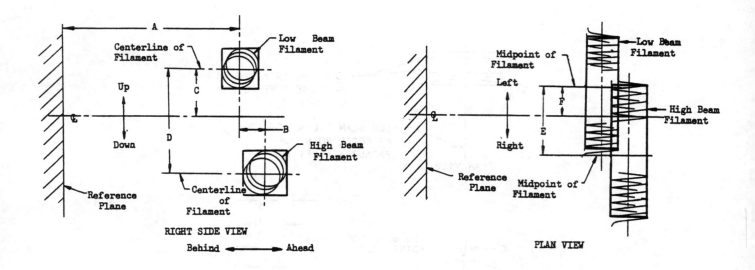

Letter	Accurate Rated Bulb Dimension (mm)
A	44.50 ± .15
B	0.00 ± .25
C	1.15 ± .20
D	2.30 ± .25
E	2.40 ± .40
F	1.20 ± .20
Low Beam Filament Length 1/3/	4.80 ± .40
High Beam Filament Length 2/3/	4.80 ± .40

1/ Low beam filament rotation shall not exceed 0.3 diameters of the coil.

2/ High beam filament rotation shall not exceed 0.4 diameters of the coil.

3/ Filament Length - The length of any filament shall be considered to be the length of the smallest rectangle which encloses the filament image in the plan view or right side view, as appropriate.

FIGURE 38—DIMENSIONAL SPECIFICATIONS FOR THE 9004 REPLACEABLE BULB
FILAMENT DIMENSION AND LOCATION—MEASUREMENT METHOD

10. Bulb Filament Dimension and Location Test for the 9005 and 9006 Replaceable Bulb—Filament locations relative to the bulb base (with O-ring removed) shall be determined for both production and accurate rated bulbs, as outlined below. For the actual conduct of these measurements, gaging standards shall be used for equipment calibration purposes.

10.1 High Beam Filament Location Test (see Figure 39)—The high beam filament location shall be determined by measuring:

    a. Axially—in the side view
    b. Vertically—in the side view
    c. Transversely—in the bottom view

10.2 Low Beam Filament Location Test (see Figure 47)—The low beam filament location shall be determined by measuring:

    a. Axially—in the side view
    b. Vertically—in the side view
    c. Transversely—in the bottom view

11. High Beam Filament Location

11.1 Production Bulbs

11.1.1 Axial—The end coil nearest to Plane A shall be within the volume "B" and the end coil farthest from Plane A shall be within the volume "C" as shown in Figure 43.

11.1.2 Vertical—Same as 11.1.1.

11.1.3 Transverse—Same as 11.1.1.

11.2 Accurate Rated Bulbs

11.2.1 Axial—The axial or fore/aft location shall be measured from Plane A to the beginning of the end coil nearest to Plane A and to the finish of the end coil farthest from Plane A. See Figure 46, Volume D and E.

11.2.2 Vertical

11.2.2.1 *End Coils*—The vertical or up/down location shall be measured from line A to the center of the smallest rectangle which encloses the end coil. See Figure 46, Volume D and E.

11.2.2.2 *Center Section*—The vertical or up/down location shall be measured from line A to the center of the smallest rectangle which encloses the center coil. See Figure 46, Section F, Area G.

11.2.3 Transverse

11.2.3.1 *End Coils*—Same as 11.2.2.1.

11.2.3.2 *Center Section*—Same as 11.2.2.2.

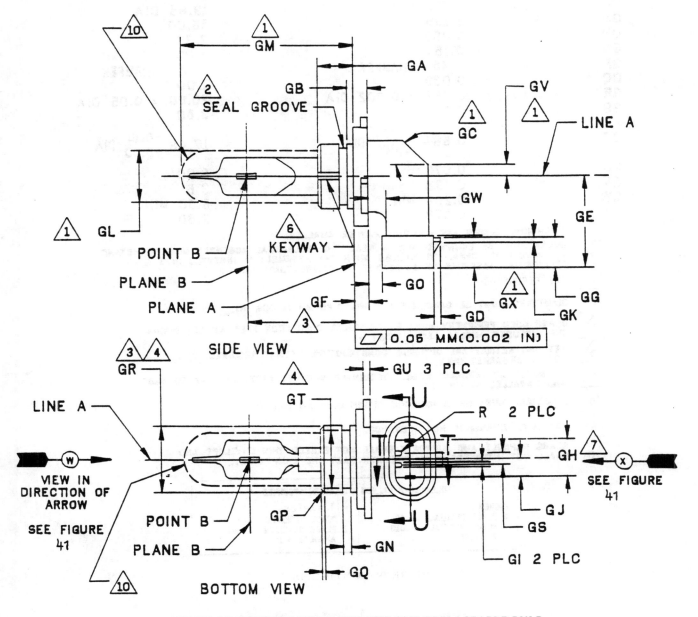

FIGURE 39—SPECIFICATION FOR THE 9005 REPLACEABLE BULB

DIMENSION	INCHES	MILLIMETERS
GA	0.591 MAX/0.217 MIN	15.00 MAX/5.50 MIN
GB	0.236	6.00
GC	45°	45°
GD	0.079	2.00
GE	1.09	27.8
GF	0.165	4.20
GG	0.346	8.80
GH	0.433	11.00
GI	0.055	1.40
GJ	0.217 ± 0.006	5.50 ± 0.15
GK	0.06	1.5
GL	0.775 DIA	19.68 DIA
GM	2.165	55.00
GN	0.093	2.36
GO	0.157	4.00
GP	45° CHAMFER	45° CHAMFER
GQ	0.039	1.00
GR	0.787 ± 0.002 DIA	20.00 ± 0.05 DIA
GS	0.138	3.50
GT	0.687 $^{+0.004}_{-0.000}$ DIA	17.46 $^{+0.10}_{-0.00}$ DIA
GU	0.079	2.00
GV	0.138	3.5
GW	0.209 MIN	5.30 MIN
GX	0.378	9.60

/1\ DIMENSIONS SHOWN ARE MAXIMUM—MAY BE SMALLER.

/2\ BULBS MUST BE EQUIPPED WITH A SEAL. THE BULB-SEAL ASSEMBLY MUST WITHSTAND A MINIMUM OF 70kPA. (10 P.S.I.G.) WHEN THE ASSEMBLY IS INSERTED INTO A CYLINDRICAL APERTURE OF 20.22±0.10 MM (0.796±0.004 IN).

/3\ SEE FIGURE 43

/4\ DIAMETERS MUST BE CONCENTRIC WITHIN 0.20 MM (0.008 IN).

/5\ GLASS BULB PERIPHERY MUST BE OPTICALLY DISTORTION FREE AXIALLY WITHIN THE INCLUDED ANGLES ABOUT POINT B.

/6\ KEY AND KEYWAY ARE OPTIONAL CONSTRUCTION. KEYWAY REQUIRED FOR AFTERMARKET ONLY.

/7\ MEASURED AT TERMINAL BASE. TERMINALS MUST BE PERPENDICULAR TO BASE AND PARALLEL WITHIN ±1.5°

/8\ DIAMETERS MUST BE CONCENTRIC WITHIN 0.20 MM (0.008 IN).

/9\ ABSOLUTE DIMENSION. NO TOLERANCE.

/10\ GLASS CAPSULE AND SUPPORTS SHALL NOT EXCEED THIS ENVELOPE AND SHALL NOT INTERFERE WITH INSERTION PAST THE LAMP'S KEY.

TOLERANCES UNLESS OTHERWISE SPECIFIED	
INCHES	millimeters
2 PLACE DECIMALS ± .02	1 PLACE DECIMALS ± 0.5
3 PLACE DECIMALS ± .013	2 PLACE DECIMALS ± 0.30
ANGULAR ± 1°	ANGULAR ± 1°

FIGURE 39 (CONTINUED)

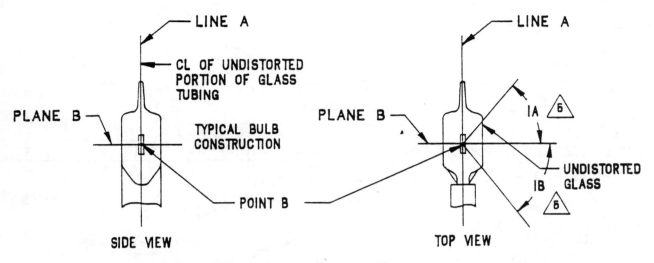

LINE A

CL OF UNDISTORTED PORTION OF GLASS TUBING

PLANE B

TYPICAL BULB CONSTRUCTION

POINT B

SIDE VIEW

LINE A

PLANE B

IA △5

UNDISTORTED GLASS

IB △5

TOP VIEW

POINT B IS INTERSECTION OF PLANE B AND CENTERLINE OF UNDISTORTED GLASS TUBING

DIMENSION	INCHES	MILLIMETERS
IA	45° MIN	45° MIN
IB	52° MIN	52° MIN

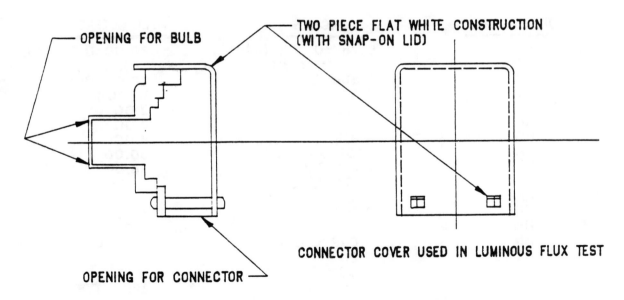

OPENING FOR BULB

TWO PIECE FLAT WHITE CONSTRUCTION (WITH SNAP-ON LID)

OPENING FOR CONNECTOR

CONNECTOR COVER USED IN LUMINOUS FLUX TEST

FIGURE 40—SPECIFICATION FOR THE 9005 REPLACEABLE BULB

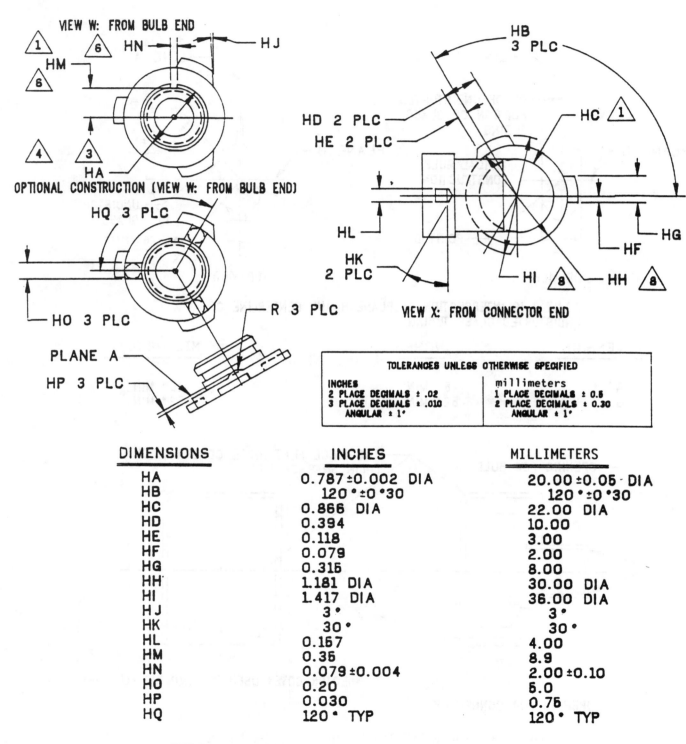

DIMENSIONS	INCHES	MILLIMETERS
HA	0.787±0.002 DIA	20.00±0.05 DIA
HB	120°±0°30	120°±0°30
HC	0.866 DIA	22.00 DIA
HD	0.394	10.00
HE	0.118	3.00
HF	0.079	2.00
HG	0.315	8.00
HH	1.181 DIA	30.00 DIA
HI	1.417 DIA	36.00 DIA
HJ	3°	3°
HK	30°	30°
HL	0.157	4.00
HM	0.35	8.9
HN	0.079±0.004	2.00±0.10
HO	0.20	5.0
HP	0.030	0.75
HQ	120° TYP	120° TYP

FIGURE 41—SPECIFICATION FOR THE 9005 REPLACEABLE BULB

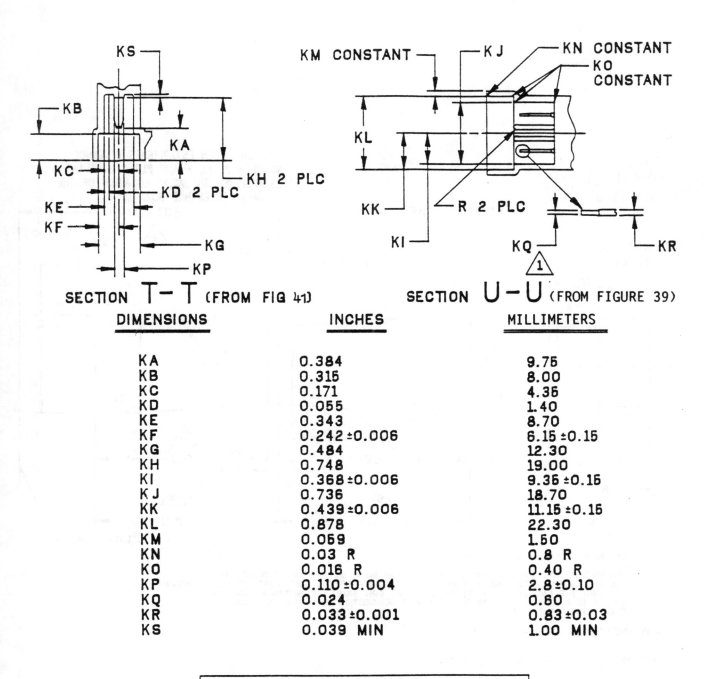

SECTION T-T (FROM FIG 41)   SECTION U-U (FROM FIGURE 39)

DIMENSIONS	INCHES	MILLIMETERS
KA	0.384	9.75
KB	0.315	8.00
KC	0.171	4.35
KD	0.055	1.40
KE	0.343	8.70
KF	0.242 ±0.006	6.15 ±0.15
KG	0.484	12.30
KH	0.748	19.00
KI	0.368 ±0.006	9.35 ±0.15
KJ	0.736	18.70
KK	0.439 ±0.006	11.15 ±0.15
KL	0.878	22.30
KM	0.059	1.50
KN	0.03 R	0.8 R
KO	0.016 R	0.40 R
KP	0.110 ±0.004	2.8 ±0.10
KQ	0.024	0.60
KR	0.033 ±0.001	0.83 ±0.03
KS	0.039 MIN	1.00 MIN

TOLERANCES UNLESS OTHERWISE SPECIFIED	
INCHES	millimeters
2 PLACE DECIMALS ± .02	1 PLACE DECIMALS ± 0.5
3 PLACE DECIMALS ± .010	2 PLACE DECIMALS ± 0.30
ANGULAR ± 1°	ANGULAR ± 1°

FIGURE 42—SPECIFICATION FOR THE 9005 REPLACEABLE BULB

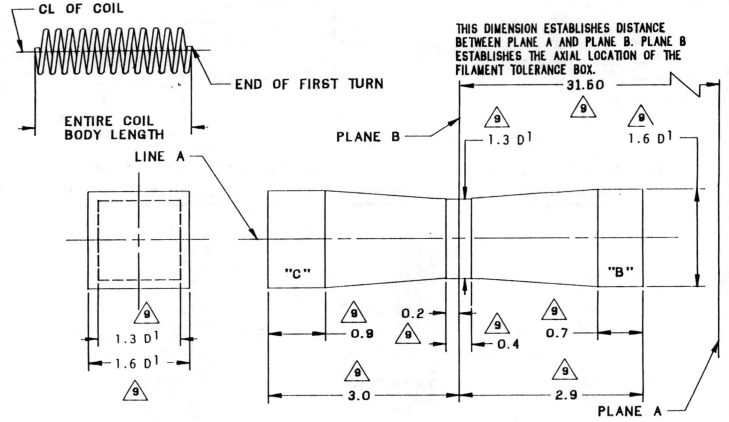

CL OF COIL

END OF FIRST TURN

ENTIRE COIL BODY LENGTH

LINE A

THIS DIMENSION ESTABLISHES DISTANCE BETWEEN PLANE A AND PLANE B. PLANE B ESTABLISHES THE AXIAL LOCATION OF THE FILAMENT TOLERANCE BOX.

PLANE B

31.50

1.3 D¹   1.6 D¹

"C"   "B"

1.3 D¹
1.6 D¹

0.2
0.9   0.4
0.7
3.0   2.9

PLANE A

PLANE B IS PARALLEL TO PLANE A.

THE ENTIRE COIL BODY AT DESIGN VOLTS (12.8) MUST BE CONTAINED WITHIN THE VOLUME AS SPECIFIED. THE END OF THE FIRST TURN OF THE COIL MUST LIE WITHIN VOLUME "B" AND THE END OF THE LAST TURN OF THE COIL MUST LIE WITHIN VOLUME "C" LINE A IS PERPENDICULAR TO PLANE A AND CONCENTRIC WITH THE 17.46 MM DIAMETER OF THE BASE.

¹D = DIAMETER OF FILAMENT COIL

DIMENSIONS SHOWN ARE IN MILLIMETERS

FIGURE 43—SPECIFICATION FOR THE 9005 REPLACEABLE BULB

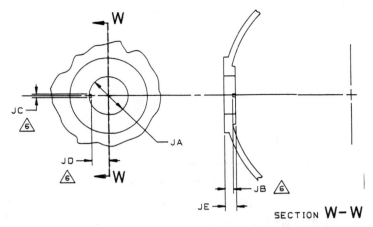

DIMENSIONS	INCHES	MILLIMETERS
JA	0.796 ±0.004 DIA	20.22 ±0.10 DIA
JB	0.172 +0.010 / -0.000	4.36 +0.30 / -0.00
JC	0.067 ±0.004	1.70 ±0.10
JD	0.352 +0.004 / -0.000	8.95 +0.10 / -0.00
JE	0.236 MIN	6.00 MIN

FIGURE 44—SPECIFICATION FOR THE 9005 REPLACEABLE BULB BULB HOLDER

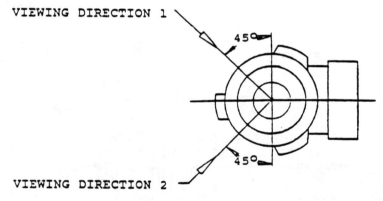

FIGURE 45—MODIFIED VIEW W FROM FIGURE 41, SIMILAR FOR 49

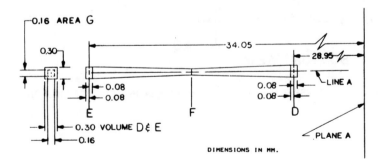

DIMENSIONS IN MM.

THE CENTROID OF THE FIRST TURN OF THE COIL MUST BE WITHIN
VOLUME D AND THE CENTROID OF THE LAST TURN OF THE COIL MUST
BE WITHIN VOLUME E. F IS AT THE MID-LENGTH OF THE COIL. THE
CENTROID AT F MUST BE WITHIN AREA G.

FIGURE 46—SPECIFICATION FOR THE 9005 REPLACEABLE BULB ACCURATE RATED BULB

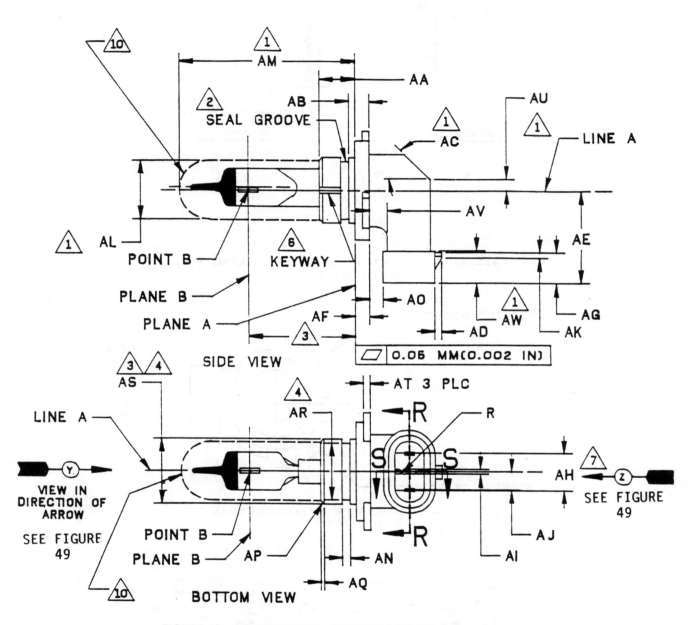

FIGURE 47—SPECIFICATION FOR THE 9006 REPLACEABLE BULB

DIMENSION	INCHES	MILLIMETERS
AA	0.591 MAX/0.217 MIN	15.00 MAX/5.50 MIN
AB	0.236	6.00
AC	45°	45°
AD	0.079	2.00
AE	1.09	27.8
AF	0.165	4.20
AG	0.346	8.80
AH	0.433	11.00
AI	0.055	1.40
AJ	0.217 ± 0.006	5.50 ± 0.15
AK	0.06	1.5
AL	0.780 DIA	19.81 DIA
AM	2.165	55.00
AN	0.093	2.38
AO	0.157	4.00
AP	45° CHAMFER	45° CHAMFER
AQ	0.039	1.00
AR	0.766 $^{+0.004}_{-0.000}$ DIA	19.46 $^{+0.10}_{-0.00}$ DIA
AS	0.866 ± 0.002 DIA	22.00 ± 0.05 DIA
AT	0.079	2.00
AU	0.138	3.5
AV	0.209 MIN	5.30 MIN
AW	0.378	9.60

1. DIMENSIONS SHOWN ARE MAXIMUM—MAY BE SMALLER.

2. BULBS MUST BE EQUIPPED WITH A SEAL. THE BULB-SEAL ASSEMBLY MUST WITHSTAND A MINIMUM OF 70kPA. (10 P.S.I.G.) WHEN THE ASSEMBLY IS INSERTED INTO A CYLINDRICAL APERTURE OF 22.22±0.10 MM (0.875±0.004 IN).

3. SEE FIGURE 51

4. DIAMETERS MUST BE CONCENTRIC WITHIN 0.20 MM (0.008 IN).

5. GLASS BULB PERIPHERY MUST BE OPTICALLY DISTORTION FREE AXIALLY WITHIN THE INCLUDED ANGLES ABOUT POINT B.

6. KEY AND KEYWAY ARE OPTIONAL CONSTRUCTION. KEYWAY REQUIRED FOR AFTERMARKET ONLY.

7. MEASURED AT TERMINAL BASE. TERMINALS MUST BE PERPENDICULAR TO BASE AND PARALLEL WITHIN ±1.5°

8. DIAMETERS MUST BE CONCENTRIC WITHIN 0.20 MM (0.008 IN).

9. ABSOLUTE DIMENSION. NO TOLERANCE.

10. GLASS CAPSULE AND SUPPORTS SHALL NOT EXCEED THIS ENVELOPE.

TOLERANCES UNLESS OTHERWISE SPECIFIED	
INCHES 2 PLACE DECIMALS ± .02 3 PLACE DECIMALS ± .010 ANGULAR ± 1°	millimeters 1 PLACE DECIMALS ± 0.5 2 PLACE DECIMALS ± 0.30 ANGULAR ± 1°

FIGURE 47 (CONTINUED)

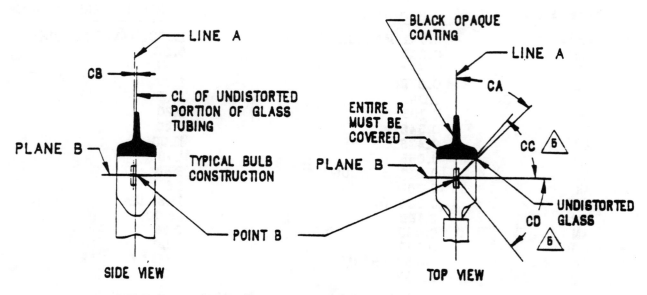

POINT B IS INTERSECTION OF PLANE B AND CENTERLINE OF
UNDISTORTED GLASS TUBING

DIMENSION	INCHES	MILLIMETERS
CA	45°±5°	45°±5°
CB	0.030±0.020	0.75±0.50
CC	50° MIN	50° MIN
CD	52° MIN	52° MIN

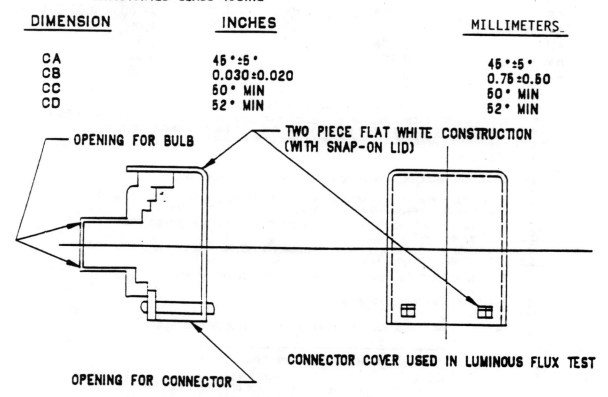

FIGURE 48—SPECIFICATION FOR THE 9006 REPLACEABLE BULB

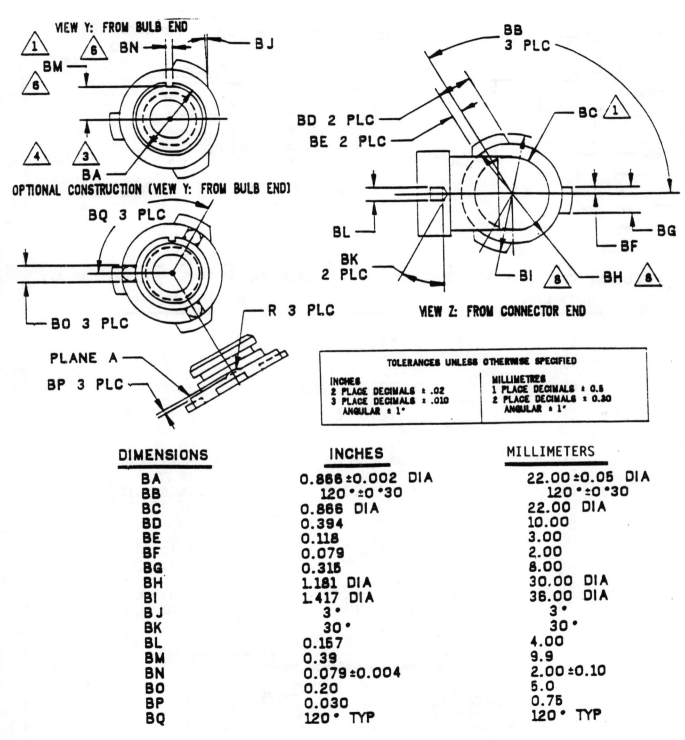

DIMENSIONS	INCHES	MILLIMETERS
BA	0.866 ±0.002 DIA	22.00 ±0.05 DIA
BB	120° ±0°30	120° ±0°30
BC	0.866 DIA	22.00 DIA
BD	0.394	10.00
BE	0.118	3.00
BF	0.079	2.00
BG	0.315	8.00
BH	1.181 DIA	30.00 DIA
BI	1.417 DIA	36.00 DIA
BJ	3°	3°
BK	30°	30°
BL	0.157	4.00
BM	0.39	9.9
BN	0.079 ±0.004	2.00 ±0.10
BO	0.20	5.0
BP	0.030	0.75
BQ	120° TYP	120° TYP

FIGURE 49—SPECIFICATION FOR THE 9006 REPLACEABLE BULB

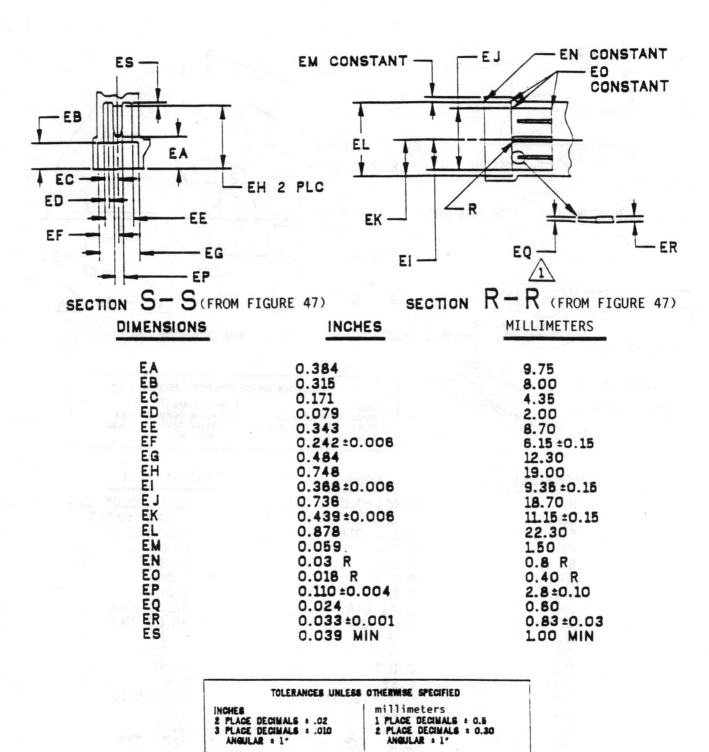

SECTION S—S (FROM FIGURE 47)　　SECTION R—R (FROM FIGURE 47)

DIMENSIONS	INCHES	MILLIMETERS
EA	0.384	9.75
EB	0.315	8.00
EC	0.171	4.35
ED	0.079	2.00
EE	0.343	8.70
EF	0.242 ±0.006	6.15 ±0.15
EG	0.484	12.30
EH	0.748	19.00
EI	0.368 ±0.006	9.35 ±0.15
EJ	0.736	18.70
EK	0.439 ±0.006	11.15 ±0.15
EL	0.878	22.30
EM	0.059	1.50
EN	0.03 R	0.8 R
EO	0.016 R	0.40 R
EP	0.110 ±0.004	2.8 ±0.10
EQ	0.024	0.60
ER	0.033 ±0.001	0.83 ±0.03
ES	0.039 MIN	1.00 MIN

TOLERANCES UNLESS OTHERWISE SPECIFIED	
INCHES	millimeters
2 PLACE DECIMALS ± .02	1 PLACE DECIMALS ± 0.5
3 PLACE DECIMALS ± .010	2 PLACE DECIMALS ± 0.30
ANGULAR ± 1°	ANGULAR ± 1°

FIGURE 50—SPECIFICATION FOR THE 9006 REPLACEABLE BULB

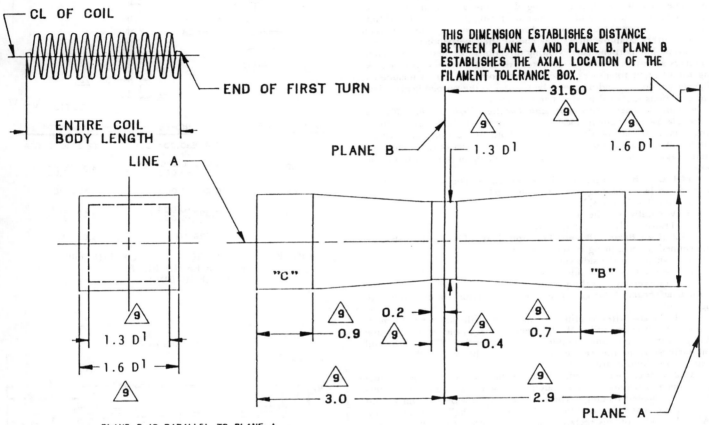

CL OF COIL

END OF FIRST TURN

ENTIRE COIL
BODY LENGTH

LINE A

THIS DIMENSION ESTABLISHES DISTANCE
BETWEEN PLANE A AND PLANE B. PLANE B
ESTABLISHES THE AXIAL LOCATION OF THE
FILAMENT TOLERANCE BOX.

31.50

PLANE B

1.3 D¹

1.6 D¹

"C"

"B"

1.3 D¹

1.6 D¹

0.2

0.9

0.4

0.7

3.0

2.9

PLANE A

PLANE B IS PARALLEL TO PLANE A.

THE ENTIRE COIL BODY AT DESIGN VOLTS (12.8) MUST BE CONTAINED WITHIN THE
VOLUME AS SPECIFIED. THE END OF THE FIRST TURN OF THE COIL MUST LIE WITHIN VOLUME
"B" AND THE END OF THE LAST TURN OF THE COIL MUST LIE WITHIN VOLUME "C".
LINE A IS PERPENDICULAR TO PLANE A AND CONCENTRIC WITH THE 19.46 MM
DIAMETER OF THE BASE.

¹D = DIAMETER OF FILAMENT COIL

DIMENSIONS SHOWN ARE IN MILLIMETERS

FIGURE 51—SPECIFICATION FOR THE 9006 REPLACEABLE BULB

12. Low Beam Filament Location

12.1 Production Bulbs

12.1.1 Axial.—Same as 11.1.1 except Figure 51.

12.1.2 Vertical.—Same as 12.1.1.

12.1.3 Transverse.—Same as 12.1.1.

12.2 Accurate Rated Bulbs

12.2.1 Axial.—Same as 11.2.1 except Figure 53.

12.2.2 Vertical.

    12.2.2.1 *End Coils*—Same as 11.2.2.1 except Figure 53.

    12.2.2.2 *Center Section*—Same as 11.2.2.2 except Figure 53.

12.2.3 Transverse.

    12.2.3.1 *End Coils*—Same as 12.2.2.1.

    12.2.3.2 *Center Section*—Same as 12.2.2.2.

13. Viewing Direction for HB3 (9005) and HB4 (9006) Bulbs—The recommended perpendicular viewing directions are listed below. Because bulb construction and bulb manufacturing procedures can differ, the actual perpendicular viewing directions used may vary between manufacturers. Manufacturers may choose their perpendicular viewing directions. The perpendicular viewing directions specified by the manufacturers are to be used by a laboratory or testing agency when checking for filament tolerances. The filament tolerance boxes included if Figures 43, 46, 51, and 53 are to be rotated to the perpendicular viewing directions specified by the manufacturer.

14. Bulb Filament Dimension and Location Test for the 9007 Replaceable Bulb—Filament locations relative to the bulb base (with O-ring removed) shall be determined for both production and accurate rated bulb, as outlined below. For the actual conduct of these measurements, gaging standards shall be used for equipment calibration purposes.

14.1 Low Beam Filament Location Test—The location shall be determined by measuring (refer to Figure 54):

    a. Axially—in the side view

    b. Vertically—in the side view

    c. Transversely—in the plan view

14.2 High Beam Filament Location Test—The location shall be determined by measuring (refer to Figure 54):

    a. Axially—in the side view

    b. Vertically—in the side view

    c. Transversely—in the plan view

15. Low Beam Filament Location—Production bulbs (refer to Figure 59).

15.1 Axial—After locating the midpoint of the low beam filament to meet "G", the end coil of the filament nearest to the reference plane shall be within the volume bounded by the dimension "C", and the end coil farthest from the reference plane shall be within the volume bounded by the dimension "B".

15.2 Vertical—The vertical location shall be measured in the side view from a horizontal plane through the base centerline to the centerline of the smallest rectangle which encloses the low beam filament and is parallel to that horizontal plane. This location shall meet dimension "A". The width of this rectangle shall not exceed 1.6X the diameter of the low beam coil.

15.3 Transverse—The transverse location shall be measured in the plan view from a vertical plane through the center of the base to the centerline of the smallest rectangle which encloses the low beam filament and is parallel to that plane. This location shall meet the dimension "L". The width of this rectangle shall not exceed 1.6X the diameter of the low beam coil.

16. High Beam Filament Location—Production bulbs (refer to Figure 59).

16.1 Axial—The filament location shall be measured from the midpoint of the low beam filament to the midpoint of the smallest rectangle which encloses the high beam filament image.

16.2 Vertical—The location shall be measured from the centerline of the low beam filament to the centerline of the smallest rectangle which encloses the high beam filament image and is parallel to the horizontal plane referenced in 15.2. This location shall not exceed dimension "J" and the width of the rectangle shall not exceed 1.6X the diameter of the high beam filament coil.

16.3 Transverse—The location shall be measured from the centerline of the low beam filament to the centerline of the smallest rectangle which encloses the high beam filament image and is parallel to that plane referenced in 15.3. This location shall not exceed dimension "H" and the width of the rectangle shall not exceed 1.6X the diameter of the high beam filament coil.

17. Methods of Measuring Internal Elements of H4/HB2 Bulbs

17.1 These paragraphs specify the methods of measuring internal elements of H4 and HB2 bulbs.

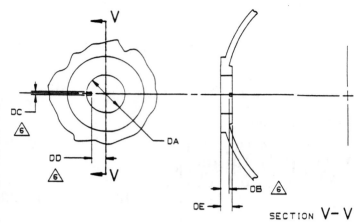

SECTION V-V

DIMENSIONS	INCHES	MILLIMETERS
DA	0.875 ±0.004 DIA	22.22 ±0.10 DIA
DB	0.172 +0.010 -0.000	4.36 +0.30 -0.00
DC	0.067 ±0.004	1.70 ±0.10
DD	0.392 +0.004 -0.000	9.95 +0.10 -0.00
DE	0.236 MIN	6.00 MIN

FIGURE 52—SPECIFICATION FOR THE 9006 REPLACEABLE BULB BULB HOLDER

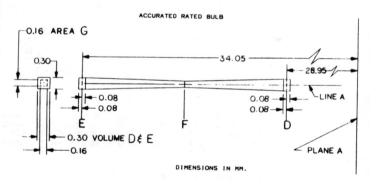

ACCURATED RATED BULB

DIMENSIONS IN MM.

THE CENTROID OF THE FIRST TURN OF THE COIL MUST BE WITHIN VOLUME D AND THE CENTROID OF THE LAST TURN OF THE COIL MUST BE WITHIN VOLUME E. F IS AT THE MID-LENGTH OF THE COIL. THE CENTROID AT F MUST BE WITHIN AREA G.

FIGURE 53—SPECIFICATION FOR THE 9006 REPLACEABLE BULB ACCURATE RATED BULB

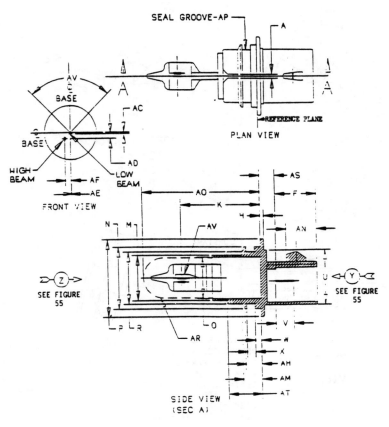

Dimension	Millimeters
A	(2.15/2.10) .05 Either Side CL
F	23.00 ± .20
H	2.00 ± .20
K Low Beam	44.50 ± .25
High Beam	CL High Beam to be within ± .64 of CL of low beam
M	24.85 Max.
N	(33.90/33.80) .05 Either Side CL
O	24.5 Max.
P	42.50 ± .20
R	(28.60/28.50).05 Either Side CL
U	30.00 ± .20
V	10.50 ± .50
W	3.25 ± .20
X	4.80 ± .20
AC	0.38 ± .38
AD	1.60 ± .64
AE	.000 ± .38
AF	1.60 ± .81
AH	9.05 ± .20
AM	10.54 ± .20
AN	17.10 ± .20
AO	70.0 Max.
AP	Seal must withstand a minimum of 70 kPa (10 PSIG) when bulb-seal assembly is inserted into a cylindrical aperture of 34.3/34.2 mm (1.350/1.346 in).
AR	Glass capsule and supports shall not exceed this envelope.
AS	8.5 ± 2.0
AT	16.00 Min.
AV	Support wires extending forward of the filaments shall be within ± 45° of vertical.

FIGURE 54—SPECIFICATION FOR THE 9007 REPLACEABLE BULB

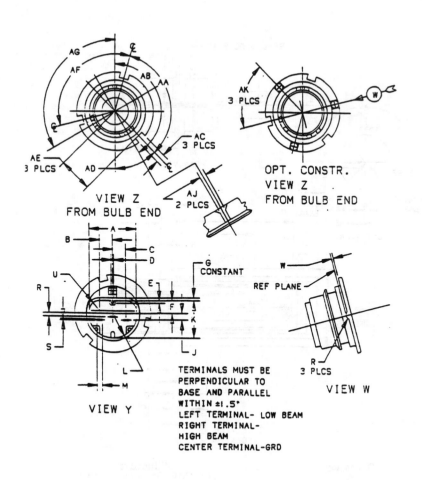

VIEW Z
FROM BULB END

OPT. CONSTR.
VIEW Z
FROM BULB END

VIEW Y

VIEW W

TERMINALS MUST BE
PERPENDICULAR TO
BASE AND PARALLEL
WITHIN ±1.5°
LEFT TERMINAL- LOW BEAM
RIGHT TERMINAL-
HIGH BEAM
CENTER TERMINAL-GRD

Dimension	Millimeters
AA	120°
AB	150°
AC	4.9 Min.
AD	44° 30'
AE	18.35 ± 0.20
AF	120°
AG	120°
AJ	3.6 ± .20
AK	60°
A	26.10 ± .20
B	7.35 ± .25
C	7.35 ± .25
D	1.30 ± .20
E	1.40 ± .20
F	7.05 ± .15
G	1.50 ± .20
J	3.60 ± .25
K	20.60 ± .20
L	13.60 ± .20R
M	3.00 ± .10
R	1.90 ± .25
S	.63 ± .05
U	5.65 ± .20R
W	.25 ± .15

TOLERANCE FOR ALL ANGULAR
DIMENSIONS ± 1°

FIGURE 55—SPECIFICATION FOR THE 9007 REPLACEABLE BULB

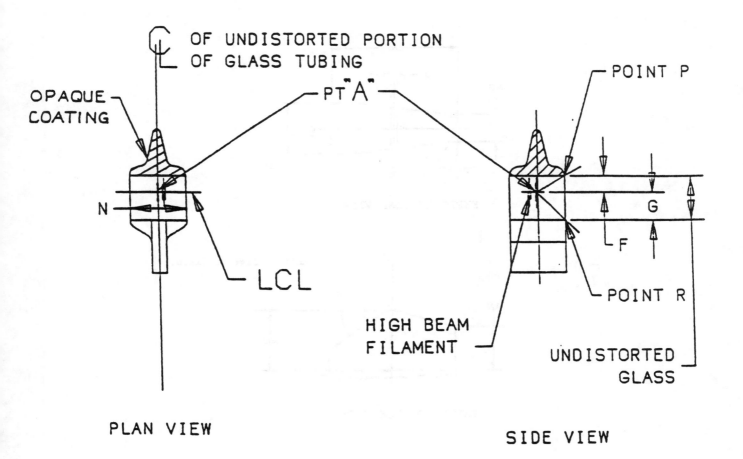

PLAN VIEW

SIDE VIEW

Dimensional Specifications
Figure 56

Dimension

F $(N/2)\tan 38° \pm 1.0\text{mm}$

G $(N/2)\tan 43°$ MIN

N   Actual Capsule Dia. (To Be Established By Manufacturer)

P   Entire Radius and Distorted Glass Shall Be Covered to the Plane Passing Through Point "P", Perpendicular to the Glass Capsule Centerline.

FIGURE 56—SPECIFICATION FOR THE 9007 REPLACEABLE BULB

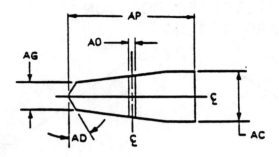

EXPLODED PLAN VIEW

Must be free of flash.

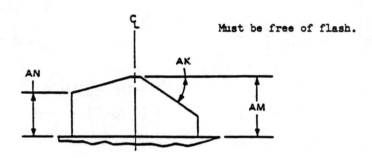

EXPLODED SIDE VIEW

Dimension	Millimeters
AC	4.55 ± .20
AD	30° ± 3°
AG	2.50 ± .20
AK	35° ± 3°
AM	5.50 ± .20
AN	4.00 ± .20
AO	.5 ± .20
AP	11.4 ± .20

FIGURE 57—SPECIFICATION FOR THE 9007 REPLACEABLE BULB
LOCKING FEATURE

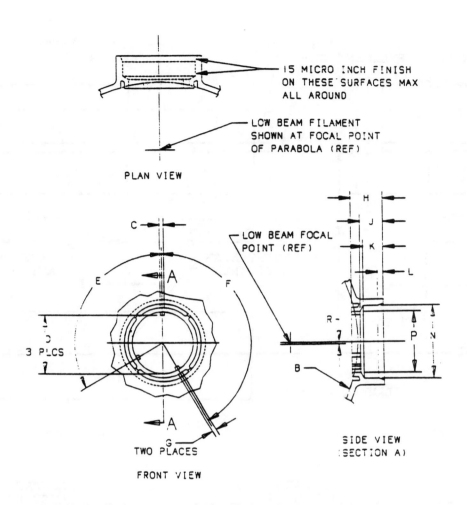

15 MICRO INCH FINISH
ON THESE SURFACES MAX
ALL AROUND

LOW BEAM FILAMENT
SHOWN AT FOCAL POINT
OF PARABOLA (REF)

PLAN VIEW

LOW BEAM FOCAL
POINT (REF)

3 PLCS

TWO PLACES

FRONT VIEW

SIDE VIEW
(SECTION A)

Dimension	Millimeters
B	Ref Line
	Lamp Parabola
C	2.00 ± .05
	.05 Either Side of CL
D	27.10 ± .20
E	120°
F	150°
G	2.00 ± .20
H	15.15 ± .20
J	11.10 ± .20
K	9.50 ± .20
L	2.75 ± .20
N	34.24 +.08/−.05
P	28.70 +.10/−.05
	Diameter P shall be concentric to diameter N within ± .05
R	0.38 ± 0.10
	TOLERANCE FOR ALL ANGULAR DIMENSIONS ± 1°

FIGURE 58—SPECIFICATION FOR THE 9007 REPLACEABLE BULB
BULB HOLDER

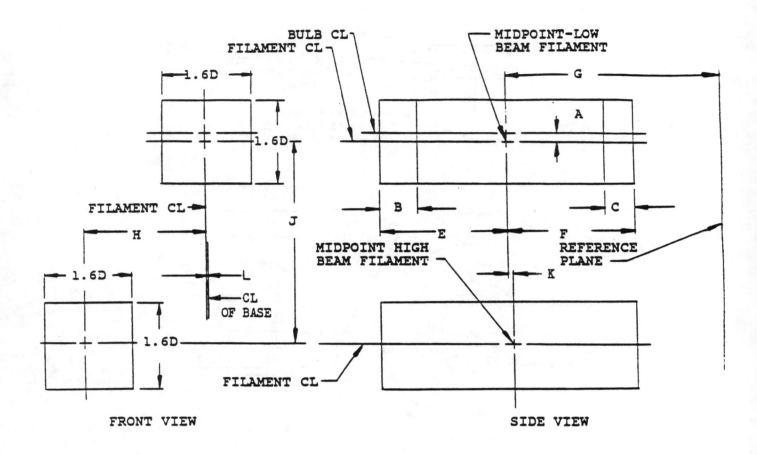

FRONT VIEW   SIDE VIEW

LETTER	STANDARD DIMENSION	ACCURATE RATED BULB
A	0.38 ± 0.38 mm	0.38 ± 0.20 mm
B	0.9 Basic	---
C	0.7 Basic	---
D	Actual Filament Diameter	---
E	3.0 Basic	---
F	2.9 Basic	---
G	44.50 ± 0.25	44.50 ± 0.15
H	1.60 ± 0.81	1.60 ± 0.25
J	1.60 ± 0.64	1.60 ± 0.25
K	000 ± 0.64	000 ± 0.40
L	000 ± 0.38	000 ± 0.25

FIGURE 59—DIMENSIONAL SPECIFICATIONS FOR THE 9006 REPLACEABLE BULB
FILAMENT DIMENSION AND LOCATION—MEASUREMENT METHOD

The drawing is not mandatory, their sole purpose is to show which dimensions must be verified.

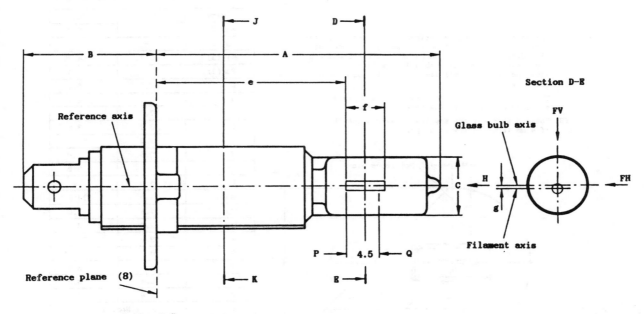

Section J-K

Definition of reference axis

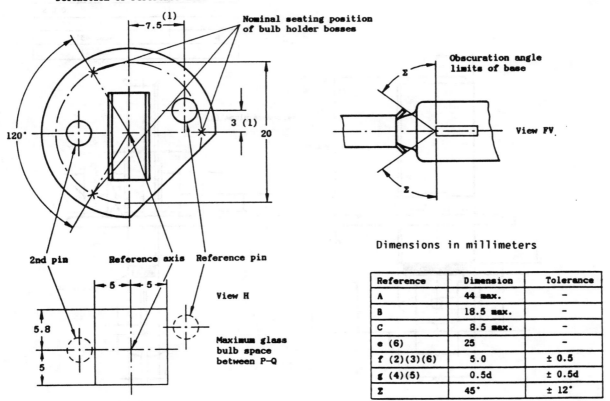

Dimensions in millimeters

Reference	Dimension	Tolerance
A	44 max.	–
B	18.5 max.	–
C	8.5 max.	–
e (6)	25	–
f (2)(3)(6)	5.0	± 0.5
g (4)(5)	0.5d	± 0.5d
Σ	45°	± 12°

FIGURE 60—SPECIFICATION FOR THE TYPE H1 REPLACEABLE BULB

The drawing is intended only to indicate
the dimensions essential for interchangeablility.

(1) The reference plane is defined by the points on the
    surface of the ring on which, taking into account
    all adverse tolerances on pages Figure 8-1 and 8-2,
    the bosses "e" of the bulb holder will rest.
    These points shall all lie on the flat surface of
    the ring.

(2) These dimensions are applicable above a plane
    situated 0.7 mm above the reference plane.

(3) These dimensions are applicable over a length
    of 4 mm from the insulator part.

Dimensions in millimeters

Dimension	Min.	Max.
A_1 (2)	5.2	5.8
A_2 (3)	–	12.0
B_1 (3)	3.75	4.25
B_2 (2)	–	6.0
C	6.2	6.4
D	1.7	2.0
E	7.8	8.1
F	3.3	3.5
G	9.0	–
H	0.5	1.0
J	–	3.0
L	5.0	–
M_1	14.3	14.5
M_2	7.4	7.6
M_3	2.9	3.1
N	23.0	25.0
Q	0.77	0.84
R	8.5	9.5
S (2)	3.4	3.5
T	2.8	3.2
V	Nom. 1.6	
Y	–	18.5
r_1	–	0.6
r_2	–	0.5 S
α	40°	50°
β	Nom. 45°	
γ	Nom. 11°	

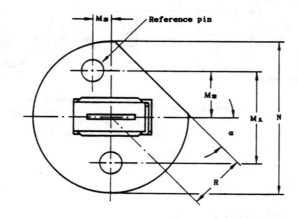

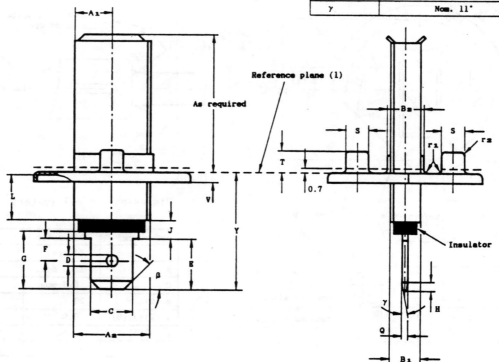

FIGURE 61—SPECIFICATION FOR THE TYPE H1 REPLACEABLE BULB
BASE P14.5s

76

The drawings are intended only to indicate
the dimensions essential for interchangeability.

Section I-I   Reference plane

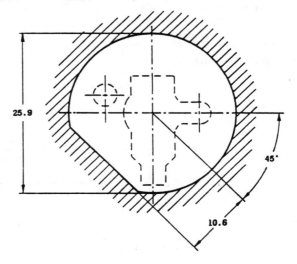

Dimensions in millimeters

Dimension	Min.	Max.
A_1	6.1	6.3
A_4	11.7	–
A_8	7.0	7.5
B_2	7.0	7.5
B_3	4.0	4.2
M_1	Nom. 14.5	
M_2	7.4	7.6
M_3	2.9	3.1
M_4	18.1	18.3
S	3.6	3.7
U_1	0.8	1.0
U_2	1.8	2.2
X	9.0	9.2
Z	19.5	20.5
δ	40°	45°
θ	59°	61°

Minimum free space for the base ring

The correct orientation of the bulb is made by the apertures "t_1" and "t_2".
The three bosses "e" determine the reference plane.

The holder shall be so designed that the means of retention can be applied only
when the bulb is in the correct position.

The means of retention shall make contact only with the prefocus ring of the base,
and the total force exerted when the bulb is in position, shall be not less
than 10 N and not greater than 60 N.

FIGURE 62—SPECIFICATION FOR THE TYPE H1 REPLACEABLE BULB
BULB HOLDER P14.5s

(1) These dimensions define the reference axis.

(2) The longer lead wire should be positioned above the filament (the bulb being viewed as shown in the figure).
The internal design of the bulb should then be such that stray light images and reflections are reduced to the minimum e.g. by fitting cooling jackets over the non-coiled parts of the filament.

(3) The cylindrical portion of the glass bulb over length "f" shall be such as not to deform the projected image of the filament to such an extend as appreciable to affect the optical results.

(4) Offset of filament in relation to glass bulb axis measured at 27.5 mm from the reference plane in direction FV.

(5) d = actual diameter of filament.

(6) The ends of the filament are defined as the points where, when the viewing direction as defined in foot-note 7, the projection of the outside of the end turns nearest to or furthest from the reference plane crosses the reference axis.

(7) The viewing direction is the perpendicular to the reference axis contained in the plane defined by the reference axis and the centre of the second pin of the base.

(8) The reference plane is the plane formed by the seating points of the three bosses of the bulb holder on the base ring.

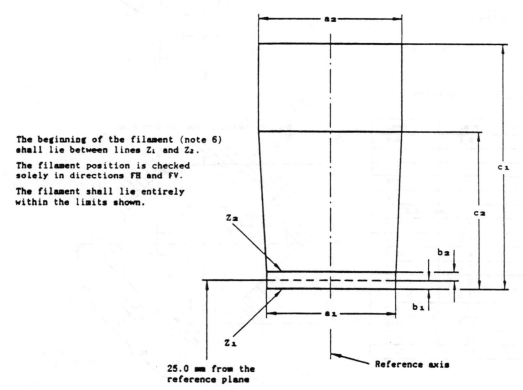

Filament position requirements

The beginning of the filament (note 6) shall lie between lines Z_1 and Z_2.

The filament position is checked solely in directions FH and FV.

The filament shall lie entirely within the limits shown.

25.0 mm from the reference plane

Dimensions in millimeters

Reference	Dimensions
a_1 (5)	1.4d
a_2 (5)	1.9d
b_1, b_2	0.25
c_1	7
c_2	4.5

FIGURE 63—SPECIFICATION FOR THE TYPE H1 REPLACEABLE BULB

78

Additional requirements for accurate rated bulbs

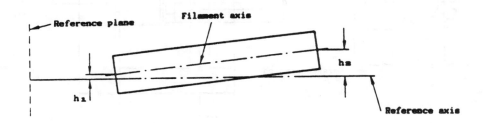

Dimensions in millimeters

Reference	Dimension	Tolerance
e (1)	25	± 0.15
f (1)	5.0	+ 0.5
g (1)	0.5d (2)	± 0.25d
Σ (1)	45°	± 3°
h₁	0	± 0.20
h₂	0	± 0.25

(1) See Figure 60
(2) d = actual filament diameter

FIGURE 64—SPECIFICATION FOR THE TYPE H1 REPLACEABLE BULB

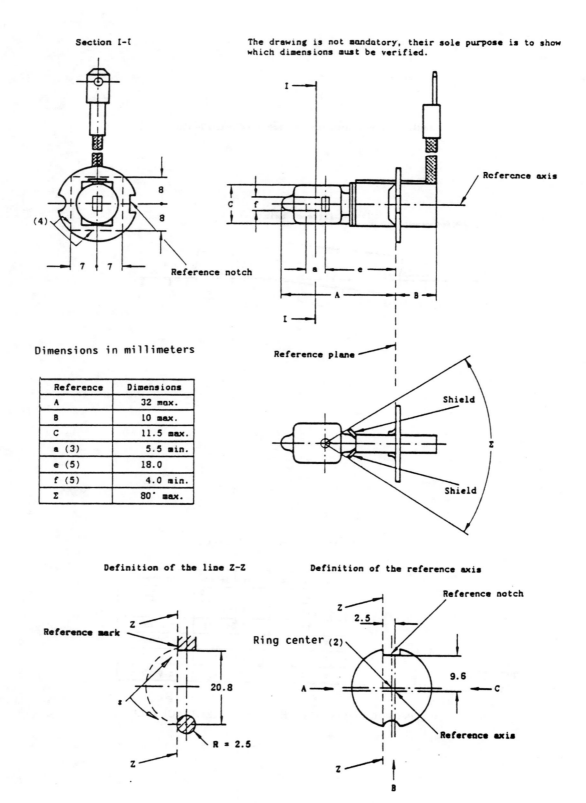

Section I-I

The drawing is not mandatory, their sole purpose is to show which dimensions must be verified.

Reference axis

Reference notch

Reference plane

Shield

Shield

Dimensions in millimeters

Reference	Dimensions
A	32 max.
B	10 max.
C	11.5 max.
a (3)	5.5 min.
e (5)	18.0
f (5)	4.0 min.
Σ	80˚ max.

Definition of the line Z-Z

Reference mark

Definition of the reference axis

Reference notch

Ring center (2)

Reference axis

The base should be pressed in these directions

FIGURE 65—SPECIFICATION FOR THE TYPE H3 REPLACEABLE BULB

80

The drawings are intended only to indicate
the dimensions essential for interchangeability.

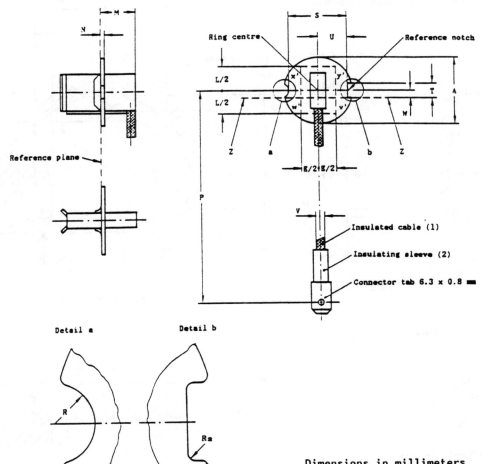

Dimensions in millimeters

Dimension	Min.	Max.
A	22.15	22.25
E (3)(6)	11.0	
L (3)(6)	16.0	
M	–	10.0
N (4)	0.7	1.1
P	95	105
R	2.5	2.6
R₁	–	0.4
R₂	–	0.5
S	18.1	18.3
T	5.0	5.1
U	9.55	9.65
V (5)	1.75	2.75
W	2.0	3.0

(1) It shall be possible to bend the cable within a cylinder
of 22.2 mm diameter co-axial with the axis of the ring.

(2) The insulating sleeve shall be securely fastened,
shall adequately overlap the wire insulation and
shall cover all metal parts up to the shoulders
of the tab.

(3) The space to be reserved for the parts of the base below
the ring—with the exception of the cable outlet,
is bounded by a rectangular box of x', y', v', w'.

(4) A reduction of the minimum value is under consideration.

(5) This dimension is not to be gauged.

(6) Outside the area defined by x', y', v' and w',
the flatness of the ring, on the reference plane side,
shall be within 0.25 mm (0.01 in).

FIGURE 66—SPECIFICATION FOR THE TYPE H3 REPLACEABLE BULB
BASE PK22s

The drawings are intended only to indicate
the dimensions essential for interchangeability.

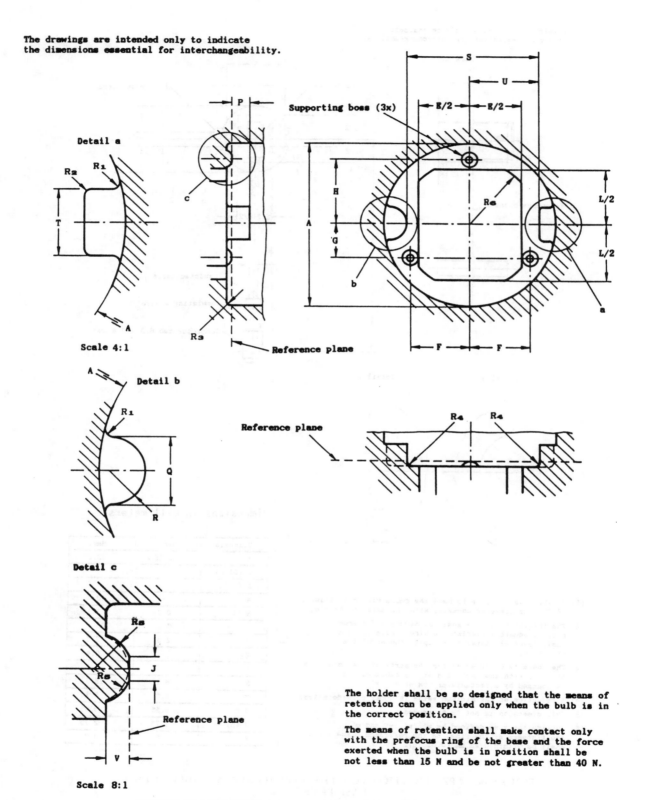

The holder shall be so designed that the means of
retention can be applied only when the bulb is in
the correct position.

The means of retention shall make contact only
with the prefocus ring of the base and the force
exerted when the bulb is in position shall be
not less than 15 N and be not greater than 40 N.

FIGURE 67—SPECIFICATION FOR THE TYPE H3 REPLACEABLE BULB
BULB HOLDER PK22s

(1) The maximum difference in height between the supporting bosses shall not exceed 0.1 mm when the value of dimension V of the smallest boss is 0.3 mm.

If this value exceeds 0.3 mm then the difference in height may be increased accordingly.

(2) If the value of dimension A exceeds A min., then the values of dimensions R₁ max. and R₄ max. may be increased accordingly.

(3) If the value of dimension V exceeds V min., then the values of dimensions R₃ max. and R₄ max. may be increased accordingly.

(4) Dimensions E, L and L₆ denote the minimum free space to be reserved for the bulb.

(5) Dimension J denotes the allowed flat area.

Dimensions in millimeters

Dimension	Min.	Max.
A (2)	24	-
E (4)	14	-
F	8.05	8.35
G	4.65	4.95
H	9.35	9.65
J (5)	-	1
L (4)	16	-
P	2.5	-
Q	4.75	4.95
R	Q/2	
R₁	-	0.5 (2)
R₂	0.3	0.5
R₃	-	0.3 (2)(3)
R₄	-	0.3 (3)
R₅	1.2	-
R₆ (4)	9.5	-
S	18.35	18.65
T	4.75	4.95
U	9.70	9.85
V (1)(3)	0.3	0.8

FIGURE 67 (CONTINUED)

(1) The distortion of the base end-portion of the glass bulb shall not be visible from any direction outside the obscuration angle of 80° max.
The shields shall produce no inconvenient reflections.
The angle between the reference axis and the plane of each shield, measured on the glass bulb side, should not exceed 90°.

(2) The permissible deviation of the ring centre from the reference axis is 0.5 mm in the direction perpendicular to the Z–Z line, and 0.05 mm in the direction parallel to the Z–Z line.

(3) Minimum length above the height of the actual light emitting centre over which the glass bulb shall be cylindrical.

(4) No part of the spring and no component of the bulb holder shall bear on the prefocus ring elsewhere than outside the rectangle shown in discontinuous outline.

(5) The positions of the first and the last turn of the filament are defined by the intersections of the outside of the first and the outside of the last light emitting turn, respectively, with the plane parallel to and 18 mm distance from the reference plane.

(6) The reference plane is the plane formed by the seating points of the three bosses of the bulb holder on the base ring.

Filament position requirements

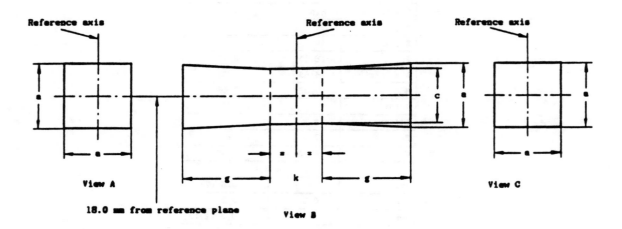

The first and last turn of the filament must lie entirely within the limits shown in respectively view A and C.
The transverse projection of the filament must lie within the limits shown in view B.
The centre of the filament shall lie within the limits of dimension k.

Dimensions in millimeters

Reference	Dimension
a	1.8d
c	1.6d
g	2.8
k	1.0

(1) d = actual filament diameter

FIGURE 68—SPECIFICATION FOR THE TYPE H3 REPLACEABLE BULB

17.2 General Test Conditions

17.2.1 The bulb shall be measured in a horizontal operating position.

17.2.2 Each filament shall be aged for approximately 1 h at test voltage. Immediately prior to a measurement the filament shall be operated for a minimum of 2 min at test voltage.

17.2.3 Measurements of filaments are carried out at test voltage.

18. Reference Plane, Reference Axis, and Planes for Measurements

18.1 Reference Plane—The reference plane is the plane formed by the seating points of the three lugs.

18.2 Reference Axis—The reference axis is perpendicular to the reference plane and passed through the center of the outer circle with diameter M of the base-ring.

18.3 Plane V-V—Plane V-V is the plane perpendicular to the reference plane and contains the reference axis and the center line of the reference lug.

18.4 Plane H-H—Plane H-H is the plane perpendicular to the reference plane and plane V-V and contains the reference axis.

18.5 Plane X-X—Plane X-X is the plane perpendicular to the reference plane, contains the reference axis, and has an angle of 15 degrees to plane H-H turned clockwise away from the reference lug.

18.6 Plane Y_1-Y_1—Plane Y_1-Y_1 is a plane parallel to the reference plane at a distance of 29.5 mm from it.

18.7 Plane Y_2-Y_2—Plane Y_2-Y_2 is a plane parallel to the reference plane at a distance of 33.0 mm from it.

18.8 Plane Y_3-Y_3—Plane Y_3-Y_3 is a plane parallel to the reference plane at a distance of 23.5 mm from it.

18.9 Plane Y_4-Y_4—Plane Y_4-Y_4 is a plane parallel to the reference plane at a distance of 26.0 mm from it.

18.10 Plane Y_5-Y_5—Plane Y_5-Y_5 is a plane parallel to the reference plane at a distance of 28.95 mm from it.

19. Viewing Directions (see Figure 74)

19.1 Viewing Direction 1—Perpendicular to plane V-V, seen from the side of the left-handed shield edge.

19.2 Viewing Direction 2—Perpendicular to plane H-H, seen from the side of the reference lug.

19.3 Viewing Direction 3—Parallel to plane X-X and reference plane, seen from the side of the right-handed shield edge.

20. Measuring Points (MP)—The following points as specified in Figures 75 and 76 shall be measured.

Measurements are to be made perpendicular to the viewing directions.

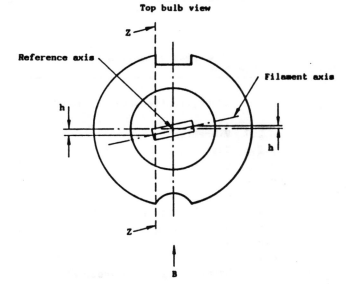

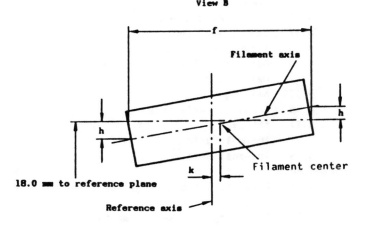

Dimensions in millimeters

Reference	Dimension	Tolerance
f	5.0	± 0.50
h	0	± 0.25
k	0	± 0.20

FIGURE 69—SPECIFICATION FOR THE TYPE H3 REPLACEABLE BULB

TABLE 8 — Test Classification

Report Section		Requirements Performance	Requirements Design	Requirements Material	Requirements Guidelines
3.	Identification Code Designation				X
4.2.1	Vibration	X			
4.2.2	Dust	X			
4.2.3	Corrosion	X			
4.2.4	Photometry	X			
4.3	Color	X			
4.4	Plastic Materials	X			
4.5	Beam Pattern Location	X			
4.6	Wattage	X			
4.7	Luminous Flux	X			
4.8	Maintenance of Luminous Flux	X			
4.9	Out-of-Focus Test	X			
4.10	Impact	X			
4.11	Aiming Adjustment	X			
4.12	Lens Inward Force	X			
4.13	Torque Deflection	X			
4.14	Deflection Test — Replaceable Headlamp Bulbs	X			
4.15	Sealing	X			
4.16	Chemical Resistance	X			
4.17	Abrasion	X		X	
4.18	Thermal Cycle	X			
4.19	Internal Heat	X			
4.20	Humidity	X			
4.21	Filament Rated Average Lab Life	X			
5.23	Retaining Ring Requirements		X		X
5.24	Dimensions		X		X
6.2	Photometric Design		X		X
6.4	Filament Life				X

The drawing is not mandatory, their sole purpose is to show
which dimensions must be verified.

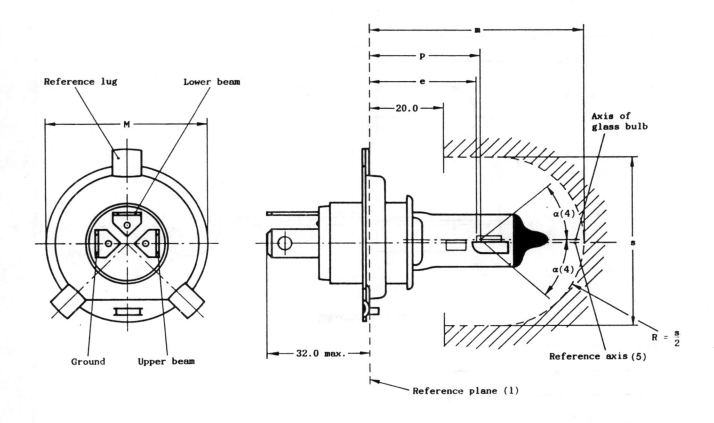

(1) The reference plane is the plane formed by the seating points of the three lugs of the base ring.

(2) "m" denotes the maximum length of the bulb.

(3) It must be possible to insert the bulb into a cylinder of diameter "s" concentric with the
    reference axis and limited at one end by a plane parallel to and 20 mm distance from the reference
    plane and at the other end by a hemisphere of radius s/2.

(4) The obscuration must extend at least as far as the cylindrical part of the glas bulb.
    It must also overlap the internal shield when the latter is viewed in a direction perpendicular to
    the reference axis.
    The effect sought by the obscuration may also be achieved by other means. *

(5) The reference axis is the line perpendicular to the reference plane and passing through the centre
    of the circle of diameter "M".

* Not applicable to HB2.

Dimensions in millimeters

Reference	Dimension	Tolerance
e	28.5	+ 0.45 − 0.25
P	28.95	−
m (2)	max. 60.0	−
s (3)	45.0	−
α (4)	max. 40°	−

FIGURE 70—SPECIFICATION FOR THE TYPE H4/HB2 REPLACEABLE BULB

The drawings are not mandatory with respect to the design of the shield.

POSITION OF SHIELD

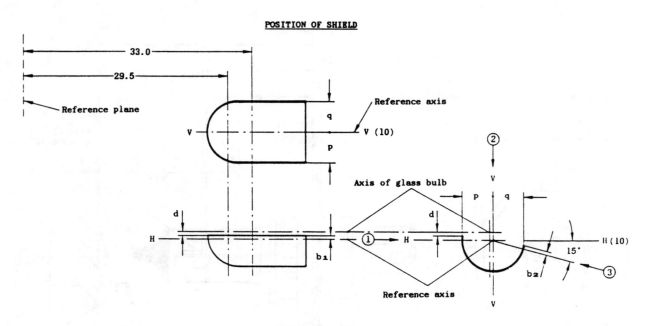

POSITION OF FILAMENTS

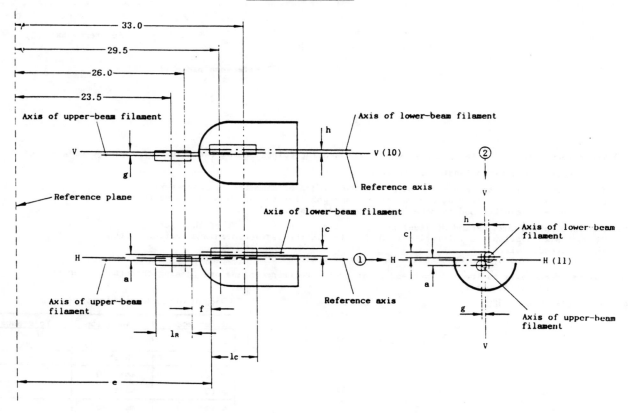

FIGURE 71—SPECIFICATION FOR THE TYPE H4/HB2 REPLACEABLE BULB

Dimensions indicated in Table are measured in three directions:

Direction ① for dimensions a, b₁, c, d, e, f, l_R and l_c;

Direction ② for dimensions g, h, p and q;

Direction ③ for dimension b₂.

Dimensions p and q are measured in a plane parallel to and 33 mm away from the reference plane.

Dimensions b₁, b₂, c and h are measured in planes parallel to and 29.5 mm and 33 mm away from the reference plane.

Dimensions a and g are measured in planes parallel to and 26.0 mm and 23.5 mm away from the reference plane.

(6) The end turns of the filaments are defined as being the first luminous turn and the last luminous turn that are at substantially the correct helix angle.

(7) For the lower-beam filament the points to be measured are the intersections, seen in direction ① , of the lateral edge of the shield with the outside of the end turns defined under footnote (6).

(8) "e" denotes the distance from the reference plane to the beginning of the lower-beam filament as defined under footnote (7).

(9) For the upper-beam filament the points to be measured are the intersections, seen in direction ① , of a plane parallel to plane HH and situated at a distance of 0.8 mm below it, with the end turns defined under footnote (6).

(10) Plane VV is the plane perpendicular to the reference plane and passing through the reference axis and through the intersection of the circle of diameter "M" with the axis of the reference lug.

(11) Plane HH is the plane perpendicular to both the reference plane and plane VV and passing through the reference axis.

Dimensions in millimeters

Reference	Dimension	Tolerances		
		H4 ***		HB2
a/26 *	0.8	± 0.35	± 0.2	+ 0.30
a/23.5 *	0.8	± 0.60	± 0.2	+ 0.40
b₁/29.5 *	0	± 0.30	± 0.2	+ 0.25
b₁/33 *	b₁/29.5vm **	± 0.30	± 0.15	± 0.20
b₂/29.5 *	0	± 0.30	± 0.2	+ 0.25
b₂/33 *	b₂/29.5vm **	± 0.30	± 0.15	+ 0.20
c/29.5 *	0.6	± 0.35	± 0.2	± 0.30
c/33 *	c/29.5vm **	± 0.35	± 0.15	± 0.30
d	min. 0.1	–	–	–
e (8)	28.5	+ 0.35 / – 0.25	+ 0.2 / – 0.0	+ 0.35 / – 0.15
f (6)(7)(9)	1.7	+ 0.50 / – 0.30	+ 0.3 / – 0.1	+ 0.30 / – 0.30
g/26 *	0	± 0.5	± 0.3	+ 0.4
g/23.5 *	0	± 0.7	± 0.3	± 0.5
h/29.5 *	0	± 0.5	± 0.3	± 0.5
h/33 *	h/29.5vm **	± 0.35	± 0.2	± 0.35
l_R (6)(9)	4.5	± 0.8	± 0.4	± 0.8
l_c (6)(7)	5.5	± 0.5	+ 0.35	+ 0.8
p/33 *	Depends on the shape of the shield	–	–	–
q/33 *	$\frac{p + q}{2}$	± 0.6	± 0.3	± 0.6
b₁ - b₂	–	–	–	± 0.25

* Dimension to be measured at the distance from the reference plane indicated in mm after the slash.

** ./29.5vm means the value measured at a distance of 29.5 mm from the reference plane.

*** Left column shows the tolerances for normal production bulbs.
Right column shows the tolerances for accurate rated bulbs.

FIGURE 71 (CONTINUED)

The drawings are intended only to indicate
the dimensions essential for interchangeability.

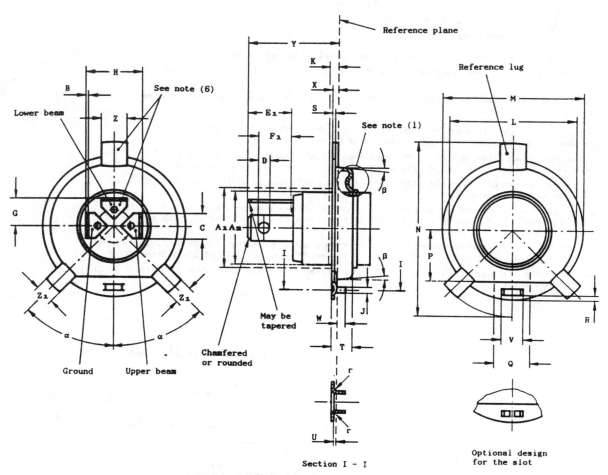

Dimensions in millimeters

Dimension	Min.	Max.
A₁ (8)	25.0	
A₂ (10)	Nom. 22*	
B	0.7	0.8
C	7.7	8.1
D	3.0	3.3
E₁	11.8	13.6
F₁	8.8	10.3
G	8.5	9.0
H	17.0	17.9
J	1.9	2.1
K (10)	2.0	
L (2)(4)	37.8	38.0
M (3) H4	42.8	43.0
M (3) HB2	42.9	43.0
N	51.6	52.0

Dimension	Min.	Max.
P (2)(7)	15.3	15.5
Q (2)(7)	8.5	–
R	1.3	1.7
S	0.50	–
T	5.0	6.0
U	(9)	
V (2)(5)	6.3	6.5
W	1.8	2.2
X	1.1	1.3
Y	–	32.0
Z	7.9	8.0
Z₁	5.8	6.2
r	(9)	
α	44°	46°
β	–	5°

FIGURE 72—SPECIFICATION FOR THE TYPE H4/HB2 REPLACEABLE BULB
BASE P43t-38

(1) The form of this annular part of the ring is optional and may be flat or recessed. However, the form shall be such that it will not cause any abnormal glare from the lower beam filament when the bulb is in its normal operating position in the vehicle.

(2) This dimension is measured at the reference plane.

(3) Dimension M is the diameter on which the bulb is centred.

(4) The maximum allowable eccentricity of cylinder L with respect to the circle of diameter M is 0.05 mm.

(5) The maximum allowable displacement of the centre of the nose from the line running through the centre of the reference lug and the circle of diameter M is 0.05 mm.
The sides of the nose shall not bend outwards.

(6) The relative positions of the contact tabs and the reference lug shall not deviate from the position shown by more than ± 20°.

(7) Dimension Q denotes the minimum width over which both the minimum and maximum limits of dimension P shall be observed.
Outside dimension Q, the maximum limit for dimension P shall not be exceeded.

(8) The means of securing the ring in the headlamp shall not encroach on this cylindrical zone, which extends over the full length of the shell shown on this side of the ring.

(9) The radius r shall be equal to or smaller than dimension U.

(10) Beyond distance K, in the direction of the contact tabs, dimension A_2* shall be observed.

* This dimension is solely for base design and is not to be gauged on the finished lamp.

FIGURE 72 (CONTINUED)

20.1 Shield and Filaments
20.1.1 VIEWING DIRECTION 1
a. MP 1 and MP 2: The intersections of the high beam filament axis with planes Y_3-Y_3 and Y_4-Y_4.
b. MP 3 and MP 4: The intersections of the shield edge with plane Y_1-Y_1 and Y_2-Y_2.
c. MP 5 and MP 6: The intersections of the envelope of the low beam filament with planes Y_1-Y_1 and Y_2-Y_2, farthest from plane H-H.
d. MP 7: The intersection of the glass bulb axis with plane Y_1-Y_1.
e. MP 8 and MP 11: The intersections of the outer part of respectively the first and last luminous turn of the low beam filament with the shield edge.
f. MP 9 and MP 10: The intersections of the outer part of respectively the first and last luminous turn of the high beam filament with the center line (axis) of that filament.
20.1.2 VIEWING DIRECTION 2
a. MP 12 and MP 13: The intersections of the high beam filament axis with planes Y_3-Y_3 and Y_4-Y_4.
b. MP 14 and MP 15: The intersections of the low beam filament axis with planes Y_1-Y_1 and Y_2-Y_2.
c. MP 16 and MP 17: The intersections of the shield edges with plane Y_2-Y_2.
20.1.3 VIEWING DIRECTION 3
a. MP 18 and MP 19: The intersections of the shield edge planes Y_1-Y_1 and Y_2-Y_2.
20.2 Top Obscuration
20.2.1 VIEWING DIRECTION 2
a. MP 23: Intersection of the glass bulb axis with plane Y_5-Y_5.
b. MP 21 and MP 22: Intersections of the top shielding with a plane parallel to plane H-H and containing the glass bulb axis.

20.2.2 VIEWING DIRECTION 1
a. MP 20: Intersection of the top shielding with a plane parallel to plane V-V and containing the glass bulb axis.

21. Dimensions to be Measured—Table 9 states the dimensions to be measured. Values and tolerances are given in Figure 65.

TABLE 9—DIMENSIONS TO BE MEASURED

Distances	Measured Perpendicular to Plane	Viewing Direction	Reference 12 V
MP 2 to MP 3	H-H	1	a/26.0
MP 1 to MP 3	H-H	1	a/23.5
MP 3 to H-H	H-H	1	b1/29.5
MP 4 to H-H	H-H	1	b1/33.0
MP 18 to X-X	X-X	3	b2/29.5
MP 19 to X-X	X-X	3	b2/33.0
MP 3 to MP 5	H-H	1	c/29.5
MP 4 to MP 6	H-H	1	c/33.0
MP 7 to MP 3	H-H	1	d
MP 8 to ref. plane	ref. plane	1	e
MP 8 to MP 9	ref. plane	1	f
MP 13 to V-V	V-V	2	g/26.0
MP 12 to V-V	V-V	2	g/23.5
MP 14 to V-V	V-V	2	h/29.5
MP 15 to V-V	V-V	2	h/33.0
MP 9 to MP 10	ref. plane	1	1R
MP 8 to MP 11	ref. plane	1	1c
MP 16 to V-V	V-V	2	p/33.0
MP 17 to V-V	V-V	2	q/33.0
Angle			
MP 21 & 22 to MP 23	V-V	2	α
MP 20 to MP 23	H-H	1	α

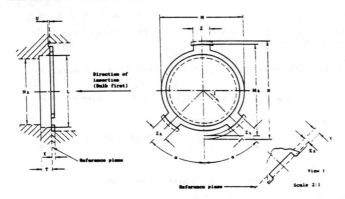
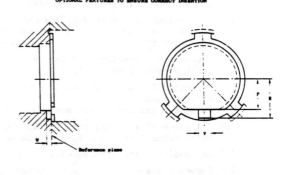

The drawings are intended only to indicate
the dimensions essential for interchangeability.

OPTIONAL FEATURES TO ENSURE CORRECT INSERTION

The holder shall be so designed that, without using undue force, the means of retention of the bulb can be applied only when it is in the correct position.

The means of retention shall make contact with the prefocus base ring only and the total force exerted, when the bulb is in position, shall be not less than 10 N and be not more than 60 N.

(1) This value shall be complied with between the rim of the holder and the reference plane (dimension X). However, it may be reduced to 38.5 mm within the dimensions Z and Z_1 which correspond with the support points for the lugs of the ring.

(2) Dimension X_1 denotes the minimum distance over which dimensions Z and Z_1 shall apply. Outside dimension X_1 the slots may be chamfered or rounded.

(3) Wrong adjustment of the bulb in the holder can be prevented in different ways e.g.:

   - by applying the additional optional features. (See figures).

   - By decreasing dimension Z_1 to 7.5 - 7.7 mm followed by a decrease of the tolerance for α to give values of 44°40' - 45°20'.

   - by using a sufficiently large value for X depending on the construction of the holder.

(4) If dimension L is smaller than 40.5 mm, dimension V, R and W shall apply.

(5) Dimension N delineates the minimum free space to be reserved for the three lugs of the ring.

(6) Dimension N_1 shall be not less than 35 mm diameter over a distance of 20 mm from the reference plane and shall be not less than 45 mm diameter at any distance greater than 20 mm from the reference plane.

Dimensions in millimeters

Dimension	Min.	Max.	Dimension	Min.	Max.
L (4)	38.2	–	U	0.4	–
M	43.02 (1)	43.2	V (4)	6.8	–
M_1	–	49.0	W (4)	2.5	–
N (5)	52.5		X (3)	1.8	–
N_1	(6)		X_1 (2)	1.4	–
P (3)	16.0	–	Z (3)	8.05	8.15
R (4)	20.5	–	Z_1 (3)	8.0	8.5
T	5.5	–	α	44°	46°

FIGURE 73—SPECIFICATION FOR THE TYPE H4/HB2 REPLACEABLE BULB
BULB HOLDER P43t

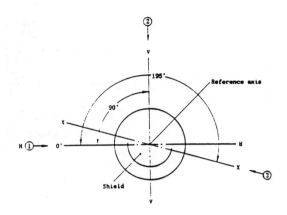

FIGURE 74—SPECIFICATION FOR THE TYPE H4/HB2
REPLACEABLE BULB
VIEWING DIRECTION SEEN FROM THE TOP OF THE BULB

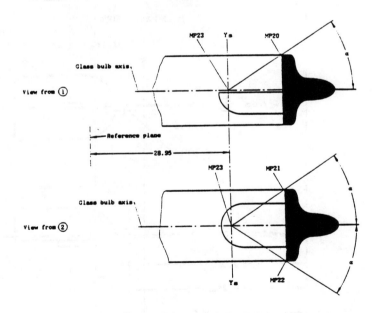

FIGURE 75—SPECIFICATION FOR THE TYPE
H4/HB2 REPLACEABLE BULB
TOP OBSCURATION

Viewing direction ①
MP 1, 2, 3, 4, 5, 6, 7, 8, 9, 10, 11

Viewing direction ②
MP 12, 13, 14, 15, 16, 17

Viewing direction ③
MP 18, 19

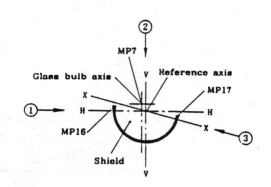

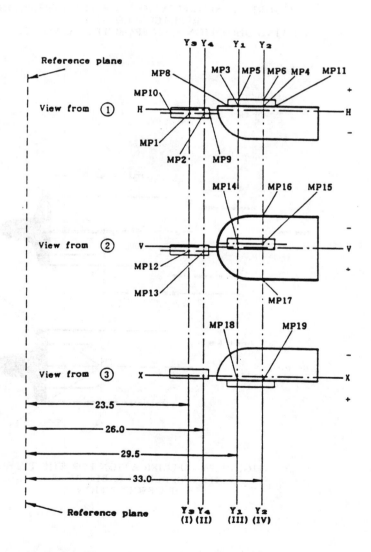

FIGURE 76—SPECIFICATION FOR THE TYPE H4/HB2 REPLACEABLE BULB
POSITIONS OF MEASURING POINTS OF H4 BULBS

HEADLAMP DESIGN GUIDELINES FOR MATURE DRIVERS—SAE J1606 MAR93

SAE Information Report

Report of the SAE Mature Driver Standards Committee approved March 1993.

Foreword—Mature drivers represent an appreciable percentage of the driving population. In 1989, the percentage of drivers of age 50 years and older represented 30% of the driving population. The number of drivers in this age group was on the order of 50 million! Demographic data such as this provides strong justification for giving specific consideration to the needs of mature drivers when developing SAE standards.

1. Scope—This SAE Information Report should be used as a supplement to SAE J1383 (Reference 2.1.1). It is intended to provide additional information which is important to the automotive designer and engineer in the process of designing, developing, and engineering the headlamps of motor vehicles which will take into account the effects of the aging process on the driver.

2. References

2.1 Applicable Documents—The following publications form a part of this specification to the extent specified herein.

2.1.1 SAE J1383—Performance Requirements for Motor Vehicle Headlamps.

2.1.2 Olson, P.L., "Problems of Nighttime Visibility and Glare for Older Drivers," SAE 881756. Warrendale: SAE (1988).

2.1.3 Yanik, A. J., "Vehicle Design Considerations for Older Drivers," SAE 885090. Warrendale: SAE (1988).

2.1.4 Kornzweig, A. C., "Physiological Effects of Age On the Visual Process," Sight Saving Review, Vol. 24, (1954).

2.1.5 Bhise, V. D., Farber, E. I. and Matle, C. C., "Predicting the Effects of Driver Age on Visual Performance in Night Driving," SAE 890873. Warrendale: SAE (1989).

2.1.6 Arens, J. B., "The Potential Impact of Automotive Headlight Changes on the Visibility of Reflectorized Highway Signs," SAE 870238. Warrendale: SAE (1987).

2.1.7 Bhise, V. D. and Matle, C. C., "Effects of Headlamp Aim and Aiming Variability on Visual Performance in Night Driving," Trans. Res. Record 1247. Transportation Research Board (1989).

2.1.8 FMVSS No. 108: Lamps, reflective devices, and associated equipment.

2.1.9 EEC 76/756 Appendix 5: Installation of lighting and light-signalling devices on motor vehicles and their trailers.

2.1.10 ECE Reg. No. 45: Uniform provisions concerning the approval of headlamp cleaners and of motor vehicles with regard to headlamp cleaners.

2.1.11 SAE J852—Front Cornering Lamps for Use on Motor Vehicles

3. General—There are a number of age-related changes that can affect the ability of persons to collect visual information while operating a motor vehicle at night (Reference 2.1.2, 2.1.3). The more important of these are:

a. Reduced visual capabilities at low levels of illumination
b. Increased sensitivity to glare
c. Longer recovery time from glare
d. Decreased visual acuity
e. Longer motor response time
f. Decreased contrast sensitivity

The primary headlamp characteristics specified or referenced in SAE J1383 (Reference 2.1.1) that have an impact on these factors are:

a. Beam candlepower
b. Candlepower distribution
c. Aim

These characteristics and their relationship to the aging process are discussed in the following section.

4. Specifics

4.1 Beam Candlepower—One of the primary effects of aging on vision is that less illumination reaches the light-sensitive portion of the eye (the retina). The reduction can be quite large. For example, for the same lighting conditions, the illumination of the retina of an 80-year-old person will be about 10% of that at the retina of a young person (Reference 2.1.4). Hence, older persons need higher levels of illumination. This is most affected by the candlepower that is directed to areas of the forward field where targets are likely to appear (Reference 2.1.5). It is also desirable that more illumination be directed to the "wing" areas to facilitate seeing driveways, close-in curbs, etc.

4.2 Candlepower Distribution—The need for increased illumination must be balanced against the fact that the aging eye is much more affected by glare. Disability glare comes about because light entering the eyes of a person is scattered somewhat, producing a veil or curtain of diffused light across the retina and thereby reducing target contrast. The amount of scattered light increases as the eye ages. Thus, it is important that the intensities above the horizontal axis of a low beam headlamp be maintained at reasonably low levels. Of course, sufficient illumination should be maintained for sign detection and legibility (Reference 2.1.5, 2.1.6).

4.3 Aim—To provide both enhanced visibility and increased glare protection to the older driver means that areas of relatively high illumination and low illumination in headlamp beam patterns must be maintained in closer proximity. This, in turn, necessitates that aim must be maintained within close tolerances (Reference 2.1.7). Major aspects of proper aim include:

a. Providing proper aim during vehicle manufacture
b. Designing mounting mechanisms that will hold aim securely while the vehicle is in use
c. Facilitating accurate aiming and checking of aim in the field
d. Minimizing aim error when bulbs are replaced
e. Considering auxiliary devices such as manual or automatic aim levelers and load levelers to maintain aim

4.4 Other Possible Assists—These assists help in maintaining proper aim and roadway illumination and in providing additional light in wing areas. They are of benefit to all drivers in all age groups but preferentially to those in the mature driver age group.

a. On-board aimers (Reference 2.1.8)
b. Aim levelers (for loading) as required in Germany (Reference 2.1.9)
c. Headlamp washers with or without wipers as required in Sweden, Norway, and Finland (Reference 2.1.10)
d. Cornering lamps (Reference 2.1.11)

Report of the SAE Road Illuminated Devices Standards Committee and the SAE Lighting Coordinating Committee approved January 1995. Rationale statement available.

1. Scope—This SAE Recommended Practice provides headlamp beam pattern test points which incorporate elements of European, Asian, and U.S. photometric tables. Alternative means of aiming headlamps are included which are consistent with methods presently used in the United States and in Europe.

2. References

2.1 Applicable Documents—The following publications form a part of this specification to the extent specified herein. The latest issue of SAE publications shall apply.

2.1.1 SAE PUBLICATIONS—Available from SAE, 400 Commonwealth Drive, Warrendale, PA 15096-0001.

SAE J599—Lighting Inspection Code

SAE J1383—Performance Requirements for Motor Vehicle

2.2 Related Documents—The following publications are provided for information purposes only and are not a required part of this document.

2.2.1 SAE PUBLICATIONS—Available from SAE, 400 Commonwealth Drive, Warrendale, PA 15096-0001.

SAE J575—Tests for Motor Vehicle Lighting Devices and Components

SAE J579 Cancelled—Sealed Beam Headlamp Units for Motor Vehicles

SAE J600—Headlamp Testing Machines

SAE J602—Headlamp Aiming Device for Mechanically Aimable Headlamp

SAE Paper 870238—The Potential Impact of Automotive Headlight Changes on the Visibility of Reflectorized Highway Signs, J. B. Arens, Office of Safety and Traffic Operations, Research and Development, Federal Highway Administration

2.2.2 ECE PUBLICATION—Available from Commission of the European Communities, 200, Rue de la Loi, B-1049 Brussels, Belgium.

ECE Regulation 20

2.2.3 JIS PUBLICATION—Available from Japanese Standards Association, 1-24, Akasaka 4, Minato-ku, Tokyo 107 Japan.

JIS D 5500

2.2.4 OTHER PUBLICATIONS

"Headlamp Beam Pattern Philosophy," Lidstrom, O., Minutes of the SAE Headlamp Beam Task Force, April 4, 1990

"Obstacle Detection Rationale for Upper Beam Intensity," Kosmatka, W.J., Minutes of the SAE Headlamp Beam Task Force, February 26, 1992

"Headlamp Beam Gradient Aim Study," Kosmatka, W.J., Minutes of the SAE Headlamp Beam Task Force, October 4, 1993

"Partial Harmonization of International Standards for Low-Beam Headlighting Patterns," Sivak, M. and Flannagan, M., UMTRI-93-11, Univ. of Mich. Trans. Res. Institute, 1993

3. Definitions

3.1 H-V Axis—See SAE J1383.

3.2 Visual Aim—A method of aiming a headlamp by visual assessment of the location of certain beam pattern characteristics, such as visual edges/cutoffs or location of the High Intensity Zone, and positioning the beam pattern, projected on a surface, with respect to prescribed coordinates on that surface. (Also see "3.12 CUTOFF.")

3.3 Low Beam Fractional Balance Aim—A method of aiming a headlamp where one or more points in the beam pattern, with specified percentage values of intensity relative to the Maximum Beam Intensity (MBI), are used to position the beam relative to the H-V axis. (Also see SAE J1383.)

3.4 High Beam Balance Aim—A method of aiming a headlamp via the upper beam such that the intensity of light at two points equidistant from a projection of the lamp's vertical plane are of equal magnitude at the same time that two points equidistant from a projection of the lamp's horizontal plane are of equal magnitude. (Also see SAE J1383.)

3.5 Mechanical Aim—A method of aiming a headlamp such that the lamp aiming plane is oriented to a predetermined mechanical feature of the lamp. "VHAD" and "REFERENCE PLANE" aim are both mechanical aiming methods.

3.6 Vehicle Headlamp Aiming Device (VHAD)—A device, permanently installed on a motor vehicle and/or headlamp by the manufacturer of the vehicle, which indicates the horizontal and vertical aim of the headlamps.

3.7 Photometric Aim—A method of aiming a headlamp using a device which measures luminous intensity at selected points of the beam pattern relative to the H-V axis.

3.8 Optical Aim—A method of aiming a headlamp based upon measurement of certain characteristics of the beam pattern. Optical aim methods include Photometric Aim, Fractional Balance Aim, and Image Processing Aim.

3.9 Aiming Reference Plane—A plane which is perpendicular to the longitudinal axis of the vehicle and tangent to the forward-most aiming pad on the headlamp.

3.10 Aiming Plane (Headlamp)—(See SAE J1383.)

3.11 Image Processing Aim—Headlamp aiming method using an image sensor to measure the intensity pattern of the headlamp, a computer to determine the position of the pattern relative to the H-V axes, and a display device showing a proportional digitized representation of the headlamp beam pattern.

3.12 Cutoff—The visual cutoff is where, by visual impression, the best separation between the lighted area of the beam pattern and the dark area above it, is located. Objectively, this will be defined as: the location in the vertical direction where the maximum rate of change in the light intensity (the highest gradient) is found.

4. Headlamp Lens Aim Marking

4.1 Visual Aim—Headlamps designed to be visually aimed using an aiming screen shall be marked with a letter "V".

4.2 Fractional Balance Aim

4.2.1 Headlamps designed to be aimed by fractional balance means shall be marked with the letter "B".

4.2.2 Following the letter designation shall be two, two-digit numbers indicating first, the "2 degrees right" and second, the "1 degree down" fractional balance percentage values chosen to represent the design aim of the headlamp.

4.2.3 The two numbers may be separated by a space, dash (-), or slash mark (/) (e.g., B25/35 or B25-35), or presented as a series of four digits preceded by a "B".

4.2.4 Lens marking shall be no less than 3 mm in height and imprinted indelibly on the lens.

4.2.5 MARKING LOCATION—Same as "Replaceable Bulb Headlamps" (see SAE J1383).

4.3 Aiming Reference Plane Aim

4.3.1 REPLACEABLE BULB HEADLAMPS—(See SAE J1383.)

4.3.2 "Reference Plane" markings are not required for standardized sealed beam headlamps.

4.4 VHAD Aim—Markings are not required for headlamps with VHAD.

4.5 Image Processing Aim—No special marking required.

5. Headlamp Aiming Procedures

5.1 Visual Aim

5.1.1 LOW BEAM

5.1.1.1 Vertical Aim—For a lamp aimed using the right cutoff, the low beam shall be adjusted such that the top cutoff is located at the horizontal line representing the projected horizontal axis of the headlamp.

For a lamp aimed using the left side cutoff, the low beam shall be aimed such that the cutoff is located approximately 0.6 degree below the horizontal line, 2 to 4 degrees left, representing the projected horizontal axis of the headlamp.

5.1.1.2 Horizontal Aim—The left edge of the HIZ shall be located at the line representing a projection of the headlamp's vertical axis V-V.

For headlamps with no prominent left edge to the HIZ (but having a straight top cutoff, which has on its left side a transition zone angling left and downward), the left/right aim of the lamp will be accomplished by orienting the left/right position of the beam so that the left end of the top cutoff is located 0.4 degree right of the vertical (V-V) as shown in Figure 1.

5.1.2 HIGH BEAM—The high beam shall be aimed so that the center of the high intensity zone is coincident with the horizontal and vertical lines on the aim screen.

5.1.3 VISUAL AIM SCREEN—Headlamp visual aiming will be conducted using a white screen with a matte surface, having a reflectance of 60% minimum. Lines indicating the horizontal and vertical coordinates should be no greater than 3 mm maximum in width. There should be no other visible marks, scuffs, or shaded areas which exceed 25 cm^2 in area.

5.1.4 SCREEN LOCATION—See SAE J599 for screen location and orientation. Where the screen is to be used in conjunction with photometric testing, the H-V axes of the screen shall be positioned perpendicular to the goniometer axis.

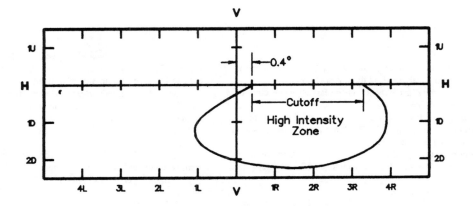

FIGURE 1—LOWER BEAM PATTERN

5.1.5 SUITABILITY FOR VISUAL AIM—Refer to 6.3.

5.2 Balance Aim

5.2.1 LOW BEAM—With the headlamp mechanical axis coincident with the axis of the goniometer or the centerline of the aiming screen, the low beam shall be adjusted to satisfy the following criteria:

5.2.1.1 The measured value at the test point designated by the triangle in Figure 2 of SAE J1383 at H - 2 degrees right, shall be a percentage of the maximum beam intensity indicated by the first two-digit number following the "B" on the headlamp lens (as defined under "Headlamp Lens Aim Marking").

5.2.1.2 The measured value at the test point designated by the square, in Figure 2 of SAE J1383, at 1 degree down-vertical, shall be the percentage of the maximum intensity indicated by the second two-digit number following the "B" on the headlamp lens.

5.2.2 HIGH BEAM—(See SAE J1383.)

5.3 Aiming Reference Plane Aim—Adjust the position of the headlamp until the aiming plane of the lamp is normal to the axis of the vehicle or the H-V axis.

5.4 VHAD Aim—Adjust the position of the headlamp until the device indicates the headlamp is properly aimed. Check manufacturer's instructions for horizontal positioning.

5.5 Image Processing—Aim the headlamp in accordance with the aimer manufacturer's instructions.

6. Photometric Tests

6.1 Low Beam Headlamps—A low beam headlamp, or the low beam of a dual beam headlamp, aimed in accordance with the appropriate procedure outlined in Section 5, shall be measured at the points and zones indicated in Figures 2 and 4.

6.2 High Beam Headlamp—A high beam headlamp, aimed in accordance with the appropriate procedure outlined in Section 5, shall be measured at the points indicated in Figures 3 and 5. (The high beam of a dual beam headlamp will retain the aim of the lower beam aimed in accordance with 6.1.)

6.3 Requirements for Lamps Marked With "V"—Adequacy of sharpness of cutoff.

6.3.1 Adjust beam location as it would be located for "visual aim."

6.3.2 Read photometric point values from 0.5 degree up to 0.5 degree down in 0.2 degree vertical increments along a line at 1 degree right. For lamps designed to be aimed using the left side of the beam, vertical 0.2 degree increments are read at 2 degrees left over the interval from 0.1 degree down to 1.1 degrees down.

6.3.3 Repeat 6.3.2 at 2 degrees right and 3 degrees right, or at 3 degrees left and 4 degrees left.

6.4 Photometric Test Voltage—(See SAE J1383.) For conversion of halogen light source photometric values to other than 12.8 V, the following factors are suggested:

  a. For 12.0 V—0.81
  b. For 12.8 V—1.0
  c. For 13.2 V—1.11

6.4.1 MEASUREMENT METHODS FOR ZONES IN FIGURE 4

Zone 1   Search for the highest intensity. The "MIN" value shall be met.

Zone II   Photometry values shall be met at all four corners of the zone.

Zone III   Photometry values shall be met at four extreme corners of the zone and at the lower boundary line from 5L to 5R.

Zone IV   Scan 4U line from 15L to 15R and along V line from 4U to 10U. "MAX" value shall not be exceeded.

Zone V   Scan 45U line from 45L to 45R and along V line form 10U to 90U. "MAX" values shall not be exceeded.

Test Point	Min (cd) (0.8 x Figure 4)	Max (cd) (1.2 x Figure 4)
0.5U, 1.5R	400	3 000
0.5U, 1.5L	100	850[1]
1.5U, 1.5R	150	1 300
2.0D, 15R, and 15L	700	—
0.86D, 3.5L	1440	14 400
4.0U, 8L	65	900
2.0U, 1.5R	65	900
10U, V	—	150
0.6D, 1.3R	8000	—
0.86D, V	3600	—

[1] Point value is 1.3 x Figure 4 value.

FIGURE 2—LOW BEAM PERFORMANCE REQUIREMENTS

Test Point	Min (cd) (0.8 x Figure 5)	Max (cd) (1.2 x Figure 5)
H-V	20 000	168 000
H-3R	12 000	168 000
H-3L	12 000	168 000

FIGURE 3—HIGH BEAM PERFORMANCE REQUIREMENTS

6.5 Re-aim Allowance—In order to accommodate slight aim differences between photometers, 1/4 degree re-aim is allowed for point measurements in Figures 2 and 3.

7. Performance Requirements

7.1 Low Beam

7.1.1 The low beam shall meet the photometric values in Figure 2.

7.1.2 LOW BEAM HIGH INTENSITY ZONE—In the zone bounded by 0.5 degree down to 2.0 degrees down, and 0.5 degree right to 2.5 degrees right, at least one point shall measure 15 000 cd.

7.2 High Beam—The high beam shall meet the photometric values shown in Figure 3.

7.3 Low Beam Cutoff—In order for a low beam to be satisfactory for visual aiming, the cutoff shall meet the following criteria.

7.3.1 CUTOFF APPEARANCE

7.3.1.1 For Lamps Designed to be Aimed Using the Top Right Cutoff —The cutoff shall appear to be approximately straight and parallel to the horizontal from at least 1 degree to 3 degrees right.

7.3.1.2 For Lamps Designed to be Aimed Using the Top Left Cutoff—The cutoff shall appear to be approximately straight and parallel to the horizontal from at least 2 degrees left to 4 degrees left.

7.3.2 A lamp aimed and measured as described in 5.3 shall meet the following:

7.3.2.1 The gradient in the vertical direction for each 0.2 degree interval shall be computed according to Equation 1:

$$\text{Gradient, } G_n = (\text{INTENSITY}_{n+1} - \text{INTENSITY}_n)/\text{INTENSITY}_n \quad \text{(Eq.1)}$$

where:

INTENSITY$_n$ = Photometric intensity at each 0.2 degree increment beginning with n = 1, at the topmost point

7.3.2.2 The maximum vertical gradient, G, is the largest value computed for the intervals along the vertical lines.

NOTE—If either the first or last interval gradient is the largest, the true maximum gradient may not have been found. The lamp may be misaimed and require re-aim or the beam may not meet the requirements in 7.3.1.

7.3.2.3 The maximum vertical gradients at 1, 2, and 3 degrees right or 2, 3, and 4 degrees left, shall be no less than 0.6 (60% change in 0.2 degree).

8. *Guidelines*

8.1 Photometric Design Guidelines

8.1.1 LOW BEAM PHOTOMETRIC GUIDELINES—For a low beam or dual beam headlamp aimed in accordance with the procedures outlined in Section 5, photometric guidelines are shown in Figure 4.

8.1.2 HIGH BEAM PHOTOMETRIC GUIDELINES—For a high beam headlamp aimed in accordance with the procedures outlined in Section 5, photometric guidelines are shown in Figure 5.

8.2 Low Beam Cutoff—In order for a low beam to be visually aimable, the cutoff shall meet the following criteria:

8.2.1 CUTOFF APPEARANCE

8.2.1.1 For Lamps Designed to be Aimed Using the Top Right Cutoff—The cutoff shall appear to be approximately straight and horizontal from at least 1 degree right to 3 degrees right.

8.2.1.2 For Lamps Designed to be Aimed Using the Top Left Cutoff—The cutoff shall appear to be approximately straight and horizontal from at least 2 degrees left to 4 degrees left.

8.2.2 A lamp aimed and measured as described in 6.3 shall meet the following:

8.2.2.1 The gradient in the vertical direction for each 0.2 degree interval shall be computed according to Equation 2:

$$\text{Gradient, } G_n = (\text{INTENSITY}_{n+1} - \text{INTENSITY}_n)/\text{INTENSITY}_n \quad \text{(Eq.2)}$$

where:

INTENSITY$_n$ = Photometric intensity at each 0.2 degree increment beginning with n = 1, at the topmost point

8.2.2.2 The maximum vertical gradient, G, is the largest value computed for the intervals along the vertical lines.

NOTE—If either the first or last interval gradient is the largest, the true maximum gradient may not be found. The lamp may be misaimed and require re-aim or the beam may not meet the requirements in 8.2.1.

8.2.2.3 The maximum vertical gradients at 1, 2, and 3 degrees right or 2, 3, and 4 degrees left shall be no less than 0.8 (80% change in 0.2 degree).

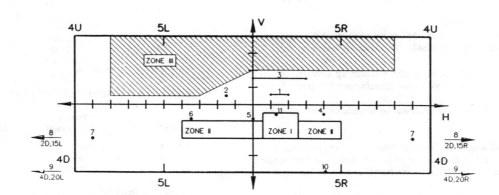

Test Points	Min (cd)	Max (cd)
1. 0.5U, 1R-2R	500	2 400
2. 0.5U, 1.5L	125	650
3. 1.5U, V-3R	200	1 000
4. 0.5D, 4R	5 000	—
5. 0.86D, V	4 500	—
6. 0.86D, 3.5L	1 800	12 000
7. 2.0D, 9R and 9L	1 250	—
8. 2.0D, 15L and 15R	1 000	—
9. 4.0D, 20L and 20R	300	—
10. 4.0D, 4R	—	50% of MAX in Zone I (but not to exceed 12 500 cd)
11. 0.6D, 1.3R	10 000	—

Zone	Description	Min (cd)	Max (cd)
Zone I	(See Above)	15000	—
Zone II	(See Above)	1875	—
Zone III	(See Above)	80	650
Zone IV	(4U-10U, 15L-15R)	—	525
Zone V	(10U-90U, 45L-45R)	—	125

NOTE—438 cd is permitted within a 2 degree conical angle.

FIGURE 4—LOW BEAM DESIGN GUIDELINES

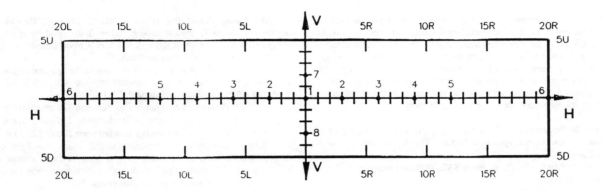

Test Points	Min (cd)	Max (cd)
1. H-V[1]	25 000	140 000
2. H-3R and 3L	1 500	—
3. H-6R and 6L	4 000	—
4. H-9R and 9L	2 500	—
5. H-12R and 12L	1 200	—
6. H-20R and 20L	250	—
7. 2U-V	1 200	—
8. 3D-V	2 500	—

[1] "H-V" includes a zone of H ± 0.5 degree, V ± 0.5 degree.

FIGURE 5—HIGH BEAM DESIGN GUIDELINES

Report of the SAE Road Illumination Devices Standards Committee approved February 1993 and revised July 1995.

(R) *1. Scope*—This SAE Recommended Practice applies to motor vehicle Forward Illumination Systems which use light generated by discharge sources. It provides test methods, requirements, and guidelines applicable to the special characteristics of gaseous discharge lighting devices which supplement those required for forward illumination systems using incandescent light sources. The document is applicable to integral beam and replaceable componet discharge forward lighting systems. This document is intended to be a guide to standard practice and is subject to change to reflect additional experience and technical advances.

2. References

2.1 Applicable Documents—The following publications form a part of this specification to the extent specified herein. The latest issue of SAE publications shall apply.

2.1.1 SAE PUBLICATIONS—Available from SAE, 400 Commonwealth Drive, Warrendale, PA 15096-0001.

SAE J575—Tests for Motor Vehicle Lighting Devices and Components

SAE J578—Color Specification

SAE J759—Lighting Identification Code

SAE J1113—Electromagnetic Susceptibility Measurement Procedures for Vehicle Components

SAE J1211—Recommended Environmental Practices for Electronic Equipment Design

SAE J1383—Performance Requirements for Vehicle Headlamps

SAE J1816—Performance Levels and Methods of Measurement of Electromagnetic Radiation From Vehicles and Devices (Narrow Band), 10 kHz - 1000 MHz

2.1.2 ANSI PUBLICATIONS—Available from American National Standards Institute, Inc., 11 West 42nd Street, New York, NY 10036.

ANSI Z311.1—Photobiological Safety for Lamps and Lighting Systems

ANSI C78.376—Spectroradiometrically Determined Assignments

2.1.3 FMVSS PUBLICATIONS—Available from the National Highway Traffic Safety Administration, 400 Seventh Street SW, Washington, DC 20024-0002.

FMVSS 108—Lamps, Reflective Devices, and Associated Equipment (Available as 49 CFR 571.108)

FMVSS 112—Headlamp Concealment Devices (Available as 49 CFR 571.112)

2.1.4 CIE PUBLICATION—Available from Commission Internationale de L'eclairage, 52 Bd Malesherbes, F-75008 Paris, France.

CIE Pub. 13.2—Method of Measuring and Specifying Color Rendering Properties of Light Sources (TC3.2) 1974

2.1.5 ACGIH PUBLICATIONS—Available from American Council of Governmental Industrial Hygienists, 6500 Glenway Avenue, Building D-7, Cincinnati, OH 45211.

Threshold Limit Values and Biological Exposure Indices for 1989-1990, American Conference of Governmental Industrial Hygienists

(R) 2.1.6 OTHER HANDBOOKS

Safety with Lasers and Other Optical Sources—Sliney and Wolbarsht (1980 Plenum Press).

3. Definitions

3.1 Discharge Forward Lighting (DFL) System—An automotive lighting system, providing forward illumination, comprised of the headlamps, discharge source, ballast/starting system, and interconnecting wiring.

3.2 Discharge Source—An electric light source in which light is produced by a stabilized arc.

3.3 Start-up Time—The period of time between the instant when the user operates a switch to power a lamp ON and the instant when the DFL system reaches a level within X% of "steady-state" output level.

3.4 Restart—The ability of the "hot" DFL system to relight before its temperature has returned to initial ambient.

3.5 Photometric Maintenance—Change in beam intensity of the test points of the beam pattern light output over time (life).

3.6 Life—Time in hours and starting cycles of a DFL system during which it meets specified operational characteristics under specified test conditions.

3.7 Rated Lab Life—Life specified by the manufacturer as the period during which the DFL system meets the performance specifications. (Rated lab life equals design life.)

3.8 Color Rendering Index (Light Source—CRI)—Measure of the degree of color shift objects undergo when illuminated by the light source as compared with the color of those same objects when illuminated by a reference source of comparable color temperature.

3.9 Ultraviolet Radiation—Radiation in the spectral region between 200 and 400 nm. Definitions and terminology are adopted in accordance with proposed ANSI specification standard Z311.

    a. UVA Flux—Radiant energy flux between 320 and 400 nm.

    b. UVB Flux—Radiant energy flux between 260 and 320 nm.

    c. UVC Flux—Radiant energy flux between 200 and 260 nm

3.10 Steady-state—A condition under which the light output of the device is considered to be stable or changing at such a slow rate as to be insignificant. A "Steady-state" condition would be generally measured in terms of a "maximum percent change per time period."

Steady-state light level (100%) is established by allowing the lamp to operate for 120 s after being switched "on." The average light level within the period from 120 to 140 s will be defined as the 100% level.

If the light output is not stable to within ±10% during the 120 to 140 s time interval, the test should be repeated on the system. If a system fails to stabilize after three attempts, a new system should be selected for a test sample.

3.11 Automotive Ballast—A device for stabilizing the operating characteristics of a discharge lamp. The ballast contains all the necessary circuitry to ignite a lamp and cause it to operate within a specified power profile range. It controls the required light output characteristics of the automotive discharge lighting system. The ballast may consist of one or more separate components.

3.12 Integral Beam—An "Integral Headlamp" produces a light pattern when normal vehicle voltage is applied. It cannot be disassembled by the user for the purpose of replacing any failed subassemblies within the lamp or housing package.

Discharge headlamps in which the ballast subunit is remote from the starter/lamp subunit may be considered integral if the user cannot disconnect the two subunits. Such a lamp may be disassembled and serviced by the manufacturer for the purpose of recycling the assembly by replacing nonfunctioning parts. It may also be disassembled and serviced by a service factory or dealer service facility. In any case, there is the assumption that the servicing facility will certify that the performance of the serviced device will meet all standards applicable to the original equipment.

4. Lighting Identification Codes, Markings, and Notices

4.1 Headlamps shall be marked in accordance with SAE J759.

4.2 The DFL system shall contain a label indicating the presence of high voltage, e.g., the international electric shock hazard symbol ("lightning bolt").

(R) *5. Tests*—All sample DFL systems shall be seasoned at 12.8 V for 20 h prior to being subjected to the tests that follow and a new DFL system may be used for each test.

NOTE—The power supply used for all testing should have its output isolated from the input to prevent any potential danger to laboratory personnel when running test as required.

5.1 Lamp/System Starting Procedures—The headlamp shall be held in its normal operating position and mechanically aimed with a photocell or cells at the test points shown in Table 1. Tests shall be conducted at room temperature (23 °C ± 3 °C), at 12.8 VDC ± 0.1 VDC, and for a duration required to obtain a reading. The response time of the measurement instrument should be less than 100 ms.

TABLE 1—TEST POINTS FOR DFL HEADLAMP STARTING TESTS

Lower Beam Lamp	Upper Beam Lamp
1.5 D - 2 R	H - V

5.1.1 INITIAL START-UP—The DFL system (ballast/starter) shall be activated and the luminous intensity at the photometric test points of Table 1 sampled and recorded for each headlamp from initial actuation through the intervals specified in Figure 1 or Figure 2. The test lamp(s) is then turned off.

5.1.2 SWITCHING (COLD LAMPS)—The DFL system (ballast/starter) shall be activated and the luminous intensity at the photometric test points of Table 1 sampled and recorded for each headlamp from initial activation through the intervals specified in Figure 1 or Figure 2.

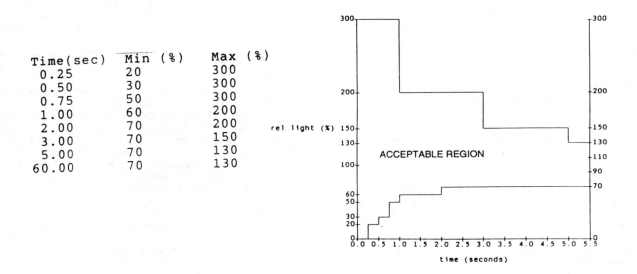

Time(sec)	Min (%)	Max (%)
0.25	20	300
0.50	30	300
0.75	50	300
1.00	60	200
2.00	70	200
3.00	70	150
5.00	70	130
60.00	70	130

(R) FIGURE 1—LAMP OUTPUT VS START-UP TIME
LOW OR HIGH BEAM NONCONTINUOUS LOW

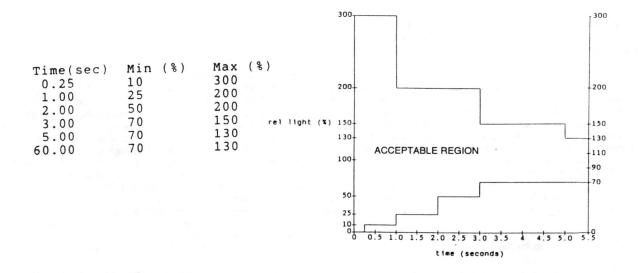

Time(sec)	Min (%)	Max (%)
0.25	10	300
1.00	25	200
2.00	50	200
3.00	70	150
5.00	70	130
60.00	70	130

(R) FIGURE 2—LAMP OUTPUT VS START-UP TIME
LOW OR HIGH BEAM CONTINUOUS LOW

NOTE—(%) = Percent of steady-state light intensity. Each beam should be measured at the point prescribed in Table 1, with the other beam blocked or not operating.

5.1.3 SWITCHING (HOT RESTART)—The lamp shall be energized for 5 min minimum. After this time period, a restart test shall be conducted once for every time interval as follows:

a. Cool down times for DFL hot restart test—1 s, 4 s, 10 s, 20 s, 30 s, 1 min

The system shall be switched off for the period of time shown as previously stated in order to simulate momentary switching to the alternate beam. The test lamp shall be energized and the luminous intensity at the applicable photometric test point shown in Table 1 sampled.

5.1.4 SWITCHING (CONTINUOUS LOW BEAM MODE)—For DFL systems designed to have the lower beam on continuously, the lower beam lamp shall be operated during the test. However, only the photometric characteristics of the upper beam switching shall be measured. The tests for "continuous low beam mode" are identical to those described in 5.1.3 except that only the upper beam lamp is tested.

5.2 Electrical Characteristics

5.2.1 SYSTEM OPERATING WATTAGE RANGE—DFL system wattage shall be measured at 12.8 VDC ± 0.1 VDC with all components in normal operating orientation using the equipment described in 5.2.3.

5.2.2 SYSTEM OPERATING VOLTAGE RANGE—The DFL system shall operate in the regulated mode from 9.0 to 18.0 VDC with all components in normal operating orientation using the equipment described in 5.2.3. Additional considerations for voltages between 9.0 and 4.5 V are presented in 7.10.

5.2.3 EQUIPMENT REQUIREMENTS—The input terminals of the DFL system shall be connected to a laboratory power supply which shall have a range of voltages from at least 4.0 to 18.5 VDC and which shall be capable of controlling voltage to ±0.1 VDC input voltage. In addition, the power supply shall be capable of satisfying the DFL system's current drain in all operational modes.

5.3 Photometric Maintenance—The DFL system shall be operated under nominal laboratory operating test conditions (23 °C ± 3 °C) at 12.8 VDC ± 0.1 VDC input voltage. The test cycle shall be the same as for the life test (7.2). The photometric maintenance test shall be performed after 70% of rated life of operation (e.g., 1400 h for a 2000 h design value of rated life).

5.4 Color and CRI

(R)   5.4.1 COLOR—The color coordinates shall be tested per SAE J578 for "White" light.

5.4.2 COLOR RENDERING—The color rendering properties of a DFL system shall be determined using the procedure outlined in CIE Publication Number 13.2 (TC 3.2) 1974, "Method of measuring and specifying color rendering properties of light sources." See 7.8 for performance criteria.

5.5 Environmental Tests—Testing shall be accomplished on a complete DFL system, i.e., ballast, interconnections, and headlamp unless otherwise specified in the specific test.

5.5.1 LEAKAGE CURRENT/BREAKDOWN TEST—The test shall be made on a system positioned in its design orientation by completely covering the exterior of the DFL system to be tested with aluminum foil. The foil is to be connected to a current-sensing device which terminates at the power source common (chassis ground). The sensing device shall be a noninductive resistor of 1000 Ω. The leakage current occurring during starting and operating (transient and steady-state) shall be measured using an oscilloscope with a bandwidth capability five times the bandwidth being measured for the observed frequencies and rise times. Current readings shall be recorded during the first 10 s of the initial start. The unit shall then continue to operate for 30 min, be turned off, and immediately restarted. The current readings shall again be recorded during the first 10 s after restart. After completion of this procedure, and without submitting the unit to any other tests, the environmental test shall be carried out on the unit. Within 30 min of the completion of the environmental test, the breakdown test shall be repeated. The final readings are then compared with the respective (initial and 30 min) readings made before the environmental test.

5.5.2 THERMAL CYCLE—A DFL system shall be mounted on a test fixture in its design orientation and shall be exposed to the test described in SAE J1383 "Thermal Cycle Test." In addition, electronic components shall be subjected to the test in SAE J1211, Section 4.1 using conditions that are appropriate for the location of the DFL system components in the vehicle.

5.5.3 HUMIDITY—The DFL system shall be mounted on a test fixture in its design orientation and shall be subjected to the test described in SAE J1383 "Humidity Test." The DFL system shall be tested before and after the humidity test in accordance with the Breakdown Test in 5.5.1. Photometric testing shall begin at 10 min ± 1 min following completion of the humidity test. In addition, electronic components shall be subjected to the test in SAE J1211 Section 4.2 using conditions that are appropriate for the location of the DFL system components in the vehicle.

5.5.4 INTERNAL HEAT TEST—The DFL system shall be subjected to the conditions specified in SAE J1383 "Internal Heat Test." The DFL system shall be tested before and after the internal heat test in accordance with the Breakdown Test in 5.5.1.

(R)   5.5.5 DUST TEST—Conducted per SAE J575 Section 3.3. "DFL System" replaces "Headlamp" in the specifications. The DFL system shall be tested before and after the dust test in accordance with the Breakdown Test in 5.5.1.

(R)   5.5.6 CORROSION TEST—Test the DFL system per J575 Section 3.4. "DFL System" replaces "Headlamp" in the test. The DFL system shall be tested before and after the corrosion test in accordance with the Breakdown Test in 5.5.1.

5.5.7 CHEMICAL RESISTANCE TEST—The DFL system shall be tested per SAE J1383 "Chemical Resistance Test," except "DFL System" replaces "Headlamp" in the test. In addition, electronic components shall be subjected to the test specified in SAE J1211 Section 4.4 using conditions that are appropriate for the location of the DFL system components in the vehicle. The DFL system shall be tested before and after the chemical test in accordance with the Breakdown Test in 5.5.1.

(R)   5.5.8 VIBRATION TEST—The DFL system shall be tested as specified in SAE J575 Section 3.1 except "DFL System" replaces "Headlamp" in the test. In addition, electronic components shall be subjected to SAE J1211 Section 4.7 and 4.8 using conditions that are appropriate for the location of the DFL system components in the vehicle. The DFL system shall be tested before and after the vibration test in accordance with the Breakdown Test in 5.5.1.

5.5.9 ALTITUDE TEST—Electronic components shall be subjected to the requirements of Section 4.6 of SAE J1211 using conditions that are appropriate for the location of the DFL system components in the vehicle. The DFL system shall also be tested before and after the altitude test in accordance with the Breakdown Test in 5.5.1.

5.6 Photometry—The DFL system shall first be seasoned (per Section 5) at the nominal ballast input voltage of 12.8 V ± 0.1 V. The seasoned DFL system shall be aimed and after attaining steady-state conditions as specified in 7.5, be photometered to SAE J1383 requirements. Photometric measurements shall be made at a minimum distance of 18.3 m (60 ft) from the unit.

5.7 Electromagnetic Susceptibility (EMS)—The DFL system shall be tested to SAE J1113 (guidelines and test methods Sections 2 through 9) to evaluate compatibility with potential sources of EMI.

5.8 Electromagnetic Radiation (EMR)—DFL systems shall be tested in accordance with the guidelines of SAE J1816.

(R)   **5.9 Life**—DFL system(s) shall be mounted in its design orientation and operated using the following cycle to determine DFL system life. The "life test cycle" is a 1 h cycle, employing three 14.75 min lighted cycles which are followed by different off cycles. The first 14.75 min lighted cycle is followed by a 0.25 min off cycle. The second 14.75 min lighted cycle is followed by a 10.25 min off cycle, and the third 14.75 lighted cycle is followed by a 5.25 off cycle. This life test cycle will yield 74% hot time for each hour of testing and address lamp restart following both short and long off times.

When the DFL system "hot time" reaches 70% of rated lab life, the DFL system shall be subjected to the tests of 5.1 (starting procedures), 5.4 (color), and 5.5.1 (breakdown). Upon completion of the previous tests, the DFL system is returned to the life test cycle listed as follows until it fails to restart (see Figure 1 or Figure 2) following any off period. Test result guidelines are covered in 7.2.

14.75 s	min on
0.25 s	min off
14.75 s	min on
10.25 s	min off
14.75 s	min on
5.25 s	min off
60.00 s	Total Cycle
44.25	min on
15.75	min off
33% Hot starts	
74% on time	

5.10 UV Test—UV radiation refers to the radiation in the spectral region between 200 and 400 nm.

a. UVA Flux—is the energy flux between 320 and 400 nm
b. UVB Flux—is the energy flux between 260 and 320 nm
c. UVC Flux—is the energy flux between 200 and 260 nm

The measurement setup shall be as shown in Figure 1 of ANSI Z311 and the radiation sensor shall be located at a specified distance from the source (typically 50 cm). The source is defined as a lamp without any outermost lens(es). Energy levels shall be recorded at 10 nm intervals over the UV range.

UV weighting factors are defined in tables in ANSI Z311. (ANSI and NIOSH use the same tables, DIN values are also defined.)

6. Performance Requirements

6.1 Lamp/System Starting Procedures

6.1.1 INITIAL START-UP—Start-up intensities shall conform to Figure 1 or Figure 2. The test lamp photometric values shall meet the percent of the minimum values specified in SAE J1383 for the test points in Table 1.

6.1.2 SWITCHING (COLD LAMPS)—Figure 1 or Figure 2 indicates the acceptable percent of steady-state light intensity versus time after a cold DFL lamp has been turned on, for DFL systems with noncontinuous and continuous low beam illumination, respectively. The lamp shall produce not less than the percent of the minimum light level specified in SAE J1383 for the test points shown in Table 1. For DFL systems which are designed for "continuous" low beam operation, see 6.1.4.

6.1.3 SWITCHING (HOT RESTART)—After a thermally stabilized DFL headlamp has been allowed to cool for varying periods of time as shown in 5.1.3a, upon restart it shall produce not less than the percentage indicated in Figure 1 or Figure 2 of the luminous intensity values given in SAE J1383 for the test points shown in Table 1. For DFL systems which are designed for "continuous" low beam operation, see 6.1.4.

6.1.4 For DFL systems which are designed for "continuous" low beam operation, the luminous intensity of the low beam at the upper beam test point is combined with that of the upper beam to determine conformance to this specification.

6.2 Electrical Characteristics

6.2.1 SYSTEM OPERATING WATTAGE RANGE—At an input voltage of 12.8 V, the power consumption of the DFL system shall stabilize at its rated value with a maximum deviation of ±7.0%.

6.2.2 SYSTEM OPERATING VOLTAGE RANGE—Ignition and hot reignition of the lamp shall occur for all voltage settings between 9.0 and 18.0 VDC. Additional considerations for voltages between 9.0 and 4.5 V are presented in 7.10. (Reduced lumen output is acceptable for the 4.5 to 8.9 VDC range.)

The DFL system manufacturer shall specify the DFL minimum system voltage and current required for DFL system start-up.

6.3 Photometric Maintenance—When tested in accordance with the described test procedure, the DFL system shall meet the appropriate photometric specifications of SAE J1383, Table 5 at 70% of rated lab life.

6.4 Color—The color of light emitted from the DFL headlamp following seasoning and attaining steady-state shall fall within the white light chromaticity boundaries as defined in SAE J578. The color of light shall be within the chromaticity limits both initially and after the photometric maintenance test of 6.3. Also see 7.1.

6.5 Environmental Requirements

6.5.1 LEAKAGE CURRENT/BREAKDOWN TEST—The acceptance criteria for this test shall be based on a comparison of the initial value of leakage current measured before the environmental test and the value measured after the test. The leakage value after the environmental test shall not exceed 200% (twice) of the initial test value.

6.5.2 THERMAL CYCLE—After the test, the DFL system shall meet SAE J1383 "Thermal Cycle Requirements" without magnification. Lens warpage shall be less than 3 mm (0.118 in) when measured normal to the lens surface at the geometric center of the lens. No breakdown shall be detected when the DFL system is tested in accordance with the Breakdown Test. In addition, electronic components shall meet the requirements of Section 5 of SAE J1211 using conditions that are appropriate for the location of the DFL system components in the vehicle.

6.5.3 HUMIDITY TEST—After the test, the DFL system shall meet SAE J1383 "Humidity Requirements" without magnification, and meet the photometric requirements of SAE J1383. There shall be no evidence of breakdown during the Breakdown Test. In addition, electronic components shall meet the requirements of Section 5 of SAE J1211 using conditions that are appropriate for the location of the DFL system components in the vehicle.

6.5.4 INTERNAL HEAT—The DFL system shall meet SAE J1383 photometry values after the internal heat test. There shall be no evidence of breakdown during the Breakdown Test. In addition, electronic components shall meet the requirements of Section 5 of SAE J1211 using conditions that are appropriate for the location of the DFL system components in the vehicle.

6.5.5 DUST TEST—The DFL system shall meet the requirements of 4.4 of SAE J575. There shall be no evidence of breakdown during the Breakdown Test. In addition, electronic components shall meet the requirements of Section 5 of SAE J1211 using conditions that are appropriate for the location of the DFL system components in the vehicle.

6.5.6 CORROSION TEST—The DFL system shall be evaluated in accordance with 4.5 of SAE J575, except "DFL System" replaces "Headlamp" in the specifications. There shall be no evidence of breakdown during the Breakdown Test. In addition, electronic components shall meet the requirements of Section 5 of SAE J1211 using conditions that are appropriate for the location of the DFL system components in the vehicle.

6.5.7 CHEMICAL RESISTANCE TEST—The DFL system shall meet SAE J1383 "Chemical Resistance Requirement," except that "DFL System" replaces "Headlamp" in the specifications. There shall be no evidence of breakdown during the Breakdown Test. In addition, electronic components shall meet the requirements of Section 5 of SAE J1211 using conditions that are appropriate for the location of the DFL system components in the vehicle.

6.5.8 VIBRATION TEST—The DFL system shall meet the requirements specified in 4.1 of SAE J575. "DFL System" replaces "Headlamp" in the specifications. There shall be no evidence of breakdown during the Breakdown Test. In addition, electronic components shall meet the requirements of Section 5 of SAE J1211 that are appropriate for vibration tests for the location of the DFL system components in the vehicle.

6.5.9 ALTITUDE TEST—The DFL system's electronics shall comply with the applicable requirements of SAE J1211. There shall be no evidence of breakdown during the Breakdown Test. In addition, electronic components shall meet the requirements of Section 5 of SAE J1211 using conditions that are appropriate for the location of the DFL system components in the vehicle.

6.6 Photometry—Each High and Low Beam of the DFL system shall meet the photometry specified in SAE J1383 Table 3.

6.7 Electromagnetic Susceptibility (EMS)—The DFL system shall meet the test requirements as specifically determined for the user's application and the environment. See applicable Sections 2 through 9 of SAE J1113 for guidance.

After exposure to the tests in SAE J1113, the DFL system shall meet the requirements specified in 6.1.1, 6.1.2, 6.1.3, and 6.2.1.

6.8 Electromagnetic Radiation (EMR)—The DFL system shall meet the test requirements as specifically determined for the user's application and environment. See applicable sections of SAE J1816 for guidance.

7. Guidelines

7.1 Colorimetric Characteristics—Until an ANSI Standard[1] for colorimetric characteristics is developed for mercury, sodium, xenon, and metal halide lamps, it is required that the color of the DFL beams be perceived as essentially white light by drivers (for the accurate perception of colors in order to interpret road signs and signals). For this purpose, a color rendering index value may be established.

The "WHITE" color of a DFL headlamp device is presumed to exhibit only minor localized variations from the integrated measurement. If significant color variations exist within the projected beam, or if color changes occur during a period of time when the device is energized, the manufacturer of the device must be assured that such color will not be confused with that of an emergency warning device.

This assurance may be realized by using a panel of observers or by comparison of colorimetric measurements to standards for signal colors.

7.2 Life—Following cycle operation per 5.9 to 70% of rated life (Example—1400 h for a 2000 h design life), the DFL system shall meet the requirements of 6.1 (starting procedures), 6.4 (color), and 6.5.1 (breakdown). Upon completion of the previous maintenance checks, the DFL system shall be returned to cycle operation.

7.3 Voltage Regulation—The DFL system electrical supply shall be designed such that an inoperative or removed lamp will not affect the operation and performance of the remaining lamp(s) in the DFL system.

7.4 Light and Near-Infrared Radiation Exposure Limits—Manufacturers and users of DFL systems should ensure that the DFL system does not exceed the maximum allowable limit value for three retinal hazards as specified in 4.3 of the ANSI Standard Z311.1 (titled Photobiological Safety). Those three hazards are retinal thermal injury from short-term viewing (ANSI Z311.1 paragraph 4.3.1), retinal photochemical injury from chronic exposure (ANSI Z311.1 paragraph 4.3.2), and long-term ocular exposure to infrared radiation (ANSI Z311.1 paragraph 4.3.3). The three hazards cover wavelengths between 400 to 1400 nm. The measurement of the exposure levels is strongly dependent on the value used for the angular subtense of the light source (the parameter, alpha, in ANSI Z311.1). The handbook "Safety With Lasers and Other Optical Sources" by Sliney and Wolbarsht (1980, Plenum Press) is recommended as a reference.

7.5 Steady-State—Steady-state light level (100%) shall be established by allowing the DFL system to operate for 120 s after being switched "on." The average light level within the period from 120 to 140 s will be defined as the 100% level. If the light output is not stable to within ±10% during the 120 to 140 s time interval, the process should be repeated. If the system selected does not stabilize within three attempts, another unit should be selected and subjected to the previous procedure. Steady-state is only used to define a system's baseline in order to evaluate test effects on the system.

7.6 High-Voltage Shock Safety—High-voltage shock from DFL systems is an important concern just as it is with other automotive components. Appropriate levels of safety must be designed in and other precautionary measures, such as use of caution labels, should be implemented to assure a sufficiently low level of risk. Since individual DFL products and vehicle applications will differ in regard to high voltage levels, power, and integrity of construction, each DFL system will require a specific evaluation with the system installed in the vehicle to assure a low problem potential. This is a vehicle design and testing issue and is beyond the scope of this document. Designs of replacement equipment will also need to be evaluated on specific vehicle models for which they are intended.

7.7 High-Voltage Vapor Ignition Safety—Protection from the possibility of vapor ignition from DFL high voltages is a concern. However, the concerns of vapor ignition are not too much different from those experienced from damaged high-voltage ignition systems, shorted and burning wiring, and exposed hot bulbs and filaments. Furthermore, the safety of a DFL system depends not only on its basic design, but also upon the design of the vehicle in which it is installed. Each vehicle application, therefore, needs to be individually evaluated as a complete DFL system in the vehicle to assure a low level of risk. This is a vehicle design and testing issue and is beyond the scope of this document.

---

[1] Current fluorescent lamp chromaticity standards in the United States are now based on spectroradiometrically determined assignments by the National Institute of Standards and Technology. Refer to ANSI C78.376-1969.

7.8 CRI—The color rendering index shall meet the general criterion of Ra = 60. Each source manufacturer and user shall determine that the light produced shall readily allow the customer to distinguish between typical road sign colors.

7.9 UV Test—UV weighting factors defined in ANSI Z311 (ANSI and NIOSH use the same tables, DIN tables are also defined) shall be used to determine time for minimum effect. Measurements shall be made in accordance with 5.10. (See Table 2 for examples.)

TABLE 2—EXAMPLE—175 W MULTIVAPOR LAMP MEASURED AT 50 CM

Standard		Type	Time for Min. Effect
NIOSH	(200-320)	ERYTH	124.4 h
DIN	(240-325)	ERYTH	677.6
DIN	(300-440)	PIGMT	26.0
DIN	(220-305)	CONJT	29435.0

The ANSI Z311 Standard shall be used (voluntary draft at present). Energy level to be determined by application.

It is recognized that ultraviolet radiation (UV) normally emitted by arc discharge sources may pose health hazards at certain levels and durations of exposure. The magnitudes of acceptable levels of exposure are outlined in documents such as those published by NIOSH or ACGIH (American Conference of Governmental Industrial Hygienists). These tables may be used as references when determining the exposure potential of DFL headlamps.

The concern with UV light may be addressed by the device manufacturer by using shields, coatings, and/or absorbing materials. It is anticipated that most lens materials will normally provide safe UV levels by absorption/reflection. However, where the possibility exists that lens protection may be lost while the arc source remains functional (stone damage or low-energy impact), it is the device manufacturer's responsibility to assure that protection from UV is provided to all who may be exposed to the light.

7.10 System Operating Voltage Range—Vehicles are designed to continue operating at voltage levels below 9.0 V. The vehicle manufacturers must define acceptable reductions in light output for voltages below 9.0 V and determine system dropout voltage.

DAYTIME RUNNING LAMPS FOR USE ON MOTOR VEHICLES
—SAE J2087 AUG91   SAE Recommended Practice

Report of the SAE DRL Task Force of the SAE Lighting Coordinating Committee approved August 1991. Rationale statement available.

1. Scope—This SAE Recommended Practice provides test procedures, requirements, and guidelines for daytime running lamps that are mounted on the exterior of a vehicle. It is applicable to daytime running lamps that are combined with or use headlamps, parking lamps, turn signal lamps, fog lamps, or other lamps on the front of the vehicle, as well as to daytime running lamps that use dedicated lamps.

2. References

2.1 Applicable Documents—The following publications form a part of this specification to the extent specified herein. The latest issue of SAE publications shall apply.

2.1.1. SAE PUBLICATIONS—Available from SAE, 400 Commonwealth Drive, Warrendale, PA 15096-0001.

SAE J567—Lamp Bulb Retention System

SAE J575—Tests for Motor Vehicle Lighting Devices and Components

SAE J576—Plastic Materials for Use in Optical Parts Such as Lenses and Reflectors of Motor Vehicle Lighting Devices

SAE J578—Color Specifications for Electric Signal Lighting Devices

SAE J759—Lighting Identification Code

SAE J1050—Describing and Measuring the Driver's Field of View

2.2 Related Publications—The following publications are provided for information purposes only and are not a required part of this document.

SAE Lighting Committee DRL Test Reports, 1974-1989, nine separate reports.

CIE TC4.13 Report—Automobile Daytime Running Lights (DRL), Third Draft, July 1990.

Canadian Motor Vehicle Safety Standard 108—Light Equipment

2.3 Definitions

2.3.1 DAYTIME RUNNING LAMPS (DRL)—Steady burning lamps that are used to improve the conspicuity of a vehicle from the front and front sides when the regular headlamps are not required for driving.

2.3.2 DAYTIME RUNNING LAMP TELLTALE—An indicator that provides a visual signal to advise the driver that only his daytime running lamps are on and he should switch on the regular headlamps.

3. Lighting Identification Code—Daytime running lamps meeting the performance requirements of Section 5 of this document may be identified by the code Y2 in accordance with SAE J759.

4. Tests

4.1 SAE J575 is a part of this document. The following tests, from that document, are applicable with the modifications as indicated.

4.1.1 VIBRATION TEST

4.1.2 MOISTURE TEST

4.1.3 DUST TEST

4.1.4 CORROSION TEST

4.1.5 PHOTOMETRY—In addition to the test procedures in SAE J575, the following applies:

Photometric measurements shall be made with the light source of the DRL at least 3 m from the photometer. If the DRL is optically combined with a headlamp or a fog lamp then the photometric measurements shall be made with the light source of the DRL at least 18.3 m from the photometer.

4.1.6 WARPAGE TEST ON DEVICES WITH PLASTIC COMPONENTS—The bulb operation for this test shall be steady burning.

4.1.7 COLOR TEST—SAE J578 is a part of this document.

5. Requirements

5.1 Performance Requirements—A DRL, when tested in accordance with the test procedures specified in Section 4, shall meet the following requirements:

5.1.1 VIBRATION—SAE J575

5.1.2 MOISTURE—SAE J575

5.1.3 DUST—SAE J575

5.1.4 CORROSION—SAE J575

5.1.5 PHOTOMETRY—SAE J575—The DRL under test shall meet the photometric requirements contained in Table 1.

5.1.6 WARPAGE—SAE J575

5.1.7 COLOR—SAE J578—The color of the light from a DRL shall be white, white to yellow, white to selective yellow, yellow, or selective yellow as specified in SAE J578.

5.2 Materials Requirements—Plastic materials used in optical parts shall meet the requirements of SAE J576.

5.3 System Requirements—A DRL system shall consist of at least two lamps.

5.3.1 LOCATION REQUIREMENTS—The DRLs shall be located on the front, at the same mounting height, and symmetrically placed laterally relative to the centerline of the vehicle.

5.3.2 AREA REQUIREMENTS—The DRLs shall have a minimum unobstructed effective projected luminous lens area of 40 cm^2. In addition the DRL must provide an unobstructed view of the outer lens surface of at least 10 cm^2 measured at 45 degrees to the longitudinal axis of the vehicle.

6. Guidelines

6.1 Photometric Design Guidelines for DRLs, when tested in accordance with 4.1.5 of this document, are contained in Table 2.

6.2 Luminous Flux Maintenance Guideline—The applicable luminous flux maintenance test cycle established to verify the performance of halogen bulbs used at reduced voltages in daytime running lamps is shown in Table 3. Testing is to be done at room temperature with a steady-state DC applied voltage as specified in Table 3. It is not required to use AC, pulse width modulators, or dropping resistors but they may be used if desired to obtain the voltage as specified in Table 3.

6.2.1 Season the filament(s) and measure the original luminous flux output of the filament(s) in a spherical photometer at 12.8 V DC. Test the light source mounted in a 100 × 165 mm sealed beam size enclosure through 24 cycles where a test cycle is as defined in Table 3 and is sequenced from the same starting point in each cycle. Measure the final luminous flux output of the filament(s) after testing.

After the testing (see equation 1):

$$\frac{LUBF}{LUBO} \geq 95\% \qquad \frac{LLBF}{LLBO} \geq 95\% \qquad\qquad \text{(Eq. 1)}$$

where:

LUBF = Lumens Upper Beam, Final

LUBO = Lumens Upper Beam, Original

LLBF = Lumens Lower Beam, Final

LLBO = Lumens Lower Beam, Original

6.3 Telltale Guidelines—A DRL Telltale, if provided, shall be located on the instrument panel or in the driver's forward field of view. If a light sensor is used to activate the telltale, the sensor should be upward pointing and activate the telltale when the ambient light level is

TABLE 1—PHOTOMETRIC REQUIREMENTS

Test Point	Minimum Candela	Maximum Candela
5U - 10L	80	
5U - V	280	
5U - 10R	80	
H - 20L	40	
H - 10L	280	
H - 5L	360	
H - V	400	7000
H - 5R	360	
H - 10R	280	
H - 20R	40	
5D - 10L	80	
5D - V	280	
5D - 10R	80	

TABLE 2—PHOTOMETRIC DESIGN GUIDELINES

Test Point	Minimum Candela	Maximum Candela
5U - 10L	100	
5U - V	350	
5U - 10R	100	
H - 20L	50	
H - 10L	350	
H - 5L	450	
H - V	500	7000
H - 5R	450	
H - 10R	350	
H - 20R	50	
5D - 10L	100	
5D - V	350	
5D - 10R	100	

TABLE 3—TEST CYCLE

Lighting Mode	Lighting Mode	Voltage(V)	H/L Using Upper Beam For DRL Double-Fil. Period (h)	H/L Using Upper Beam For DRL Single-Fil. Period (h)	H/L Using Lower Beam For DRL Double-Fil. Period (h)	H/L Using Lower Beam For DRL Single-Fil. Period (h)
Headlamp	Upper Beam	12.8	0.25	0.25	0.25	–
(Nighttime)	Lower Beam	12.8	1.0	–	1.0	1.0
DRL	Upper Beam	6.4	6.25	6.25	–	–
(Daytime)	Lower Beam	10.5	–	–	6.25	6.25
OFF	OFF	0	0.5	1.5	0.5	0.75
Total (1 Cycle)	Total (1 Cycle)		8.0	8.0	8.0	8.0

less than 1000 lux, indicating dusk, night, or other reduced light conditions. If a light sensor is not used the telltale should provide a visual signal when the ambient light level, as measured by an upward pointing sensor, is less than 1000 lux, indicating dusk, night, or other reduced light conditions. The telltale is used to indicate to the driver:

 a. The DRLs are still illuminated and the ambient light level indicates the headlamps should be illuminated or
 b. The headlamps should be turned on.

The telltale may deactivate when the headlamps are switched on.

6.3.1 The telltale may also function as a bulb failure indicator for any exterior lighting functions.

6.3.2 The telltale should emit yellow colored light and have a minimum projected illuminated area of 18 mm². The minimum required illuminated area of the telltale shall be visible according to the procedures contained in SAE J1050. The steering wheel shall be turned to a straight-ahead position and in the design location for an adjustable wheel or column.

6.3.3 A DRL telltale need not be installed on vehicles having the following lighting equipment:

 a. Lower beam headlamps operating at full voltage used as DRLs, with all exterior marking lamps activated by the DRL system or
 b. An automatic photocell system for switching between DRL and night exterior lighting modes, unless this device can be manually switched to an inoperative status.

6.4 **Operating Guidelines**—These guidelines apply to how DRLs are used on the vehicle and are not part of the requirements.

6.4.1 The DRLs are to be activated without any switching by the operator (apart from the ignition switch).

6.4.2 No other lights are required to be illuminated with the DRLs unless full intensity low beam headlamps are used as the DRLs. In this case those exterior lamps that are required to be illuminated with the low beam headlamps are to be illuminated with the DRLs.

6.4.3 The DRLs are to be deactivated when the low beam or high beam headlamps are turned on.

6.5 **Installation Guidelines**—For DRLs to be most effective they should be spaced as far apart laterally as practicable, to maximize the field of view and to facilitate estimation of distances by drivers in approaching vehicles.

DRLs should be designed to be mounted on the vehicle so the centers of the lenses are not less than 380 mm (15 in) nor more than 1820 mm (72 in) above the road surface.

6.6 **Color Guidelines**—The color of the emitted light from all DRLs on a vehicle shall be designed to be the same (see 5.1.7).

Appendix A

A.1 For information on requirements and gages used in socket design, refer to SAE J567.

SAE The Engineering Society
For Advancing Mobility
Land Sea Air and Space®

I N T E R N A T I O N A L®

400 Commonwealth Drive, Warrendale, PA 15096-0001

| SURFACE VEHICLE DRAFT TECHNICAL REPORT | **SAE** J2338 |
| | Issued   1996-10 |

RECOMMENDATIONS OF THE SAE TASK FORCE ON HEADLAMP MOUNTING HEIGHT

1. Scope—The Society of Automotive Engineers task force on headlamp mounting height has considered the ramifications of reducing the maximum mounting height of headlamps on highway vehicles. The task force has concluded that it is in the best interest of the driving public to make a significant reduction in the recommended maximum height at which headlamps, particularly lower beam headlamps, may be mounted. Heights as low as 36 to 40 in (0.9 to 1.0 m) have been considered. New tractor vehicles are in fact being designed with headlamps mounted in this range. Further recommendations were withheld in anticipation of tests to demonstrate the effect of mounting height on the legibility of certain overhead signs.

1.1 Background—For the past several years there has been increasing concern on the part of automotive lighting committees within SAE and automotive lighting regulators at National Highway Traffic Safety Administration (NHTSA) over the glare from vehicle headlamps. Complaints to NHTSA from users indicate that both mirror glare and glare from opposing vehicles contribute to the problem.

Present mounting height standards allow headlamps to be mounted up to a height of 54 in (from the ground plane to the center of the headlamp). Generally, passenger vehicle occupants are seated such that their eye-level is much lower. Driver eye level ranges from about 40 in to 45 in. By comparing the range of vehicle driver's eyes and mirrors, with the range of headlamp heights, it can be shown that passenger vehicle drivers' eyes and the vehicle's rearview mirrors can be located below the top cutoff of the projected beam of a following vehicle. In this high gradient zone, the light intensity from a lower beam headlamp beam, located 40 ft behind a driver's rearview mirror, will increase at least 20% (40% in some lamps) for every 1/10 degree (0.84 in) below the top cutoff of the beam pattern.

For a rearview mirror located 5 in below the top cutoff of a headlamp beam pattern, the beam gradients of 20 to 30% per 1/10 degree would cause an increase of 300% to 500% of the light that a driver would experience if the mirror were located exactly at the top cutoff. A 1000% increase in eye illumination could be experienced in comparison to that from a mirror located at an approximately equal distance above the top cutoff. These numbers give us a clue as to why passenger vehicle drivers are noticing the differences in glare from high-mounted headlamps.

QUESTIONS REGARDING THIS DOCUMENT: (412) 772-8512 **FAX** (412) 776-0243
TO PLACE A DOCUMENT ORDER: (412) 776-4970 **FAX** (412) 776-0790

Printed in U.S.A.

1.2 History—The discrepancy between where passenger car drivers are located and where vehicle headlamps can be mounted can be traced by reviewing historical trends in vehicle lighting.

Passenger vehicle sizes and heights are decreasing as many vehicles are being downsized and, as a result, the elevation of drivers' eyes and rearview mirrors has been reduced accordingly. Light trucks (pickups, vans, minivans and sport utility vehicles) on the other hand, are not decreasing in either size or market share. With headlamps routinely mounted well above those on passenger cars, light trucks are more popular than ever. The higher mounting heights on these vehicles most likely represent a substantial part of the increase in complaints about headlamp glare.

In the years when headlamp mounting height standards were first written, headlamps on passenger vehicles were routinely mounted at 30 or even 32 in above the ground plane, 8 to 10 in above the 22 to 24 in mounting height we see today. It is probably safe to assume that the eyepoint of the driver was also higher by 8 to 10 in. If we use 44 in for today's passenger car driver, a rearview mirror mounted 2 or 3 in above the driver's eye in the old standard-setting vehicles would have an elevation of from 54 to 57 in (44 + 8 + 2 to 44 + 10 + 3 in). This is essentially identical with the maximum mounting height of the headlamp that was prescribed at that time.

Another reason for the recent trend of dissatisfaction and irritation with vehicle lighting among passenger vehicle drivers may be found in the headlamp beam intensity distribution itself. In one of the first SAE photometric standards, J579a, the required light level was only about 75% of the present standard and only 60% of more advanced standards in Federal Code 49 CFR Part 571.108. In fact, contemporary halogen headlamps generally achieve 100% more light at the 1/2-degree-down seeing point than was available from the "brightest" of the SAE J579a design headlamps. At the time the mounting height standard was defined, a driver would have been exposed to roughly about 2800 cd viewing a following vehicle's 54 inch mounting height headlamps (designed to SAE J579a) in his rearview mirror.

Today rearview mirrors (front surface, prism) in their "night" position may reflect as little as 4% of the incident light. In spite of their elevation in the headlamp beam, the glare concern for rearview mirrors is low compared to driver's side view mirrors. A side view mirror (no "night" adjustment; 50% reflectance), mounted at about 40 in or less, could theoretically be over 1.6 degrees below the horizontal of a 54 in mounting-height headlamp. At a distance of 40 ft on some halogen headlamps using axial sources, this is the approximate location of the "maximum beam intensity" (MBI). MBIs of over 30 000 cd are possible. This represents more than a ten-fold increase of the exposure intensity over that which was typical when the standard was formulated.

It is apparent that mounting height or aiming guidelines must be revised to accommodate the changes in aerodynamic vehicle styling and headlighting technology. The most technically defensible solution is to lower the current maximum mounting height for headlamps in order to reduce the maximum exposure level to a reasonable value.

2. References

2.1 Applicable Documents—The following publications form a part of this specification to the extent specified herein.

2.1.1 Sivak, M., Flannagan, M., Gellatly, A.W., "Influence of Truck Driver Eye Position on Effectiveness of Retroreflective Traffic Signs," Ltg. Res. Technology, 25(1) 31-36, (1993)

2.1.2 Cobb, J., "Roadside Survey of Vehicle Lighting 1989," Transport and Road Research Laboratory, U.K., Research Report 290, (1989)

2.1.3 Kosmatka, W.J., "Obstacle Detection with Headlamps: Threshold Luminance or Contrast," Proceedings of IES, IENSA Conference - 1995, (1995)

2.1.4 Kosmatka, W.J., "Obstacle Detection Rationale for Vehicle Headlamps," J of the IES, Winter 1995, 36-40, (1994)

3. *Revelant Issues in Lowering Recommended Headlamp Mounting Heights*—It is certain that the greatest effect of such recommendations would be felt in the truck, tractor-trailer and pickup vehicle manufacturing industries. Passenger vehicles, with few exceptions, already have their headlamps mounted in the range of 22 to 26 in. The body contours and bumper location preclude higher mounting in most passenger vehicles; vans are the notable exception. With this background one can understand why most of the following discussion centers on truck types of vehicles.

Two issues are frequently raised on the subject of lowering the mounting height of headlamps:

a. The resulting increase in the vertical separation between the driver's eyepoint and the headlamp light source on large trucks will decrease the conspicuity and legibility of retroreflective traffic control devices and highway information signs which are illuminated solely by the vehicle headlamps.

b. There will be a reduction in the visibility distance of the operator and this will reduce the chances of stopping the tractor-trailer or truck vehicle within the obstacle detection distance.

4. *Unlit Traffic Control Devices*—Luminance of retroreflective overhead highway information signs (which are not illuminated by other than vehicle headlamps) will be reduced by virtue of the increased "observation angle." The observation angle is the angle formed by a line between the driver's eye and the sign, and another line between the light source and the sign. As the driver's eye position moves upward, away from the headlamp, or as the headlamp height is lowered, the observation angle increases. For retroreflective materials, the level of light returned to an observer is reduced as the observation angle is increased. The implications of separation distances are discussed by Sivak, Flannagan and Gellatly (see 2.1.1).

Without a doubt, a loss of legibility of the sign information is undesirable. But, this reasoning may be overly simplistic in the assumptions that it makes. It implies that a driver cannot take measures to compensate for the loss of visual information. Moreover, the argument ignores precedent. Some vehicles being driven on highways today already have extreme observation angles with no documented ill effects.

In order for the driver to suffer the loss of sign legibility as the direct result of headlamp location, the headlamps must be the only source of illumination on the sign. On heavily traveled highways where lower beams are generally required, sign illumination is frequently the result of illumination by multiple sources, each having its own particular intensity and observation angle for the drivers in the immediate vicinity. A loss of 20 or 30% of sign luminance from one vehicle may not even be noticeable, let alone constitute a safety issue under these conditions.

In low traffic situations, a single vehicle's headlamps are sometimes the only source of sign illumination. If the operator needs the sign only as a reminder of a predetermined route or direction, then it is difficult to argue the safety implications of reduced sign legibility. Assuming that the vehicle operator really does need the information presented to make a decision, the driver is still able to exert control over the time available to view a sign. In this situation vehicle operators are able, at their option, to control the time available to formulate a decision by a reduction in the vehicle's speed. If the roadway traffic is light as postulated, then a reduction in speed, a lane change or momentary switch to high beam are all possible.

A comparison of truck headlamp mounting heights and vertical separation of the driver's eyes from the headlamps is depicted in Figure 1. This is a compilation of recent data provided by truck and tractor vehicle manufacturers. The parameter of the driver's eye height is noted also. The chart makes several important points:

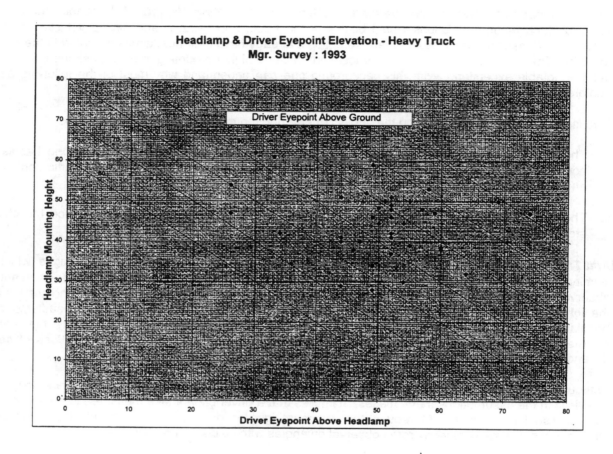

FIGURE 1—HEADLAMP AND DRIVER EYEPOINT ELEVATION—HEAVY TRUCK MGR. SURVEY: 1993

a. The average (or median) mounting height of a headlamp is about 45 in.

b. There are situations where a relatively great separation between the driver's eyes and the light source (e.g., the observation angle) already exists. There are several instances in which the location of the driver's eyepoint is above the headlamp by 60 to 70 in.

c. There are trucks on the road with headlamps mounted at 40 in and below.

A study of vehicle lighting (see 2.1.2) also shows that there are a significant number of European trucks with headlamps mounted at 0.9 m (36 in) and below. Interpolation of Cobb's data would indicate that the vast majority of "articulated" vehicles measured had headlamps mounted below the 0.9 m height.

Based on these data, and having no information that the vehicles noted above have caused drivers to experience problems with large observation angles, the argument that a loss of sign legibility will have dramatic negative safety effects does not appear to be substantiated. As will be explained in a later paragraph, drivers viewing oncoming traffic from elevated positions actually experience a significant reduction in glare and a reduction in the dark-adaptation effect resulting from this reduced glare.

5. Detection Distance Effect—The detection or discernibility distance for headlighting systems has been studied in real roadway situations and with mathematical algorithms over the years. In almost all cases these studies concentrated on passenger vehicles. In most of these cases mounting height was not the issue.

In the limited situations in which headlamp mounting location was studied, there was a detection distance loss noted as a result of lowered mounting height of the vehicle headlamps. While numbers such as "10 ft loss per 1-in mounting height reduction" are stated, this was for passenger vehicle headlamps which were already mounted relatively low; in the range of 25 in. The obstacles in some detection distance tests conducted by Roper or Meese, were 40 cm x 40 cm (16 in^2) targets. The "targets" were generally detected at 200 to 250 ft depending on the headlamp system. The "center" of the target (at 8 in above the roadway) is located 17 in below the center of the headlamp at a distance of 225 ft. At this point in the beam, it is illuminated by light at about 0.36 degree below the top of the beam cutoff. This is in the area where the beam gradient is very large. A reduction of 2 in in mounting height implies that the location of the target center would now be located slightly over 0.04 degree higher in the beam pattern. Beam gradients in this area are generally 25%, or even 35% per 1/10 degree, and a change of one-half of 1/10 degree would imply that 12 to 16% less light illuminates the obstacle.

Application of the inverse distance law would dictate that if the headlamps are lowered 2 in, the detection distance should fall by approximately 6 to 8% of 225 ft or 14 to 18 ft. So for a 1-in mounting height change, a loss of 7 to 9 ft is implied. This analysis confirms (approximately) the generalization of "10 ft detection loss per 1 in" mounting height reduction. This applies, in a general sense at least, to passenger vehicles. We will see in the following sections that the rule is not generally applicable to headlamps mounted at greater mounting heights in large truck types of vehicles.

5.1 Detection Distance With Lowered Mounting Height—It is possible to determine the effect of mounting height differences by actual dynamic testing similar to that described above. However, this would be difficult and costly to do with actual trucks and tractors.

The implications of performing static testing using mock-ups of vehicle front ends, stationary targets, and "driver-observers" at varying heights has been discussed. Even this task was daunting for the amount and relevance of the information which might be gained. There are some who feel that static obstacle detection tests do not fairly depict actual roadway obstacle detection distances. Some of the reasons for this are the absence of secondary tasks such as lane-keeping and speed maintenance, as well as longer (or artificial) target acquisition time intervals. For these reasons, the data acquired from static tests are always somewhat insensitive to subtle light level differences. Longer, sometimes significantly longer, detection distances are typical of static tests relative to distances found in dynamic tests.

5.2 Detection Distance Model—In the interest of defining the effect of lowered mounting height, without incurring the expense and time penalty of dynamic road tests, a simpler modeling experiment was undertaken. The distance at which a roadway obstacle would be discerned by the driver of a motor vehicle is a function of the obstacle luminance and contrast with the background. For many roadway situations, the background is the distant roadway surface and therefore it is at a significantly lower luminance than the illuminated obstacle. The contrast requirement is generally satisfied in this situation. At any rate over a short distance the contrast ratio can be shown to be relatively invariant and we can infer that the detection distance becomes simply a function of threshold luminance.

A model (see 2.1.3) which compares the distance-related headlamp illumination with the distance-related illumination required for detection of the obstacle was used to predict the (relative) effect of reducing headlamp height from the average noted previously (45 in) to a reduced (36 in) height. The obstacle characteristics selected for the calculations were: 3 ft^2 in area, 1.5 ft high, 0.10 reflectance (.1 ft-lambert/Fc). The vehicle headlamp spacing used was 60 inches. An H6054 (Type 2B1) lamp was chosen for the experiment because of its widespread use in the industry and its known level of photometric performance.

In order to determine the illumination of the obstacle at various distances from the vehicle, the angular position of the obstacle's center was calculated as a function of distance for each headlamp at the two mounting heights of interest. A representative GE H6054 headlamp was evaluated at each of these angular displacements. A programmable LMT G-1200 gonio-photometer was used to make the photometric readings with the lamp aimed photometrically to its nominal fractional balance aim. The light falling on the obstacle center is the simple summation of the separate contributions of the right and left headlamps. Use of the inverse-square relationship then yields the obstacle illumination as a function of distance from the headlamps to the obstacle.

The detection requirements as a function of distance were calculated by the algorithms proposed by Kosmatka (see 2.1.4). This was done for each of two cases: one in which the driver is nonexpectant (i.e., not reasonably anticipating a roadway obstacle), and one in which the driver is "expectant" and has reason to anticipate that there will be an obstacle in or near the path of the vehicle.

5.3 Detection Distance Model Results—Comparison of the illumination provided by the headlamp system and the illumination required for detection or discernibility of the obstacle yielded the approximate distance at which the detection criterion is satisfied. This is shown in Table 1:

TABLE 1—DETECTION DISTANCE

MOUNTING HEIGHT	EXPECTANT DRIVER	NONEXPECTANT DRIVER
at 45 in	264 ft (80 m)	157 ft (47.5 m)
at 36 in	251 ft (76 m)	144 ft (43.6 m)
% change	5%	8%

5.4 Discussion of Detection Distance Results—The detection distance loss predicted by the detection distance model contradicts conventional lore based on previous studies of the distance "lost" per inch of mounting height reduction. There are several reasons for this. As discussed previously, the "10 ft/in rule" may take some license in rounding numbers that are somewhat less than "10 ft."

However, there is another, more profound reason that we find less of a reduction at severely elevated mounting heights. It is an artifact of the beam patterns made by halogen lamps. In general, halogen type lamps have smaller, more compact coils than did their standard incandescent counterparts. The wire temperature is (generally) elevated, resulting in more lumens per watt. Also, as a general rule, the filament wire's diameter is smaller. This increases the resistance-per-unit-length and results in a shorter wire segment for a given wattage and life rating. The coiled filament is smaller in length and diameter in halogen cycle headlamps.

The combination of more lumens and smaller coiled tungsten filaments allows a "brighter" and more "luminous" source. This results in a smaller, more compact, and brighter projected beam pattern with more light a the top of the beam, compared to the relatively inferior non-halogen headlamps. The center of the high intensity zone is closer to the top cutoff of the beam. The beam is more compact from top to bottom, with the center of "maximum beam intensity" (MBI) located closer to the top of the beam than the bottom, in the range of 1.5 to 2 degrees below the horizontal. This was not the case in the older style of headlamps. In the standard incandescent designs, the MBI was located farther down from the top of the beam pattern, frequently at 2.5 and even 3 degrees down. The gradient continued to increase and provide more light on obstacles located lower in the beam.

The gradients commonly found in modern halogen lamps have already had their most significant effect at locations of zero to 1 degree down. Placing an obstacle lower in the beam pattern by elevating the lamp's mounting height has a diminished effect. A corollary statement might be that some lowering of the mounting height will have a much smaller effect on the light falling on the obstacle than would have been the case for earlier headlamp designs. (It is worth noting that at some point, raising the mounting height will place the object on the down-side of the gradient and there will actually be less light falling on the obstacle.)

6. *Glare Reduction Considerations for Truck Vehicles*—While most arguments point out the negative effects of having the driver's eyes at elevated heights, few recognize the counter-effecting advantages. High density traffic situations are the most critical for drivers for two reasons. First, there is a loss of visual acuity due to glare and elevated adaptation levels. Second, the traffic density may make alternative means of prolonging the observation time more difficult. In this situation it is easy to argue that driver needs are most critical.

The driver of a large vehicle is located such that the eyepoint is at approximately eight feet above the road. A passenger vehicle driver's eye height is approximately 3.5 ft. For the sake of argument we'll assume the oncoming vehicles' headlamps are located at a two-foot elevation. The position of the drivers' eyes in the beams is described by Equation 1:

$$\alpha = a \tan (h / d) \hspace{3cm} \text{(Eq.1)}$$

where:

h is the eyepoint elevation with respect to the headlamp and d is the distance from the headlamp to the eyepoint.

On a roadway with one 12-ft-wide lane in each direction, a vehicle driver will view an opposing passenger vehicle's closest (driver's side) headlamp from a point about nine feet left of the headlamp, seeing the light on the left side of the headlamp beam pattern. The relative location of a driver's eyes in the beam pattern is show in Table 2 for a driver at 8 ft eye height versus one at 3.5 ft eye height.

TABLE 2—LATERAL EYE LOCATION AND DRIVER'S EYE ELEVATION IN VEHICLE

Distance	Lateral Eye Location (9 ft left)	Driver's Eye Elevation in Vehicle (3.5 ft up, h=1.5)	Driver's Eye Elevation in Vehicle (8.0 ft up, h=6.0)
100 ft	5.1 degrees left	0.9 degree up	3.4 degrees up
200 ft	2.1 degrees left	0.4 degree up	1.7 degrees up
300 ft	1.7 degrees left	0.3 degree up	1.1 degrees up
400 ft	1.3 degrees left	0.2 degree up	0.9 degree up

Observation of a typical ISO-candela diagram for an automotive headlamp with an SAE beam pattern will show that the glare light directed at the eyepoint above will be about one-half as much for the more elevated (8 ft) driver's eyepoint than for the driver with his eyes at an elevation of only 3.5 ft. At a 200 ft distance, a passenger car driver would view about 800 cd from an oncoming headlamp. A driver at a height of 8 ft would be exposed to only 450 cd. At 300 ft we find similar results: about 1200 cd for a passenger car and around 600 cd for a truck driver. At 400 ft the respective levels are about 1500 cd and 800 cd.

Adaptation level (and the object luminance required) is approximately in proportion to the glare light differential; then it would follow that compared to a passenger car driver, a driver with an eyepoint at 8 ft will require only about one-half as much luminance (as of a sign for instance). Drivers of truck vehicles, who would be more disadvantaged by a reduction in headlamp mounting height, are also located in the beams of oncoming traffic in such a way that in the more demanding situation of "opposing traffic glare" they require less target luminance than vehicle drivers who are located in the more intense portion of oncoming headlamp beams.

7. Recommendations—Although the task force considered the implied ill effects of decreased lamp height on legibility of retroreflective highway marking signs, it noted that there are large "driver eyes versus headlamp" separation distances with truck vehicles today. Taken in combination with potential actions which the driver may take to prolong the time available to study sign messages, and a partially compensating reduction in glare, the task force is not convinced that this single issue should by itself be allowed to override the safety needs of the vast majority of passenger vehicle drivers.

Based on the known and reconstructed history of headlamp mounting height rationale, and having a fair deal of confidence that there will be a minimal effect on detection distance, the Mounting Height Task Force members agreed that the maximum headlamp mounting height limit for motor vehicles should be reduced significantly from the present limit of 54 in, though there was no clear majority agreement on a recommended limit at this time.

The task force recognized that there are vehicles which, because of ground clearance needs, or because they are equipped with special equipment, cannot have their headlamps mounted in conventional locations. The task force does not wish to encumber these vehicles, which constitute a small minority of vehicular traffic, with restrictive headlamp mounting specifications.

The task force notes that there are new headlighting systems with the potential to create very high "maximum beam intensity" levels very close to the top cutoff of the beam. It would be prudent and timely for standards organizations, vehicle and lighting designers and manufacturers, highway safety equipment manufacturers and engineers to consider the long term needs of the driving public in the context of new headlighting systems. These systems have the potential to project light down the road at much higher intensities while maintaining glare control above the top cutoff. As the use of these headlamp systems becomes more widespread, the situation noted today, of passenger vehicle driver discomfort glare, can conceivably escalate to one of severe glare-induced detection distance loss from sideview mirror or opposing vehicle high-mounted headlamps.

The question of "how much to reduce" still remains to be answered. The task force has discussed rationale in support of a limit of 36 in (0.9 m) or 40 in (1.0 m) limit. Though there were members favoring both 36 in and 40 in recommendations, there was no definitive majority opinion. There may be some reason to consider the European limit of 47 in (1.2 m), to the *bottom edge* of the headlamp, in the interests of harmonization. Based on data which the task force has studied, this would have no significant effect since it would encompass the majority of the mounting heights already found in service and which are presumably responsible for the level of driver complaints which led to the concerns stated in this report. The task force believes that a 47 in recommendation has little allure other than unilateral harmonization.

A minority opinion expressed by engineers involved with retroreflective sign materials and performance suggested that other "of the many components contributing to glare" should be studied along with the legibility effect of increased observation angles. They did not agree that a "significant reduction in mounting height" was in the best interest of the road user but suggested that beam distribution, headlight output, glare limits and rearview mirror efficiency should all be studied. These factors do in some fashion all contribute to passenger car driver glare; however, this proposal does not address the dichotomous situation where truck vehicle headlamps are simply located above the passenger vehicle driver's eyepoint, or above the side view mirror. The light intensity levels here are ten or twenty times that in the "glare" portion of the pattern upon which the existing standard was based. It is this same high intensity light upon which drivers depend to illuminate the distant roadway.

It is the recommendation of the Mounting Height Task Force that the transportation industry and standards associations consider significantly reducing the limit of mounting height for headlamps on vehicles whose basic purpose is transportation of people and goods over public roadways. The task force does not believe it is necessary to apply a new definition of headlamp mounting height to specialized vehicles which require headlamps mounted above the normal range as dictated by the vehicle's intended use (i.e., "construction" vehicles such as bulldozers, "special purpose" vehicles such as snow plows or vehicles whose only function is nonhighway use such as vehicles used for open or underground mining operations).

The task force recommendation is based on the information available and the belief that the marginal detection distance loss for some vehicles is offset by the greater good of reducing glare for the vast majority of passenger vehicle drivers. The task force understands that sign legibility is still a salient issue but has considered the precedent of current practice on many contemporary truck vehicles.

PREPARED BY THE SAE MOUNTING HEIGHT TASK FORCE OF THE
LIGHTING COORDINATING COMMITTEE

PARKING LAMPS (FRONT POSITION LAMPS)—SAE J222 DEC94   SAE Standard

Report of the Lighting Committee approved October 1951 and revised March 1986. Rationale statement available. Revised by the SAE Signalling and Marking Devices Standards Committee and the SAE Lighting Coordinating Committee December 1991 and December 1994. Rationale statement available.

1. Scope—This SAE Standard provides test procedures, requirements, and guidelines of parking lamps (front position lamps).

2. References

2.1 Applicable Documents—The following publications form a part of this specification to the extent specified herein. Unless otherwise specified, the latest issue of SAE publications shall apply.

2.1.1 SAE PUBLICATIONS—Available from SAE, 400 Commonwealth Drive, Warrendale, PA 15096-0001.

SAE J567—Lamp Bulb Retention System

SAE J575—Tests for Motor Vehicle Lighting Devices and Components

SAE J576—Plastic Materials for Use in Optical Parts Such as Lenses and Reflectors of Motor Vehicle Lighting Devices

SAE J578—Color Specification

SAE J759—Lighting Identification Code

(R)   **2.2 Related Publications**—The following publications are provided for information purposes only and are not a required part of this document.

(R)   2.2.1 SAE PUBLICATIONS—Available from SAE, 400 Commonwealth Drive, Warrendale, PA 15096-0001.

SAE J592—Clearance, Side Marker, and Identification Lamps

SAE J585—Tail Lamps (Rear Position Lamps) for Use on Motor Vehicles Less Than 2032 mm in Overall Width

SAE J586 FEB84—Stop Lamps for Use on Motor Vehicles Less Than 2032 mm in Overall Width

SAE J588 NOV84—Turn Signal Lamps for Use on Motor Vehicles Less Than 2032 mm in Overall Width

SAE J594—Reflex Reflectors

SAE J1395 APR85—Front and Rear Turn Signal Lamps for Use on Motor Vehicles 2032 mm or More in Overall Width

SAE J1398 MAY85—Stop Lamps for Use on Motor Vehicles 2032 mm or More in Overall Width

SAE J1957—Central High Mounted Stop Lamp Standard for Use on Vehicles Less than 2032 mm Overall Width

SAE J2040—Tail Lamps (Rear Position Lamps) for Use on Vehicles 2032 mm or More in Overall Width

SAE J2042—Clearance, Sidemarker, and Identification Lamps for Use on Motor Vehicles 2032 mm or More in Overall Width

(R) 2.2.2 FEDERAL PUBLICATION—Available from the Superintendent of Documents, U. S. Government Printing Office, Washington, DC 20402.

FMVSS No. 108—Turn Signal Geometric Visibility Requirements (56 FR 64733-64737)

2.3 Definitions

2.3.1 PARKING LAMPS—Whether separate or in combination with other lamps, parking lamps are located on both the front left and right of the vehicle which show to the front and are intended to mark the vehicle when parked. In addition, these front lamps serve as a reserve front position indicating system in the event of headlamp failure.

3. Lighting Identification Code—Parking lamps may be identified by the code "P" in accordance with SAE J759.

4. Tests

4.1 SAE J575 is a part of this report. The following tests are applicable with the modifications as indicated:

4.1.1 VIBRATION TEST

4.1.2 MOISTURE TEST

4.1.3 DUST TEST

4.1.4 CORROSION TEST

4.1.5 PHOTOMETRY TEST—In addition to the test procedures in SAE J575, the following apply:

4.1.5.1 Photometric measurements shall be made with the light source of the lamp at least 3 m from the photometer. The H-V axis shall be taken as parallel to the axis of reference of the lamp as mounted on the vehicle.

4.1.6 WARPAGE TEST FOR DEVICES WITH PLASTIC COMPONENTS

116

4.2 Color Test—SAE J578 is a part of this report.

5. *Requirements*

5.1 Performance Requirements—A device, when tested in accordance with the test procedures specified in Section 4, shall meet the following requirements.

5.1.1 VIBRATION—SAE J575.

5.1.2 MOISTURE—SAE J575.

5.1.3 DUST—SAE J575.

5.1.4 CORROSION—SAE J575.

5.1.5 PHOTOMETRY—In addition to the photometric requirements in SAE J575, the following apply:

5.1.5.1 The lamp under test shall meet the photometric performance requirements contained in Table 1. The summation of the luminous intensity measurements at the specified test points in a zone shall be at least the value shown.

TABLE 1—PHOTOMETRIC REQUIREMENTS[1,2]

Zone	Test Points (Degrees)	Minimum Luminous Intensity (Candela)
1	10U - 5L	2.4
	5U - 20L	2.4
	5D - 20L	2.4
	10D - 5L	2.4
2	5U - 10L	3.0
	H - 10L	3.0
	5D - 10L	3.0
3	5U - V	16.8
	H - 5L	16.8
	H - V	16.8
	H - 5R	16.8
	5D -V	16.8
4	5U - 10R	3.0
	H - 10R	3.0
	5D - 10R	3.0
5	10U - 5R	2.4
	5U - 20R	2.4
	5D - 20R	2.4
	10D - 5R	2.4

[1] The measured values at each test point shall not be less than 60% of the minimum values in Table 2.

[2] Ratio requirements of 5.1.5.2 apply.

TABLE 2—PHOTOMETRIC DESIGN GUIDELINES[1]

Test Points (Degrees)	Test Points (Degrees)	Minimum Luminous Intensity (Candela)
10U, 10D	5L, 5R	0.8
5U, 5D	20L, 20R	0.4
5U, 5D	10L, 10R	0.8
5U, 5D	V	2.8
H	10L, 10R	1.4
H	5L, 5R	3.6
H	V	4.0

[1] Ratio requirements of 5.1.5.2 apply.

5.1.5.2 When a parking lamp is combined with the turn signal lamp, the signal lamp shall not be less than three times the luminous intensity of the parking lamp at any test point on or above horizontal; except that at H-V, H-5L, H-5R, and 5U-V, the (turn signal) lamp shall not be less than five times the luminous intensity of the parking lamp.

5.1.6 WARPAGE—SAE J575.

5.1.7 COLOR—The color of the light from a parking lamp shall be white or yellow as specified in SAE J578.

5.2 Materials Requirements—Plastic materials used in optical parts shall meet the requirements of SAE J576.

5.3 Design Requirements

5.3.1 If a turn signal lamp is optically combined with the parking lamp and a two-filament replaceable bulb is used, the bulb shall have an indexing base and the socket shall be designed so that bulbs with nonindexing bases cannot be used. Removable sockets shall have an indexing feature so that they cannot be reinserted into lamp housings in random positions, unless the lamp will perform its intended function with random light source orientation.

(R) 5.4 Installation Requirements—Parking lamps shall meet the following requirements as installed on the vehicle.

5.4.1 Each parking lamp shall be designed to comply with all photometric requirements of Table 1 with all vehicular obstructions considered.

5.4.2 Each parking lamp shall be designed to comply with one of the following visibility requirements:

a. Each lamp must provide a minimum of 13 cm^2 of unobstructed projected area when the light emitting surface area of the lens, excluding reflex reflector area, is projected parallel to a horizontal plane in any direction from 45 degrees outboard to 20 degrees inboard of the vehicle longitudinal axis, and parallel to a longitudinal, vertical plane in any direction from 15 degrees above to 15 degrees below the horizontal (see Figure 1).

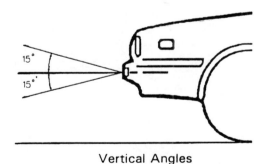

Vertical Angles

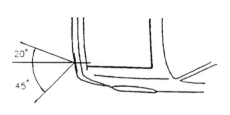

Horizontal Angles**

FIGURE 1—GEOMETRIC VISIBILITY—DESIGN METHOD

b. Each lamp must provide a luminous intensity not less than 0.05 cd throughout the photometric pattern defined by the corner points specified in Figure 2:

15 degrees above horizontal, 45 degrees inwards and 80 degrees outwards
15 degrees below horizontal,* 45 degrees inwards and 80 degrees outwards

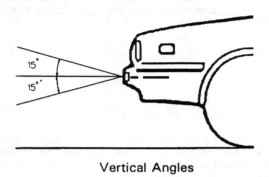

Vertical Angles

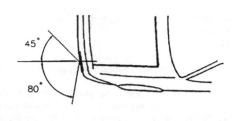

Horizontal Angles**

* The downward angle may be reduced to 5 degrees if the lower lighted edge of the lamp is less than 750 mm above the ground.
** Left side shown; right side symmetrically opposite.

FIGURE 2—GEOMETRIC VISIBILITY—PHOTOMETRIC METHOD

6. Guidelines

6.1 Photometric Design Guidelines for parking lamps, when tested in accordance with 4.1.5 of this report, are contained in Table 2.

6.2 Installation Guidelines—The following guidelines apply to parking lamps as used on the vehicle and shall not be considered part of the requirements.

6.2.1 Parking lamps on the front of the vehicle should be spaced as far apart laterally as practicable so that the signal will be clearly visible and its intent clearly understood.

6.2.2 The luminous intensity of incandescent filament bulbs will vary with applied voltage. The electrical wiring in the vehicle should be adequate to supply design voltage to the lamp filament.

6.2.3 Performance of lamps may deteriorate significantly as a result of dirt, grime, and/or snow accumulation on their optical surfaces. Installation of lamps on vehicles should be considered to minimize the effect of these factors.

6.2.4 Where it is expected that lamps must perform in extremely severe environments, such as in off-highway, mining, fuel haulage, or where it is expected that they will be totally immersed in water, the user should specify lamps specifically designed for such use.

APPENDIX A

A.1 As a matter of additional information, attention is called to SAE J567 for requirements and gages used in socket design.

118

Report of Lighting Division aproved march 1918 and last revised by Lighting committee December 1976. Rationale statement available. Completely revised by the Signalling and Marking Devices Standards Committee December 1989. Rationale statement available.

1. Scope—Many of the lighting devices on motor vehicles are required and essential to operation on public roadways. To assure field replacement, it is important that the bulb types employed be readily available, when needed, in normal service channels. Therefore, this document lists an assortment of current popular types, together with their design characteristics, which are recommended for use wherever practicable. It is recognized that because of constantly changing and improving technology, the list may be incomplete. Also, instances may arise in the design of some devices that require the employment of other types while achieving the desired performance.

Some of the design characteristics in this document are listed solely for the sake of standardization and have no bearing on how lamp bulbs perform in lighting devices on the highway.

2. Definition

2.1 Accurate Rated Miniature Bulb—A bulb operated at design mean spherical candela (Table 2) and having its filament(s) within ±0.25 mm of nominal design position. This applies to No. 1156, 1157,

1157NA, 2057, and 2057NA only. (See Figure 1 for the spacing between the major and minor filaments of these bulbs.)

2.2 Seasoned Bulb—A bulb that has been lighted at 1% of its average lab life, or 10 h maximum, whichever is shorter.

3. Tests

3.1 Samples for Test—Test samples shall be new, unused lamp bulbs fabricated from production processes.

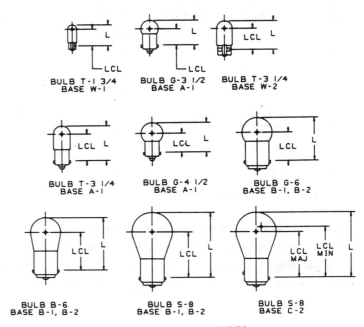

FIG. 1—BULB TYPES

TABLE 1—BULB DIMENSIONS (SEE FIGURE 1)

Bulb	Base	Max Bulb Dia (D) in	Max Bulb Dia (D) mm	Max Exposed Length (L) in	Max Exposed Length (L) mm
G – 3-1/2	A–1	0.460	11.7	0.700	17.8
T – 1-3/4	W–1	0.230	5.8	0.598	15.2
T – 3-1/4	W–2	0.405	10.3	0.815	20.7
T – 3-1/4	A–1	0.433	11.0	0.941	23.9
G – 4-1/2	A–1	0.590	15.0	0.843	21.4
G – 6	B–1, B–2	0.748	19.0	1.189	30.2
B – 6	B–1, B–2	0.775	19.7	1.469	37.3
S – 8	B–1, B–2	1.043	26.5	1.772	45.0
S – 8	C–2	1.043	26.5	1.772	45.0

See Table 2 for LCL dimensions and tolerances.

TABLE 2—TYPICAL LAMP BULBS FOR MOTOR VEHICLES

Typical[a] Service	Trade No.	Mean Spherical Candela	Cd Tol. ±%	Volts	Design Amps	Amp Tol. ±%	Rated Average Lab Life. H.	Type[b]	LCL in	LCL mm	LCL Tolerance ±in	LCL Tolerance ±mm	Axial Alignment Tolerance ±in	Axial Alignment Tolerance ±mm	Bulb[c] Type	Type[d]	Designation
C	74	0.7	30	14.0	0.1	15	500	C–2F	0.402	10.2	0.040	1.0	0.040	1.0	T 1 3/4	W1	Sub–Min–Wedge
C	53	1	20	14.4	0.12	10	1000	C–2V	0.500	12.7	0.090	2.3	0.090	2.3	G 3 1/2	A1	Min Bay
C.M	57	2	20	14.0	0.24	10	500	C–2V	0.560	14.2	0.090	2.3	0.090	2.3	G 4 1/2	A1	Min Bay
C.M	1895	2	20	14.0	0.27	10	1500	C–2F	0.560	14.2	0.090	2.3	0.090	2.3	G 4 1/2	A1	Min Bay
T.P.M.L	67	4	15	13.5	0.59	8	2000	C–2R	0.811	20.6	0.090	2.3	0.090	2.3	G6	B1	SC Bay
T.P.M.L	97	4	15	13.5	0.69	8	2000	C–2V	0.811	20.6	0.090	2.3	0.090	2.3	G6	B1	SC Bay
C	161	1	20	14.0	0.19	10	1500	C–2F	0.560	14.2	0.090	2.3	0.090	2.3	T 3 1/4	W2	Wedge
C.M	168	3	20	14.0	0.35	10	1500	C–2F	0.560	14.2	0.090	2.3	0.090	2.3	T 3 1/4	W2	Wedge
C.M.T.L	194	2	20	14.0	0.27	10	1500	C–2F	0.560	14.2	0.040	1.0	0.060	1.5	T 3 1/4	W2	Wedge
D.S.B	1156	32	10	12.8	2.10	5	600	C–6	1.252	31.8	0.040	1.0	0.040	1.0	S8	B1	SC Bay[f]
P.S.T.D	1157	32	10	12.8	2.10	5	600	C–6	1.252	31.8	0.040	1.0	0.040	1.0	S8	C2	DC Bay
		3	12	14.0	0.59	8	2000	C–6	e		e		e				Index[f]
D.M.P	1157NA	24	30	12.8	2.10	5	600	C–6	1.252	31.8	0.040	1.0	0.040	1.0	S8	C2	DC Bay
		2.2	30	14.0	0.59	8	2000	C–6	e		e		e				Index[f]
P.S.T.D	2057	32	10	12.8	2.10	5	600	C–6	1.252	31.8	0.040	1.0	0.040	1.0	S8	C2	DC Bay
		2	12	14.0	0.48	8	5000	C–6	e		e		e				Index[f]
D.M.P	2057NA	24	30	12.8	2.10	5	600	C–6	1.252	31.8	0.040	1.0	0.040	1.0	S8	C2	DC Bay
		1.5	30	14.0	0.48	8	5000	C–6	e		e		e				Index[f]

[a]Letter designations are defined as follows: B–Backup; C–Indicator; D–Turn Signal; M–Marker, Clearance, Identification; P–Parking; S–Stop; T–Tail; L–License

[b]Filament types – see Figure 3

[c]Bulb types – see Figure 1

[d]Base types – see Figures 4, 5, and 6

[e]See Figure 2 for filament spacing and light center length

[f]Plane of pins with respect to filament is 90° ± 5

TABLE 3—BASE DIMENSIONS^A (SEE FIGURE 4)

Dim	Bayonet (A–1)				Bayonet (B–1, B–2, C–2)			
	inches		mm		inches		mm	
	Min	Max	Min	Max	Min	Max	Min	Max
A^b	0.357	0.366	9.0	9.3	0.593	0.602	15.0	15.3
B	0.383	0.400	9.7	10.1	0.616	0.636	15.6	16.1
C	—	0.431	—	10.97	—	0.668	—	16.9
D	0.025	—	0.6	—	0.025	—	0.6	—
E	0.060	0.067	1.5	1.7	0.071	0.087	1.8	2.2
F	0.180	0.255	4.5	6.48	0.248	0.316	6.3	8.0^c
H	0.095	0.131	2.4	3.33	0.138	0.170	3.5	4.3
J	0.300	—	7.6	—	0.492	—	12.5	—
K	0.180	—	4.5	—	0.350	—	8.8	—
L	—	0.409	—	10.4	—	0.642	—	16.3
M	0.031	—	0.8 NOM	—	0.031	—	0.8 NOM	—
N	0.157	—	4 NOM	—	0.189	—	4.8 NOM	—
P	—	—	—	—	0.117	0.133	2.9	3.3
S	—	—	—	—	0.255	0.280	6.4	7.0

^a Apply to base on complete lamp bulbs.

^b Both minimum and maximum to be measured with a ring gauge. Applies to all parts of base shell except within 3 mm from the bulb and base junction.

^c On bases B–2 and C–2, heights of solder contacts are to be within 0.5 mm of each other.

4. Requirements

The test samples shall comply with the following requirements:

4.1 Candela—Seasoned bulbs shall be measured at design volts in a properly calibrated photometer in accordance with accepted photometric procedures. See Table 2 for candela requirements. An acceptable seasoning schedule at rated volts is 1% of rated average lab life as shown in Table 1 or 10 h maximum, whichever is shorter. For lamp bulbs not listed in Table 1, use the manufacturer's published design life for rated average lab life.

4.2 Physical Dimensions:

4.2.1 Table 1 lists the bulb dimensions necessary to allow interchangeability.

4.2.2 Table 2 lists the electrical rating and physical locations of the filaments.

4.2.3 Table 3 lists the base dimensions considered important for metal based bulbs to insure that lamp bulbs will perform satisfactorily in a bulb retaining device (socket) made in accordance with SAE J567. Appendix A contains the following ANSI Standards:

Base Type/Description	ANSI Pub./Std. Sheet No.	IEC Designation
SAE A-1 Miniature Bayonet	C81.30,1-1	BA9s
SAE B-1 Candelabra Bayonet	C81.30,1-3	BA15s
SAE B-2 Candelabra Bayonet	C81.30,1-3	BA15d
SAE C-2 Candelabra Bayonet	C81.30,1-11	BAY15d

TABLE 4—WEDGE BASE DIMENSIONS (SEE FIGURE 5)
TYPE W-2

Dimension	mm	
	Min	Max
A^a	3.43	4.45
B	4.83	—
C	—	6.35
D	1.5 NOM	—
E	8.89	9.50
F	—	3.04
G	—	4.06
H	5.6 NOM	—
J	0.8 NOM	—
K^b	0.8R NOM	—
P	1.90	2.41
N	1.65	—

^a To be measured on longest side only with the wire in intimate contact with the bottom of the glass wedge.

^b Optional construction, radius under wire not required, and dimension J becomes 1.2 nominal.

4.2.4 Table 4 lists the base dimensions considered important for wedge base (Type W-2) lamps to insure that the lamp bulbs will perform satisfactorily in a bulb retaining device (socket) made in accordance with SAE J567.

4.2.5 Table 5 lists the base dimensions considered important for subminiature wedge base (Type W-1) lamps to insure that lamp bulbs will perform satisfactorily in a bulb retaining device (socket) made in accordance with SAE J567.

TABLE 5—SUBMINIATURE WEDGE BASE DIMENSIONS (SEE FIGURE 6)
TYPE W-1

Dimension	mm	
	Min	Max
A[a]	2.03	3.04
B	3.05	5.08
C	—	5.08
E	4.83	5.08
G	—	3.10
H	3.3 NOM	—
P	1.78	2.20
N	1.65	—
M	1.5 NOM	—
Q	0.50	—

[a]To be measured on longest side only with the wire in intimate contact with the bottom of the glass wedge.

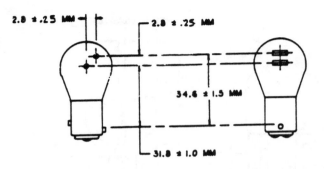

USE DIMENSIONS OF LOWER FILAMENT FOR 1156 BULB

FIG. 2—BULB FILAMENT DESIGN LOCATION

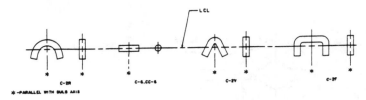

FIG. 3—FILAMENT TYPES

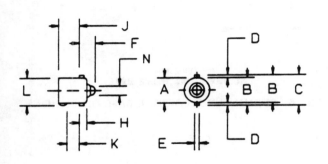

TYPE A-1
MINIATURE BAYONET
SINGLE CONTACT

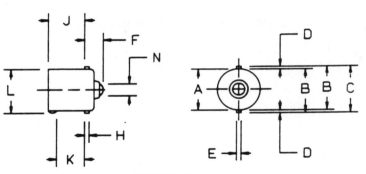

TYPE B-1
BAYONET
SINGLE CONTACT

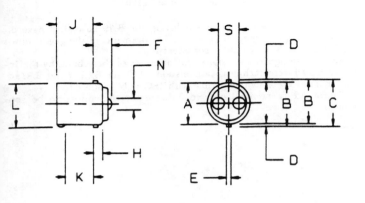

TYPE B-2
BAYONET
DOUBLE CONTACT

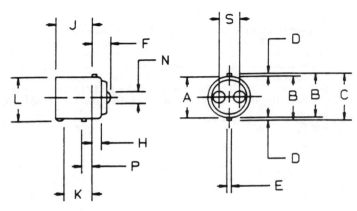

TYPE C-2
INDEXING BAYONET
DOUBLE CONTACT

FIG. 4—BASE TYPES

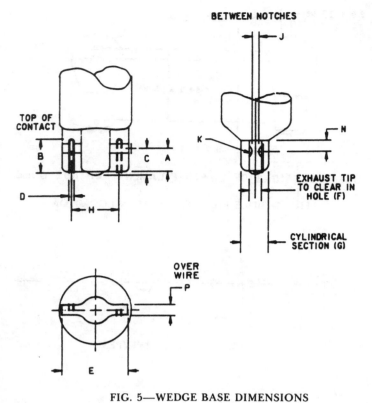

FIG. 5—WEDGE BASE DIMENSIONS

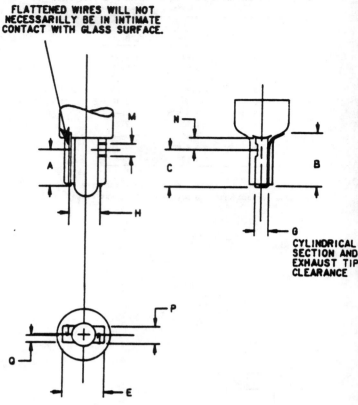

TYPE W-1
SUBMINIATURE WEDGE BASE

FIG. 6—SUBMINIATURE WEDGE BASE DIMENSIONS

APPENDIX A

A1. The designation assigned to this base by the International Electrotechnical Commission (IEC) is BA9. This base is fully compatible with IEC Publication 61.

Figure A1 is intended only to indicate the dimensions to be controlled.

NOTES:

1. Bases may be made with a flare, with the diameter not to be more than 0.50 mm (0.20 in) greater than dimension A max.

2. On a finished lamp, the maximum pin diameter is checked in conjunction with the allowance for misalignment of pins. The "go" gage shown on Std Sheet X-X-X (under consideration) is used.

3. Dimension M lists The OAL limits of the BA9/13 base. For the BA9/14 base, the limits are 13.75 to 14.25 mm (0.541 to 0.561 in).

4. Dimension N denotes the minimum length of shell that shall conform to the limits of dimension A.

5. Dimension U includes allowance for side-solder. It is measured from opposite the barrel or the flare, if present.

6. Rounded edge recommended to aid insertion.

A2. Gaging: Finished lamps employing the BA9 base shall have dimensions such that they will meet the requirements of the gages shown on Std Sheets X-X-X (under consideration).

A3. The designations assigned to variations of these bases by the International Electrotechnical Commission (IEC) are BA15s and BA15d. These bases are fully compatible with IEC Publication 61.

Figure A2 is intended only to indicate the dimensions to be controlled.

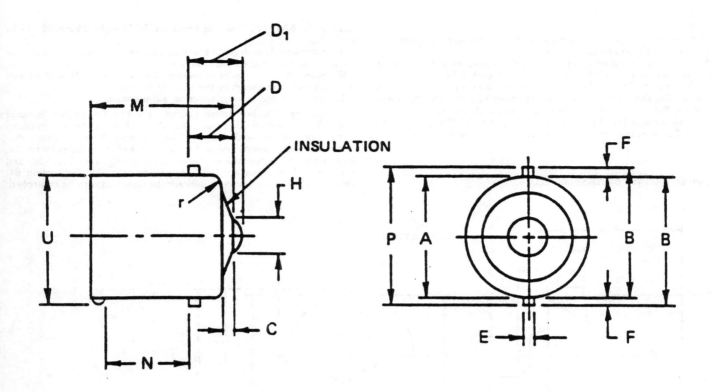

Reference	Standard Dimension (millimeters)				Nearest Equivalent (inches)			
	Unmounted*		Finished Lamp		Unmounted*		Finished Lamp	
	Min	Max	Min	Max	Min	Max	Min	Max
A (Note 1)	9.08	9.20	9.08	9.25	0.357	0.362	0.357	0.364
B	9.75	10.11	9.75	10.16	0.384	0.398	0.384	0.400
C	1.50	–	–	–	0.059	–	–	–
D	4.30	5.20	–	–	0.169	0.205	–	–
D_1	–	–	4.30	5.90	–	–	0.169	0.232
E (Note 2)	1.50	1.70	1.50	1.70	0.059	0.067	0.059	0.067
F	0.64	–	0.64	–	0.025	–	0.025	–
H	3.50	4.00	3.50	4.00	0.138	0.157	0.138	0.157
M (Note 3)	12.90	13.30	–	–	0.508	0.524	–	–
N (Note 4)	4.50	–	4.50	–	0.177	–	0.177	–
P	–	10.95	–	11.00	–	0.431	–	0.433
U (Note 5)	–	–	–	10.41	–	–	–	0.410
r (Note 6)	–	–	–	–	–	–	–	–

*These dimensions are solely for base design and are not to be gaged on the finished lamp.

FIG. A1

NOTES:

1. Bases may be made with a flare, with the diameter not more than 1 mm (0.39 in) greater than dimension A.

2. On double circular[1] contact bases, the solder height of the two contacts shall be within 0.50 mm (0.20 in) of each other.

3. On a finished lamp, the maximum pin diameter is checked in conjunction with the allowance for misalignment of pins. The "go" gage shown on Std Sheet X-X-X (under consideration) is used.

4. Dimension M lists The OAL limits of the BA15/19 base. For the BA15/17.5 base, the limits are 17.25 to 17.75 mm (0.679 to 0.699 in),

and for the BA15/21 base, the limits are 20.75 to 21.25 mm (0.817 to 0.837 in).

5. Dimension N denotes the minimum length of the shell that shall conform to the limits of dimension A.

6. Dimension U includes allowance for side-solder. It is measured from opposite the barrel or the flare, if present.

7. Rounded edge recommended to aid insertion.

A4. Gaging: Finished lamps employing BA15 Candelabra Bayonet bases shall have dimensions such that they will meet the requirements of the gages shown on Std Sheets X-X-X (under consideration).

A5. The designations assigned to variations of these bases by the International Electrotechnical Commission (IEC) are BAY15s and BAY15d. These bases are fully compatible with IEC Publication 61. Figure A3 is intended only to indicate the dimensions to be controlled.

[1] Change approved by ANSI and IEC.

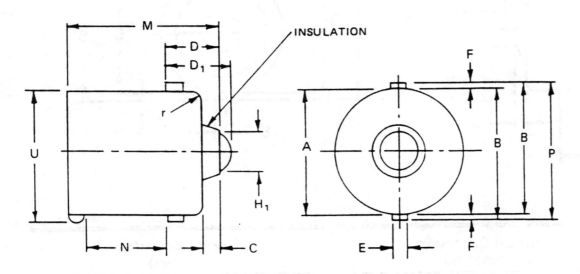

SINGLE CONTACT
BA15s

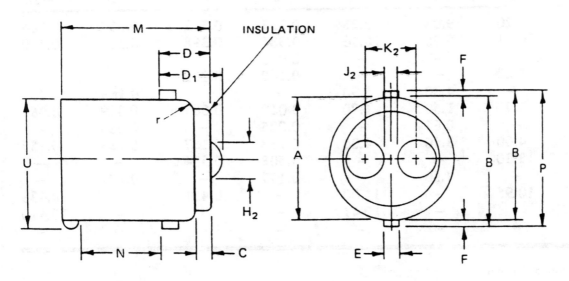

DOUBLE CONTACT
BA15d

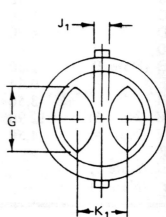

OPTIONAL CONTACT
CONFIGURATION

FIG. A2

124

Reference	Standard Dimension (millimeters)				Nearest Equivalent (inches)			
	Unmounted*		Finished Lamp		Unmounted*		Finished Lamp	
	Min	Max	Min	Max	Min	Max	Min	Max
A (Note 1)	15.05	15.25	15.05	15.30	0.5925	0.6004	0.5925	0.6025
B	15.65	16.10	15.65	16.10	0.616	0.634	0.616	0.636
C	1.50	–	–	–	0.059	–	–	–
D	6.00	6.60	–	–	0.236	0.260	–	–
D$_1$ (Note 2)	–	–	6.32	7.50	–	–	0.249	0.295
E (Note 3)	1.80	2.20	1.80	2.20	0.071	0.087	0.071	0.087
F	0.64	–	0.64	–	0.025	–	0.025	–
G	9.00 Nom		–		0.354 Nom		–	
H$_1$	4.50	5.20	–	–	0.177	0.204	–	–
H$_2$	4.50	–	–	–	0.177	–	–	–
J$_1$	3.00	–	–	–	0.118	–	–	–
J$_2$	1.70	–	–	–	0.067	–	–	–
K$_1$	7.00	8.00	–	–	0.276	0.315	–	–
K$_2$	6.50	7.10	–	–	0.256	0.280	–	–
M (Note 4)	18.75	19.25	–	–	0.738	0.758	–	–
N (Note 5)	8.90	–	8.90	–	0.350	–	0.350	–
P	–	16.95	–	17.00	–	0.667	–	0.669
U (Note 6)	–	–	–	16.26	–	–	–	0.640
r (Note 7)	–	–	–	–	–	–	–	–

*These dimensions are for base design only, and are not to be gaged on the finished lamp.

FIG. A2 (Continued)

NOTES:
1. Bases may be made with a flare, with the diameter not more than 1 mm (0.39 in) greater than dimension A.
2. On double circular[1] contact bases, the solder height of the two contacts shall be within 0.50 mm (0.20 in) of each other.
3. On a finished lamp, the maximum pin diameter is checked in conjunction with the allowance for misalignment of pins. The "go" gage shown on Std Sheet X-X-X (under consideration) is used.

[1] Change approved by ANSI and IEC.

4. Dimension M lists the OAL limits of the BAY15/19 Base. For the BAY15/21 base, the limits are 20.75 to 21.25 mm (0.817 to 0.837 in).
5. Dimension N denotes the minimum length of the shell that shall conform to the limits of dimension A.
6. Dimension U includes allowance for side-solder. It is measured from opposite the barrel or the flare, if present.
7. Rounded edge recommended to aid insertion.

A6. Gaging: Finished lamps employing BAY15 Candelabra Bayonet bases shall have dimensions such that they will meet the requirements of the gages shown on Std Sheets X-X-X (under consideration).

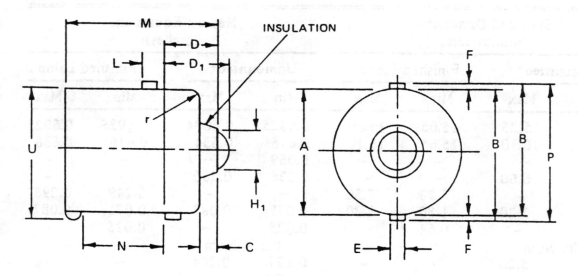

SINGLE CONTACT
BAY15s

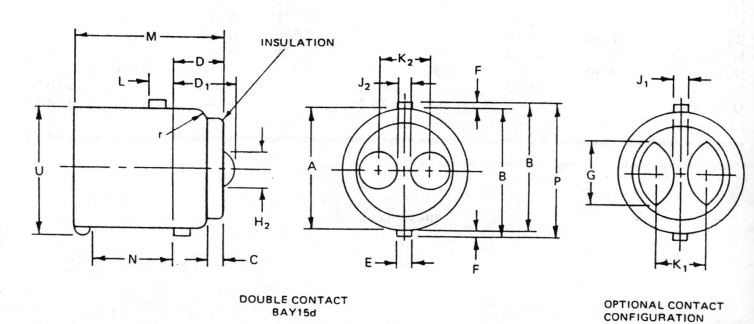

DOUBLE CONTACT
BAY15d

OPTIONAL CONTACT
CONFIGURATION

FIG. A3

| Reference | Standard Dimension (millimeters) | | | | Nearest Equivalent (inches) | | | |
| | Unmounted* | | Finished Lamp | | Unmounted* | | Finished Lamp | |
	Min	Max	Min	Max	Min	Max	Min	Max
A (Note 1)	15.05	15.25	15.05	15.30	0.5925	0.6004	0.5925	0.6025
B	15.65	16.10	15.65	16.15	0.616	0.634	0.616	0.636
C	1.50	–	–	–	0.059	–	–	–
D	6.00	6.60	–	–	0.236	0.260	–	–
D_1 (Note 2)	–	–	6.32	7.50	–	–	0.249	0.295
E (Note 3)	1.80	2.20	1.80	2.20	0.071	0.087	0.071	0.087
F	0.64	–	0.64	–	0.025	–	0.025	–
G	9.00 Nom		–		0.354 Nom		–	
H_1	4.50	5.20	–	–	0.177	0.204	–	–
H_2	4.50	–	–	–	0.177	–	–	–
J_1	3.00	–	–	–	0.118	–	–	–
J_2	1.70	–	–	–	0.067	–	–	–
K_1	7.00	8.00	–	–	0.276	0.315	–	–
K_2	6.50	7.10	–	–	0.256	0.280	–	–
L	3.00	3.40	3.00	3.40	0.118	0.134	0.118	0.134
M (Note 4)	18.75	19.25	–	–	0.738	0.758	–	–
N (Note 5)	8.90	–	8.90	–	0.350	–	0.350	–
P	–	16.95	–	17.00	–	0.667	–	0.669
U (Note 6)	–	–	–	16.26	–	–	–	0.640
r (Note 7)	–	–	–	–	–	–	–	–

*These dimensions are for base design only, and are not to be gaged
on the finished lamp.

FIG. A3 (Continued)

TAIL LAMPS (REAR POSITION LAMPS) FOR USE ON MOTOR VEHICLES LESS THAN 2032 mm IN OVERALL WIDTH—SAE J585 DEC94   SAE Standard

Report of the Lighting Division approved March 1918. Revised by the Lighting Committee March 1986. Rationale statement available. Completely revised by the SAE Lighting Coordinating Committee and the SAE Signalling and Marking Devices Standards Committee December 1991, and revised December 1994. Rationale statement available.

1. *Scope*—This SAE Standard provides test procedures, requirements, and guidelines for tail lamps (rear position lamps).

2. *References*

2.1 Applicable Documents—The following publications form a part of this specification to the extent specified herein. Unless otherwise specified, the latest issue of SAE publications shall apply.

SAE J567—Lamp Bulb Retention System

SAE J575—Tests for Motor Vehicle Lighting Devices and Components

SAE J576—Plastic Materials for Use in Optical Parts Such as Lenses and Reflectors of Motor Vehicle Lighting Devices

SAE J578—Color Specification

SAE J759—Lighting Identification Code

SAE J2040—Tail Lamps (Rear Position Lamps) for Use on Vehicles 2032 mm or More in Overall Width

(R)   **2.2 Related Publications**—The following publications are provided for information purposes only and are not a required part of this document.

2.2.1 SAE PUBLICATIONS—Available from SAE, 400 Commonwealth Drive, Warrendale, PA 15096-0001.

SAE J586 FEB84—Stop Lamps for Use on Motor Vehicles Less Than 2032 mm in Overall Width

SAE J588 NOV84—Turn Signal Lamps for Use on Motor Vehicles Less Than 2032 mm in Overall Width

SAE J594—Reflex Reflectors

SAE J1395 APR85—Front and Rear Turn Signal Lamps for Use on Motor Vehicles 2032 mm or More in Overall Width

SAE J1398 MAY85—Stop Lamps for Use on Motor Vehicles 2032 mm or More in Overall Width

SAE J1957—Central High Mounted Stop Lamp Standard for Use on Vehicles Less than 2032 mm Overall Width

SAE J2042—Clearance, Sidemarker, and Identification Lamps for Use on Motor Vehicles 2032 mm or More in Overall Width

2.2.2 FMVSS SPECIFICATION—Available from the Superintendent of Documents, U.S. Government Printing Office, Washington, D.C. 20402.

FMVSS 108 (56 FR 64733 - 64737)—Lamps, Reflective Devices, and Associated Equipment

2.3 Definitions

2.3.1 TAIL LAMPS—Lamps used to designate the rear of a vehicle by a steady burning low intensity light.

2.3.2 MULTIPLE COMPARTMENT LAMP—A device which gives its indication by two or more separately lighted areas which are joined by one or more common parts such as a housing or lens.

2.3.3 MULTIPLE LAMP ARRANGEMENT—An array of two or more separated lamps on each side of the vehicle which operate together or give a signal.

3. *Lighting Identification Code*—Tail lamps may be identified by the code "T" in accordance with SAE J759.

4. *Tests*

4.1 SAE J575 is a part of this report. The following tests are applicable with the modifications as indicated:

4.1.1 VIBRATION TEST

4.1.2 MOISTURE TEST

4.1.3 DUST TEST

4.1.4 CORROSION TEST

4.1.5 PHOTOMETRY TEST—In addition to the test procedure in SAE J575, the following apply:

4.1.5.1 Photometric measurements shall be made with the light source of the lamp at least 3 m from the photometer. The H-V axis shall be taken as parallel to the axis of reference of the lamp as mounted on the vehicle.

4.1.5.2 Photometric measurements shall be made with the bulb filament steadily burning. Photometric measurement of multiple compartment lamps or multiple lamp arrangements shall be made by either of the following methods:

4.1.5.2.1 All compartments or lamps shall be photometered together provided that a line from the light source of each compartment or lamp to the center of the photometer sensing device does not make an angle of more than 0.6 degree with the photometer H-V axis. When compartments or lamps are photometered together, the H-V axis shall intersect the midpoint between their light sources.

4.1.5.2.2 Each compartment or lamp shall be photometered separately by aligning the axis of each lamp or compartment with the photometer. The photometric measurement for the entire multiple compartment lamp or multiple lamp arrangement shall be determined by adding the photometric outputs from each individual lamp or component at corresponding test points.

4.1.6 WARPAGE TEST FOR DEVICES WITH PLASTIC COMPONENTS

4.2 Color Test—SAE J578 is a part of this report.

5. *Requirements*

5.1 Performance Requirements—A device when tested in accordance with the test procedures specified in Section 4 shall meet the following requirements:

5.1.1 VIBRATION—SAE J575.

5.1.2 MOISTURE—SAE J575.

5.1.3 DUST—SAE J575.

5.1.4 CORROSION—SAE J575.

5.1.5 PHOTOMETRY—SAE J575.

5.1.5.1 The lamp under test shall meet the photometric performance requirements contained in Table 1. The summation of the luminous intensity measurements at the specified test points in a zone shall be at least the value shown.

5.1.5.2 A multiple compartment lamp or multiple lamps may be used to meet the photometric requirements. If a multiple compartment lamp or multiple lamps are used and the distance between adjacent light sources does not exceed 560 mm for two compartments or lamp arrangements and does not exceed 410 mm for three compartments or lamp arrangements, then the combination of the compartments or lamps must be used to meet the photometric requirements for the corresponding number of lighted sections in Table 1. If the distance between adjacent light sources exceeds the previous dimensions, each compartment or lamp shall comply with the photometric performance requirements for one lighted section in Table 1.

5.1.5.3 When a tail lamp is combined with the turn signal or stop lamp, the signal lamp intensity shall not be less than three times the luminous intensity of the tail lamp at any test point, except that at H-V, H-5L, H-5R, and 5U-V, the turn signal or stop lamp intensity shall not be less than five times the luminous intensity of the tail lamp. If a multiple compartment or multiple lamp arrangement is used and the distance between optical axes for both the tail lamp and the turn signal or stop lamp is within the dimensions specified in 5.1.5.2, the ratio of the turn signal or stop lamp to the tail lamp shall be computed with all the compartments or lamps lighted. If a multiple compartment or multiple lamp arrangement is used and the distance between optical axes for one of the functions exceeds the dimensions specified in 5.1.5.2, the ratio shall be computed for only those compartments or lamps where the tail lamp and turn signal or stop lamp are optically combined. When the tail lamp is combined with the turn signal or stop lamp and the maximum luminous intensity of the tail lamp is located below horizontal and within an area generated by a 1.0 degree radius around a test point, the ratio for the test point may be computed using the lowest value of the tail lamp luminous intensity within the generated area.

5.1.6 WARPAGE—SAE J575.

5.1.7 COLOR—The color of the light from a tail lamp shall be red as specified in SAE J578.

5.2 Material Requirements—Plastic materials used in optical parts shall meet the requirements of SAE J576.

5.3 Design Requirements

5.3.1 If a turn signal or stop lamp is optically combined with the tail lamp and a two-filament replaceable bulb is used, the bulb shall have an indexing base and the socket shall be designed so that bulbs with nonindexing bases cannot be used. Removable sockets shall have an indexing feature so that they cannot be reinserted into lamp housings in random positions, unless the lamp will perform its intended function with random light source orientation.

(R)   **5.4 Installation Requirements**—Tail lamps shall meet the following requirements as installed on the vehicle:

5.4.1 Each tail lamp shall be designed to comply with all photometric requirements of Table 1 with all vehicular obstructions considered.

5.4.2 Each tail lamp shall be designed to comply with one of the following visibility requirements:

a. Each lamp must provide a minimum of 13 cm² of unobstructed projected area when the light emitting surface area of the lens, excluding reflex reflector area, is projected parallel to a horizontal plane in any direction from 45 degrees outboard to 45 degrees inboard of the vehicle longitudinal axis, and parallel to a longitudinal, vertical plane in any direction from 15 degrees above to 15 degrees below the horizontal (see Figure 1).

TABLE 1—PHOTOMETRIC REQUIREMENTS[1,2,3]

Zone	Test Points (Degrees) Lighted Sections	Minimum Luminous Intensity (cd) 1	Minimum Luminous Intensity (cd) 2	Minimum Luminous Intensity (cd) 3
1	10U-5L 5U-20L 5D-20L 10D-5L	1.4	2.4	3.5
2	5U-10L H-10L 5D-10L	2.4	4.2	6.0
3	5U-V H-5L H-V H-5R 5D-V	9.6	16.8	24.0
4	5U-10R H-10R 5D-10R	2.4	4.2	6.0
5	10U-5R 5U-20R 5D-20R 10D-5R	1.4	2.4	3.5
MAXIMUM LUMINOUS INTENSITY (cd) H AND ABOVE (See Note 2)	MAXIMUM LUMINOUS INTENSITY (cd) H AND ABOVE (See Note 2)	18	20	25

[1] The measured values at each test point shall not be less than 60% of the minimum values in Table 2.
[2] The listed maximum shall not be exceeded over any area larger than that generated by an 0.5 degree readius within the solid angle defined by the test points in Table 1.
[3] Ratio requirements of 5.1.5.3 apply.

b. Each lamp must provide a luminous intensity not less than 0.05 cd throughout the photometric pattern defined by the corner points specified as follows:

(1) 15 degrees above horizontal, 45 degrees inwards, and 80 degrees outwards
(2) 15 degrees below horizontal, 45 degrees inwards, and 80 degrees outwards

6. Guidelines

6.1 Photometric Design Guidelines for tail lamps, when tested in accordance with 4.1.5 of this report, are contained in Table 2.

6.2 Installation Guidelines—The following guidelines apply to tail lamps as used on the vehicle and shall not be considered part of the requirements:

6.2.1 Tail lamps on the rear of the vehicle should be spaced as far apart laterally as practicable so that the signal will be clearly visible and its intent clearly understood.

6.2.2 The luminous intensity of incandescent filament bulbs will vary with applied voltage. The electrical wiring in the vehicle should be adequate to supply design voltage to the lamp filament.

6.2.3 Performance of lamps may deteriorate significantly as a result of dirt, grime, and/or snow accumulation on their optical surfaces. Installation of lamps on vehicles should be considered to minimize the effect of these factors.

6.2.4 Where it is expected that lamps must perform in extremely severe environments, such as in off-highway, mining, fuel haulage, or where it is expected that they will be totally immersed in water, the user should specify lamps specifically designed for such use.

TABLE 2—PHOTOMETRIC DESIGN GUIDELINES[1,2]

Test Points (Degrees)	Test Points (Degrees)	Minimum Luminous Intensity (cd) Lighted Sections 1	Minimum Luminous Intensity (cd) Lighted Sections 2	Minimum Luminous Intensity (cd) Lighted Sections 3
10U, 10D	5L, 5R	0.4	0.7	1.0
5U, 5D	20L, 20R 10L, 10R V	0.3 0.8 1.8	0.5 1.4 3.1	0.7 2.0 4.5
H	10L, 10R 5L, 5R V	0.8 2.0 2.0	1.4 3.5 3.5	2.0 5.0 5.0
MAXIMUM LUMINOUS INTENSITY (cd) H AND ABOVE (See Note 1)	MAXIMUM LUMINOUS INTENSITY (cd) H AND ABOVE (See Note 1)	18	20	25

[1] The maximum design value of a lamp intended for the rear of the vehicle should not exceed the listed design maximum over any area larger than that generated by an 0.25 degree radius within the solid angle defined by the test points in this table.
[2] Ratio requirements of 5.1.5.3 apply.

APPENDIX A

A.1 As a matter of additional information, attention is called to SAE J567 for requirements and gages used in socket design.

A.2 For vehicles over 2032 mm wide see SAE J2040.

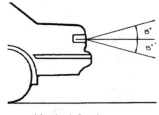 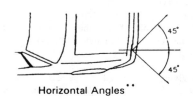

Vertical Angles

Horizontal Angles **

* The downward angle may be reduced to 5 degrees if the lower lighted edge of the lamp is less than 750 mm above the ground
** Left side shown; right side symmetrically opposite.

FIGURE 1—TAIL LAMP VISIBILITY REQUIREMENTS—UNOBSTRUCTED PROJECTED AREA

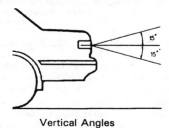 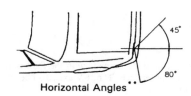

Vertical Angles

Horizontal Angles **

* The downward angle may be reduced to 5 degrees if the lower lighted edge of the lamp is less than 750 mm above the ground
** Left side shown; right side symmetrically opposite.

FIGURE 2—TAIL LAMP VISIBILITY REQUIREMENTS—LUMINOUS INTENSITY

(R) STOP LAMPS FOR USE ON MOTOR VEHICLES LESS THAN 2032 mm IN OVERALL WIDTH—SAE J586 SEP95 — SAE Standard

Report of the Lighting Division, approved February 1927, completely revised by the Lighting Committee February 1984. Rationale statement available. Reaffirmed by the Signalling and Marking Devices Standards Committee December 1989. Completely revised by the SAE Signalling and Marking Devices Standards Committee and the SAE Lighting Coordinating Committee September 1995. Rationale statement available.

1. Scope
This SAE Standard provides test procedures, requirements, and guidelines for stop lamps intended for use on vehicles of less than 2032 mm in overall width.

2. References

2.1 Applicable Documents—The following publications form a part of this specification to the extent specified herein. The latest issue of SAE publications shall apply.

2.1.1 SAE PUBLICATIONS—Available from SAE, 400 Commonwealth Drive, Warrendale, PA 15096-0001.

SAE J567—Lamp Bulb Retention System

SAE J575—Tests for Motor Vehicle Lighting Devices and Components

SAE J576—Plastic Materials for Use in Optical Parts Such as Lenses and Reflectors of Motor Vehicle Lighting Devices

SAE J578—Color Specification

SAE J579—Lighting Code Identification

SAE J1050—Describing and Measuring the Driver's Field of View

2.2 Related Publications—The following publications are provided for information purposes only and are not a required part of this document.

2.2.1 SAE PUBLICATIONS—Available from SAE, 400 Commonwealth Drive, Warrendale, PA 15096-0001.

SAE J222—Parking Lamps (Front Position Lamps)

SAE J585—Tail Lamps (Rear Position Lamps) for Use on Motor Vehicles Less Than 2032 mm in Overall Width

SAE J586 FEB84—Stop Lamps for Use on Motor Vehicles Less Than 2032 mm in Overall Width

SAE J588 NOV84—Turn Signal Lamps for Use on Motor Vehicles Less Than 2032 mm in Overall Width

SAE J592—Clearance, Side Marker, and Identification Lamps

SAE J594—Reflex Reflectors

SAE J1395 MAY85—Front and Rear Turn Signal Lamps for Use on Motor Vehicles 2032 mm or More in Overall Width

SAE J1398—Stop Lamps for Use on Motor Vehicles 2032 mm or More in Overall Width

SAE J1957—Central High Mounted Stop Lamp Standard for Use on Vehicles Less than 2032 mm Overall Width

SAE J2040—Tail Lamps (Rear Position Lamps) for Use on Vehicles 2032 mm or More in Overall Width

SAE J2042—Clearance, Sidemarker, and Identification Lamps for Use on Motor Vehicles 2032 mm or More in Overall WIdth

2.2.2 NHTSA PUBLICATION—Available from the Superintendent of Documents, U.S. Government Printing Office, Washington, DC 20402.

FMVSS108 56 FR 64733 - 64737

3. Definitions

3.1 Stop Lamps—Lamps giving a steady light to the rear of a vehicle to indicate the intention of the operator of a vehicle to stop or diminish speed by braking.

4. Lighting Identification Code
Stop lamps for use on vehicles less than 2032 mm in overall width may be identified by the code "S" in accordance with SAE J759.

5. Tests

5.1 SAE J575 is a part of this document. The following tests are applicable with modifications as indicated.

5.1.1 VIBRATION TEST

5.1.2 MOISTURE TEST

5.1.3 DUST TEST

5.1.4 CORROSION TEST

5.1.5 PHOTOMETRY TEST

5.1.5.1 Photometric measurements shall be made with the light source of the signal lamp at least 3 m from the photometer. The H-V axis shall be taken as parallel to the longitudinal axis of the vehicle.

5.1.5.2 Photometric measurements shall be made with the bulb filament steadily burning. Photometric measurements of multiple compartment lamps or multiple lamp arrangements shall be made by either of the following methods by aligning the axis of each lamp or compartment with the photometer:

5.1.5.2.1 All compartments or lamps shall be photometered together provided that a line from the light source of each compartment or lamp to the center of the photometer sensing device does not make an angle of more than 0.6 degree with the photometer H-V axis. When compartments or lamps are photometered together, the H-V axis shall intersect the midpoint between their light sources.

5.1.5.2.2 Each compartment or lamp shall be photometered separately. The photometric measurement for the entire multiple compartment lamp or multiple lamp arrangement shall be determined by adding the photometric outputs from each individual lamp or component at corresponding test points.

5.1.6 WARPAGE TEST FOR DEVICES WITH PLASTIC COMPONENTS

5.2 Color Test—SAE J578 is a part of this document.

6. Requirements

6.1 Performance Requirements—A device when tested in accordance with the test procedures specified in Section 5, shall meet the following requirements:

6.1.1 VIBRATION—SAE J575

6.1.2 MOISTURE—SAE J575

6.1.3 DUST—SAE J575

6.1.4 CORROSION—SAE J575

6.1.5 PHOTOMETRY—SAE J575

6.1.5.1 The lamp shall meet the photometric performance requirements contained in Table 1 and its footnotes. The summation of the luminous intensity measurements at the specified test points in a zone shall be at least the value shown.

TABLE 1—PHOTOMETRIC REQUIREMENTS[3]

Zone	Test Points[1] (deg)	Minimum Luminous Intensity (cd) Lighted Sections[4] 1	Minimum Luminous Intensity (cd) Lighted Sections[4] 2	Minimum Luminous Intensity (cd) Lighted Sections[4] 3
1	10U-5L 5U-20L 5D-20L 10D-5L	50	60	70
2	5U-10L H-10L 5D-10L	100	115	135
3	5U-V H-5L H-V H-5R 5D-V	380	445	520
4	5U-10R H-10R 5D-10R	100	115	135
5	10U-5R 5U-20R 5D-20R 10D-5R	50	60	70
Maximum Luminous Intensity (cd)[2]		300	360	420

[1] The measured values at each test point shall not be less than 60% of the minimum value in Table 2.
[2] The listed maximum shall not be exceeded over any area larger than that generated by a 0.5 degree radius within the solid angle defined by the test points in Table 1.
[3] Ratio requirements of 6.1.5.3 apply.
[4] A multiple device signaling unit gives its indication by two or more separately lighted sections which may be separate lamps, or areas that are joined by common parts. The photometric values are to apply when all sections that provide the same signal are considered as a unit except when the dimensions between optical centers exceed those given in 6.1.5.2. For a separate lamp arrangement, where lamps are interchangeable, each lamp shall be of approximately the same performance.

6.1.5.2 A multiple compartment lamp or multiple lamps may be used to meet the photometric requirements of a stop lamp. If a multiple compartment or multiple lamps are used and the distance between adjacent light sources does not exceed 560 mm for two compartments or lamp arrangements and does not exceed 410 mm for three compartments or lamp arrangements, then the combination of the compartments or lamps must be used to meet the photometric requirements for the corresponding number of lighted sections (Table 1). If the distance between adjacent light sources exceeds the dimensions, each compartment or lamp shall comply with the photometric requirements for one lighted section (Table 1).

6.1.5.3 When a tail lamp is combined with the stop lamp, the stop lamp shall not be less than three times the luminous intensity of the tail lamp at any test point; except that at H-V, H-5L, H-5R, and 5U-V, the stop lamp shall not be less than five times the luminous intensity of the tail lamp. If a multiple compartment or multiple lamp arrangement is used and the distance between optical axis for both the tail lamp and stop lamp is within the dimensions specified in 6.1.5.2, the ratio of the stop lamp to the tail lamp shall be computed with all the compartments or lamps lighted. If a multiple compartment or multiple lamp arrangement is used and the distance between optical axes for one of the functions exceeds the dimensions specified in 6.1.5.2, the ratio shall be computed for only those compartments or lamps where the tail lamp and stop lamp are optically combined. When the tail lamp is combined with the stop lamp, and the maximum luminous intensity of the tail lamp is located below horizontal and within an area generated by a 0.5 degree radius around a test point, the ratio for the test point may be computed using the lowest value of the tail lamp luminous intensity within the generated area.

6.1.6 WARPAGE—SAE J575

6.1.7 COLOR—The color of light from the stop lamps shall be red as specified in SAE J578.

6.2 Materials Requirements—Plastic materials used in the optical parts shall meet the requirements of SAE J576.

6.3 Design Requirements

6.3.1 If a stop signal is optically combined with the tail lamp and a two-filament bulb used, the bulb shall have an indexing base and the socket shall be designed so that bulbs with nonindexing bases cannot be used. Removable sockets shall have an indexing feature so that they cannot be reinserted into lamp housings in random positions, unless the lamp will perform its intended function with random light source orientation.

6.3.2 The functional lighted lens area of a single compartment lamp shall be at least 37.5 cm^2.

6.3.3 If a multiple compartment lamp or multiple lamps are used to meet the photometric requirements, the functional lighted lens area of each compartment or lamp shall be at least 22 cm^2 provided the combined area is at least 37.5 cm^2.

6.4 Installation Requirements—Stop lamps shall meet the following requirements as installed on the vehicle:

6.4.1 Each stop lamp shall be designed to comply with all photometric requirements of Table 1 with all vehicular obstructions considered.

6.4.2 Each stop lamp shall be designed to comply with one of the following visibility requirements:

a. Each lamp must provide a minimum of 13 cm^2 of unobstructed projected area when the light emitting surface area of the lens, excluding reflex reflector area, is projected parallel to a horizontal plane in any direction from 45 degrees outboard to 45 degrees inboard of the vehicle longitudinal axis, and parallel to a longitudinal, vertical plane in any direction from 15 degrees above to 15 degrees below* the horizontal (see Figure 1).

or

b. Each lamp must provide a luminous intensity not less than 0.3 cd throughout the photometric pattern defined by the corner points specified in Figure 2:
    15 degrees above horizontal, 45 degrees inwards and outwards
    15 degrees below horizontal*, 45 degrees inwards and outwards

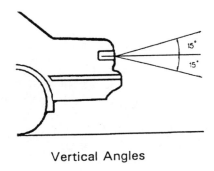

Vertical Angles

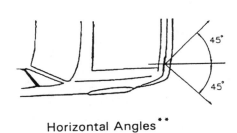

Horizontal Angles**

* The downward angle may be reduced to 5 degrees if the lower lighted edge of the lamp is less than 750 mm above the ground.
** Left side shown; right side symmetrically opposite.

FIGURE 1—TAIL LAMP VISIBILITY REQUIREMENTS—UNOBSTRUCTED PROJECTED AREA

OR

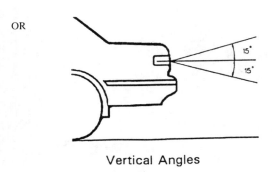

Vertical Angles

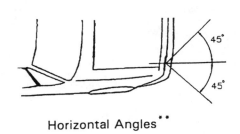

Horizontal Angles**

* The downward angle may be reduced to 5 degrees if the lower lighted edge of the lamp is less than 750 mm above the ground.
** Left side shown; right side symmetrically opposite.

FIGURE 2—TAIL LAMP VISIBILITY REQUIREMENTS—LUMINOUS INTENSITY

7. Guidelines

7.1 Photometric design guidelines for stop lamps, when tested in accordance with 5.1.5 of this document, are contained in Table 2 and its footnotes.

TABLE 2—PHOTOMETRIC DESIGN GUIDELINES

Test Points (degrees)		Minimum Luminous Intensity (cd) Lighted Sections 1	Minimum Luminous Intensity (cd) Lighted Sections 2	Minimum Luminous Intensity (cd) Lighted Sections 3
10U, 10D	5L, 5R	16	19	22
	20L, 20R	10	12	15
5U, 5D	10L, 10R	30	35	40
	V	70	82	95
	10L, 10R	40	47	55
H	5L, 5R	80	95	110
	V	80	95	110
Maximum Luminous Intensity[1] (cd)		300	360	420

[1] The maximum design value of a stop lamp should not exceed the listed design maximum over any area larger than that generated by 0.25 degree radius within the solid angle defined by the test points in Table 2.

7.2 Installation Guidelines—The following apply to stop lamps as used on the vehicle and shall not be considered part of the requirements:

7.2.1 Stop lamps on the rear of the vehicle should be spaced as far apart laterally as practicable, so that the signal will be clearly visible.

7.2.2 The luminous intensity of incandescent filament bulbs will vary with applied voltage. The electrical power system of the vehicle should, under normal running conditions, provide design voltage to the lamp as closely as practical bearing in mind the inherent variability of such systems.

7.2.3 Performance of lamps may deteriorate significantly as a result of dirt, grime, and/or snow accumulation on the optical surfaces. Installation of lamps on vehicles should be considered to minimize the effect of these factors.

7.2.4 Where it is expected that lamps must perform in severe environments, for example, be totally immersed in water periodically, the user should specify lamps designed for such use.

8. Additional Information—As a matter of additional information, attention is called to SAE J567 for requirements and gages to be used in socket design.

Report of the Lighting Division, approved March 1918, completely revised, Lighting Committee, August 1985. Rationale statement available. Completely revised by the SAE Signalling and Marking Devices Standards Committee March 1993. Rationale statement available.

1. Scope—This SAE Standard provides test procedures, requirements, and guidelines for vehicular license plate illumination devices.

2. References

2.1 Applicable Documents—The following publications form a part of this specification to the extent specified herein. The latest issue of SAE publications shall apply.

2.1.1 SAE PUBLICATIONS—Available from SAE, 400 Commonwealth Drive, Warrendale, PA 15096-0001.

SAE J567—Lamp Bulb Retention System

SAE J575—Tests for Motor Vehicle Lighting Devices and Components

SAE J576—Plastic Materials for Use in Optical Parts Such as Lenses and Reflectors of Motor Vehicle Lighting Devices

SAE J578—Color Specification

SAE J759—Lighting Identification Code

2.1.2 ASTM PUBLICATION—Available from ASTM, 1916 Race Street, Philadelphia, PA 19103-1187.

ASTM E 179—Selection of Geometric Conditions for Measurement of Reflection and Transmission Properties of Materials

2.2 Definitions

2.2.1 A LICENSE PLATE ILLUMINATION DEVICE is a device that illuminates the license plate on the rear of a vehicle.

3. Lighting Identification Code—License plate illumination devices may be identified by the code "L" in accordance with SAE J759.

4. Tests

4.1 SAE J575 is a part of this document. The following tests are applicable with modifications as indicated.

4.1.1 VIBRATION TEST

4.1.2 MOISTURE TEST

4.1.3 DUST TEST

4.1.4 CORROSION TEST

4.1.5 WARPAGE TEST ON DEVICES WITH PLASTIC COMPONENTS

4.2 Color Test—SAE J578 is part of this document.

4.3 Photometry Test

4.3.1 TEST EQUIPMENT

4.3.1.1 Test Plate—All luminance measurements shall be made on a rectangular test plate of clean, smooth, matte white blotting paper or an equivalent material with a diffuse white surface. The test plate shall have a total reflectance factor of 85% ± 5% when measured in accordance with ASTM E 179 (0/t illumination/viewing geometry). The size of the test plate is shown in Figure 1 or 2, as applicable. For devices used on vehicles other than motorcycles and motor-driven cycles, test stations shall be located on the face of the test plate as shown in Figure 1. For devices used on motorcycles and motor-driven cycles, the test stations shall be located on the face of the test plate as shown in Figure 2.

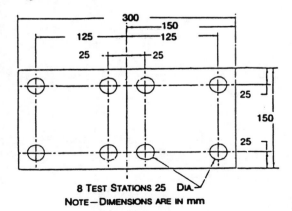

FIGURE 1—TEST PLATE FOR VEHICLES OTHER THAN MOTORCYCLES AND MOTOR-DRIVEN CYCLES

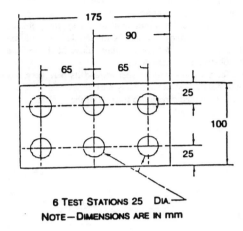

6 TEST STATIONS 25 DIA.

NOTE—DIMENSIONS ARE IN mm

FIGURE 2—TEST PLATE FOR MOTORCYCLES AND MOTOR-DRIVEN CYCLES

4.3.1.2 Luminance Meter—A luminance meter shall be used to measure the luminance over the entire area of each circular test station on the test plate. The meter shall be calibrated to measure luminance in cd/m². Measurements shall not include any area beyond that of the test station.

4.3.2 TEST PROCEDURE

4.3.2.1 The test plate shall be mounted in the position ordinarily taken by the license plate. The face of the test plate shall be located 2 mm from the plane of the license plate holder toward the luminance meter.

4.3.2.2 Luminance measurements shall be made with the optical axis of the luminance meter perpendicular to the test plate surface within ±5 degrees. Measurements shall be recorded at each of the circular test station areas specified in Figure 1 or Figure 2, as applicable.

4.3.2.3 Calculate and record the ratio of the maximum to the minimum luminance over all specified test points. For test plates conforming to Figure 1, the average of the two highest and the two lowest luminance values recorded at the eight test stations shall be taken as maximum and minimum, respectively. For test plates conforming to Figure 2, the highest luminance value and the average of the two lowest luminance values recorded at the six test stations shall be taken as maximum and minimum, respectively.

5. Requirements

5.1 Performance Requirements—A device, when tested in accordance with the test procedures specified in Section 4, shall meet the following requirements:

5.1.1 Vibration—SAE J575

5.1.2 Moisture—SAE J575

5.1.3 Dust—SAE J575

5.1.4 Corrosion—SAE J575

5.1.5 Warpage—SAE J575

5.2 Color—The color of the light from the license plate illumination device(s) shall be white as specified in SAE J578.

5.3 Photometry—Upon completion of the photometry test procedure (paragraph 4.3), the following requirements shall apply:

5.3.1 The luminance at each of the test station areas on the applicable test plate shall be at least 2.5 cd/m².

5.3.2 For tests based on Figure 1, the ratio of maximum to minimum luminance shall not exceed 20/1. For tests based on Figure 2, the ratio of maximum to minimum luminance shall not exceed 15/1.

5.3.3 If a tail or stop lamp is combined with a license plate illumination device, the combination shall also meet the requirements for these devices.

5.4 Materials Requirements—Plastic materials used in the optical parts shall meet the requirements of SAE J576. Since some license plate illumination devices are mounted in shaded or protected locations, attention is called to the section of SAE J576 which covers exposure time and conditions.

5.5 Design Requirements

5.5.1 License plate illumination devices for vehicles other than motorcycle and motor-driven cycles shall be of such size and design as to provide illumination on all parts of a 150 × 300 mm test plate, except for a 13 mm wide border around the plate periphery. License plate illumination devices for motorcycle and motor-driven cycles shall be of such size and design as to provide illumination on all parts of a 100 × 175 mm test plate.

5.5.2 The design shall be such that, when the plate is mounted on a vehicle as intended, the angle between the plane of the license plate and the plane on which the vehicle stands shall be 90 degrees ± 15 degrees.

5.6 Installation Requirements

5.6.1 The license plate illumination device(s) for vehicles other than motorcycles or motor-driven cycles shall be mounted so as to illuminate the plate without obstruction from any designed feature unless the device(s) is designed to comply with the obstructions considered.

5.6.2 Except for a 13 mm wide border around its periphery, visibility of the license plate shall not be obstructed by any part of the vehicle when any point on the license plate is projected directly to the rear of the vehicle.

5.6.3 The license plate illumination device(s) shall be installed so that no white light is projected from the illumination device(s) directly to the rear of the vehicle.

5.6.4 The license plate illumination device(s) for vehicles other than motorcycles and motor-driven cycles shall be mounted so as to illuminate the plate from the top or sides. Illumination from the bottom of the plate is permitted provided other illumination is also provided from the top or sides of the plate.

6. Guidelines

6.1 **Installation Guidelines**—The following apply to license plate illumination devices as used on the vehicle and shall not be considered part of the requirements.

6.1.1 The license plate holding device shall be designed and constructed to provide a substantial plane surface on which to mount the plate.

APPENDIX A

A.1 As a matter of information, attention is called to SAE J567 for requirements and gages to be used in socket design.

TURN SIGNAL LAMPS FOR USE ON MOTOR VEHICLES LESS THAN 2032 mm IN OVERALL WIDTH—SAE J588 DEC94

SAE Standard

Report of the Lighting Division approved February 1927. Completely revised by the Lighting Committee November 1984. Rationale statement available. Revised by the SAE Lighting Coordinating Committee and the SAE Signalling and Marking Devices Standards Committee June 1991 and December 1994. Rationale statement available.

1. Scope—This SAE Standard provides test procedures, requirements, and guidelines for turn signal lamps intended for use on vehicles of less than 2032 mm in overall width.

2. References

2.1 Applicable Documents—The following publications form a part of this specification to the extent specified herein. The latest issue of SAE publications shall apply.

2.1.1 SAE PUBLICATIONS—Available from SAE, 400 Commonwealth Drive, Warrendale, PA 15096-0001.

SAE J567—Lamp Bulb Retention System

SAE J575—Tests for Motor Vehicle Lighting Devices and Components

SAE J576—Plastic Materials for Use in Optical Parts Such as Lenses and Reflectors of Motor Vehicle Lighting Devices

SAE J578—Color Specification

SAE J579—Lighting Code Identification

SAE J1050—Describing and Measuring the Driver's Field of View

2.2 Related Publications—The following publications are provided for information purposes only and are not a required part of this document.

2.2.1 SAE PUBLICATIONS—Available from SAE, 400 Commonwealth Drive, Warrendale, PA 15096-0001.

SAE J222—Parking Lamps (Front Position Lamps)

SAE J585—Tail Lamps (Rear Position Lamps) for Use on Motor Vehicles Less Than 2032 mm in Overall Width

SAE J586 FEB84—Stop Lamps for Use on Motor Vehicles Less Than 2032 mm in Overall Width

SAE J588 NOV84—Turn Signal Lamps for Use on Motor Vehicles Less Than 2032 mm in Overall Width

SAE J592—Clearance, Side Marker, and Identification Lamps

SAE J594—Reflex Reflectors

SAE J1395 MAY85—Front and Rear Turn Signal Lamps for Use on Motor Vehicles 2032 mm or More in Overall Width

SAE J1398—Stop Lamps for Use on Motor Vehicles 2032 mm or More in Overall Width

SAE J1957—Central High Mounted Stop Lamp Standard for Use on Vehicles Less than 2032 mm Overall Width

SAE J2040—Tail Lamps (Rear Position Lamps) for Use on Vehicles 2032 mm or More in Overall Width

SAE J2042—Clearance, Sidemarker, and Identification Lamps for Use on Motor Vehicles 2032 mm or More in Overall WIdth

2.2.2 NHTSA PUBLICATION—Available from the Superintendent of Documents, U.S. Government Printing Office, Washington, DC 20402.

FMVSS108 56 FR 64733 - 64737

3. Definitions

3.1 Turn Signal Lamps—The signalling elements of a turn signal system which indicate an intention to turn by giving a flashing light on the side toward which the turn will be made.

4. Lighting Identification Code—Turn signal lamps for use on vehicles less than 2032 mm in overall width may be identified by the codes I, I2, I3, I4, or I5 in accordance with SAE J759.

5. Tests

5.1 SAE J575 is a part of this document. The following tests are applicable with modifications as indicated.

5.1.1 VIBRATION TEST

5.1.2 MOISTURE TEST

5.1.3 DUST TEST

5.1.4 CORROSION TEST

5.1.5 PHOTOMETRY TEST

5.1.5.1 Photometric measurements shall be made with the light source of the signal lamp at least 3 m from the photometer. The H-V axis shall be taken as parallel to the longitudinal axis of the vehicle.

5.1.5.2 Photometric measurements shall be made with the bulb filament steadily burning. Photometric measurements of multiple compartment lamps or multiple lamp arrangements shall be made by either of the following methods by aligning the axis of each lamp or compartment with the photometer:

5.1.5.2.1 All compartments or lamps shall be photometered together provided that a line from the light source of each compartment or lamp to the center of the photometer sensing device does not make an angle of more than 0.6 degree with the photometer H-V axis. When compartments or lamps are photometered together, the H-V axis shall intersect the midpoint between their light sources.

5.1.5.2.2 Each compartment or lamp shall be photometered separately. The photometric measurement for the entire multiple compartment lamp or multiple lamp arrangement shall be determined by adding the photometric outputs from each individual lamp or component at corresponding test points.

5.1.6 WARPAGE TEST FOR DEVICES WITH PLASTIC COMPONENTS

5.2 Color Test—SAE J578 is a part of this document.

6. Requirements

6.1 Performance Requirements—A device when tested in accordance with the test procedures specified in Section 5, shall meet the following requirements:

6.1.1 VIBRATION—SAE J575

6.1.2 MOISTURE—SAE J575

6.1.3 DUST—SAE J575

6.1.4 CORROSION—SAE J575

6.1.5 PHOTOMETRY—SAE J575

6.1.5.1 The lamp under test shall meet the photometric performance requirements contained in Table 1 and its footnotes. The summation of the luminous intensity measurements at the specified test points in a zone shall be at least the value shown.

6.1.5.2 A multiple compartment lamp or multiple lamps may be used to meet the photometric requirements of a turn signal lamp. If a multiple compartment or multiple lamps are used and the distance between adjacent light sources does not exceed 560 mm for two compartments or lamp arrangements and does not exceed 410 mm for three compartments or lamp arrangements, then the combination of the compartments or lamps must be used to meet the photometric requirements for the corresponding number of lighted sections (see Table 1). If the distance between adjacent light sources exceeds the previous dimensions, each compartment or lamp shall comply with the photometric requirements for one lighted section (see Table 1).

6.1.5.3 When a tail lamp or parking lamp is combined with the turn signal lamp, the signal lamp shall not be less than three times the luminous intensity (a) of the tail lamp at any test point, or (b) of the parking lamp at any test point on or above horizontal except that at H-V, H-5L, H-5R, and 5U-V, the signal lamp shall not be less than five times the luminous intensity of the tail lamp or parking lamp. If a multiple compartment or multiple lamp arrangement is used and the distance between optical axis for both the tail lamp (parking lamp) and the turn signal is within the dimensions specified in 6.1.5.2, the ratio of the signal to the tail lamp (parking lamp) shall be computed with all the compartments or lamps lighted. If a multiple compartment or multiple lamp arrangement is used and the distance between optical axis for one of the functions exceeds the dimensions specified in 6.1.5.2, the ratio shall be computed for only those compartments or lamps where the tail lamp (parking lamp) and turn signal are optically combined. Where the tail lamp is combined with the turn signal lamp, and the maximum luminous intensity of the tail lamp is located below horizontal and within an area generated by a 0.5 degree radius around a test point, the ratio for the test point may be computed using the lowest value of the tail lamp luminous intensity within the generated area.

6.1.5.4 In the case where the front turn signal is mounted in close proximity to the low beam headlamp or any additional lamp used to supplement or used in lieu of the low beam, such as an auxiliary low beam or fog lamp, Table 2 shall be used to modify Table 1 as follows:

6.1.5.4.1 Spacing for a direct light source type design front turn signal lamp, that is, a lamp primarily employing a lens to meet photometric requirements (for example, a lamp that does not employ a reflector) shall be measured from the light source to the lighted edge of the low beam headlamp or any additional lamp used to supplement or used in lieu of the lower beam, such as an auxiliary low beam or fog lamp.

6.1.5.4.2 Spacing for a front turn signal lamp which primarily employs a reflector (for example, one of parabolic section) in conjunction with a lens to meet photometric requirements, shall be measured from the geometric centroid of the front turn signal functional lighted area to the lighted edge of the low beam headlamp or any additional lamp used to supplement or used in lieu of the lower beam, such as an auxiliary low beam or fog lamp.

6.1.6 WARPAGE—SAE J575

6.1.7 COLOR—The color of light from the turn signal lamps shall be red or yellow to the rear and yellow to the front of the vehicle as specified in SAE J578.

TABLE 1—PHOTOMETRIC REQUIREMENTS[3]

Zone Lighted Sections	Test Points[1] (deg) Lighted Sections	Minimum Luminous Intensity (cd)[4] Front Signals Yellow 1	Minimum Luminous Intensity (cd)[4] Front Signals Yellow 2	Minimum Luminous Intensity (cd)[4] Front Signals Yellow 3	Minimum Luminous Intensity (cd)[4] Rear Signals Red 1	Minimum Luminous Intensity (cd)[4] Rear Signals Red 2	Minimum Luminous Intensity (cd)[4] Rear Signals Red 3	Minimum Luminous Intensity (cd)[4] Rear Signals Yellow 1	Minimum Luminous Intensity (cd)[4] Rear Signals Yellow 2	Minimum Luminous Intensity (cd)[4] Rear Signals Yellow 3
1	10U-5L 5U-20L 5D-20L 10D-5L	130	155	180	50	60	70	80	100	120
2	5U-10L H-10L 5D-10L	250	295	340	100	115	135	165	185	220
3	5U-V H-5L H-V H-5R 5D-V	950	1130	1295	380	445	520	610	710	825
4	5U-10R H-10R 5D-10R	250	295	340	100	115	135	165	185	220
5	10U-5R 5U-20R 5D-20R 10D-5R	130	155	180	50	60	70	80	100	120

Maximum Luminous Intensity (cd)

Rear Lamps Only[2]		—	—	—	300	360	420	750	900	1050

[1] The measured values at each test point shall not be less than 60% of the minimum value in Table 3.
[2] The listed maximum shall not be exceeded over any area larger than that generated by a 0.5 degree radius within the solid angle defined by the test points in Table 1.
[3] Ratio requirements of 6.1.5.3 apply.
[4] Multipliers of Table 2 are applicable per 6.1.5.4.

TABLE 2—LUMINOUS INTENSITY MULTIPLIERS FOR FRONT TURN SIGNAL SPACINGS

Spacing to Lighted Edge of Low Beam Headlamp[1]	Multiplier of Table 1 and 3 Values to Obtain Required Minimum Luminous Intensities
100 mm or greater	1.0
75 mm to less than 100 mm	1.5
60 mm to less than 75 mm	2.0
Less than 60 mm	2.5

[1] See 6.1.5 for methods to be used for measurements of spacings.

6.2 Materials Requirements—Plastic materials used in the optical parts shall meet the requirements of SAE J576.

6.3 Design Requirements

6.3.1 If a turn signal is optically combined with the tail lamp and a two-filament bulb used, the bulb shall have an indexing base and the socket shall be designed so that bulbs with nonindexing bases cannot be used. Removable sockets shall have an indexing feature so that they cannot be reinserted into lamp housings in random positions, unless the lamp will perform its intended function with random light source orientation.

6.3.2 The functional lighted lens area of a single compartment lamp shall be at least 37.5 cm² for a rear lamp and at least 22 cm² for a front lamp.

6.3.3 If a multiple compartment lamp or multiple lamps are used to meet the photometric requirements of a rear turn signal lamp, the functional lighted lens area of each compartment or lamp shall be at least 22 cm² provided the combined area is at least 37.5 cm².

6.4 Installation Requirements—Turn signal lamps shall meet the following requirements as installed on the vehicle:

6.4.1 Each turn signal lamp shall be designed to comply with all photometric requirements of Table 1 with all vehicular obstructions considered.

6.4.2 Turn signal lamps shall be designed to comply with one of the following visibility requirements:

a. Each lamp must provide a minimum of 13 cm² of unobstructed projected area when the light emitting surface area of the lens, excluding reflex

reflector area, is projected parallel to a horizontal plane in any direction from 45 degrees outboard to 20 degrees inboard of the vehicle longitudinal axis, and parallel to a longitudinal, vertical plane in any direction from 15 degrees above to 15 degrees below* the horizontal (see Figure 1).

b. Each lamp must provide a luminous intensity not less than 0.3 cd throughout the photometric pattern defined by the corner points specified in Figure 2:

15 degrees above horizontal, 45 degrees inward, and 80 degrees outward
15 degrees below horizontal*, 45 degrees inward, and 80 degrees outward

7. Guidelines

7.1 Photometric Design Guidelines—Guidelines for turn signal lamps, when tested in accordance with 5.1.5 of this document, are contained in Table 3 and its footnotes. Depending on the spacing of the front turn signal relative to the forward illumination lamps as defined in 6.1.5 of this document, the multipliers specified in Table 2 are applicable to the values to Table 3.

7.2 Installation Guidelines—The following guidelines apply to front and/or rear signal lamps as used on the vehicle and shall not be considered part of the requirements.

7.2.1 Signal lamps on the front and rear of the vehicle should be spaced as far apart laterally as practicable, so that the direction of turn will be clearly understood.

7.2.2 The luminous intensity of incandescent filament bulbs will vary with applied voltage. The electrical power system of the vehicle should, under normal running conditions, provide design voltage to the lamp as closely as practical bearing in mind the inherent variability of such systems.

7.2.3 Performance of lamps may deteriorate significantly as a result of dirt, grime, and/or snow accumulation on the optical surfaces. Installation of lamps on vehicles should be considered to minimize the effect of these factors.

7.2.4 Where it is expected that lamps must perform in severe environments, e.g., be totally immersed in water periodically, the user should specify lamps designed for such use.

8. Additional Information—As a matter of additional information, attention is called to SAE J567 for requirements and gages to be used in socket design.

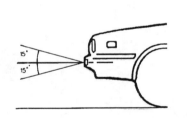
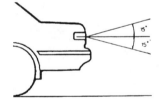

Vertical Angles   Horizontal Angles**

* The downward angle may be reduced to 5 degrees if the lower lighted edge of the lamp is less than 750 mm above the ground.
** Left side shown; right side symmetrically opposite.

FIGURE 1—TAIL LAMP VISIBILITY REQUIREMENTS—UNOBSTRUCTED PROJECTED AREA

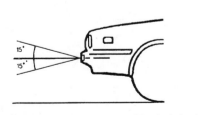
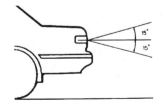

Vertical Angles   Horizontal Angles**

* The downward angle may be reduced to 5 degrees if the lower lighted edge of the lamp is less than 750 mm above the ground.
** Left side shown; right side symmetrically opposite.

FIGURE 2—TAIL LAMP VISIBILITY REQUIREMENTS—LUMINOUS INTENSITY

TABLE 3—PHOTOMETRIC DESIGN GUIDELINES

Test Points (deg)	Lighted Sections	Minimum Luminous Intensity (cd) Front Signals Yellow 1	Minimum Luminous Intensity (cd) Front Signals Yellow 2	Minimum Luminous Intensity (cd) Front Signals Yellow 3	Minimum Luminous Intensity (cd) Rear Signals Red 1	Minimum Luminous Intensity (cd) Rear Signals Red 2	Minimum Luminous Intensity (cd) Rear Signals Red 3	Minimum Luminous Intensity (cd) Rear Signals Yellow 1	Minimum Luminous Intensity (cd) Rear Signals Yellow 2	Minimum Luminous Intensity (cd) Rear Signals Yellow 3
10U, 10D	5L, 5R	40	48	55	16	19	22	26	30	35
	20L, 20R	25	30	35	10	12	15	15	20	25
5U, 5D	10L, 10R	75	88	100	30	35	40	50	55	65
	V	175	205	235	70	82	95	110	130	150
H	10L, 10R	100	120	140	40	47	55	65	75	90
	5L, 5R	200	240	275	80	95	110	130	150	175
	V	200	240	275	80	95	110	130	150	175

Maximum Luminous Intensity (cd)

Rear Lamps Only[1]		—	—	—	300	360	420	750	900	1050

[1] The maximum design value of a lamp intended for the rear of the vehicle should not exceed the listed design maximum over any area larger than that generated by 0.25 degree radius within the solid angle defined by the test points in Table 3.

) SPOT LAMPS
—SAE J591 JUL95

Report of the Lighting Committee approved October 1951 and completely revised by the Lighting Coordinating Committee May 1989. Rationale statement available. Completely revised by the SAE Road Illumination Devices Standards Committee and the SAE Lighting Coordinating Committee July 1995.

1. Scope—This SAE Standard provides test procedures and performance requirements for spot lamps.

2. References

2.1 Applicable Documents—The following publications form a part of this specification to the extent specified herein. Unless otherwise specified, the latest issue of SAE publications shall apply.

2.1.1 SAE PUBLICATIONS—Available from SAE, 400 Commonwealth Drive, Warrendale, PA 15096-0001.

SAE J567—Lamp Bulb Retention System

SAE J575—Test Methods and Equipment for Lighting Devices and Components for Use on Vehicles Less than 2032 mm in Overall Width

SAE J578—Color Specification

SAE J759—Lighting Identification Code

3. Definition

3.1 Spot Lamps—Lamps which are designed to be installed on a motor vehicle and which provide a substantially parallel beam of light and are capable of being aimed as desired by the user for non-driving purposes.

4. Lighting Definition Code—Spot light for vehicles may be identified with "0" in accordance with SAE J759 and designed to comply with SAE J575 and SAE J578.

5. Tests

5.1 SAE J575—The following test procedures in SAE J575 tests for motor vehicle lighting devices and components are part of this document with modifications as indicated.

5.1.1 VIBRATION TEST

5.1.2 MOISTURE TEST

5.1.3 DUST TEST—The dust test shall not be required for sealed units.

5.1.4 CORROSION TEST

5.1.5 WARPAGE

5.2 Color Test—SAE J578 is part of this document.

6. Requirements

6.1 Performance Requirements—A device, when tested in accordance with the test procedures specified in Section 5, shall meet the following requirements indicated in SAE J575:

6.1.1 VIBRATION

6.1.2 MOISTURE

6.1.3 DUST

6.1.4 CORROSION

6.1.5 WARPAGE

6.1.6 COLOR—The color of the emitted light shall be white as defined in SAE J578.

6.1.7 BEAM PATTERN—The spot lamp beam pattern shall be well defined and generally round or oval in shape, without voids or dark areas.

APPENDIX A

A.1 As a matter of additional information, attention is called to SAE J567 for requirements and gages in socket design.

CLEARANCE, SIDE MARKER, AND
IDENTIFICATION LAMPS—SAE J592 DEC94

Report of the Lighting Division approved January 1937. Completely revised by the Lighting Committee January 1984. Rationale statement available. Reaffirmed by the Lighting Coordinating Committee March 1990. Revised by the Signalling and Marking Devices Standards Committee and the SAE Lighting Coordinating Committee June 1992 and December 1994. Rationale statement available.

1. Scope—This SAE Information Report provides test procedures, requirements, and guidelines for clearance, side marker, and identification lamps.

2. References

2.1 Applicable Documents—The following publications form a part of this specification to the extent specified herein. The latest issue of SAE publications shall apply.

2.1.1 SAE PUBLICATIONS—Available from SAE, 400 Commonwealth Drive, Warrendale, PA 15096-0001.

SAE J567—Lamp Bulb Retention System

SAE J575—Tests for Motor Vehicle Lighting Devices and Components

SAE J576—Plastic Materials for Use in Optical Parts Such as Lenses and Reflectors of Motor Vehicle Lighting Devices

SAE J578—Color Specification for Electric Signal Lighting Devices

SAE J759—Lighting Identification Code

2.2 Related Publications—The following publications are provided for information purposes only and are not a required part of this document.

2.2.1 SAE PUBLICATIONS—Available from SAE, 400 Commonwealth Drive, Warrendale, PA 15096-0001.

SAE J222—Parking Lamps (Front Position Lamps)

SAE J585—Tail Lamps (Rear Position Lamps) for Use on Motor Vehicles Less Than 2032 mm in Overall Width

SAE J586 FEB84—Stop Lamps for Use on Motor Vehicles Less Than 2032 mm in Overall Width

SAE J588 NOV84—Turn Signal Lamps for Use on Motor Vehicles Less Than 2032 mm in Overall Width

SAE J592—Clearance, Side Marker, and identification Lamps

SAE J594—Reflex Reflectors

SAE J1395 APR85—Front and Rear Turn Signal Lamps for Use on Motor Vehicles 2032 mm or More in Overall Width

SAE J1398 MAY85—Stop Lamps for Use on Motor Vehicles 2032 mm or More in Overall Width

SAE J1957—Central High Mounted Stop Lamp Standard for Use on Vehicles Less Than 2032 mm Overall Width

SAE J2040—Tail Lamps (Rear Position Lamps) for Use on Vehicles 2032 mm or More in Overall Width

SAE J2042—Clearance, Sidemarker, and Identification Lamps for Use on Motor Vehicles 2032 mm or More in Overall Width

2.2.2 FMVSS PUBLICATION—Available from the Superintendent of Documents, U.S. Government Printing Office, Washington, DC 20402-9371.

FMVSS 108 56 FR 64733 - 64737

3. Definitions

3.1 Clearance Lamps—Lamps mounted on the permanent structure of the vehicle as near as practicable to the upper left and right extreme edges that provide light to the front or rear to indicate the overall width and height of the vehicle.

3.2 Side Marker Lamps—Lamps mounted on the permanent structure of the vehicle as near as practicable to the front and rear edges, that provide light to the side to indicate the overall length of the vehicle. Additional lamps may also be mounted at intermediate locations on the sides of the vehicle.

3.3 Combination Clearance and Side Marker Lamps—Single lamps which simultaneously fulfill the performance requirements of clearance and side marker lamps.

3.4 Identification Lamps—Lamps used in groups of three, in a horizontal row, that provide light to the front or rear or both, having lamp centers that are spaced not less than 150 mm nor more than 310 mm apart, mounted on the permanent structure as near as practicable to the vertical centerline and the top of the vehicle to identify vehicles 2032 mm or more in overall width.

4. Lighting Identification Code—Clearance, side marker, or identification lamps may be identified by the code "P2," and combination clearance and marker lamps may be identified with the code "PC," and in accordance with SAE J759.

5. Tests

5.1 SAE J575 is a part of this report. The following tests are applicable with the modifications as indicated.

5.1.1 VIBRATION TEST

5.1.2 MOISTURE TEST

5.1.3 DUST TEST

5.1.4 CORROSION TEST

5.1.5 PHOTOMETRY TEST

5.1.5.1 Photometric tests shall be made at a lamp distance of at least 3 m. The H-V axis of a clearance lamp shall be taken as parallel with the longitudinal axis of the vehicle. The H-V axis of a combination clearance and side marker lamp shall be taken as parallel with the longitudinal axis of the vehicle when measuring clearance lamp test points, and normal to this vehicle axis when measuring side marker test points. In all cases, the H-V axis shall be taken as parallel to the surface on which the vehicle stands.

5.1.6 WARPAGE TEST ON DEVICES WITH PLASTIC COMPONENTS

5.2 Color Test—SAE J578 is a part of this report.

6. Requirements

6.1 Performance Requirements—A device which, when tested in accordance with the test procedures specified in Section 5, shall meet the following requirements:

6.1.1 VIBRATION—SAE J575

6.1.2 MOISTURE—SAE J575

6.1.3 DUST—SAE J575

6.1.4 CORROSION—SAE J575

6.1.5 PHOTOMETRY—SAE J575

6.1.5.1 The lamp under test shall meet the photometric performance requirements contained in Table 1 and its footnotes. The summation of the luminous intensity measurements at the specified test points in a zone shall be at least the value shown.

TABLE 1—PHOTOMETRIC REQUIREMENTS

Zone	Test Points[1,2] (degrees)	Minimum Luminous Intensity (cd) See Notes[3,4] Red	Minimum Luminous Intensity (cd) See Notes[3,4] Yellow
1	45L-10U 45L-H 45L-10D V-10U	0.75	1.86
2	V-H V-10D	0.75	1.86
3	45R-10U 45R-H 45R-10D	0.75	1.86

[1] Maximum luminous intensities of red clearance and identification lamps shall not exceed 18 cd within the solid cone angle 45L to 45R and 10U to 10D. When red clearance lamps are optically combined with stop or turn signal lamps, the maximum applies only on or above horizontal. The maximum luminous intensity shall not be exceeded over any area larger than that generated by a 0.5 degree radius within the solid cone angle prescribed by the test points.

[2] The requirements for side markers used on vehicles less than 2032 mm wide need only be met for inboard test points at a distance of 4.6 m from the vehicle on a vertical plane that is perpendicular to the longitudinal axis of the vehicle and located midway between the front and rear side marker lamps.

[3] When calculating zone totals, the measured value at each test point shall not be less than 60% of the minimum values in Table 2.

[4] Combination clearance and side marker lamps shall conform with both clearance and side marker photometric performance requirements.

6.1.6 WARPAGE—SAE J575

6.1.7 COLOR—The color of light from front clearance lamps, front and intermediate side marker lamps, and front identification lamps shall be yellow.

The color of light from rear clearance, side marker, and identification lamps shall be red. Color shall be as specified in SAE J578.

6.2 Materials Requirements—Plastic materials used in optical parts shall meet the requirements of SAE J576.

6.3 Design Requirements

6.3.1 A clearance lamp and/or side marker lamp may be combined optically with a turn signal and/or a stop lamp. A clearance lamp may not be combined optically with a tail lamp or an identification lamp.

6.3.2 If a clearance lamp or a side marker lamp is optically combined with a turn signal lamp or a stop lamp and a two-light source (two filament) bulb is used, the bulb shall have an indexing base and the socket shall be designed so that bulbs with nonindexing bases cannot be inserted. In addition, removable sockets shall have an indexing feature so that they cannot be reinserted into lamp housings in random positions, unless the lamp will perform its intended function with random light source orientation.

(R) 6.4 Installation Requirements—Clearance, side marker, and identification lamps shall be designed to comply with all photometric requirements of Table 1 as installed on the vehicle, with all vehicular obstructions considered.

7. Guidelines

7.1 Photometric Design Guidelines—Photometric design guidelines for clearance, side marker, and identification lamps, when tested in accordance with 5.1.5 of this report, are contained in Table 2 and its footnotes.

TABLE 2—PHOTOMETRIC DESIGN GUIDELINES

	Test Points (degrees)	Minimum Luminous Intensity (cd) See Notes[2] Red[1]	Minimum Luminous Intensity (cd) See Notes[2] Yellow
10U	45L	0.25	0.62
	V	0.25	0.62
	45R	0.25	0.62
H	45L	0.25	0.62
	V	0.25	0.62
	45R	0.25	0.62
10D	45L	0.25	0.62
	V	0.25	0.62
	45R	0.25	0.62

[1] The maximum design value of a lamp intended for the rear of the vehicle should not exceed the listed design maximum over any area larger than that generated by 0.25 degree radius within the solid angle defined by the test points in Table 2.

[2] For combined clearance and side marker lamps, both the clearance and side marker photometric design values should apply.

7.2 Installation Guidelines—The following guidelines apply to clearance, side marker, and identification lamps as used on the vehicle and shall not be considered part of the requirements.

7.2.1 The luminous intensity of incandescent filament bulbs will vary with applied voltage. The electrical wiring in the vehicle should be adequate to supply design voltage to the lamp filament.

7.2.2 Performance of lamps can deteriorate significantly as a result of dirt, grime, and/or snow accumulation on their optical surfaces. Installation of lamps on vehicles should be considered to minimize the effect of these factors.

7.2.3 Where it is expected that lamps must perform in extremely severe environments, such as in off-highway, mining, fuel haulage, or where it is expected that they will be totally immersed in water, the user should specify lamps specifically designed for such use.

APPENDIX A

A.1 As a matter of additional information, attention is called to SAE J567 for requirements and gages used in socket design.

Report of the Lighting Committee approved August 1947 and completely revised June 1987. Rationale statement available. Completely revised by the SAE Signalling and Marking Devices Standards Committee and the Lighting Coordinating Committee February 1995 and October 1995. Rationale statement available.

1. Scope—This SAE Standard provides installation requirements, test procedures, design guidelines, and performance requirements for backup lamps.

2. References

2.1 Applicable Documents—The following publications form a part of this specification to the extent specified herein. The latest issue of SAE publications shall apply.

2.1.1 SAE PUBLICATIONS—Available from SAE, 400 Commonwealth Drive, Warrendale, PA 15096-0001.

SAE J567—Lamp Bulb Retention System

SAE J575—Test Methods and Equipment for Lighting Devices and Components for Use on Vehicles Less than 2032 mm in Overall Width

SAE J576—Plastic Materials for use in Optical Parts such as Lenses and Reflectors of Motor Vehicle Lighting Devices

SAE J578—Color Specification

SAE J759—Lighting Identification Code

SAE J1330—Photometry Laboratory Accuracy Guidelines

3. Definitions

3.1 Backup Lamp—A lighting device used to provide illumination behind the vehicle and to provide a warning signal to pedestrians and other drivers when the vehicle is backing up or is about to back up.

3.2 Point of Visibility—Any point on the lens surface which is within an area bounded by the intersection of the lens surface with a 25 mm diameter cylinder, the centerline of which passes through the light source center and is oriented horizontally and parallel with the longitudinal axis of the vehicle.

4. Lighting Identification Code—Backup Lamps may be identified by the code "R" in accordance with SAE J759.

5. Tests

5.1 SAE J575 is a part of this report. The following tests are applicable with modifications as indicated:

5.1.1 VIBRATION TEST

5.1.2 MOISTURE TEST

5.1.3 DUST TEST

5.1.4 CORROSION TEST

5.1.5 PHOTOMETRIC TEST

5.1.5.1 Photometric tests shall be made with the photometer at a distance of at least 3 m from the lamp. The H-V Axis shall be taken as the horizontal line through the light source and parallel with the longitudinal axis of the vehicle.

5.1.5.2 Photometric measurements shall be made with the bulb filament steadily burning.

5.1.6 WARPAGE TEST ON DEVICES WITH PLASTIC COMPONENTS

5.2 Color Test—SAE J578 is part of this report.

5.3 Materials Test—SAE J576 is part of this report.

6. Requirements

6.1 Performance Requirements—A device when tested in accordance with the test procedures specified in Section 5 shall meet the following requirements:

6.1.1 VIBRATION—SAE J575

6.1.2 MOISTURE—SAE J575

6.1.3 DUST—SAE J575

6.1.4 CORROSION—SAE J575

6.1.5 PHOTOMETRY—SAE J575

6.1.5.1 A single lamp, when used in a two-lamp system, shall meet the photometric performance requirements contained in Table 1 and its footnotes. The summation of luminous intensity measurements at the specified test points in a zone shall be at least the value shown. When two lamps of the same or symmetrically opposite design are used, the photometric readings along the vertical axis and the averages of the readings for the same angles left and right of vertical for one lamp may be used to determine compliance with the requirements of Table 1. If two lamps of differing designs are used, they shall be tested individually, and the photometric values added to determine that the combined units meet twice the candela requirements of Table 1.

6.1.5.2 When only one backup lamp is used on the vehicle, it shall meet twice the photometric requirements of Table 1.

TABLE 1—PHOTOMETRIC PERFORMANCE REQUIREMENTS[1,2]

Zone	Minimum Luminous Intensity Test Points (deg)	Minimum Luminous Intensity Zone (cd)
1	45L-5U 45L-H 45L-5D	45
2	30L-H 30L-5D	50
3	10L-10U 10L-5U V-10U V-5U 10R-10U 10R-5U	100
4	10L-H 10L-5D V-H V-5D 10R-H 10R-5D	360
5	30R-H 30R-5D	50
6	45R-5U 45R-H 45R-5D	45

[1] The measured value for any test point in a given zone, shall not be less than 60% of the minimum value for that test point specified in Table 2.

[2] Maximum candela per lamp at H and above shall be 300 for a two lamp system and 500 for a single lamp system.

TABLE 2—PHOTOMETRIC DESIGN GUIDELINES
(MINIMUM LUMINOUS INTENSITY (CD))

Test Points (degrees)	45L	30L	10L	V	10R	30R	45R
10U	—	—	10	15	10	—	—
5U	15	—	20	25	20	—	15
H	15	25	50	80	50	25	15
5D	15	25	50	80	50	25	15

NOTE—Maximum candela per lamp at H and above shall be 300 for a two lamp system and 500 for a single lamp system.

6.1.5.3 If a backup lamp has portions of its lens which project nonwhite light, that light shall be excluded from measurements made to determine compliance with 6.1.5.1 and 6.1.5.2. The lamp or lamps shall meet the photometric requirements of this document with white light alone.

6.1.6 WARPAGE—SAE J575

6.1.7 COLOR—The color of the light from a backup lamp shall be white, as specified in SAE J578. A backup lamp may project incidental red, yellow, or white light through the reflectors or lenses that are adjacent to, close to, or part of the lamp assembly. If a lamp has portions of its lens which project nonwhite light, that light shall be regarded as incidental if, when only the nonwhite light is measured at each test point specified in Table 1, the sum of such measurements does not exceed 20% of the sum of the test point measurements of the total light output (white plus nonwhite).

6.2 Material Requirements—Plastic materials used in optical parts shall meet the requirements of SAE J576.

6.3 Installation Requirements

6.3.1 Backup lamps shall be mounted so that the point of visibility of at least one of the lamps is visible from any eye point that is (a) 0.6 to 1.8 m above the horizontal plane on which the vehicle is standing and (b) rearward of a vertical plane perpendicular to the longitudinal axis of the vehicle, 0.9 m to the rear of the vehicle and extending 0.9 m beyond each side of the vehicle.

6.3.2 Visibility and photometric performance of the backup lamp within the test angles shown in Tables 1 and 2 shall not be obstructed by any portion of the vehicle unless the lamp is designed to comply with all requirements when the obstruction is considered.

6.3.3 The backup lamp shall be lighted only when the ignition switch is energized and reverse gear is engaged.

7. Guidelines

7.1 Photometric design guidelines for backup lamps, when tested in accordance with 5.1.5 of this document, are contained in Table 2 and its footnote. When two asymmetrical lamps of the same or symmetrically opposite design are used, the photometric readings along the vertical axis and the averages of the readings for the same angles left and right of vertical for one lamp may be used to determine compliance with the requirements of Table 2. If two lamps of differing designs are used, they shall be tested individually, and the photometric values added to determine that the combined units meet twice the candlepower requirements of Table 2.

7.2 **Installation Guidelines**—The following guidelines apply to the backup lamps as used on the vehicle and shall not be considered to be part of the requirements.

7.2.1 The luminous intensity of incandescent filament bulbs will vary with applied voltage. The electrical wiring in the vehicle should be adequate to supply design voltage to the lamp filament.

7.2.2 Performance of lamps may deteriorate significantly as a result of dirt, grime and/or snow accumulation on their optical surfaces. Installation of lamps on vehicles should be considered to minimize the effect of these factors.

7.2.3 Where it is expected that lamps must perform in extremely severe environments, such as off-highway, mining or fuel haulage, or where it is expected that they will be totally immersed in water, the user should specify lamps specifically designed for such use.

7.3 For requirements and gauges to be used in socket designs, refer to SAE J567.

7.4 For additional information on photometric test accuracy guidelines, refer to SAE J1330.

APPENDIX A

As a matter of information, attention is called to SAE J567, for requirements and gauges to be used in socket design.

SAE Standard

Report of the Lighting Division approved January 1951. Completely revised by the Lighting Committee May 1989. Rationale statement available. Completely revised by the Geometric Visibility Task Force of the SAE Signaling and Marking Devices Standards Committee and the SAE Lighting Coordinating Committee December 1994, and revised July 1995. Rationale statements available.

1. Scope—This SAE Standard provides test procedures, requirements, and guidelines for reflex reflectors.

2. References

2.1 Applicable Documents—The following publications form a part of this specification to the extent specified herein. Unless otherwise specified, the latest issue of SAE publications shall apply.

2.1.1 SAE PUBLICATIONS—Available from SAE, 400 Commonwealth Drive, Warrendale, PA 15096-0001.

SAE J575—Tests for Motor Vehicle Lighting Devices and Components

SAE J576—Plastic Materials for Use in Optical Parts Such as Lenses and Reflectors of Motor Vehicle Lighting Devices

SAE J578—Color Specifications

SAE J759—Lighting Identification Code

2.2 Related Publications—The following publications are provided for information purposes only and are not a required part of this document.

2.2.1 SAE PUBLICATIONS—Available from SAE, 400 Commonwealth Drive, Warrendale, PA 15096-001.

SAE J585—Tail Lamps (Rear Position Lamps) for Use on Motor Vehicles Less Than 2032 mm in Overall Width

SAE J586 FEB84—Stop Lamps for Use on Motor Vehicles Less Than 2032 mm in Overall WIdth

SAE J588 NOV84—Turn Signal Lamps for Use on Motor Vehicles Less Than 2032 mm In Overall Width

SAE J592—Clearance, Side Marker, and Identification Lamps

SAE J1395 APR85—Front and Rear Turn Signal Lamps for Use on Motor Vheicles 2032 mm or More in Overall Width

SAE J1398 MAY85—Stop Lamps for Use on Motor Vehicles 2032 mm or More in Overall Width

SAE J2040—Tail Lamps (Rear Position Lamps) for Use on Vehicles 2032 mm or More in Overall Width

SAE J2041—Reflex Reflectors for Use on Vehicles 2032 mm or More in Overall Width

SAE J2042—Clearance, Sidemarker, and Identification Lamps for Use on Motor Vehicles 2032 mm or More in Overall Width

2.2.2 FEDERAL SPECIFICATIONS—Available from the Superintendent of Documents, U.S. Government Printing Office, Washington, DC 20402.

FMVSS 108 56FR 64733 - 64737—Turn Signal Geometric Visibility Requirements

3. Definitions

3.1 Reflex Reflectors are devices that are used on vehicles to give an indication of presence to an approaching driver by reflected light from the headlamps on the approaching vehicle.

3.2 The Observation Angle is the angle between a line from the observation point to the center of the reflector and a second line from the center of the reflector to the source of illumination.

3.3 The Entrance Angle is the angle between the axis of the reflex reflector and a line from the center of the reflector to the source of illumination.

4. Identification Code—Reflex reflectors may be identified by the Code "A" in accordance with SAE J759.

5. Tests

5.1 SAE J575 is a part of this report. The following tests are applicable with the modifications as indicated.

5.1.1 VIBRATION TEST

5.1.2 MOISTURE

5.1.3 DUST TEST

5.1.4 CORROSION TEST

5.1.5 PHOTOMETRY—In addition to the test procedures in SAE J575, the following apply:

5.1.5.1 Test Setup—Photometric measurement shall be made at a test distance of at least 30 m with the reflex reflector setup for testing as shown in Figure 1. The reflex reflector shall be mounted in a goniometer with the center of the reflex area at the center of rotation and at the same horizontal level as the source of illumination.

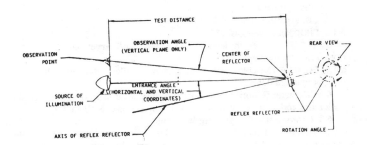

FIGURE 1—SETUP FOR TESTING

5.1.5.2 Light Source and Sensor—The source of illumination shall be a projector with a 50 mm ± 5 mm effective diameter and a lamp filament operating at 2856 K (nominal) color temperature. In making photoelectric measurements, the opening to the photo cell shall not be more than 13 mm vertical by 25 mm horizontal with the observation point above (geometrically) the source of illumination.

5.1.5.3 Measurements—Reflex reflectors shall be photometered at the observation and entrance angles shown in Table 1. The entrance angle shall be designated left, right, up, and down in accordance with the position of the source of illumination with respect to the axis of the reflex reflector as viewed from behind the reflector. The H-V axis of reflex reflectors shall be taken parallel to the longitudinal axis of the vehicle for rear reflectors and perpendicular to a vertical plane parallel to the longitudinal axis of the vehicle for side reflectors.

Photometric measurements shall be made photoelectrically. The recorded value for each test point shall be the quotient of luminous intensity of the reflected light expressed as millicandela (candela[1]) divided by the illumination on the reflector measured in lux (foot candle). Also, the illumination on the reflex reflector from the source of illumination shall be measured in lux (foot candle). Reflex reflectors may have any linear or area dimension; but, for the photometric test, a maximum projected area of 7740 mm² contained within a 254 mm diameter circle shall be exposed.

5.1.5.4 Rotational Position—Reflex reflectors that do not have a fixed rotational position with respect to the vehicle shall be rotated 360 degrees about their axis to find the minimum millicandela per incident lux (candela per incident foot candle), which shall be reported for each test point. If the output falls below the minimum requirement at any test point, the reflector shall be rotated ±5 degrees about its axis from the angle where the minimum output occurred; and the maximum millicandela per lux (candela per foot candle) within the angular range reported as a tolerance value.

Reflex reflectors that, by their design or construction, permit mounting on the vehicle in fixed rotational position shall be tested in this position. A visual locator, such as the word TOP, shall not be considered adequate to establish a fixed rotational position on the vehicle.

5.1.5.5 Uncolored Reflections—If uncolored reflections from the front surface interfere with photometric readings at any test point, the operator shall check 1 degree above, below, right, and left of the test point, and report the lowest reading and location. The latter must meet the minimum requirement for the test point.

(R) **5.2 Color Test**—SAE J578 is a part of this report. Additionally, the test sample may be either the reflex reflector or a disc of the same material, technique of fabrication, and dye formulation as the reflex reflector. If a disc is used for color determination by the transmission technique, the thickness should be twice the thickness of the reflector as measured from the face of the lens to the apexes of the reflecting elements. For either sample, a Source "A" illumination shall be used for color measurement.

---

[1] "Candela" is used rather than "candlepower" as the preferred term in either metric or English units.

6. Requirements

6.1 Performance Requirements—A reflex reflector, when tested in accordance with the test procedures specified in Section 5, shall meet the following requirements:

6.1.1 VIBRATION—SAE J575

6.1.2 MOISTURE—SAE J575, except that in the case of sealed units the alternate water submersion test (5.2.4) is required.

6.1.3 DUST—SAE J575

6.1.4 CORROSION—SAE J575

6.1.5 PHOTOMETRY—SAE J575

6.1.5.1 The reflex reflectors under test shall meet the photometric performance requirement contained in Table 1 or Table 1A.

6.1.6 COLOR—The color of the light from a reflex reflector shall be red, yellow, or white as defined in SAE J578.

6.2 Material Requirements—Plastic materials used in the optical portion of each reflex reflector unit shall meet the requirements of SAE J576.

6.3 Photometric Design Requirements

6.3.1 If a reflex reflector is optically combined with signaling or marking bulb type devices, it shall be photometered independently by masking from the other functions and shall meet the performance values contained in Table 1 or 1A.

6.4 Installation Requirements—Reflex reflectors shall be designed to comply with all photometric requirements of Table 1 as installed on the vehicle, with all vehicular obstructions considered.

7. Guidelines

7.1 Photometric Design Guidelines—Reflex reflectors, when tested in accordance with 5.1.5, should be designed at least equal to the values contained in Table 1 or 1A.

7.2 Installation Guidelines—The following guidelines apply to reflex reflectors as used on the vehicle and shall not be considered a part of this report:

7.2.1 Reflex reflectors when used on the exterior of vehicles should be mounted to minimize the accumulation of dirt, grime, and/or snow so that adequate illumination is maintained from the low beam headlamps of approaching vehicles.

7.2.2 If reflex reflectors must perform in severe environments, such as periodic total immersion in water, the user should specify reflex reflector designs suitable for such use.

TABLE 1—MINIMUM MILLICANDELAS PER INCIDENT LUX FOR A RED REFLEX REFLECTOR[1]

Observation Angle (deg)	Entrance Angle (deg) 0 deg	Entrance Angle (deg) 10 deg Up	Entrance Angle (deg) 10 deg Down	Entrance Angle (deg) 20 deg Left	Entrance Angle (deg) 20 deg Right
0.2	420	280	280	140	140
1.5	6	5	5	3	3

[1] Yellow values shall be 2.5 times indicated red values and white values shall be 4 times indicated red values.

TABLE 1A—MINIMUM CANDLEPOWER PER INCIDENT FOOTCANDLE FOR A RED REFLEX REFLECTOR[1]

Observation Angle (deg)	Entrance Angle (deg) 0 deg	Entrance Angle (deg) 10 deg Up	Entrance Angle (deg) 10 deg Down	Entrance Angle (deg) 20 deg Left	Entrance Angle (deg) 20 deg Right
0.2	4.5	3.0	3.0	1.5	1.5
1.5	0.07	0.05	0.05	0.03	0.03

[1] Yellow values shall be 2.5 times indicated red values and white values shall be 4 times indicated red values.

(R) SIDE TURN SIGNAL LAMPS FOR VEHICLES LESS THAN 12 m IN LENGTH—SAE J914 JAN95

SAE Standard

Report of the Lighting Committee approved February 1965 and completely revised November 1987. Rationale statement available. Completely revised by the Lighting Coordinating Committee and the SAE Signaling and Marking Devices Standards Committee, January 1995. Rationale statement available.

1. Scope—This SAE Standard provides installation requirements, test procedures, design guidelines, and performance requirements for side turn signal lamps for vehicles less than 12 m in length.

2. References

2.1 Applicable Documents—The following publications form a part of this specification to the extent specified herein. The latest issue of SAE publications shall apply.

2.1.1 SAE PUBLICATIONS—Available from SAE, 400 Commonwealth Drive, Warrendale, PA 15096-0001.

SAE J567—Lamp Bulb Retention System

SAE J575—Test Methods and Equipment for Lighting Devices and Components for Use on Vehicles Less Than 2032 mm in Overall Width

SAE J576—Plastic Materials for Use in Optical Parts Such as Lenses and Reflectors of Motor Vehicle Lighting Devices

SAE J578—Color Specification

SAE J588—Turn Signal Lamps for Use on Motor Vehicles Less Than 2032 mm in Overall Width

SAE J759—Lighting Identification Code

2.2 Related Publication—The following publication is provided for information purposes only and is not a required part of this specification.

2.2.1 SAE PUBLICATION—Available from SAE, 400 Commonwealth Drive, Warrendale, PA 15096-0001.

SAE J2039—Side Turn Signal Lamps for Large Vehicles

3. Definition

3.1 Side Turn Signal Lamp—A lighting device normally mounted on the side of a vehicle at or near the front, and used as part of the turn signal system to indicate a change in direction by means of a flashing warning signal on the side toward which the vehicle operator intends to turn or maneuver.

NOTE—Side turn signals, when used, are supplemental to, and should not be confused with turn signals described in SAE J588, which, in some cases, may be mounted on the side of the vehicle.

4. Lighting Identification Code—Side Turn Signal Lamps for use on vehicles less than 12 m in length may be identified by the code "E2" in accordance with SAE J759.

5. Tests

5.1 SAE J575 is a part of this document. The following tests are applicable with modifications as indicated:

5.1.1 VIBRATION TEST

5.1.2 MOISTURE TEST

5.1.3 DUST TEST

5.1.4 CORROSION TEST

5.1.5 PHOTOMETRIC TEST

5.1.5.1 Photometric tests shall be made with the photometer at a distance of at least 3 m from the lamp. The H-V axis shall be taken as the horizontal line through the light source and normal to the longitudinal axis of the vehicle.

5.1.5.2 Photometric measurements shall be made with the bulb filament steadily burning.

5.1.6 WARPAGE TEST ON DEVICES WITH PLASTIC COMPONENTS

5.2 Color Test—SAE J578 is part of this document.

6. Requirements

6.1 Performance Requirements—A device when tested in accordance with the test procedures specified in Section 5 shall meet the following requirements:

6.1.1 VIBRATION—SAE J575

6.1.2 MOISTURE—SAE J575

6.1.3 DUST—SAE J575

6.1.4 CORROSION—SAE J575

6.1.5 PHOTOMETRY—SAE J575

6.1.5.1 The lamp under test shall meet the photometric performance requirements contained in Table 1 and its footnotes. The summation of luminous intensity measurements at the specified test points in a zone shall be at least the value shown.

6.1.6 WARPAGE—SAE J575

6.1.7 COLOR—The color of the light from a side turn signal lamp shall be yellow, as specified in SAE J578.

TABLE 1—PHOTOMETRIC PERFORMANCE REQUIREMENTS[1,2,3]

Position (Degrees)	Minimum Zone Total (Candela)
15U-30L	2.4
5U-30L	
H-30L	
5D-30L	
15U-70L	2.4
5U-70L	
H-70L	
5D-70L	

[1] Angles shown are for lamps mounted on left-hand side of vehicle. For lamps mounted on right-hand side, substitute right-hand angles.
[2] The measured value for any test point shall not be less than 60% of the minimum value for that test point specified in Table 2.
[3] Maximum candela at any test point: 200.

6.2 Material Requirements—Plastic materials used in optical parts shall meet the requirements of SAE J576.

6.3 Installation Requirements

6.3.1 Visibility and photometric performance of the side turn signal lamp within the test angles shown in Tables 1 and 2 shall not be obstructed by any portion of the vehicle unless the lamp is designed to comply with all requirements when the obstruction is considered.

6.3.2 Side turn signal lamps shall flash simultaneously or alternately with the required front turn signal lamps.

6.3.3 Side turn signal lamps shall be mounted on vehicles with a length of less than 12 m at a height of no more than 1220 mm and no less than 500 mm.

TABLE 2—PHOTOMETRIC DESIGN GUIDELINES[1,2]

Position (Degrees)	Minimum (Candela)
15U-30L	0.6
15U-70L	0.6
5U-30L	0.6
5U-70L	0.6
H-30L	0.6
H-70L	0.6
5D-30L	0.6
5D-70L	0.6

[1] Angles shown are for lamps mounted on left-hand side of vehicle. For lamps mounted on right-hand side, substitute right-hand angles.
[2] Maximum candela at any test point: 200.

7. Guidelines

7.1 Photometric design guidelines for side turn signal lamps, when tested in accordance with 5.1.5 of this document are contained in Table 2 and its footnotes.

7.2 Installation Guidelines—The following guidelines apply to the side turn signal lamps as used on the vehicle and shall not be considered to be part of the requirements.

7.2.1 Side turn signal lamps should be located as close to the front of the vehicle as practicable.

7.2.2 The electrical wiring in the vehicle should be adequate to supply design voltage to the lamp filament.

7.2.3 Installation of lamps on vehicles should be such that the effect of dirt, grime, and/or snow accumulation on optical surfaces is minimized.

7.2.4 Where it is expected that lamps must perform in extremely severe environments, such as off-highway, mining or fuel haulage, or where it is expected that they will be totally immersed in water, the user should specify lamps specifically designed for such use.

APPENDIX A

As a matter of information, attention is called to SAE J567 for requirements and gauges to be used in socket design.

FOG TAIL LAMP (Rear Fog Light)
SYSTEMS—SAE J1319 JUN93   **SAE Recommended Practice**

Report of the Lighting Committee approved August 1987. Rationale statement available. Revised by the Signalling and Marking Devices Standards Committee June 1993. Rationale statement available.

1. Scope—This SAE Recommended Practice provides test procedures, requirements, and guidelines for fog tail lamp systems. See Appendices A and B.

(R) *2. References*

(R) **2.1 Applicable Documents**—The following publications form a part of this specification to the extent specified herein. The latest issue of SAE publications shall apply.

(R) 2.1.1 SAE PUBLICATIONS—Available from SAE, 400 Commonwealth Drive, Warrendale, PA 15096-0001.

SAE J567—Lamp Bulb Retention System

SAE J575—Test Methods and Equipment for Lighting Devices and Components for Use on Vehicles Less Than 2032 mm in Overall Width

SAE J576—Plastic Materials for Use in Optical Parts Such as Lenses and Reflectors of Motor Vehicle Lighting Devices

SAE J578—Color Specification

SAE J585—Tail Lamps (Rear Position Lamps) for Use on Motor Vehicles Less Than 2032 mm in Overall Width

SAE J759—Lighting Identification Code

2.2 Definitions

(R) 2.2.1 FOG TAIL LAMP—A lighting device providing a continuous red light of higher intensity than a tail lamp (SAE J585) for the purpose of marking the rear of a vehicle during fog or similar conditions of reduced visibility.

2.2.2 FOG TAIL LAMP SYSTEM—One or two fog tail lamps with their **(R)** respective wiring, connectors, switch, and a function indicator.

3. Lighting Identification Code—Fog tail lamps may be identified by the code F2 in accordance with SAE J759.

4. Tests

4.1 SAE J575 is a part of this report. The following tests are applicable:

4.1.1 VIBRATION TEST

4.1.2 MOISTURE TEST

4.1.3 DUST TEST

4.1.4 CORROSION TEST

4.1.5 PHOTOMETRY TEST

(R) *4.1.5.1* Photometric measurements shall be made with light source of the lamp at least 3 m from the photometer. The H-V axis shall be taken as parallel to the axis of reference of the lamp as mounted on the vehicle.

4.1.6 WARPAGE TEST FOR DEVICES WITH PLASTIC COMPONENTS

4.2 Color Test—SAE J578 is a part of this report.

5. Requirements

5.1 Performance Requirements—A device, when tested in accordance with the test procedures specified in Section 4, shall meet the following requirements with the modifications indicated:

5.1.1 VIBRATION—SAE J575

5.1.2 MOISTURE—SAE J575

5.1.3 DUST—SAE J575

5.1.4 CORROSION—SAE J575

5.1.5 PHOTOMETRY—SAE J575

5.1.5.1 The lamp shall meet the photometric performance requirements contained in Table 1 and its footnotes. The summation of the luminous intensities at the test points specified for each zone in column 2 of Table 1 shall be at least the value shown for that zone in column 3.

TABLE 1—PHOTOMETRIC REQUIREMENTS

Zone	Test Points[1] (deg)	Minimum Luminous Intensity (candela)
1	10U-5L 5U-20L 5D-20L 10D-5L	50
2	5U-10L H-10L 5D-10L	100
3	5U-V H-5L H-V H-5R 5D-V	380
4	5U-10R H-10R 5D-10R	100
5	10U-5R 5U-20R 5D-20R 10D-5R	50
Maximum Luminous Intensity (candela[2])		300

[1] The measured values of each test point shall not be less than 60% of the minimum value in Table 2.

(R) [2] The listed maximum at any test point shall not be exceeded over any area larger than that generated by a 0.5 degree radius with the solid angle defined by the test points in Table 1.

5.1.6 WARPAGE—SAE J575

5.1.7 COLOR—The color of light from a fog tail lamp shall be red as specified in SAE J578.

5.2 Materials Requirements—Plastic materials used in the optical parts shall meet the requirements of SAE J576.

5.3 Design Requirements

5.3.1 A fog tail lamp shall not be optically combined with any lamp other than a tail lamp. If a fog tail lamp is optically combined with the tail lamp and a two-filament bulb is used, the bulb shall have an indexing base and the socket shall be designed so that bulbs with nonindexing bases cannot be used.

(R) **6. Guidelines**—The following guidelines are intended to provide optimal performance of the system and uniformity in use but shall not be considered part of the requirements.

6.1 Photometric design guidelines for a fog tail lamp, when tested in accordance with 4.1.5 of this document, are contained in Table 2.

6.2 Installation Guidelines—The user is cautioned that the mounting and use of fog tail lamps are specified by various regulatory agencies.

6.2.1 The illuminated edge of a fog tail lamp lens should be no closer than 100 mm from the illuminated edge of any stop lamp lens when projected on a vertical transverse plane.

6.2.2 The fog tail lamp system should consist of either: (a) one lamp mounted on or to the left of a vertical plane through the longitudinal centerline of the vehicle, or (b) two lamps symmetrically located about the vehicle centerline.

6.2.3 The fog tail lamp system should be wired so that it can be turned on only when the headlamps and/or front fog lamps are on, and should have a switch that allows the fog tail lamp to be turned off when headlamps are on.

6.2.4 Visibility of the fog tail lamp should not be obstructed by any part of the vehicle throughout the photometric test angles for the lamp unless the lamp is designed to comply with all photometric and visibility requirements with these obstructions considered. The signal from the lamp should be visible through a horizontal angle from 45 degrees to the left to 45 degrees to the right.

(R) **6.2.5** The fog tail lamp system should include a continuous yellow indicator that illuminates when the system is switched on that should be mounted in a location readily visible to the driver of the vehicle.

TABLE 2—PHOTOMETRIC DESIGN GUIDELINES

	Test Points (deg)	Minimum Luminous Intensity (candela)
10U, 10D	10L, 10R 5L, 5R V	10 16 25
5U, 5D	20L, 20R 10L, 10R 5L, 5R V	10 30 50 70
H	20L, 20R 10L, 10R 5L, 5R V	15 40 80 80
Maximum Luminous Intensity (candela)		300

APPENDIX A

As a matter of additional information, attention is called to SAE J567c for requirements and gages used in socket design.

(R) APPENDIX B

A fog tail lamp is a lighting device, required within the European Economic Community (EEC), which provides a steady burning marker on the rear of vehicles during conditions of reduced visibility. As a consequence of this regulation, many vehicle manufacturers already have vehicle designs which can accommodate fog tail lamps, but do not provide a completely operable system because of the absence of an SAE Standard; this Recommended Practice could be adopted by U.S. governmental agencies thereby permitting such a device through uniform, harmonized regulations.

The SAE Recommended Practice was developed to harmonize the existing EEC requirements and State of California Administrative Code, Title 13; it is believed that devices designed to comply with this SAE Recommended Practice will satisfy both the current California and the EEC requirements.

The EEC regulation was used as the basis for this document but differs from those European requirements in several areas:

a. Photometric test point location requirements and environmental test procedures were adopted from the SAE practice for stop lamps. Photometric design guidelines were adopted from the State of California requirements.

b. Minimum design candela requirements correspond to those for an SAE stop lamp and the California specifications. (Maximum permissible candela values, however, are the same as the EEC and California standards.)

c. The EEC mounting height requirements were not incorporated into this standard as this traditionally has been left to the discretion of government regulatory agencies. No other SAE Standard contains mounting height requirements.

d. Lateral visibility requirements were taken from the SAE stop lamp requirements which are more stringent than the EEC requirements (45 degrees versus 25 degrees).

e. The service performance requirements are identical to those for SAE stop lamps.

f. This SAE Recommended Practice specifies the installation of one fog tail lamp on the vehicle centerline or to the left of this position or two lamps displayed symmetrically about the centerline. The EEC requirements also specify that not more than two lamps may be installed.

g. Wiring of this lamp type is proposed so as to permit operation only with the headlamps to ensure compatibility with existing state governmental regulations for front fog lamps. Selectivity with beam switching was not included in order to correspond with the EEC requirements.

147

(R) REAR CORNERING LAMPS FOR USE ON MOTOR VEHICLES LESS THAN 9.1 m IN OVERALL LENGTH—SAE J1373 APR96

SAE Recommended Practice

Report of the Lighting Committee approved June 1982, and completely revised October 1987. Rationale statement available. Completely revised by the SAE Signaling and Marking Devices Standards Committee April 1996. Rationale statement available.

1. Scope—This SAE Recommended Practice provides test procedures, requirements, and guidelines for rear cornering lamps for use on vehicles less than 9.1 m in overall length.

2. References

2.1 Applicable Documents—The following publications form a part of this specification to the extent specified herein. Unless otherwise specified, the latest issue of SAE publications shall apply.

2.1.1 SAE PUBLICATIONS—Available from SAE, 400 Commonwealth Drive, Warrendale, PA 15096-0001.

SAE J567—Lamp Bulb Retention System

SAE J575—Test Methods and Equipment for Lighting Devices and Components for Use on Vehicles Less Than 2032 mm in Overall Width

SAE J576—Plastic Materials for Use in Optical Parts Such as Lenses and Reflex Reflectors of Motor Vehicle Lighting Devices

SAE J578—Color Specification

SAE J759—Lighting Identification Code

3. Definitions

3.1 Rear Cornering Lamps—Supplemental lamps used to provide illumination to an area to the side and rearward of the vehicle when it is backing up.

3.2 Incidental Light—Light emitted from a lamp that is projected from other than the intended light emitting surface. Incidental light is typically a color other than that of the intended lighting function.

4. Lighting Identification Code—Rear cornering lamps may be identified by the code K2 in accordance with SAE J759.

5. Tests

5.1 SAE J575 is a part of this document. The following tests are applicable with the modifications as indicated:

5.1.1 VIBRATION TEST

5.1.2 MOISTURE TEST

5.1.3 DUST EXPOSURE TEST

5.1.4 CORROSION TEST

5.1.5 PHOTOMETRY TEST—In addition to the test procedure in SAE J575, the following shall apply:

5.1.5.1 Photometric measurements shall be made with the light source of the lamp at least 3 m from the photometer. The H-V axis shall be taken as the horizontal line through the light source and perpendicular to the longitudinal axis of the vehicle.

5.1.6 WARPAGE TEST ON DEVICES WITH PLASTIC COMPONENTS

5.2 Color Test—SAE J578 is part of this document.

5.3 Plastic Optical Materials Test—SAE J576 is part of this document.

6. Requirements

6.1 A device, when tested in accordance with the test procedures specified in Section 5, shall meet the following requirements:

6.1.1 VIBRATION—Per SAE J575

6.1.2 MOISTURE—Per SAE J575

6.1.3 DUST EXPOSURE—Per SAE J575

6.1.4 CORROSION—Per SAE J575

6.1.5 PHOTOMETRY—Per SAE J575

6.1.5.1 The lamp under test shall meet the performance requirements contained in Table 1. Test points shown are for a lamp mounted on the left side of the vehicle. Right-hand angles should be substituted for left-hand angles for a lamp mounted on the right side of the vehicle.

6.1.5.2 If the lamp has portions of its lens which project nonwhite light, that light shall be excluded from measurements made to determine compliance with 6.1.5.1. The lamp shall meet the photometric requirements of this document with white light alone.

6.1.6 WARPAGE—Per SAE J575 (for devices with plastic components).

TABLE 1—PHOTOMETRIC REQUIREMENTS

Test Position Degrees	Luminous Intensity Candela (cd)
2-1/2 D - 30 L	30 min
2-1/2 D - 45 L	60 min
2-1/2 D - 60 L	30 min
Horizontal and Above	600 max

6.2 Color—The color of the light from a rear cornering lamp shall be white as specified in SAE J578. The lamp may project incidental red, yellow, or white light through reflectors or lenses that are adjacent, close to, or a part of the lamp assembly. If a lamp has portions of its lens which project nonwhite light, that light shall be regarded as incidental if, when only the nonwhite light is measured at each test point specified in Table 1, the sum of such measurements does not exceed 20% of the sum of the test point measurements of the total light output (white plus nonwhite).

6.3 Material Requirements—Plastic materials used in optical parts shall meet the requirements of SAE J576.

7. Guidelines

7.1 Photometric Design Guidelines—The photometric design guidelines for rear cornering lamps, when tested in accordance with 5.1.5 of this document are contained in Table 2. Test points shown are for a lamp mounted on the left side of the vehicle. Right-hand angles should be substituted for left-hand angles for a lamp mounted on the right side of the vehicle.

TABLE 2—PHOTOMETRIC DESIGN GUIDELINES

Test Position Degrees	Luminous Intensity Candela (cd)
2-1/2 D - 30 L	40 min
2-1/2 D - 45 L	80 min
2-1/2 D - 60 L	40 min
Horizontal and Above	500 max

7.2 Installation Guidelines—The following guidelines apply to rear cornering lamps as used on the vehicle and shall not be considered part of the requirements:

7.2.1 Rear cornering lamps should be mounted on each side, near or at the rear of the vehicle. These lamps may be combined with other lamps on the vehicle provided each function of the combined lamp meets its respective requirements.

7.2.2 Performance of the lamps may deteriorate significantly as a result of dirt, grime, and/or snow accumulation on their optical surfaces. Installation of lamps on vehicles should be considered to minimize the effects of these factors.

7.2.3 Where it is expected that lamps must perform in extremely severe environments, such as in off-highway, mining, fuel haulage, or where it is expected that they will be totally immersed in water, the user should specify lamps specifically designed for such use.

7.3 Mechanization Guidelines—The following guidelines apply to rear cornering lamps as used on the vehicle and shall not be considered part of the requirements:

7.3.1 The rear-cornering lamp should be illuminated only when the ignition switch is energized and reverse gear is engaged.

7.3.2 The luminous intensity of the light source will vary with applied voltage. The electrical wiring in the vehicle should be adequate to supply design voltage to the lamp filament.

7.4 For requirements and gages to be used in socket designs, refer to SAE J567.

CARGO LAMPS FOR USE ON VEHICLES
UNDER 12 000 LB GVWR—SAE J1424 JUN93   SAE Recommended Practice

Report of the Signalling and Marking Devices Standards Committee and The Sae Lighting Coordinating Committee approved August 1991 and revised June 1993. Rationale statements available.

1. Scope—This SAE Recommended Practice provides test procedures, performance requirements, design guidelines, and installation requirements for cargo lamps that are mounted on the exterior of vehicles weighing under 12 000 lb GVWR (Gross Vehicle Weight Rating).

2. References

2.1 Applicable Documents—The following publications form a part of this specification to the extent specified herein. The latest issue of SAE publications shall apply.

2.1.1 SAE PUBLICATIONS—Available from SAE, 400 Commonwealth Drive, Warrendale, PA 15096-0001.

SAE J567—Lamp Bulb Retention System

SAE J575—Tests for Motor Vehicle Lighting Devices and Components

SAE J576—Plastic Material for Use in Optical Parts Such as Lenses and Reflectors of Motor Vehicle Lighting Devices

SAE J578—Color Specification

SAE J759—Lighting Identification Code

2.2 Definition

2.2.1 A CARGO LAMP(S) is a supplemental lamp mounted on the exterior of a vehicle weighing under 12 000 lb GVWR for the purpose of providing illumination to load and unload cargo in an environment of otherwise insufficient light.

3. Lighting Identification Code—A cargo lamp for use on vehicles weighing less than 12 000 lb GVWR may be identified with the code "G" in accordance with SAE J759.

4. Tests

4.1 SAE J575 is a part of this report. The following tests are applicable with the modifications as indicated:

4.1.1 VIBRATION TEST

4.1.2 MOISTURE TEST

4.1.3 DUST TEST

4.1.4 CORROSION TEST

4.1.5 PHOTOMETRY TEST—In addition to the test procedures in SAE J575, the following apply:

4.1.5.1 Photometric measurements shall be made with the light source of the lamp at a distance of at least 3 m from the photometer.

4.1.6 WARPAGE TEST ON DEVICES WITH PLASTIC COMPONENTS—The device shall be operated with the bulb burning steadily during the test period.

4.2 Color Test—SAE J578 is a part of this report.

5. Requirements

5.1 Performance Requirements—A device when tested in accordance with the test procedures specified in Section 4 shall meet the following requirements:

5.1.1 VIBRATION—SAE J575

5.1.2 MOISTURE—SAE J575

5.1.3 DUST—SAE J575

5.1.4 CORROSION—SAE J575

5.1.5 PHOTOMETRY—SAE J575

5.1.5.1 A single lamp mounted on a test stand to simulate mounting attitude on the vehicle shall meet the photometric performance requirements contained in Table 1 and its footnotes.

5.1.6 WARPAGE TEST—SAE J575

5.2 Color—The color of the light from a cargo lamp shall be white as specified in SAE J578.

5.3 Material Requirements—Plastic materials used in optical parts shall meet the requirements of SAE J576.

6. Guidelines

6.1 Photometric Design Guidelines for cargo lamps, when tested in accordance with 4.1.5 of this report, are contained in Table 2.

6.2 Installation Guidelines

6.2.1 These guidelines apply to the device as used on the vehicle and are not a part of the design requirements, performance requirements, or test procedures.

6.2.1.1 The cargo lamp shall be wired in one of the following ways:

a. Into the vehicle dome light circuit so that it cannot be energized unless the dome light is also energized, or

b. In such a manner that it can be turned on only when the vehicle is stopped, or

c. Independent with a separate on-off switch and a dash-mounted telltale lamp with an appropriate label to indicate the lamp operation.

6.2.1.2 The cargo lamp shall be mounted on the rear of the vehicle, or the vehicle cab, or in the cargo bed. One or more lamps may be used.

TABLE 1—PHOTOMETRIC PERFORMANCE REQUIREMENTS[2]

Zone	Test Points (degrees)	Minimum Luminous Intensity[1] Zone (cd)
1	10D - V	
	40D - V	67
	40D - 10L	
	40D - 10R	
2	10D - 10L	
	10D - 30L	
	40D - 30L	69
	70D - 30L	
	70D - 10L	
3	10D - 10R	
	10D - 30R	
	40D - 30R	69
	70D - 30R	
	70D - 10R	

[1] The measured value at each test point shall not be less than 60% of the minimum value for that test point in Table 2.

(R) [2] The maximum per lamp at 1.5 degrees down and above shall be 300 cd.

TABLE 2—PHOTOMETRIC DESIGN GUIDELINES

Test Points (degrees)	Luminous Intensity (cd)
1.5D & Above	300 max
10D - V	22 min
10D - 10L	22 min
10D - 10R	22 min
10D - 30L	22 min
10D - 30R	22 min
40D - V	15 min
40D - 10L	15 min
40D - 10R	15 min
40D - 30L	15 min
40D - 30R	15 min
70D - 10L	5 min
(R) 70D - 10R	5 min
70D - 30L	5 min
70D - 10R	5 min

APPENDIX A

A.1 As a matter of information, attention is called to SAE J567 for requirements and gages used in socket design.

HIGH MOUNTED STOP LAMPS
FOR USE ON VEHICLES
2032 mm OR MORE IN OVERALL WIDTH—
SAE J1432 OCT88

SAE Information Report

Report of the Lighting Committee approved October 1988. Rationale statement available.

1. Scope—This SAE Information Report will provide a uniform arrangement with which to evaluate the concept of high-mounted lamps on large vehicles. The report provides test procedures, requirements, and guidelines for high-mounted stop lamps intended for use on certain vehicles 2032 mm (80 in) or more in overall width.

This information report applies to trucks, motor coaches, closed and open top van trailers and other vehicles with permanent structures greater than 2.8 m high. They are not intended for use on school busses, truck tractors, flat bed, pole, and boat trailers and all other trailers or trucks/truck bodies whose permanent structures are less than 2.8 m (approximately 112 in) high. These lamps are for the purpose of providing a signal over intervening vehicles to following drivers.

Additionally, four widely spaced lamps will make a more conspicuous stop lamp pattern, thus making it easier to identify a large vehicle as slowing or stopping when approaching it from the rear.

2. Definitions

2.1 High Mounted Stop Lamp—A lamp mounted high on the vehicle giving a steady light to the rear to indicate the intention of the operator to stop or diminish speed by braking. These lamps are supplemental and are in addition to the regular stop lamps.

3. Lighting Identification Code—High mounted stop lamps for use on vehicles 2032 mm or more in overall width may be identified by the code "U2" in accordance with SAE J759.

4. Tests

4.1 The device shall be tested according to the procedures specified in SAE J575. The following tests are applicable with the modifications as indicated:

4.1.1 VIBRATION TEST

4.1.2 MOISTURE TEST

4.1.3 DUST TEST

4.1.4 CORROSION TEST

4.1.5 PHOTOMETRY, with the following addition:

4.1.5.1 Photometric measurements shall be made with the light source of the signal lamp at least 3 m from the photometer. If the location and the intended orientation of the H-V axis of the lamp is not obvious from its physical configuration, the lamp manufacturer shall provide explicit instructions concerning the method of installing the lamp so that its H-V axis is horizontal and coincident with the O-O or H-V axis of the goniometer.

4.1.6 WARPAGE TEST ON DEVICES WITH PLASTICS COMPONENTS

TABLE 1 – PHOTOMETRIC REQUIREMENTS[a]

Zone	Test Results (deg)		Minimum Luminous Intensity Total for Zone (cd)
1	5U	V 10R – 10L 20R – 20L	150
2	H	V 5R – 5L 10R – 10L	320
3	5D	V 10R – 10L 20R – 20L	150
4	10D	5R – 5L 20R – 20L	52
Maximum Luminous Intensity (cd)[b]			300

[a]The measured value at each test point shall not be less than 60% of the minimum in Table 2.
[b]The maximum value shall not be exceeded over any area larger than that generated by a 0.5 deg radius within the solid cone angle defined by the test points in Table 2.

4.2 Color Test—The device shall be tested according to the procedures specified in SAE J578.

5. Requirements

5.1 Performance Requirements

5.1.1 SAE J575—A device, when tested in accordance with the test procedures specified in Section 4, shall meet the requirements indicated in the following sections of SAE J575:

5.1.1.1 Vibration
5.1.1.2 Moisture
5.1.1.3 Dust
5.1.1.4 Corrosion
5.1.1.5 Photometry

5.1.1.5.1 The lamp under test shall meet the photometric performance requirements contained in Table 1 - Photometric Requirements and its footnotes. The summation of the luminous intensity measurements at the specified test points in a zone shall be at least the value shown.

5.1.1.6 Warpage

5.1.2 COLOR—The color of the emitted light shall be red as specified in SAE J578.

5.2 Materials Requirements—Plastic materials used in optical parts shall meet the requirements of SAE J576.

5.3 Design Requirements

5.3.1 No other lamp or reflex reflector functions shall be combined with a high mounted stop lamp.

5.3.2 The effective projected luminous lens area of a single lamp shall be at least 50 cm^2.

5.4 Installation Requirements—The following requirements apply to the device as installed on the vehicle, and are not part of the laboratory test procedures and requirements.

5.4.1 Visibility of the lamp shall not be obstructed by any part of the vehicle throughout photometric test angles for the lamp unless the lamp is designed to comply with all photometric and visibility requirements with these obstructions considered.

5.4.2 Two high-mounted stop lamps are required. Both lamps must be mounted at the same height, as far apart laterally as practicable, at a minimum height of 2.7 m (approximately 108 in), measured from the road surface to the center of the lens with the vehicle unladen.

Only one lamp is required on vehicles, such as tankers, whose structure does not permit mounting two lamps at the same height as required above. Where only one lamp is required, it shall be mounted on vehicle centerline at a minimum height of 2.7 m (approximately 108 in).

5.4.3 The lamps shall be mounted so that their H-V axes are horizontal and parallel to the longitudinal axis of the vehicle with the vehicle unladen.

6. Guidelines:

6.1 Photometric Design Guidelines—for high-mounted stop lamps, when tested in accordance with paragraph 4.1.5 of this report, are contained in Table 2 - Photometric Design Guidelines and its footnotes.

6.2 Installation Guidelines—The following guidelines apply to high-mounted stop lamps as used on the vehicle and shall not be considered part of the requirements.

6.2.1 High-mounted stop lamps should be spaced as far apart laterally as practicable so that the signal will be clearly visible.

6.2.2 The luminous intensity of the light source will vary with applied voltage. The electrical wiring in the vehicle should be adequate to supply design voltage to the stop lamp.

6.2.3 Performance of lamps may deteriorate significantly as a result of dirt, grime or snow accumulation, or both, on their optical surfaces. Installation of lamps on vehicles should be considered to minimize the effect of these factors.

6.2.4 Where it is expected that lamps must perform in extremely severe environments, such as in off-highway, mining, fuel haulage, etc., the user should specify lamps designed for such use.

7. Appendix—As a matter of additional information, attention is called to SAE J567 for requirements and gages used in socket design.

TABLE 2 – PHOTOMETRIC DESIGN GUIDELINES

Test Points (deg)		Minimum Luminous Intensity (cd)
10D	5L and 5R 20L and 20R	16 10
5U and 5D	20L and 20R 10L and 10R V	10 30 70
H	10L and 10R 5L and 5R V	40 80 80
Maximum Luminous Intensity (cd)[a]		300

[a]The maximum design value should not be exceeded over any area larger than that generated by a 0.25 deg radius within the solid angle defined by the test points in Table 2.

Report of the Lighting Committee approved June 1988. Rationale statement available. Revised by the SAE Signalling and Marking Devices Standards Committee October 1993. Rationale statement available.

1. Scope—This SAE Recommended Practice applies to motor vehicle signalling and marking lighting devices which use light emitting diodes (L.E.D.) as light sources. This report provides test methods, requirements, and guidelines applicable to the special characteristics of L.E.D. lighting devices. These are in addition to those required for devices designed with incandescent light sources. This report is intended as a guide to standard practice and is subject to change to reflect additional experience and technical advances.

(R)   *2. References*

2.1 Applicable Documents—The following publications form a part of this specification to the extent specified herein. The latest issue of SAE publications shall apply.

2.1.1 SAE PUBLICATIONS—Available from SAE, 400 Commonwealth Drive, Warrendale, PA 15096-0001.

SAE J387—Terminology—Motor Vehicle Lighting

SAE J575—Test Methods and Equipment for Lighting Devices and Components for Use on Vehicles Less than 2032 mm in Overall Width

SAE J576—Plastic Materials for Use in Optical Parts Such as Lenses and Reflex Reflectors of Motor Vehicle Lighting Devices

SAE J578—Color Specification

SAE J1330—Photometry Laboratory Accuracy Guidelines

2.2 Definitions

2.2.1 SEMICONDUCTOR—A material whose resistivity lies in the broad range between conductors and insulators.

2.2.2 L.E.D.—An indivisible, discrete light source unit containing a semiconductor junction in which visible light is nonthermally produced when a forward current flows as a result of applied voltage.

2.2.3 L.E.D. LIGHTING DEVICE—A lighting device in which light is produced by an array of L.E.D. light sources.

2.2.4 INCANDESCENCE—The generation of light caused by heating a body to a high temperature. Generally this heating is obtained by passing an electric current through a wire filament. The resistance of the filament to the current causes the filament to heat up and emit radiant energy, some of which is in the visible range. Ordinary automotive bulbs have incandescent light sources.

2.2.5 L.E.D. LIGHT SOURCE CENTER—For a single L.E.D., the point that is located at the geometric center of the junction where the luminescence takes place.

2.2.6 LIGHTING DEVICE LIGHT CENTER—The geometric center of all the single L.E.D. light source centers within the L.E.D. array(s) used to illuminate the device function, or the geometric center of the illuminated area if the light output is produced indirectly.

3. Tests—The following section describes individual tests which need not be performed in any particular sequence. Testing may be expedited by performing two or more tests simultaneously on separate samples.

3.1 SAE J575 is a part of this report. Unless otherwise specified, the following tests are applicable with modifications as indicated.

3.1.1 VIBRATION TEST—The evaluation of the sample at the completion of the test shall also include a functional lighting check. If a partial outage is observed, a photometry test (see 3.1.5) shall be performed and the results recorded.

3.1.2 MOISTURE TEST

3.1.3 DUST TEST—If dust is found, the change in the maximum photometric luminous intensity of the sample shall be determined by using the photometric measurement procedures in 3.1.5.

3.1.4 CORROSION TEST

(R)   3.1.5 PHOTOMETRY TEST—Due to the near monochromatic nature of the color emitted by most L.E.D. light sources, the color response of the photometer detector shall be accurately calibrated in the spectral range of the L.E.D. device being measured. The photometric output (luminous intensity) of a L.E.D. lighting device typically decreases as the temperature of the L.E.D. light sources increases. In addition to the test procedures in SAE J575, the following shall apply:

3.1.5.1 Design Voltage—The device shall be operated at its design voltage during all photometric tests.

3.1.5.2 Photometric Maximums—For measurements to photometric maximum requirements, first allow the test device to stabilize at laboratory ambient temperature (23 °C ± 5 °C) unenergized. After all the device

components are at laboratory ambient temperature, energize the test device and record the maximum photometric value(s) within 60 s of the initial on-time.

3.1.5.3 Photometric Minimums—For measurements to photometric minimum requirements, the test device light output shall first be stabilized by energizing the device at laboratory ambient temperature (23 °C ± 5 °C) until either internal heat buildup saturation has occurred or 30 min has elapsed, whichever occurs first.

3.1.6 WARPAGE TEST ON DEVICES WITH PLASTIC COMPONENTS—Not required.

3.2 Color Test—SAE J578 is a part of this report.

3.3 Thermal Cycle Test

3.3.1 SCOPE—This test evaluates the ability of the sample device to resist optical, electrical, or physical malfunctions due to exposures to repeated changes from hot to cold temperature extremes. Devices installed in vehicle locations that could produce temperatures outside the test range specified may necessitate special test requirements.

3.3.2 TEST EQUIPMENT—A thermal cycle chamber capable of providing the temperature extremes and rates of change of temperature in the temperature-time profile specified in Figure 1.

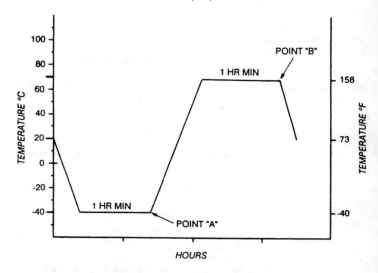

AMBIENT TEMPERATURE TRANSITION RATES
MINIMUM 0.6 °C (1 °F) PER MINUTE
MAXIMUM 5 °C (9 °F) PER MINUTE

FIGURE 1—THERMAL CYCLE PROFILE

3.3.3 TEST PROCEDURE—The sample device, mounted on a test fixture shall be subjected to thermal cycles as follows:

3.3.3.1 Thermal Cycle—The device shall be exposed to the thermal cycle profile shown in Figure 1.

3.3.3.2 Device Operation—The device shall be energized at design voltage commencing at point "A" of Figure 1 and de-energized at point "B" of each cycle. When energized, the lighting function(s) shall be cycled as specified in SAE J575, Table 1.

3.3.3.3 Test Duration—The test shall consist of 25 complete cycles of the thermal cycle profile shown in Figure 1.

3.3.3.4 Sample Evaluation—During the final thermal cycle, the sample lighting function(s) shall be continuously checked for permanent or intermittent outages while energized from Point "A" (cold temperature) to Point "B" (hot temperature) on Figure 1 and the results recorded. If partial outage is observed, a photometry test (see 3.1.5) with the remaining functional L.E.D. segments lighted shall be performed and the results recorded. Upon completion of the thermal cycle exposure the sample device shall be visually examined for any cracking, rupture, or warpage of parts and the results recorded. If any of the previous changes are observed that could result in failure of the other tests contained in Section 3, these test(s) shall be performed on the same sample used for the thermal cycle test and the results recorded.

4. Requirements

4.1 Performance Requirements—A L.E.D. lighting device when tested in accordance with the test procedures specified in Section 3 shall meet the following requirements.

4.1.1 VIBRATION—SAE J575. The following requirements also apply:

4.1.1.1 After completion of test procedure 3.1.1, all L.E.D. light sources contained within the device shall function or the device shall comply with the photometric requirements in 4.1.5 of this report.

4.1.2 MOISTURE—SAE J575.

4.1.3 DUST—SAE J575.

4.1.4 CORROSION—SAE J575.

4.1.5 PHOTOMETRY—SAE J575. The photometric performance requirements in the applicable SAE technical report for the lighting function being tested shall also apply. Specified photometric maximum and minimum test points shall be determined as specified in 3.1.5.2 and 3.1.5.3 of this report. The following requirements shall also apply:

4.1.5.1 Lighted Sections—Applicable photometric requirements specified in other SAE technical reports which are based on the number of lighted sections shall instead be applied based on the dimensions of the L.E.D. lighting device function being tested. The maximum horizontal or vertical projected lighted linear dimension of the function shall be equivalent to the number of lighted sections in Table 1:

TABLE 1

Maximum Projected Linear Dimension	Equivalent Number of Lighted Sections
150 mm or less	1
151 to 300 mm	2
301 mm or greater	3

4.1.6 WARPAGE—SAE J575. Not required.

4.1.7 COLOR—The color of light shall be as specified in SAE J578 and in the SAE report of the applicable device function.

4.1.8 THERMAL CYCLE—After completion of the thermal cycle test procedure in 3.3.3, there shall be no observed cracking, rupture, displacement, or warpage of parts of the test device which would result in failure of other tests contained in 4.1 of this technical report. There shall also be no loss of function of any L.E.D. light sources while energized during the last thermal cycle which would result in failure of the photometry requirements of 4.1.5 of this technical report.

(R) **4.2 Materials Requirements**—Plastic materials used in optical parts in the device, including the individual L.E.D. light source units, shall meet the requirements of SAE J576 when exposed directly, or when covered by another lens material, depending on the actual use in the device.

4.3 Design Requirements

(R) 4.3.1 REVERSE VOLTAGE—Some L.E.D. light sources may be damaged by the application of a voltage of reverse polarity. Protection shall be provided to prevent any damage when the voltage polarity to the lighting device is reversed.

5. Guidelines

5.1 Photometric Design Guidelines—The photometric design guidelines in the applicable SAE technical report for the lighting function design shall be required. Specified photometric maximum and minimum values shall be measured as specified in 3.1.5.2 and 3.1.5.3 of this report. Requirements using the number of lighted sections shall apply as specified in 4.1.5.1 of this report.

5.2 Installation Guidelines—The following guidelines are provided due to the special characteristics of L.E.D. lighting devices:

5.2.1 The luminous intensity of L.E.D. lighting devices typically vary with applied voltage. The electrical system of a vehicle should, under normal operating conditions, provide design voltage to the device as closely as practicable bearing in mind the inherent variability of such systems.

5.2.2 The luminous intensity of a L.E.D. lighting device typically decreases as the temperature of the L.E.D. light sources increases. Installation of lamps on vehicles should be considered to minimize the effect of accumulating excessive temperatures in the device.

5.2.3 While L.E.D. light sources typically have a very long energized life, outage of a segment of a L.E.D. light source array may occur when one of the L.E.D. light sources within the array segment malfunctions. The user should be cautioned to replace or repair the device since the luminous intensity of the device is reduced by such an outage.

(R) **6. Notes**

(R) **6.1** As a matter of additional information, attention is called to SAE J387 and SAE J1330.

CENTER HIGH MOUNTED STOP LAMP STANDARD FOR VEHICLES LESS THAN 2032 mm OVERALL WIDTH—SAE J1957 JUN93

SAE Standard

Report of the Signalling and Marking Devices Standards Committee approved June 1993. Rationale statement available.

1. Scope—This SAE Standard provides test procedures, requirements, and guidelines for center high mounted stop lamps (CHMSL) for use on vehicles less than 2032 mm in overall width.

2. References

2.1 Applicable Documents—The following publications form a part of this specification to the extent specified herein. The latest issue of SAE publications shall apply.

2.1.1 SAE PUBLICATIONS—Available from SAE, 400 Commonwealth Drive, Warrendale, PA 15096-0001.

SAE J575—Tests for Motor Vehicle Lighting Devices and Components

SAE J576—Plastic Materials for Use in Optical Parts Such as Lenses and Reflectors of Motor Vehicle Lighting Devices

SAE J578—Color Specification

SAE J759—Lighting Identification

2.2 Definitions

2.2.1 The center high mounted stop lamp (CHMSL) is an additional lamp of the stop lamp system, giving a brake actuated steady warning light to the rear of the vehicle. The CHMSL is intended to provide a signal to both the operator of the following vehicle as well as through intervening vehicles.

3. Lighting Identification Code

3.1 CHMSL for passenger vehicles may be identified with U3 code in accordance with SAE J759.

4. Tests

4.1 SAE J575—The following test procedures in SAE J575 are part of this document, with the modifications indicated:

4.1.1 VIBRATION TEST

4.1.2 MOISTURE TEST

4.1.3 DUST TEST

4.1.4 CORROSION TEST

4.1.5 PHOTOMETRY

4.1.5.1 Photometric tests shall be made with the photometer at least 3 m from the light source. The lamp axis shall be taken as the horizontal line through the light source and parallel to what would be the longitudinal axis of the vehicle if the lamp were mounted in its normal position on the vehicle.

4.1.6 WARPAGE TEST ON DEVICES WITH PLASTIC COMPONENTS—Stop lamp cycle time and temperature in Table 1 of SAE J575 shall be used for evaluating a CHMSL.

4.2 Color Test—SAE J578 is a part of this report.

5. Requirements

5.1 Performance Requirements—Center high mounted stop lamps, when tested in accordance with the test procedures specified in 4.1 shall meet the requirements indicated in the following sections of SAE J575.

5.1.1 VIBRATION TEST

5.1.2 MOISTURE TEST—Does not apply to CHMSLs mounted inside the vehicle.

5.1.3 DUST TEST—Does not apply to CHMSLs mounted inside the vehicle.

5.1.4 CORROSION TEST—Does not apply to CHMSLs mounted inside the vehicle.

5.1.5 PHOTOMETRY TEST—The lamp, when tested in accordance with 4.1 of this document, shall meet the photometric requirements contained in Table 1. For interior mounted CHMSLs, the photometry test shall include the vehicle manufacturer's specified glazing in the design position.

a. The luminous intensity values at each test point shall not be less than 60% of the minimum value specified in Table 2.

b. The listed maximum shall not be exceeded over any area larger than that generated by a 0.5 degree radius within the solid angle defined by the test points in Table 1.

5.1.6 WARPAGE TEST—There shall be no evidence of warpage which results in failure of any test contained in 4.1 of this document.

5.2 Color Test—The light emitted by the CHMSL shall be red.

5.3 Material Requirements—Plastic materials used in CHMSL optic parts shall conform to the requirements in SAE J576.

5.4 Dimensional Requirements—The effective projected luminous lens area measured on a plane at right angles to the lamp axis shall not be less than 29 cm^2 (4.5 in^2).

5.5 Installation Requirements

5.5.1 The CHMSL shall not be optically combined with any other signal lamp or reflective device other than with a cargo lamp.

5.5.2 The center of the CHMSL shall be mounted on the vertical centerline of the vehicle.

5.5.3 If the lamp is mounted below the rear window, no portion of the lens shall be lower than 152 mm (6 in) below the rear window on convertibles, or 76 mm (3 in) on other passenger cars.

5.5.4 CHMSL shall have a signal visible from 45 degrees to the left to 45 degrees to the right of the longitudinal axis of the vehicle.

5.5.5 The CHMSL shall be activated only upon application of the service brakes.

5.5.6 If the CHMSL is mounted inside the vehicle, means shall be provided to minimize reflections at the rear window glazing that might be visible to the driver when viewed directly, or indirectly in the rearview mirror.

6. Guidelines

6.1 Photometric design guidelines for center high mounted stop lamps, when tested in accordance with 4.1.5 of this document, are contained in Table 2.

6.2 Serviceability/Cleanability—The CHMSL shall be designed to be serviced and cleaned with either commonly available tools or no tools. The number of trim pieces that must be removed for this purpose should be minimized. This guideline applies to lamp servicing, bulb replacement, and access to the rear window glazing for cleaning purposes.

6.3 Replacement bulb identification should be permanently located on the lamp housing.

6.4 The vertical location is specified with the intent of positioning the lamp higher than the conventional stop lamps. The lamp shall be mounted high to insure its visibility through intervening vehicles. It may be located forward of the tail, stop, and rear turn signal lamps.

6.5 Heat test cycle time and temperature cycle may be increased to represent a more severe heat test based on CHMSL mounting environment and/or performance cycle.

TABLE 1—MINIMUM ZONAL PHOTOMETRIC REQUIREMENTS FOR CENTER HIGH MOUNTED STOP LAMPS

Group	Test Points (degrees)	Minimum Total Intensity (candela)
1	5U-V H-5L H-V H-5R 5D-V	125
2	5U-5R 5U-10R H-10R 5D-10R 5D-5R	98
3	5U-5L 5U-10L H-10L 5D-10L 5D-5L	98
4	10U-10L 10U-V 10U-10R	32

TABLE 2—DESIGN PHOTOMETRIC GUIDELINES FOR CENTER HIGH MOUNTED STOP LAMPS

Test Points		Minimum Intensity (candela)
10U	10L	8
	V	16
	10R	8
5U and 5D	10L	16
	5L	25
	V	25
	5R	25
	10R	16
H	10L	16
	5L	25
	V	25
	5R	25
	10R	16
	Maximum[1]	130

[1] The lamp shall not exceed the listed maximum over an area larger than that generated by a 0.25 degree radius within a solid cone angle from 10 degrees L to 10 degrees R and from 10 degrees U to 5 degrees D.

SIDE TURN SIGNAL LAMPS FOR LARGE VEHICLES—SAE J2039 JUN94

SAE Recommended Practice

Report of the SAE Heavy-Duty Lighting Standards Committee approved June 1994. Rationale statement available.

1. Scope—This SAE Recommended Practice provides test procedures, requirements, and guidelines for side turn signal lamps intended for use on trailers 12 m or more in overall length except pole trailers. Side turn signal lamps conforming to the requirements of this document may be used on other large vehicles such as trucks, truck tractors, buses, and other applications where this type of lighting device is desirable.

2. References

2.1 Applicable Documents—The following publications form a part of this specification to the extent specified herein. The latest issue of SAE publications shall apply.

2.1.1 SAE PUBLICATIONS—Available from SAE, 400 Commonwealth Drive, Warrendale, PA 15096-0001.

SAE J387—Terminology—Motor Vehicle Lighting

SAE J567—Lamp Bulb Retention System for Requirements and Gages Used in Retention System Design

SAE J576—Plastic Material for Use in Optical Parts Such as Lenses and Reflectors of Motor Vehicle Lighting Devices

SAE J578—Color Specification

SAE J588—Turn Signal Lamps for Use on Vehicles Less than 2032 mm in Overall Width

SAE J590—Turn Signal Flashers

SAE J759—Lighting Identification Code

SAE J1395—Front and Rear Turn Signal Lamps Used on Vehicles 2032 mm or More in Overall Width

SAE J1889—LED Lighting Devices

SAE J2139—Tests for Lighting Devices, Reflective Devices, and Components Used on Vehicles 2032 mm or More in Overall Width

2.2 Related Publications—Attention is called to the following documents for additional information on lamp design and installation.

2.2.1 TMC PUBLICATIONS—Available from The American Trucking Association, Alexandria, VA.

TTMA #RP-9—Location of Lighting Devices for Trailers

TMC #RP-702A—Trailer Lamp and Reflector Placement

TMC #RP-704B—Heavy-Duty Lighting Systems for Trailers

TMC #AV7-1—Heavy-Duty Lighting Systems for Trailers

2.3 Definitions

2.3.1 A side turn signal lamp is the signaling element of a turn signal system which indicates a change in direction by giving a flashing light on the side toward which the turn or lane change will be made. Side turn signal lamps are

supplemental to, and should not be confused with front- and rear-mounted turn signal lamps described in SAE J588 or J1395. See SAE J590 for flash rate and percent on time.

3. Lighting Identification Code—Side turn signal lamps for use on trailers 12 m or more in overall length or for other large vehicles may be identified by the Code "E" in accordance with SAE J759.

4. Tests

4.1 SAE J2139 is a part of this document. The following tests are applicable with modification as indicated.

4.1.1 VIBRATION

4.1.2 MOISTURE

4.1.3 DUST

4.1.4 CORROSION

4.1.5 PHOTOMETRY

4.1.5.1 Photometric measurements shall be made with the light source of the device at least 3 m from the photometer.

4.1.5.2 The H-V axis of the device shall be taken as the horizontal line through the light source and normal to the longitudinal axis of the vehicle, when the device is mounted in its design position.

4.1.5.3 Photometric measurement shall be made with the light source steadily burning.

4.1.6 WARPAGE TEST ON DEVICES WITH PLASTIC COMPONENTS

4.2 Color—SAE J578 is a part of this document.

4.3 Plastic Materials—SAE J576 is a part of this document.

5. Requirements

5.1 Performance Requirements—The device when tested in accordance with the test procedures of this document shall meet the requirements of SAE J2139 or as indicated.

5.1.1 VIBRATION

5.1.2 MOISTURE

5.1.3 DUST

5.1.4 CORROSION

5.1.5 PHOTOMETRY—The device tested shall meet the photometric performance requirements of Table 1 and its footnotes.

5.1.5.1 The summation of the luminous intensity measurements at the specified test points in a zone shall be at least the value shown.

5.1.5.2 When a sidemarker lamp is combined with the side turn signal lamp, the side turn signal lamp intensity shall not be less than five times the luminous intensity of the sidemarker lamp at any test point of Table 2.

5.1.6 WARPAGE

5.2 Color—The color of the light from the side turn signal lamp shall be yellow as specified in SAE J578.

5.3 Plastic Materials—The plastic materials used in the optical parts shall meet the requirements of SAE J576.

5.4 Design Requirements

5.4.1 If a side turn signal lamp is optically combined with a sidemarker lamp and a replaceable multiple light source is used, the light source retention system shall be designed with an indexing means so that the light source is properly indexed. Removable light source retention systems shall have an indexing feature so that they cannot be reinserted into the lamp housing in a random position, unless the lamp will perform its intended function with random light source orientation.

5.4.2 The effective projected luminous lighted lens area, as defined in SAE J387, shall be at least 20 cm^2.

5.5 Installation Requirements—The side turn signal lamp shall meet the following requirements as installed on the vehicle.

5.5.1 Visibility of each side turn signal lamp shall not be obstructed by any part of the vehicle throughout the photometric test pattern of Table 2 unless the lamp is designed to comply with all photometric and visibility requirements with these obstructions considered. The visibility and photometric requirements below the lamp horizontal axis are not applicable when the lower lighted edge of the lamp is less than 750 mm above the ground.

5.5.2 To be considered visible, the lamp must provide a minimum of 13 cm^2 of unobstructed projected area when the illuminated portion of the outer lens surface, excluding reflex reflector, is projected parallel to a horizontal plane in any direction from 85 degrees left to 85 degrees right and to a vertical plane in any direction from 50 degrees above to 20 degrees below the horizontal with respect to the lamp H-V axis as defined in 4.1.5.2 (see Figure 1).

5.5.3 The side turn signal lamp shall flash in conjunction with the required front and rear turn signal lamps.

5.5.4 Side turn signal lamps need not meet the H-85 degree right test point performance requirements for a left side mounted lamp or the H-85 degree left test point performance requirements for a right side mounted lamp of Table 1 or the 60% requirement of notes 2 and 3, Table 1, between this same test point and the nearest corresponding 75 degree test point. The intent is to permit the

manufacturer to provide glare protection for the driver against light reflecting in the rearview mirror from the forward facing portion of the side turn signal lamp.

5.5.5 The side turn signal lamp shall be wired so that when it is in its flashing mode it shall continue to flash even with the vehicle brakes applied.

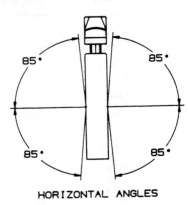

HORIZONTAL ANGLES

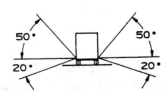

VERTICAL ANGLES

FIGURE 1—VISIBILITY REQUIREMENTS

TABLE 1—SIDE TURN SIGNAL LAMP PHOTOMETRIC PERFORMANCE REQUIREMENTS

Zone	Test Point Degrees	Zone Total Luminous Intensity, Candela, Yellow
1	50U-30L	
	35U-60L	
	20U-75L	
	H-85L	138
	5D-75L	
	10D-60L	
	20D-30L	
2	50U-V	
	H-30L	
	H-V	158
	H-30R	
	20D-V	
3	50U-30R	
	35U-60R	
	20U-75R	
	H-85R	138
	5D-75R	
	10D-60R	
	20D-30R	
Maximum Luminous Intensity, Candela		750

[1] The maximum luminous intensity shall not be exceeded over any area larger than that generated by a 0.5 degree radius within the area defined by the test point pattern of Table 2.

[2] Unless otherwise specified, the lamp shall be considered to have failed the photometric requirements of this document if the luminous intensity at any test point is less than 60% of the values specified in Table 2.

[3] Unless otherwise specified, the lamp shall be considered to have failed the photometric requirements of this document if the minimum luminous intensity between test points is less than 60% of the lower design values of Table 2 for the closest adjacent test points on a horizontal and vertical line as defined by the test point pattern.

[4] The summation of the luminous intensity measurements at the specified test points in the zone shall be at least the values shown.

[5] When a sidemarker lamp is combined with a side turn signal lamp, see 5.1.5.2 of this document for luminous intensity ratio requirements.

TABLE 2—SIDE TURN SIGNAL LAMP PHOTOMETRIC DESIGN GUIDELINES

Test Point Degrees	Luminous Intensity, Candela, Yellow
50U-30L	12
V	12
30R	12
35U-60L	20
60R	20
20U-75L	20
75R	20
H-85L	30
30L	40
V	50
30R	40
85R	30
5D-75L	20
75R	20
10D-60L	20
60R	20
20D-30L	16
V	16
30R	16
Maximum Luminous Intensity, Candela	750

[1] The maximum luminous intensity shall not be exceeded over any area larger than that generated by a 0.25 degree radius within the area defined by the test point pattern of Table 2.

[2] When a sidemarker lamp is combined with a side turn signal lamp, see 5.1.5.2 of this document for luminous intensity ratio requirements.

6. Guidelines

6.1 Design Guidelines

6.1.1 Photometric design guidelines are contained in Table 2 and its footnotes.

6.2 Installation Guidelines—The following guidelines apply to side turn signal lamps as used on the vehicle and shall not be considered part of the requirements.

6.2.1 Performance of lamps may deteriorate significantly as a result of dirt, grime, snow, and ice accumulation on the optical surfaces. Installation of the device on the vehicle should be considered to minimize the effects of these factors.

6.2.2 Where it is expected that the device must perform in extremely severe environments, or where it is expected to be totally immersed in water, the user should specify devices specifically designed for such use.

6.2.3 The side turn signal lamp should be mounted, one on each side of the trailer, with the optical center of the lamp mounted on or forward of the midpoint of the trailer and at a height not less than 380 mm and not more than 1650 mm.

TAIL LAMPS (REAR POSITION LAMPS) FOR USE ON VEHICLES 2032 mm OR MORE IN OVERALL WIDTH—SAE J2040 JUN91

SAE Standard

Report of the SAE Lighting Coordinating Committee and the Heavy-Duty Lighting Standards Committee approved June 1991. Rationale statement available.

1. Scope—This SAE Standard provides test procedures, requirements, and guidelines for tail lamps intended for use on vehicles 2032 mm or more in overall width. Tail lamps conforming to the requirements of this document may also be used on vehicles less than 2032 mm in overall width.

2. References

2.1 Applicable Documents—The following publications form a part of this specification to the extent specified herein. The latest issue of SAE publications shall apply.

2.1.1 SAE PUBLICATIONS—Available from SAE, 400 Commonwealth Drive, Warrendale, PA 15096-0001.

SAE J567—Lamp Bulb Retention System for Requirements and Gages Used in Retention System Design

SAE J576—Plastic Material for Use in Optical Parts Such as Lenses and Reflectors of Motor Vehicle Lighting Devices

SAE J578—Color Specification

SAE 585—Tail Lamps (Rear Position Lamps)

SAE J759—Lighting Identification Code

SAE J2139—Tests for Lighting Devices, Reflective Devices and Components Used on Vehicles 2032 mm or More in Overall Width

SAE Technical Paper 830566, "Motor Vehicle Conspicuity," R.L. Henderson, K. Ziedman, W.J. Burger, and K.E. Cavey, National Highway Traffic Safety Administration

2.1.2 OTHER PUBLICATIONS—Attention is called to the following documents for additional information on lamp design and installation requirements.

FMVSS 108
FHWA 393 Subpart B
TTMA #RP-9
TMC #RP-702

2.2 Definitions

2.2.1 A tail lamp is a lamp used to designate the rear of a vehicle by a steady burning low intensity light.

3. Lighting Identification Code—Tail lamps for use on vehicles 2032 mm or more in overall width may be identified by the code "T2" in accordance with SAE J759.

4. Tests

4.1 SAE J2139 is a part of this document. The following tests are applicable with modification as indicated.

4.1.1 VIBRATION

4.1.2 MOISTURE

4.1.3 DUST

4.1.4 CORROSION

4.1.5 PHOTOMETRY

4.1.5.1 Photometric measurements shall be made with the light source of the device at least 3 m from the photometer.

4.1.5.2 The H-V axis of the device shall be taken to be parallel to the longitudinal axis of the vehicle, when the device is mounted in its design position.

4.1.5.3 Photometric measurements shall be made with the light source steadily burning. Photometric measurements of multiple compartment lamps or multiple lamp arrangements shall be made by either of the following methods.

4.1.5.3.1 All compartments or lamps shall be photometered together provided that a line from the light source of each compartment or lamp to the center of the photometer sensing device does not make an angle of more than 0.6 degrees with the photometer H-V axis. When compartments or lamps are photometered together, the H-V axis shall intersect the midpoint between their light sources.

4.1.5.3.2 Each compartment or lamp shall be photometered separately by aligning the axis of each lamp or compartment with the axis of the photometer. The photometric measurement for the entire multiple compartment lamp or multiple lamp arrangement shall be determined by adding the photometric outputs from each individual lamp or component at corresponding test points.

4.1.6 WARPAGE TEST ON DEVICES WITH PLASTIC COMPONENTS

4.2 Color—SAE J578 is a part of this document.

4.3 Plastic Materials—SAE J576 is a part of this document.

5. Requirements

5.1 Performance Requirements—The device when tested in accordance with the test procedures of this document shall meet the requirements of SAE J2139 or as indicated.

5.1.1 VIBRATION

5.1.2 MOISTURE

5.1.3 DUST

5.1.4 CORROSION

5.1.5 PHOTOMETRY—The device tested shall meet the photometric performance requirements of Table 1 and its footnotes.

The summation of the luminous intensity measurements at the specified test points in a zone shall be at least the value shown.

5.1.5.1 A multiple compartment lamp or multiple lamps may be used to meet the photometric requirements. If a multiple compartment lamp or multiple lamps are used and the distance between adjacent light sources does not exceed 560 mm for two compartments or lamp arrangements and does not exceed 410 mm for three compartments or lamp arrangements, then the combination of the compartments or lamps must be used to meet the photometric requirements of Table 1. If the distance between adjacent light sources exceeds the above dimensions, each compartment or lamp shall comply with the photometric requirements of Table 1.

5.1.5.2 When a tail lamp is combined with the stop lamp or turn signal lamp, the stop lamp or turn signal lamp intensity shall be not less than three times the luminous intensity of the tail lamp at any test point, except that at H-V, H-5L, H-5R, and 5U-V, the stop lamp or turn signal lamp intensity shall be not less than five times the luminous intensity of the tail lamp.

When a tail lamp is combined with the stop lamp or turn signal lamp, and the maximum luminous intensity of the tail lamp is located below the horizontal and is within an area generated by a 1.0 degree radius around the test point, the ratio for the test point may be computed using the lowest value of the tail lamp intensity within the generated area.

5.1.6 WARPAGE

5.2 Color—The color of the light from the tail lamp shall be red as specified in SAE J578.

5.3 Plastic Materials—The plastic materials used in the optical parts shall meet the requirements of SAE J576.

5.4 Design Requirements

5.4.1 If a tail lamp is combined with a stop lamp or a turn signal lamp and a replaceable multiple light source is used, the light source retention system shall be designed with an indexing means so that the light source is properly indexed. Removable light source retention systems shall have an indexing feature so that they cannot be reinserted into the lamp housing in a random position, unless the lamp will perform its intended function with random light source orientation.

5.4.2 The effective projected luminous lighted lens area of a single lamp shall be at least 75 cm^2.

5.4.3 If a multiple compartment lamp or multiple lamps are used to meet the photometric requirements, the effective projected luminous lens area of each compartment or lamp shall be at least 40 cm^2 provided the combined area is at least 75 cm^2.

5.4.4 A tail lamp shall not be combined with a clearance lamp.

5.5 Installation Requirements—The tail lamp shall meet the following requirements as installed on the vehicle.

5.5.1 The tail lamps shall be mounted on the permanent structure of the vehicle, facing rearward, at the same height and spaced as far apart laterally as practicable, so that the signal will be clearly visible.

5.5.2 Visibility of each tail lamp shall not be obstructed by any part of the vehicle throughout the photometric test pattern unless the lamp is designed to comply with all photometric and visibility requirements with the obstructions considered.

To be considered visible, the lamp must provide an unobstructed view of a portion of the lighted outer lens surface, excluding reflex reflector area, of at least 13 cm^2 measured at a horizontal angle of 45 degrees to the left and 45 degrees to the right of the longitudinal axis of the vehicle and a vertical angle from 20 degrees up to 10 degrees down.

See Table 1, Note 6. Where more than one lamp or optical area is lighted on each side of the vehicle, only one such area on each side need comply.

6. Guidelines

6.1 Design Guidelines

6.1.1 Photometric design guidelines are contained in Table 2 and its footnotes.

6.2 Installation Guidelines—The following guidelines apply to tail lamps as used on the vehicle and shall not be considered part of the requirements.

6.2.1 Performance of lamps may deteriorate significantly as a result of dirt, grime, snow, and ice accumulation on the optical surfaces. Installation of the device on the vehicle should be considered to minimize the effects of these factors.

6.2.2 Where it is expected that the device must perform in extremely severe environments, or where it is expected to be totally immersed in water, the user should specify devices specifically designed for such use.

7. Advance Requirements—This section of the document gives advance notice to manufacturers and users of the device of a pending change in the requirements for a tail lamp. The change in the requirements shall be effective on devices marketed and used on or after January 1, 1996.

See Tables 3 and 4 and the footnotes.

TABLE 1—TAIL LAMP PHOTOMETRIC PERFORMANCE REQUIREMENTS

Zone	Test Point Deg.	Zone Total Luminous Intensity, Candela, Red
1	10U— 5L 5U—20L 5D—20L 10D— 5L	1.4
2	5U—10L H—10L 5D—10L	2.4
3	5U— V H— 5L H— V H— 5R 5D— V	9.6
4	5U—10R H—10R 5D—10R	2.4
5	10U— 5R 5U—20R 5D—20R 10D— 5R	1.4
Maximum Luminous Intensity, Candela		18.0 H and above

[1] The maximum luminous intensity shall not be exceeded over any area larger than that generated by a 0.5 degree radius within the area defined by the test point pattern of Table 2.

[2] Unless otherwise specified, the lamp shall be considered to have failed the photometric requirements of this document if the luminous intensity at any test point is less than 60% of the values specified in Table 2.

[3] Unless otherwise specified, the lamp shall be considered to have failed the photometric requirements of this document if the minimum luminous intensity between test points is less than 60% of the lower design values of Table 2 for the closest adjacent test points on a horizontal and vertical line as defined by the test point pattern.

[4] The summation of the luminous intensity measurements at the specified test points in the zone shall be at least the values shown.

[5] When a tail lamp or a clearance lamp is combined with a stop lamp or a turn signal lamp, see 5.1.5.2 of this document for luminous intensity ratio requirements.

[6] Throughout the photometric pattern defined by the corner points of 20U-45L, 20U-45R, 10D-45R, and 10D-45L, the light intensity shall be not less than 0.10 candela in red.

TABLE 2—TAIL LAMP PHOTOMETRIC DESIGN GUIDELINES

Test Point Deg.	Luminous Intensity, Candela, Red
10U— 5L 5R	0.4 0.4
5U—20L 10L V 10R 20R	0.3 0.8 1.8 0.8 0.3
H—10L 5L V 5R 10R	0.8 2.0 2.0 2.0 0.8
5D—20L 10L V 10R 20R	0.3 0.8 1.8 0.8 0.3
10D— 5L 5R	0.4 0.4
Maximum Luminous Intensity, Candela	18.0 H and above

[1] The maximum luminous intensity shall not be exceeded over any area larger than that generated by a 0.25 degree radius within the area defined by the test point pattern of Table 2.

[2] When a tail lamp is combined with a stop lamp or a turn signal lamp, see 5.1.5.2 of this document for luminous intensity ratio requirements.

[3] Throughout the photometric pattern defined by the corner points of 20U-45L, 20U-45R, 10D-45R, and 10D-45L, the light intensity shall be not less than 0.10 candela in red.

TABLE 3—TAIL LAMP PHOTOMETRIC PERFORMANCE REQUIREMENTS—ADVANCE REQUIREMENTS

Zone	Test Point Deg.	Zone Total Luminous Intensity, Candela, Red
1	20U—45L 20U—20L 10D—20L 10D—45L	1.0
2	10U— 5L 5U—20L 5D—20L 10D— 5L	1.4
3	5U—10L H—10L 5D—10L	2.4
4	5U— V H— 5L H— V H— 5R 5D— V	9.6
5	5U—10R H—10R 5D—10R	2.4
6	10U— 5R 5U—20R 5D—20R 10D— 5R	1.4
7	20U—20R 20U—45R 10D—45R 10D—20R	1.0
Maximum Luminous Intensity, Candela		18.0 H and above

[1] The maximum luminous intensity shall not be exceeded over any area larger than that generated by a 0.5 degree radius within the area defined by the test point pattern of Table 4.

[2] Unless otherwise specified, the lamp shall be considered to have failed the photometric requirements of this document if the luminous intensity at any test point is less than 60% of the values specified in Table 4.

[3] Unless otherwise specified, the lamp shall be considered to have failed the photometric requirements of this document if the minimum luminous intensity between test points is less than 60% of the lower design values of Table 4 for the closest adjacent test points on a horizontal and vertical line as defined by the test point pattern.

[4] The summation of the luminous intensity measurements at the specified test points in the zone shall be at least the values shown.

[5] When a tail lamp is combined with a stop lamp or a turn signal lamp, see 5.1.5.2 of this document for luminous intensity ratio requirements.

TABLE 4—TAIL LAMP PHOTOMETRIC DESIGN GUIDELINES—ADVANCE REQUIREMENTS

Test Point Deg.	Luminous Intensity, Candela, Red
20U—45L 20L 20R 45R	0.25 0.25 0.25 0.25
10U— 5L 5R	0.4 0.4
5U—20L 10L V 10R 20R	0.3 0.8 1.8 0.8 0.3
H—10L 5L V 5R 10R	0.8 2.0 2.0 2.0 0.8
5D—20L 10L V 10R 20R	0.3 0.8 1.8 0.8 0.3
10D—45L 20L 5L 5R 20R 45R	0.25 0.25 0.4 0.4 0.25 0.25
Maximum Luminous Intensity, Candela—	18.0 H and above

[1] The maximum luminous intensity shall not be exceeded over any area larger than that generated by a 0.25 degree radius within the area defined by the test point pattern of Table 4.

[2] When a tail lamp is combined with a stop lamp or a turn signal lamp, see 5.1.5.2 of this document for luminous intensity ratio requirements.

REFLEX REFLECTORS FOR USE ON VEHICLES 2032 mm OR MORE IN OVERALL WIDTH—SAE J2041 JUN92

SAE Information Report

Report of the SAE Heavy-Duty Lighting Standards Committee approved June 1992. Rationale statement available.

1. Scope—This SAE Information Report provides test procedures, requirements, and guidelines for reflex reflectors used on vehicles 2032 mm or more in overall width and 7.6 m or more in length. Reflex reflectors conforming to these requirements may also be used on vehicles less than 2032 mm in overall width.

2. References

2.1 Applicable Documents—The following publications form a part of this specification to the extent specified herein. The latest issue of SAE publications shall apply.

2.1.1 SAE PUBLICATIONS—Available from SAE, 400 Commonwealth Drive, Warrendale, PA 15096-0001.

SAE J576—Plastic Material for Use in Optical Parts Such as Lenses and Reflectors of Motor Vehicle Lighting Devices

SAE J578—Color Specifications

SAE J594—Reflex Reflectors

SAE J759—Lighting Identification

SAE J2139—Test Methods and Equipment for Lighting Devices and Components for Use on Vehicles 2032 mm or More in Overall Width

2.2 Definitions

2.2.1 REFLEX REFLECTORS—Reflex reflectors are devices used on vehicles to alert an approaching driver by reflected light from the lamps on the approaching vehicle of a possible hazard.

2.2.1.1 Type 1 Reflex Reflectors—Type 1 reflex reflectors are devices having a photometric pattern ranging from 20 degrees left to 20 degrees right along the horizontal axis and from 10 degrees up to 10 degrees down along the vertical axis. (See SAE J594.)

2.2.1.2 Type 2 Wide Angle Reflex Reflectors—Type 2 wide angle reflex reflectors are devices having an expanded photometric pattern beyond that for a Type 1 reflex reflector. The photometric pattern covers the area defined by the entrance angle corner points of 45L-5U, 45R-5U, 45R-5D, 45L-5D and from 10 U and 10 D along the vertical axis.

Wide angle reflex reflectors may be directional and may require that they be mounted on the vehicle in a fixed orientation to be effective.

2.2.2 OBSERVATION ANGLE—The observation angle is the angle formed by a line from the observation point to the center of the reflective area and a second line from the center of the reflective area to the center of the source of illumination in the vertical plane only.

2.2.3 ENTRANCE ANGLE—The entrance angle is the angle between the axis of the reflex reflector and a line from the center of the reflective area to the center of the source of illumination, with both horizontal and vertical coordinates.

The entrance angle shall be designated left, right, up, and down in accordance with the position of the source of illumination with respect to the axis of the reflex reflector as viewed from behind the reflector.

3. Identification Code

3.1 Type 1 Reflex Reflectors may be identified by the code "A" in accordance with SAE J759.

3.2 Type 2 Wide Angle Reflex Reflectors may be identified by the code "A2" in accordance with SAE J759.

4. Tests

4.1 SAE J2139 is a part of this document. The following tests are applicable with the modifications as indicated.

4.1.1 VIBRATION—The device shall be mounted on the test fixture in accordance with the manufacturer's instruction and the horizontal mounting line marked.

The device shall be conditioned in a circulating air oven with the temperature controlled at 46 °C to 49 °C for 60 min. The device and test fixture shall be removed from the oven and without remounting (repressing of adhesive tape or tightening of mounting screws) placed on the vibration test machine and vibrated for 60 min.

4.1.2 MOISTURE

4.1.2.1 Either the Water Spray Moisture Test or Water Submersion Test may be used to test reflex reflectors.

4.1.2.2 Water Spray Moisture Test

4.1.2.2.1 If the reflex reflector is a separate unit and not combined with a lighting device, the light source on-off cycle during the water spray moisture test is not applicable.

4.1.2.2.2 Upon completion of the drain period, the interior of the device shall be observed for moisture accumulation that can be formed by tapping or tilting the device.

4.1.3 DUST

4.1.3.1 If the reflex reflector is a separate unit and not combined with a lighting device, the light source on-off cycle during the dust test is not applicable.

4.1.4 CORROSION

4.1.4.1 If the reflex reflector is a separate unit and not combined with a lighting device, the light source on-off cycle during the corrosion test is not applicable.

4.1.5 PHOTOMETRY

4.1.5.1 The reflex reflector shall be set up for testing as shown in Figure 1.

4.1.5.2 The reflex reflector shall be mounted on the goniometer in accordance with the manufacturer's instructions and with the center of the reflex area at the center of rotation and at the same horizontal level as the source of illumination.

4.1.5.3 The test distance shall be 30 m. The source of illumination shall be a lamp with a 50 mm ± 5 mm effective diameter and with a filament operating at nominal 2856 K color temperature.

4.1.5.4 The observation point shall be located directly above the source of illumination and the opening to the photocell shall not be more than 13 mm vertical by 25 mm horizontal.

4.1.5.5 The H-V axis of the reflex reflector shall be taken as being parallel to the longitudinal axis of the vehicle for front and rear reflectors and perpendicular to a vertical plane passing through the longitudinal axis of the vehicle for side reflectors.

4.1.5.6 Reflex reflectors may have any linear or area dimension but for the photometric test a maximum projected area of 7740 mm² contained within a 254 mm diameter circle shall be exposed.

4.1.5.7 If uncolored reflections from the front surface interfere with the photometric readings at any test point, the operator shall check 1 degree above, below, right, and left of the test point, and report the lowest reading and location. The lowest reading shall meet the minimum requirements for that test point.

4.1.5.8 Type 1 reflex reflectors, which do not require a fixed mounted position on the vehicle, shall be rotated about their axis through 360 degrees to find the millicandela per incident lux (minimum candela per incident footcandle) which shall be reported for each test point. If the output falls below the minimum requirements at any test point, the reflector shall be rotated ±5 degrees about its axis from the angle where the minimum output occurred and highest reading and location reported. The highest reading shall meet the minimum requirements for the test point.

4.1.5.9 Type 2, Wide Angle Reflex Reflectors, that maybe directional and may require a fixed orientation shall be mounted in their design position and in accordance with the manufacturer's instructions.

4.1.6 WARPAGE—The device mounted in its design position shall be placed in a circulating air oven with the temperature controlled at 46 °C to 49 °C for 60 min.

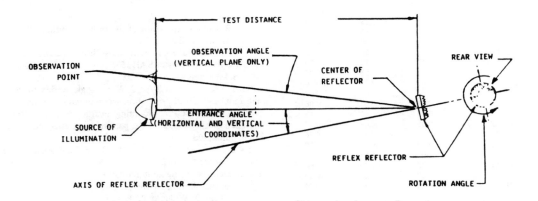

FIGURE 1—REFLEX REFLECTOR SETUP FOR TESTING

4.2 Color—The test sample may be either the reflex reflector or a disc of the same material, technique of fabrication and dye formulation as the reflex reflector.

If a disc is used, the thickness shall be twice the thickness of the reflector as measured from the face of the lens to the apexes of the reflecting elements.

4.3 Plastic Material—SAE J576.

5. Requirements

5.1 Performance Requirements—A device when tested in accordance with the test procedures of this document shall meet the requirements, of SAE J2139.

5.1.1 VIBRATION—Upon completion of the vibration test the reflector shall not have become separated from its mounting means. A Type 2 Wide Angle Reflex Reflector that is directional and requires a fixed orientation when mounted on the vehicle shall not rotate more than 2 degrees above or below the horizontal mounting line, unless the reflector meets all photometric requirements of Table 1 or Table 1A at the maximum rotation.

TABLE 1—WIDE ANGLE REFLEX REFLECTORS PHOTOMETRIC PERFORMANCE REQUIREMENTS
MILLICANDELA PER INCIDENT LUX

Obs. Angle (deg)	Ent. Angle (deg)		Red	Yellow	White
	10U	V	420	1050	1680
	5U	45L	50	125	200
		45R	50	125	200
		30L	185	465	740
		20L	280	700	1120
0.2	H	V	420	1050	1680
		20R	280	700	1120
		30R	185	465	740
	5D	45L	50	125	200
		45R	50	125	200
	10D	V	420	1050	1680
	10U	V	5	12	20
	5U	45L	2	5	8
		45R	2	5	8
		30L	3	7	12
		20L	3	7	12
1.5	H	V	6	15	24
		20R	3	7	12
		30R	3	7	12
	5D	45L	2	5	8
		45R	2	5	8
	10D	V	5	12	20

NOTE—Unless otherwise specified, the reflector shall be considered to have failed the photometric requirements of this document if the millicandela per incident lux between test points is less than the lowest values specified for the closest adjacent test points on a horizontal and vertical line defined by the test point pattern of Table 1A.

TABLE 1A—TYPE 2 WIDE ANGLE REFLEX REFLECTORS PHOTOMETRIC PERFORMANCE REQUIREMENTS
CANDELA PER INCIDENT FOOTCANDLE

Obs. Angle (deg)	Ent. Angle (deg)		Red	Yellow	White
	10U	V	4.50	11.25	18.00
	5U	45L	0.50	1.25	2.00
		45R	0.50	1.25	2.00
		30L	2.00	5.00	8.00
		20L	3.00	7.50	12.00
0.2	H	V	4.50	11.25	18.00
		20R	3.00	7.50	12.00
		30R	2.00	5.00	8.00
	5D	45L	0.50	1.25	2.00
		45R	0.50	1.25	2.00
	10D	V	4.50	11.25	18.00
	10U	V	0.05	0.12	0.20
	5U	45L	0.02	0.05	0.08
		45R	0.02	0.05	0.08
		30L	0.03	0.07	0.12
		20L	0.03	0.07	0.12
1.5	H	V	0.07	0.17	0.28
		20R	0.03	0.07	0.12
		30R	0.03	0.07	0.12
	5D	45L	0.02	0.05	0.08
		45R	0.02	0.05	0.08
	10D	V	0.05	0.12	0.20

NOTE—Unless otherwise specified, the reflector shall be considered to have failed the photometric requirements of this document if the candela per incident footcandle between test points is less than the lowest values specified for the closest adjacent test points on a horizontal and vertical line defined by the test point pattern of Table 1.

5.1.2 MOISTURE

5.1.2.1 Upon completion of the moisture test, the reflex reflector shall not have become separated from its mounting means.

5.1.3 DUST

5.1.3.1 Upon completion of the dust test, the reflex reflector shall not have become separated from its mounting means.

5.1.4 CORROSION

5.1.4.1 Upon completion of the corrosion test, the reflex reflector shall not have become separated from its mounting means.

5.1.5 PHOTOMETRY

5.1.5.1 Type 1, Reflex Reflectors shall meet the photometric performance requirements of Table 2 or Table 2A and the footnotes.

5.1.5.2 Type 2, Wide Angle Reflex Reflectors shall meet the photometric performance requirements of Table 1 or Table 1A and the footnotes.

TABLE 2—TYPE 1 REFLEX REFLECTORS PHOTOMETRIC PERFORMANCE REQUIREMENTS
MILLICANDELA PER INCIDENT LUX

Obs. Angle (deg)	Ent. Angle (deg)		Red	Yellow	White
	10U	V	280	700	1120
		20L	140	350	560
0.2	H	V	420	1050	1680
		20R	140	350	560
	10D	V	280	700	1120
	10U	V	5	12	20
		20L	3	7	12
1.5	H	V	6	15	24
		20R	3	7	12
	10D	V	5	12	20

TABLE 2A—TYPE 1 REFLEX REFLECTORS PHOTOMETRIC PERFORMANCE REQUIREMENTS
CANDELA PER INCIDENT FOOTCANDLE

Obs. Angle (deg)	Ent. Angle (deg)		Red	Yellow	White
	10U	V	3.0	7.5	12.00
		20L	1.5	3.75	6.00
0.2	H	V	4.5	11.25	18.00
		20R	1.5	3.75	6.00
	10D	V	3.0	7.5	12.00
	10U	V	0.05	0.12	0.20
		20L	0.03	0.07	0.12
1.5	H	V	0.07	0.17	0.28
		20R	0.03	0.07	0.12
	10D	V	0.05	0.12	0.20

5.1.6 WARPAGE

5.2 Color—The color of the reflected light shall be red, yellow, or white as specified in SAE J578.

5.3 Material Requirements—Plastic materials used in optical parts shall meet the requirements of SAE J576.

5.4 Design Requirements

5.4.1 The face of a Type 2 Wide Angle Reflex Reflector that is directional and requires a fixed orientation when mounted on the vehicle shall be marked with the word TOP. Mounting instructions, including a diagram, shall be included on the outside of the packaging or attached to the reflector and visible when purchased.

5.4.2 Means shall be provided to keep fixed orientation reflex reflectors from rotating more than 2 degrees unless the reflector meets all photometric requirements at the maximum rotation.

5.5 Installation Requirements

5.5.1 Type 2, Wide Angle Reflex Reflectors that are directional may require mounting on the vehicle in a fixed orientation to be effective and shall be mounted on the vehicle in accordance with the manufacturer's instructions.

5.5.2 Type 1 and Type 2 reflectors shall be mounted not less than 380 mm nor more than 1525 mm above the road surface as measured from the center of the reflector at vehicle curb weight.

5.5.3 Visibility of the reflected light shall not be obstructed by any part of the vehicle throughout the specified photometric test pattern unless the reflector is designed to comply with these obstructions in place.

5.5.4 The reflex reflector shall be mounted on the rigid structure of the vehicle.

6. Guidelines—The following guidelines apply to Type 1 and/or Type 2 Reflex Reflectors used on the vehicle and shall not be considered a part of the requirements.

6.1 Design Guidelines

6.1.1 A Type 1 or a Type 2 reflex reflector may be combined with a stop lamp, turn signal lamp, tail lamp, clearance lamp, side marker lamp, identification lamp, or side turn signal lamp.

6.2 Installation Guidelines

6.2.1 It is suggested that Type 2 wide angle reflex reflectors be mounted on the corners of the vehicle facing front and rear and to each side. Type 1 reflex reflectors may be used at other mounting locations as one method of improving passive vehicle delineation.

(R) CLEARANCE, SIDEMARKER, AND IDENTIFICATION LAMPS FOR USE ON MOTOR VEHICLES 2032 mm OR MORE IN OVERALL WIDTH—SAE J2042 JUN96

SAE Standard

Report of the SAE Lighting Coordinating Committee and the Heavy-Duty Lighting Standards Committee approved June 1991. Rationale statement available. Completely revised by the SAE Lighting Forum Committee and the Heavy-Duty Lighting Standards Committee June 1996. Rationale statement available.

1. Scope—This SAE Standard provides test procedures, requirements, and guidelines for clearance, sidemarker, and identification lamps intended for use on vehicles 2032 mm or more in overall width. A clearance lamp, sidemarker lamps, or an identification lamp conforming to the requirements of this document may be used on vehicles less than 2032 mm in overall width.

2. References

2.1 Applicable Documents—The following publications form a part of this specification to the extent specified herein. The latest issue of SAE publications shall apply.

2.1.1 SAE PUBLICATIONS—Available from SAE, 400 Commonwealth Drive, Warrendale, PA 15096-001.

SAE J387—Terminology—Motor Vehicle Lighting

SAE J567—Lamp Bulb Retention System

SAE J576—Plastic Material for Use in Optical Parts Such as Lenses and Reflectors of Motor Vehicle Lighting Devices

SAE J578—Color Specification

SAE J592—Clearance, Sidemarker, and Identification Lamps

SAE J759—Lighting Identification Code

SAE J1889—L.E.D. Lighting Devices

SAE J2139—Tests for Lighting Devices, Reflective Devices, and Components Used on Vehicles 2032 mm or More in Overall Width.

2.1.2 OTHER PUBLICATIONS—Attention is called to the following documents for additional information on lamp design and installation requirements.

Federal Motor Vehicle Safety Standards 49CFR 571.108

Federal Highway Administration 49CFR Part 393 Subpart B

Truck Trailer Manufacturers Association RP-9

The Maintenance Council RP-702

3. Definitions

3.1 Clearance Lamp—A clearance lamp provides light to the front or rear of a vehicle to indicate the overall width and height.

3.2 Sidemarker Lamp—A sidemarker lamp provides light to the side of a vehicle to indicate the overall length of the vehicle. Additional sidemarker lamps may also be mounted at intermediate locations on the side of the vehicle. The rear sidemarker lamp used on a trailer is also referred to as a tracking lamp.

3.3 Identification lamp—An identification lamp is a group of three lamps in a horizontal row which provide light to the front or rear or both, having a light center spacing of not less than 150 mm nor more than 300 mm apart, to identify vehicles 2032 mm or more in overall width.

3.4 Combination Clearance and Sidemarker Lamp—A combination clearance and sidemarker lamp is a single lamp which simultaneously meets the requirements of a clearance and a sidemarker lamp.

4. Lighting Identification Code—Clearance, sidemarker, or identification lamps may be identified by the code "P3"; combination clearance and sidemarker lamps may be identified by the code "PC2," in accordance with SAE J759.

5. Tests

5.1 SAE J2139 is a part of this document. The following tests are applicable with modification as indicated.

5.1.1 VIBRATION

5.1.2 MOISTURE

5.1.3 DUST

5.1.4 CORROSION

5.1.5 PHOTOMETRY

5.1.5.1 The photometric test shall be made at a device distance of at least 3 m from the photometer.

5.1.5.2 The H-V axis of a clearance or identification lamp shall be taken to be parallel to the longitudinal axis of the vehicle, when the device is mounted in its design position.

5.1.5.3 The H-V axis of a sidemarker lamp shall be taken to be perpendicular to a vertical plane passing through the longitudinal axis of the vehicle, when mounted in its design position.

5.1.5.4 The H-V axis of a combination clearance and sidemarker lamp shall be taken to be parallel to the longitudinal axis of the vehicle when testing the clearance lamp function, and perpendicular to a vertical plane passing through the longitudinal axis of the vehicle when testing the sidemarker lamp function, when the device is mounted in its design position.

5.1.6 WARPAGE TEST ON DEVICES WITH PLASTIC COMPONENTS

5.2 Color—SAE J578 is a part of this document.

5.3 Plastic Materials—SAE J576 is a part of this document.

6. Requirements

6.1 Performance Requirements—The device when tested in accordance with the test procedures of this document shall meet the requirements of SAE J2139 or as indicated.

6.1.1 VIBRATION

6.1.2 MOISTURE

6.1.3 DUST

6.1.4 CORROSION

6.1.5 PHOTOMETRY—The device tested shall meet the photometric performance requirements of Table 1 and its footnotes, except that front yellow clearance and identification lamps that are roof mounted on the vehicle need not meet the photometric requirements at 20 degrees down; 45 degrees left to 45 degrees right. Zone totals should be reduced by the values as listed in Table 2, when testing a lamp designed for this application.

The summation of the luminous intensity measurements at the specified test points in a zone shall be at least the value shown.

6.1.5.1 When a clearance lamp is combined with a stop lamp or a turn signal lamp, the stop lamp or turn signal lamp intensity shall be not less than three times the luminous intensity of the clearance lamp at any test point, except that at H-V, H-5L, H-5R, and 5U-V, the stop lamp or turn signal lamp intensity shall be not less than five times the luminous intensity of the clearance lamp.

6.1.6 WARPAGE

6.2 Color—The color of the light from the front clearance lamps, the front identification lamps, and the front and intermediate sidemarker lamps shall be yellow.

The color of the light from the rear clearance lamps, rear identification lamps, and the rear sidemarker lamp (aka a tracking lamp on a trailer) shall be red.

The color shall meet the requirements of SAE J578.

6.3 Plastic Materials—The plastic materials used in the optical parts shall meet the requirements of SAE J576.

6.4 Design Requirements

6.4.1 A clearance lamp shall not be combined with a tail lamp.

6.4.2 A clearance lamp may be combined with a turn signal lamp or a stop lamp.

6.4.3 A sidemarker lamp may be combined with a side turn signal lamp.

6.4.4 A clearance lamp, identification lamp, or a sidemarker lamp may be combined with a reflex reflector.

6.4.5 If a clearance lamp is combined with a turn signal lamp or a stop lamp, or if a sidemarker lamp is combined with a side turn signal lamp, and a replaceable multiple light source is used, the light source retention system shall be designed with an indexing feature in order to insure that the light source is properly indexed. Removable light source retention systems shall have an indexing feature so that they cannot be reinserted into the lamp housing in a random position, unless the lamp will perform its intended function with random light source orientation.

6.5 Installation Requirements

6.5.1 Clearance lamps shall be mounted on the permanent structure of the vehicle as near as practicable to the upper left and right extreme edges of the vehicle.

6.5.2 Sidemarker lamps shall be mounted on the permanent structure of the vehicle not less than 380 mm above the road surface measured from the center of the device at vehicle curb weight.

An intermediate yellow sidemarker lamp shall be mounted at the midpoint on vehicles 7.6 m or more in overall length.

The red, rear sidemarker lamp, used on trailers, also referred to as a tracking lamp, shall be mounted on the permanent structure of the trailer not less than 380 mm nor more than 1525 mm above the road surface measured from the center of the lamp at trailer curb weight.

6.5.3 Identification lamps shall be mounted on the permanent structure of the vehicle as near as practicable to the vehicle centerline and to the top of the vehicle.

6.5.4 When the rear identification lamps are mounted at the extreme height of the vehicle, rear clearance lamps need not meet the requirement that they be mounted as close as practicable to the top of the vehicle.

6.5.5 The lamps shall be designed to comply with all photometric requirements of Table 1 as installed on the vehicle, with all vehicular obstructions considered, except that yellow clearance and identification lamps that are roof mounted need not meet the photometric requirements of 20 degrees down, 45 degrees left to 45 degrees right.

7. Guidelines
7.1 Design Guidelines

7.1.1 Photometrics—Photometric design guidelines are contained in Table 2 and its footnotes.

7.2 Installation Guidelines

7.2.1 The following guidelines apply to devices used on the vehicle and shall not be considered part of the requirements.

7.2.2 Performance of the lamps may deteriorate significantly as a result of dirt, grime, snow, and ice accumulation on the optical surfaces. Installation of the device on vehicles should be considered to minimize the effect of these factors.

7.2.3 In instances where severe environments are expected, such as in off-highway, mining, fuel haulage, or where it is expected to be totally immersed in water, the user should specify devices specifically designed for such use.

TABLE 1—CLEARANCE, SIDEMARKER, AND IDENTIFICATION LAMP PHOTOMETRIC PERFORMANCE REQUIREMENTS

Zone	Test Points (Degrees)	Zone Total Luminous Intensity-Red (Candela)	Zone Total Luminous Intensity-Yellow (Candela)
1	20U - 45L		
	10U - 45L		
	H - 45L	1.4	3.4
	10D - 45L		
	20D - 45L		
2	10U - V		
	H - V	1.2	3.0
	10D - V		
3	20U - 45R		
	10U - 45R		
	H - 45R	1.4	3.4
	10D - 45 R		
	20D - 45R		
Maximum Luminous Intensity, Candela Red, rear only		18.0	

1. The maximum luminous intensity shall not be exceeded over any area larger than that generated by a 0.5 degree radius within the area defined by the test point pattern of Table 2. When red clearance lamps are optically combined with stop and turn signal lamps the maximum applies only on or above the horizontal.
2. Unless otherwise specified, the lamp shall be considered to have failed the photometric requirements of this document if the luminous intensity at any test point is less than 60% of the values specified in Table 2.
3. Combination clearance and sidemarker lamps shall conform with both clearance and sidemarker lamp photometric performance requirements.
4. The summation of the luminous intensity measurements at the specified test points in a zone shall be at least the values shown.
5. When a clearance lamp is combined with a stop lamp or a turn signal lamp, see 6.1.5.1 of this document for luminous intensity ratio requirements.

TABLE 2—CLEARANCE, SIDEMARKER, AND IDENTIFICATION LAMP PHOTOMETRIC DESIGN GUIDELINES

Test Points (Degrees)	Luminous Intensity-Red (Candela)	Luminous Intensity-Yellow (Candela)
20U - 45L	0.10	0.20
45R	0.10	0.20
10U - 45L	0.40	1.0
V	0.40	1.0
45R	0.40	1.0
H - 45L	0.40	1.0
V	0.40	1.0
45R	0.40	1.0
10D - 45L	0.40	1.0
V	0.40	1.0
45R	0.40	1.0
20D - 45L	0.10	0.20
45R	0.10	0.20
Maximum Luminous Intensity, Candela Red, rear only	18.0	

1. The maximum luminous intensity shall not be exceeded over any area larger than that generated by a 0.25 degree radius within the solid angle defined by the test points in Table 2.
2. For combined clearance and sidemarker lamps, both clearance and sidemarker photometric design guidelines shall apply.
3. When a clearance lamp is combined with a stop lamp or a turn signal lamp, see 6.1.5.1 of this document for luminous intensity ratio requirements.
4. When making photometric measurements at specific test points, the minimum candela values between test points shall not be less than the lower specified value of the two closet adjacent test points on a horizontal or vertical line.

STOP LAMPS AND FRONT- AND REAR-TURN SIGNAL LAMPS FOR USE ON MOTOR VEHICLES 2032 mm OR MORE IN OVERALL WIDTH—SAE J2261 MAR96   SAE Standard

Report of the SAE Heavy-Duty Lighting Standards Committee approved March 1996. Rationale statement available.

1. Scope—This SAE Standard provides test procedures, requirements, and guidelines for stop lamps and turn signal lamps intended for use on vehicles 2032 mm or more in overall width. Stop lamps and front- and rear-turn signal lamps conforming to the requirements of this document may be used on vehicles less than 2032 mm in overall width.

2. References

2.1 Applicable Documents—The following publications form a part of this specification to the extent specified herein. Unless otherwise specified, the latest issue of SAE publications shall apply.

2.1.1 SAE PUBLICATIONS—Available from SAE, 400 Commonwealth Drive, Warrendale, PA 15096-0001.

SAE J576—Plastic Material for Use in Optical Parts Such as Lenses and Reflectors of Motor Vehicle Lighting Devices

SAE J578—Color Specification

SAE J1050—Describing and Measuring the Drivers Field of View

SAE J1889—LED Lighting Devices

SAE J2139—Tests for Lighting Devices, Reflective Devices and Components Used on Vehicles 2032 mm or More in Overall Width

2.2 Related Publications—The following publications are provided for information purposes only and are not a required part of this document.

2.2.1 SAE PUBLICATIONS—Available from SAE, 400 Commonwealth Drive, Warrendale, PA 15096-0001.

SAE J387—Terminology—Motor Vehicle Lighting

SAE J567—Lamp Bulb Retention System for Requirements and Gages Used in Retention System Design

SAE J586—Stop Lamps for Use on Motor Vehicles Less Than 2032 mm in Overall Width

SAE J588—Turn Signal Lamps for Use on Motor Vehicles Less Than 2032 mm in Overall Width

SAE J590—Turn Signal Flashers

SAE J759—Lighting Identification Code

SAE Technical Paper 830566—"Motor Vehicle Conspicuity," R.L. Henderson, K. Ziedman, W.J. Burger, and K.E. Cavey, National Highway Traffic Safety Administration

2.2.2 FMVSS PUBLICATION—Available from The Superintendent of Documents, U.S. Government Printing Office, Washington, DC 20402.

Federal Motor Vehicle Safety Standard 49CFR 571.108

2.2.3 OTHER

Federal Highway Administration 49CFR Part 393 Subpart B

Truck Trailer Manufacturers Association RP-9

The Maintenance Council RP-702

3 Definitions

3.1 Effective Projected Luminous Lens Area—That area of the light emitting surface projected on a plane at right angles to the axis of a lamp, excluding reflex reflectors (but including congruent reflexes), which is not obstructed by opaque objects such as mounting screws, mounting rings, bezels, or trim, or similar ornamental feature areas. Areas of optical or other configurations, for example, molded-optical rings or markings, shall be considered part of the total effective projected luminous lens area. The axis of the lamp corresponds to the H-V axis used for photometric requirements.

3.2 Stop Lamp—A lamp giving a steady light to the rear of a vehicle to indicate the intention of the operator of the vehicle to stop or diminish speed by application of the service brakes.

3.3 Turn Signal Lamp—The signaling element of a turn signal system which indicates intent to change vehicle direction by giving a flashing light on the side toward which the turn or lane change will be made. See SAE J590 for flash rate and percent on time.

4. Lighting Identification Code

4.1 Turn signal lamps for use on vehicles 2032 mm or more in overall width may be identified by the code:

    a. "I6" for a rear-mounted turn signal lamp and for a front-turn signal lamp mounted 100 mm or more from the headlamp.

    b. "I7" for a front-mounted turn signal lamp mounted less than 100 mm from the headlamp, in accordance with SAE J759.

4.2 Stop lamps for use on vehicles 2032 mm or more in overall width may be identified by the code "S2" in accordance with SAE J759.

5. Tests

5.1 SAE J2139 is a part of this document. The following tests are applicable with modification as indicated.

5.1.1 VIBRATION

5.1.2 MOISTURE

5.1.3 DUST

5.1.4 CORROSION

5.1.5 PHOTOMETRY

5.1.5.1 Photometric measurements shall be made with the light source of the device at least 3 m from the photometer.

5.1.5.2 The H-V axis of the device shall be taken to be parallel to the longitudinal axis of the vehicle when the device is mounted in its design position.

5.1.5.3 Photometric measurement shall be made with the light source steady burning. Photometric measurements of multiple lamp arrangements may be made by either of the following methods.

5.1.5.3.1 All lamps of a multiple lamp arrangement shall be photometered together provided that a line from the light source of each lamp to the center of the photometer sensing device does not make an angle of more than 0.6 degrees with the photometer H-V axis. When lamps are photometered together, the H-V axis shall intersect the midpoint between the light sources of the lamps on the extremities of a multiple lamp arrangement.

5.1.5.3.2 Each lamp of a multiple lamp arrangement shall be photometered separately. The photometric value for the entire multiple lamp arrangement at any test point shall be determined by adding the photometric outputs from each individual lamp at the corresponding test point.

5.1.6 WARPAGE TEST ON DEVICES WITH PLASTIC COMPONENTS

5.2 Color—SAE J578 is a part of this document.

5.3 Plastic Materials—SAE J576 is a part of this document.

6. Requirements

6.1 Performance Requirements—The device when tested in accordance with the test procedures of this document shall meet the requirements of SAE J2139 or as indicated.

6.1.1 VIBRATION

6.1.2 MOISTURE

6.1.3 DUST

166

6.1.4 CORROSION

6.1.5 PHOTOMETRY—The device tested shall meet the photometric performance requirements of Table 1 and its footnotes.

The summation of the luminous intensity measurements at the specified test points in a zone shall be at least the value shown.

6.1.5.1 Any multiple lamp arrangement may be used to meet the photometric requirements of a stop or turn signal lamp. If multiple lamp arrangements are used and the distance between adjacent light sources does not exceed 560 mm for two-lamp arrangements and does not exceed 410 mm for multiple lamp arrangements, then the combination of the lamps may be used to meet the photometric requirements of Table 1 (see 5.1.5.3.2). If the distance between adjacent light sources exceeds the above dimensions, each lamp shall comply with the photometric requirements of Table 1.

6.1.5.2 When a tail lamp, or clearance lamp is combined with the stop or turn signal lamp, or a parking lamp is combined with a turn signal lamp, the lamp's intensity shall be not less than three times the luminous intensity of the tail lamp, clearance lamp, or a parking lamp at any test point, except that at H-V, H-5L, H-5R, and 5U-V the stop or turn signal lamp's intensity shall be not less than five times the luminous intensity of the tail lamp, clearance lamp, or parking lamp.

When a tail lamp or a clearance lamp is combined with a stop or turn signal lamp and the maximum intensity of the tail lamp or clearance lamp is located below the horizontal and is within an area generated by a 1.0 degree radius around the test point, the ratio for the test point may be computed using the lowest value of the tail lamp or clearance lamp luminous intensity within the generated area.

TABLE 1—STOP AND TURN SIGNAL LAMP PHOTOMETRIC PERFORMANCE REQUIREMENTS

Zone	Test Point Degrees	Zone Total Luminous Intensity Candela, Yellow Front-Turn Lamp	Zone Total Luminous Intensity Candela, Red Rear Stop or Turn Lamp	Zone Total Luminous Intensity Candela, Yellow Rear-Turn Lamp
1	20U-45L 20U-20L 10D-20L 10D-45L	30	12	20
2	10U-5L 5U-20L 5D-20L 10D-5L	130	50	84
3	5U-10L H-10L 5D-10L	250	100	165
4	5U-V H-5L H-V H-5R 5D-V	950	380	610
5	5U-10R H-10R 5D-10R	250	100	165
6	10U-5R 5U-20R 5D-20R 10D-5R	130	50	84
7	20U-45R 20U-20R 10D-20R 10D-45R	30	12	20
	MAXIMUM LUMINOUS INTENSITY, CANDELA	—	300	750

1 The maximum luminous intensity shall not be exceeded over any area larger than that generated by a 0.5 degree radius within the area defined by the test point pattern of Table 2.

2 The measured values at each test point shall not be less than 60% of the minimum value in Table 2.

3 The summation of the luminous intensity measurements at the specified test points in the zone shall be at least the values shown.

4 When a tail lamp or a clearance lamp is combined with a stop or turn signal lamp, or a parking lamp is combined with a turn signal lamp, see 6.1.5.2 of this document for luminous intensity ratio requirements.

5 Photometric requirements beyond 20 degrees inboard do not apply to turn signal lamps. Adjust zone totals accordingly.

6.1.5.3 Rear signals from a forward mounted double-faced turn signal lamp need only meet the performance requirements contained in Table 1 from directly to the rear to the left for a left-hand lamp, and from directly to the rear to the right for a right-hand lamp. The intent is to permit the manufacturer to provide glare protection for the driver.

6.1.5.4 When a front-turn signal lamp is mounted less than 100 mm from the low beam headlamp as measured from the closest lighted edge of the low beam headlamp (or any additional lamp used to supplement or used in lieu of the low beam, such as a daytime running lamp, auxiliary low beam or fog lamp) to the optical center of the turn signal lamp, the turn signal lamps luminous intensity shall not be less than 2.5 times the values specified in Table 1 for a front-turn signal lamp.

6.1.5.5 When a front-turn signal lamp is mounted less than 100 mm from a daytime running lamp, as measured from the closest lighted edge of the daytime running lamp to the optical center of the turn signal lamp, the daytime running lamp shall not have more than 2600 candela throughout the pattern and the turn signal lamps luminous intensity shall not be less than 2.5 times the values specified in Table 1 for a front-turn signal lamp.

6.1.5.6 Paragraph 6.1.5.5 does not apply if the daytime running lamp adjacent to the turn signal lamp is deactivated when that turn signal lamp is activated.

6.1.6 WARPAGE

6.2 Color—The color of the light from the front-turn signal lamp shall be yellow and the color from the rear-turn signal lamp may be red or yellow as specified in SAE J578. The color of the light from the stop lamp shall be red as specified in SAE J578.

6.3 Plastic Materials—The plastic materials used in the optical parts shall meet the requirements of SAE J576.

6.4 Design Requirements

6.4.1 If a stop lamp or a turn signal lamp is combined with a tail lamp or a clearance lamp (or a parking lamp is combined with a turn signal lamp), and a replaceable multiple light source is used, the light source retention system shall be designed with an indexing means so that the light source is properly indexed. Removable light source retention systems shall have an indexing feature so that they cannot be reinserted into the lamp housing in a random position, unless the lamp will perform its intended function with random light source orientation.

6.4.2 The effective projected luminous lighted area of a lamp shall be at least 75 cm².

6.5 Installation Requirements—The stop or turn signal lamp shall meet the following requirements as installed on the vehicle.

6.5.1 The stop or turn signal lamps, facing rearward for the rear lamp and the turn signal lamp facing forward for the front lamp, shall be rigidly mounted on the permanent structure of the vehicle, at the same height, and spaced as far apart laterally as practicable, so that the signal will be clearly visible.

6.5.2 Each stop lamp and front and rear-turn signal lamp shall be designed to comply with all photometric requirements of Table 1 with all vehicular obstructions considered.

6.5.3 Each front- and rear-turn signal lamp shall be designed to comply with one of the following visibility requirements.

6.5.3.1 The lamp must provide a minimum of 13 cm² of unobstructed projected area when the light emitting surface of the lens, excluding reflex reflector area, is projected parallel to a horizontal plane in any direction from 45 degrees outboard to 20 degrees inboard of the vehicle longitudinal axis, and parallel to a longitudinal, vertical plane in any direction from 15 degrees above to 15 degrees below (see 6.5.5) the horizontal (see Figure 1):

6.5.3.2 The lamp must provide a luminous intensity not less than 0.3 candela throughout the photometric pattern defined by the corner points specified as follows and as shown in Figure 2:

a. Driver side front lamp and passenger side rear lamp: 15U-80L, 15U-45R, 15D-80L, 15D-45R (see 6.5.5).

b. Passenger side front lamp and drivers side rear lamp: 15U-45L, 15U-80R, 15D-45L, 15D-80R (see 6.5.5).

6.5.4 Each stop lamp shall be designed to comply with one of the following visibility requirements.

6.5.4.1 The lamp must provide a minimum of 13 cm² of unobstructed projected area when the light emitting surface area of the lens, excluding reflex reflector area, is projected parallel to a horizontal plane in any direction from 45 degrees outboard to 45 degrees inboard of the vehicle longitudinal axis, and parallel to a longitudinal, vertical plane in any direction from 15 degrees above to 15 degrees below (see 6.5.5) the horizontal (see Figure 3):

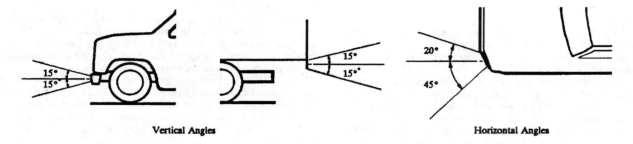

Vertical Angles

Horizontal Angles

FIGURE 1—LEFT SIDE SHOWN RIGHT SIDE SYMMETRICAL

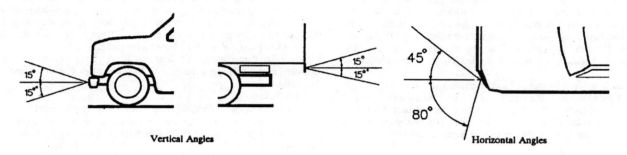

Vertical Angles

Horizontal Angles

FIGURE 2—LEFT SIDE SHOWN RIGHT SIDE SYMMETRICAL

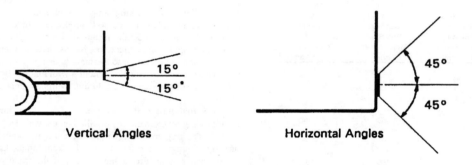

Vertical Angles

Horizontal Angles

FIGURE 3—LEFT SIDE SHOWN RIGHT SIDE SYMMETRICAL

6.5.4.2 The lamp must provide a luminous intensity not less than 0.3 candela throughout the photometric pattern defined by the corner points 15U,-45L, 15U-45R, 15D-45L, 15D-45R (see 6.5.5). See Figure 4.

6.5.5 The downward angle (see 6.5.3.1, 6.5.3.2, 6.5.4.1, and 6.5.4.2) may be reduced to 5 degrees if the lower lighted edge of the lamp is less than 750 mm above the ground.

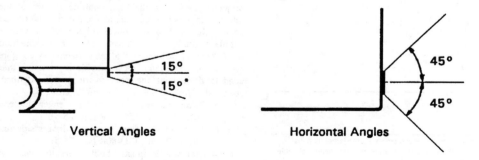

Vertical Angles

Horizontal Angles

FIGURE 4—LEFT SIDE SHOWN RIGHT SIDE SYMMETRICAL

6.5.6 Where more than one stop lamp or front- or rear-turn signal lamp or optical area is lighted on each side of the vehicle, only one such area need comply.

6.5.7 TURN SIGNAL PILOT INDICATOR

6.5.7.1 If one right and one left turn signal lamp are not readily visible to the driver, there shall be an illuminated indicator provided to give a clear and unmistakable indication that the turn signal system is activated. The illuminated indicator shall consist of one or more lights flashing at the same frequency as the turn signal lamps.

6.5.7.2 If the illuminated indicator is located inside the vehicle, it shall emit a green colored light and have a minimum functional lighted area of 18 mm^2.

6.5.7.3 If the illuminated indicators are located outside of the vehicle, they shall emit a yellow colored light and have a minimum functional lighted area of 60 mm^2.

6.5.7.4 The minimum required illuminated lighted area of the indicators shall be visible according to the procedures described in SAE J1050.

The steering wheel shall be turned to a straight-ahead driving position and in the design location for an adjustable wheel or column.

7. Guidelines

7.1 Design Guidelines

7.1.1 Photometric design guidelines are contained in Table 2 and its footnotes.

7.2 Installation Guidelines—The following guidelines apply to stop and turn signal lamps as used on the vehicle and shall not be considered part of the requirements.

7.2.1 Performance of lamps may deteriorate significantly as a result of dirt, grime, snow, and ice accumulation on the optical surfaces. Installation of the device on the vehicle should be considered to minimize the effects of these factors.

7.2.2 Where it is expected that the device must perform in extremely severe environments, or where it is expected to be totally immersed in water, the user should specify devices specifically designed for such use.

7.2.3 The luminous intensity of the light source will vary with applied voltage. The electrical wiring in the vehicle should be designed to supply adequate voltage to the lamp.

7.2.4 When designing the wiring circuit for the stop lamps the extra load that anti-lock braking systems (ABS) contribute must be considered and wiring should be sized accordingly so that adequate power is provided for the lamps to function as well as the braking system.

TABLE 2—STOP AND TURN SIGNAL LAMP PHOTOMETRIC DESIGN GUIDELINES

Test Point Degrees	Minimum Luminous Intensity Candela, Yellow Front-Turn Lamp	Minimum Luminous Intensity Candela, Red Rear Stop or Turn Lamp	Minimum Luminous Intensity Candela, Yellow Rear-Turn Lamp
20U-45L	2.5	1	2
20L	12.5	5	8
20R	12.5	5	8
45R	2.5	1	2
10U-5L	40	16	27
5R	40	16	27
5U-20L	25	10	15
10L	75	30	50
V	175	70	110
10R	75	30	50
20R	25	10	15
H-10L	100	40	65
5L	200	80	130
V	200	80	130
5R	200	80	130
10R	100	40	65
5D-20L	25	10	15
10L	75	30	50
V	175	70	110
10R	75	30	50
20R	25	10	15
10D-45L	2.5	1	2
20L	12.5	5	8
5L	40	16	27
5R	40	16	27
20R	12.5	5	8
45R	2.5	1	2
MAXIMUM LUMINOUS INTENSITY	—	300	750

1 The maximum luminous intensity shall not be exceeded over any area larger than that generated by a 0.25 degree radius within the area defined by the test point pattern of Table 2.

2 When a tail lamp or a clearance lamp is combined with a stop or turn signal lamp, or a parking lamp is combined with a turn signal lamp, see 6.1.5.2 of this document for luminous intensity ratio requirements.

3 Photometric requirements beyond 20 degrees inboard do not apply to turn signal lamps.

4 When making photometric measurements at specific test points, the candela values between test points shall not be less than the lower specified value of the two closest adjacent test points on a horizontal or vertical line for minimum values.

Report of Lighting Committee approved February 1972, and completely revised June 1988.

1. Purpose—This standard defines the test conditions, procedures, and performance specifications for 6-, 12-, and 24-V manually actuated mechanical stop lamp switches.

2. Definition—The mechanical stop lamp switch is an operator activated mechanical device intended primarily to control the functioning of the stop lamp and high mounted stop lamp circuits. Secondarily, the device may control the functioning of various accessories, such as disengaging cruise control, with operator actuation of brake pedal.

3. Test Requirements

3.1 Test Equipment and Instrumentation

3.1.1 POWER SUPPLY—The power supply shall comply with the following specifications:

    a. Output Current—capable of supplying the continuous and in-rush currents of the design load (reference paragraph 3.2.1.1).

    b. Regulation:

    Dynamic—the output voltage at the supply shall not deviate more than 1.0 V from zero to maximum load (including in-rush current) and should recover 63% of its maximum excursion within 100 ms.

    Static—the output voltage at the supply shall not deviate more than 2% with changes in static load from zero to maximum (not including in-rush current), and means shall be provided to compensate for static input line voltage variations.

    c. Ripple Voltage—maximum 300 mV peak-to-peak.

3.1.2 VOLTMETER—0 - 30 maximum full scale deflection, accuracy ± ½%.

NOTE—A digital meter having at least 3½ digit readout with an accuracy of ±1% plus one digit is recommended for millivolt readings.)

3.1.3 AMMETER—Capable of carrying full system load current, accuracy ±3%.

3.2 Test Procedures—Environmental conditions have been selected for this standard to help assure satisfactory operation under general customer use conditions. It is essential to duplicate specific environmental conditions under which the device is expected to function.

3.2.1 ELECTRICAL LOADS

3.2.1.1 The design load applied to the switch is the electrical load specified by the number and type of bulbs (or other electrical load devices) to be operated by each circuit of the switch. For example, the design load for the stop lamp circuit may be two #1157 (high current filament) and high mounted stop lamp circuit may be two #922 bulbs.

The switch shall be operated at 6.4 ± 0.2 V DC for a 6 V system, 12.8 ± 0.2 V DC for a 12 V system, or 25.6 ± 0.2 V DC for a 24 V system. These voltages shall be open circuit voltage measured at the input termination on the switch.

3.2.2 TEMPERATURE TEST PROCEDURES

3.2.2.1 The switch shall be exposed for 1 h without electrical load to each of the following temperatures: 25 ± 5°C; 74 + 0°C, −3°C; −32 + 3°C, −0°C. The switch shall be manually cycled at each temperature for ten cycles at design load.

3.2.2.2 The same switch shall be used for the endurance test described in Section 3.2.3.

3.2.3 ENDURANCE TEST PROCEDURE

3.2.3.1 The switch shall be electrically connected to operate its design load (both primary and secondary circuit function design electrical loads) at a temperature of 25 ± 5°C.

3.2.3.2 The switch shall be operated for a minimum of 300 000 cycles. One complete cycle shall consist of energizing and de-energizing the design load (with a dwell in each position).

The test equipment shall be arranged to provide the following switch operating time requirements:

Travel Time: 0.1 - 0.5 s (time from one position to next)
Dwell Time: 1.0 - 2.0 s (time in each position)
Make & Break Rate: 10 - 15 mm/s

NOTE—300 000 cycles represents 82 cycles of switch operation every day for approximately 10 years, or 3 cycles for each 1.0 mile driven 100 000 miles.

3.2.4 VOLTAGE DROP TEST PROCEDURE

3.2.4.1 The voltage drop from the input terminal(s) to the corresponding output terminal(s) shall be measured at design load before and after the completion of the endurance test and shall be average of three consecutive readings. If wiring is an integral part of the switch, the voltage drop measurement shall be made including 75 ± 6 mm of wire on each side of the switch terminals.

4. Performance Requirements

4.1 During and after each of the cycles described in paragraph 3.2.2.1 and Section 3.2.3, the switch shall be electrically and mechanically operable.

4.2 The voltage drop shall not exceed 0.3 V when measured as in Section 3.2.4, at the beginning and after the test described in Section 3.2.3.

HEADLAMP SWITCH—SAE J253 DEC89

SAE Standard

Report of the Lighting Committee, approved July 1971, completely revised April 1984. Rationale statement available. Reaffirmed by the Auxiliary Devices Standards Committee and the Lighting Coordinating Committee December 1989.

1. Scope—This document defines the test conditions, procedures, and performance specifications for 6-, 12-, and 24-volt manually actuated headlamp switches (circuit breaker(s) may be incorporated for circuit overload protection).

2. Definition—The headlamp switch is an operator-activated device intended primarily to control functioning of headlamps, parking lamps, tail lamps, and certain marking lamps. Secondarily, the device may control functioning of various accessory and instrument lights.

3. Test Requirements

3.1 Test Equipment and Instrumentation

3.1.1 POWER SUPPLY—The power supply shall comply with the following specifications:

a. Output Current—capable of supplying the continuous and in-rush currents of the design load (Reference 3.2.1.1).

b. Regulation

Dynamic—the output voltage at the supply shall not deviate more than 1.0 V from zero to maximum load (including in-rush current) and should recover 63% of its maximum excursion within 100 ms.

Static—the output voltage at the supply shall not deviate more than 2% with changes in static load from zero to maximum (not including in-rush current), and means shall be provided to compensate for static input line voltage variations.

c. Ripple Voltage—maximum 300 mV peak-to-peak.

3.1.2 VOLTMETER—0 to 30 V maximum full scale deflection, accuracy ± ½%.

NOTE: A digital meter having at least a 3-½ digit readout with an accuracy of ± 1% plus one digit is recommended for millivolt readings.

3.1.3 AMMETER—Capable of carrying full system load current, accuracy ± 3%.

3.2 Test Procedures—Environmental conditions have been selected for this document to help assure satisfactory operation under general customer use conditions. It is essential to duplicate specific environmental conditions under which the device is expected to function.

3.2.1 ELECTRICAL LOADS

3.2.1.1 The design load applied to the switch is the electrical load specified by the number and type of bulbs (or other electrical load devices) to be operated by each circuit of the switch. For example, the design load for the headlamp circuit may be four sealed beam headlamp units (2-4651 and 2-4652) and four—#194 bulbs.

3.2.1.2 The switch shall be operated at 6.4 V DC ± 0.2 for a 6-V system, 12.8 V DC ± 0.2 for a 12-V system, or 25.6 V DC ± 0.2 for a 24-V system. These voltages shall be the open circuit voltage measured at the input termination on the switch.

3.2.2 TEMPERATURE TEST PROCEDURES

3.2.2.1 The switch shall be exposed for 1 h without electrical load to each of the following temperatures: 25°C ± 5; 74 + 0°C, −3°C; −32 + 3°C, −0°C. The switch shall be manually cycled at each temperature for ten cycles at design load.

3.2.2.2 The same switch shall be used for the endurance test described in 3.2.3.

3.2.3 ENDURANCE TEST PROCEDURE

3.2.3.1 The switch shall be electrically connected to operate its design load (both primary and secondary circuit function design electrical loads) at a temperature of 25°C ±5.

3.2.3.2 The switch shall be operated for a minimum of 11 000 cycles[1]. One complete cycle shall consist of sequencing through each position (with dwell in each position) and return without dwell in intermediate positions to the initial position.

The test equipment shall be arranged to provide the following switch operating time requirements:

Travel Time:	0.1-0.5 s	(time from one position to the next)
Dwell Time:	1.0-2.0 s	(time in each position)
Make and Break Rate:	130-150	mm/s

3.2.3.3 At the completion of the cycle testing, the switch shall be operated for 1 h in the headlamp position with the design load(s) connected.

3.2.4 VOLTAGE DROP TEST PROCEDURE

3.2.4.1 The voltage drop from the input terminal(s) to the corresponding output terminal(s) shall be measured at design load before and after the completion of the endurance test and shall be the average of three consecutive readings. These voltage drop readings should exclude the voltage drop across the circuit breaker(s). If wiring is an integral part of the switch, the voltage drop measurement shall be made including 75 mm ± 6 of wire on each side of the switch; otherwise the measurement shall be made at the switch terminals.

4. Performance Requirements

4.1 During and after each of the cycles described in 3.2.2.1 and 3.2.3, the switch shall be electrically and mechanically operable.

4.2 The voltage drop shall not exceed 0.3 V when measured as in 3.2.4, before and after completion of the tests described in 3.2.3.

---

[1] 11 000 cycles represents three cycles of headlamp switch operation every day for approximately 10 years, or one cycle for each 4.5 miles driven for 100 000 miles with 50% night driving.

(R) HEADLAMP BEAM SWITCHING— SAE J564 MAR90

SAE Standard

Report of Lighting Division approved January 1934 and last revised by Lighting Committee June 1971. Editorial change October 1977. Completely revised by the Auxiliary Devices Standards Committee March 1990. Rationale statement available.

1. Scope—This SAE Standard defines the test conditions, procedures and performance specification for 6, 12, and 24 V manually actuated headlamp beam control switches.

2. Definition—The headlamp beam control switch is an operator activated device intended primarily to select the high or low beam headlamp circuit. A secondary function may incorporate an auxiliary circuit for override of the semiautomatic beam switching control.

3. Test

3.1 Test Equipment and Instrumentation

3.1.1 POWER SUPPLY—The power supply shall comply with the following specifications:

a. Output current—Capable of supplying the continuous and inrush currents of the design load (reference: 3.2.1.1.).

b. Regulation—

(1) Dynamic—The output voltage at the supply shall not deviate more than 1.0 V from zero to maximum load (including inrush current) and should recover 63% of its maximum excursion within 100 ms.

(2) Static—The output voltage at the supply shall not deviate more than 2% with changes in static load from zero to maximum (not including inrush current), and means shall be provided to compensate for static input line variations.

c. Ripple Voltage—Maximum 300 mV peak-to-peak.

3.1.2 VOLTMETER—0 to 30 V maximum full-scale deflection, accuracy ±1/2%.

NOTE: A digital meter having at least a 3-1/2 digit readout with an accuracy of ±1% plus 1 digit is recommended for mV readings.

3.1.3 AMMETER—Capable of carrying full system load current, accuracy ±3%.

3.2 Test Procedures—Environmental conditions have been selected for this document to help assure satisfactory operations under general use conditions. It is essential to duplicate specific environmental conditions under which the device is expected to function.

3.2.1 ELECTRICAL LOADS

3.2.1.1 The design load applied to the switch is the electrical load specified by the number and type of bulbs (or other electrical load devices) to be operated by each circuit of the switch. For example, the design load for the headlamp circuit may be four sealed beam headlamp units (2-4651 and 2-4652) and four - No. 194 bulbs.

3.2.1.2 The switch shall be operated at 6.4 V DC ± 0.2 V for a 6 V system, 12.8 V DC ± 0.2 for a 12 V system, or 25.6 V DC ± 0.2 V for a 24 V system. These voltages shall be the open circuit voltage measured at the input termination on the switch.

3.2.2 TEMPERATURE TEST PROCEDURE

3.2.2.1 The switch shall be exposed for 1 h without electrical load to each of the following temperatures: 25°C ± 5°C; 74 + (0°C − 3°C); −32 + (3°C, −0°C). The switch shall be manually cycled at each temperature for 10 cycles at design load.

3.2.2.2 The same switch shall be used for the endurance test described in 3.2.3.

3.2.3 ENDURANCE TEST PROCEDURE

3.2.3.1 The switch shall be electrically connected to operate its design load (both primary and secondary circuit function design electrical loads) at a temperature of 25°C ± 5°C.

3.2.3.2 *Beam Control Switch (primary function)*—The switch shall be operated for a minimum of 50 000 cycles.[1] One complete cycle shall consist of sequencing through each position (high beam – low beam – high beam with dwell in each position) and return without dwell in any of the intermediate positions to the initial position.

---

[1] 50 000 cycles represents 14 cycles of headllamp switch operation every day for approximately 10 years, or 1 cycle for each 2 miles driven for 100 000 miles with 50% night driving.

The test equipment shall be arranged to provide the following switch operating time requirements:
a. Travel Time: 0.1 to 0.5 s
   (time from one position to the next)
b. Dwell Time: 0.5 to 2.0 s
   (time in each position)
c. Make and
   Break Rate: 130 to 150 mm per s

3.2.3.3 *Semiautomatic Beam Control Switch (secondary function):* The switch shall meet all the requirements of the beam control switch except as follows:

One complete cycle shall consist of sequencing through each position (with dwell in each beam position):
a. High beam
b. Override mechanism
c. Low beam
d. Override mechanism
e. High beam

The test equipment shall be arranged to provide the operating time requirements.

The semiautomatic beam control switch shall be operated for 25 000 cycles.[2]

---

[2] 25 000 cycles represents 14 manual override beam changes every day for approximately 10 years or cycle for each 4 miles driven for 100 000 miles with 50% night driving.

3.2.3.4 At the completion of the cycle testing, the switch shall be operated for 1 h in the headlamp position with the design load(s) connected.

3.2.4 VOLTAGE DROP TEST PROCEDURE:

3.2.4.1 The voltage drop from the input terminal(s) to the corresponding output terminal(s) shall be measured at design load before and after the completion of the endurance test and shall be the average of three consecutive readings. These voltage drop readings should exclude the voltage drop across the circuit breaker(s). If wiring is an integral part of the switch, the voltage drop measurement shall be made including 75 mm ± 6 mm of wire on each side of the switch; otherwise the measurement shall be made at the switch terminals.

4. Performance Requirements

4.1 During and after each of the cycles described in 3.2.2 and 3.2.3, the switch shall be electrically and mechanically operable.

4.2 The voltage drop shall not exceed 0.3 V when measured as in 3.2.4, before and after completion of the tests described in 3.2.3.

φSEMIAUTOMATIC HEADLAMP BEAM SWITCHING DEVICES—SAE J565 JUN89

SAE Standard

Report of the Lighting Committee, approved August 1954, completely revised by the Lighting Coordinating Committee June 1989.

1. Scope—This SAE Standard provides test procedures, performance requirements, and guidelines for semiautomatic headlamp beam switching devices.

2. Definitions

2.1 Semiautomatic Headlamp Beam Switching Device—A device that provides either automatic or manual control of beam switching at the option of the driver. When the control is automatic, the headlamps switch from the upper beam to the lower beam when a photosensor is illuminated by the headlamps of an approaching car and switch back to the upper beam when the light from the road ahead is at an appropriate intensity. When the control is manual, the driver may obtain either beam manually regardless of the condition of light ahead of the vehicle.

2.2 "Dim" Sensitivity Light Intensity—The emitted candela of the light source at the time the device switches from upper beam to lower beam as the intensity of the light source is gradually increased.

2.3 "Hold" Sensitivity Light Intensity—The emitted candela of the light source at the time the device switches from lower beam to upper beam as the intensity of the light source is gradually decreased.

3. Identification Code Designation—Not applicable.

4. Tests

4.1 Test Facilities and Environment

4.1.1 LABORATORY FACILITIES—See SAE J575.

4.1.2 LIGHT SOURCES—The light sources used for sensitivity testing shall be of the incandescent tungsten filament type operating as C.I.E. Illuminant A (2856 K).

4.2 Equipment and Instrumentation

4.2.1 TESTING DISTANCE—The testing distance for sensitivity shall not be less than 3 m with the lamp intensity and test distance adjusted

to give the same results as that obtained when using 30 m.

4.2.2 AIM—The device shall be mounted and operated in the laboratory in the same environment as that encountered on the vehicle, that is behind tinted glass, grille work, etc. The H-V position/axis shall be taken as parallel to the longitudinal axis of the vehicle.

4.3 Test Samples

4.3.1 See SAE J575.

4.4 Test Procedures—The following sections describe individual tests, which need not be performed in any particular sequence unless otherwise specified. The completion of the tests may be expedited by performing the tests simultaneously on separately mounted samples. For all tests unless otherwise specified, the device shall be set up, adjusted, and operated in accordance with paragraphs 4.4.3.1 and 4.2.2 in an ambient temperature of 25°C ± 5 with an input of 13 V ± 0.1. All light intensity values should normally be measured at 30 m unless otherwise specified.

4.4.1 DUST TEST—The device shall be subjected to the dust test of SAE J575. The device shall not be operated during the dust test.

4.4.2 CORROSION TEST—The device and all components, which are located outside the driver compartment of the vehicle, shall be subjected to corrosion testing in accordance with SAE J575 with the device not operating. (Water should not be allowed to collect on any connector socket).

4.4.3 SENSITIVITY TEST

4.4.3.1 With the device in the design position and aimed with the H-V position per paragraph 4.2.2 facing a light source of 15 cd, the voltage output of the sensitivity control shall be gradually increased until the device switches from upper beam to lower beam. The voltage at this setting of the sensitivity control shall be noted and maintained throughout the remainder of the sensitivity test. The "dim" sensitivity and the "hold" sensitivity, shall be determined at each test position.

4.4.3.2 To provide more complete information on sensitivity, a "dim" curve shall be made radially in intervals not exceeding 10 deg around the H-V axis at a light level of 25 cd $\pm$ 0.5. The sensitivity control output voltage shall be maintained as found in paragraph 4.4.3.1 for establishing the "dim" curve. The device shall be aimed a sufficient amount from the H-V position that it will remain on upper beam. The aim of the device shall gradually be changed along a radial line towards the H-V position until the device switches from upper beam to lower beam to establish a point on the "dim" curve. As the change in aim of the device continues to the H-V axis, the device shall remain on lower beam. A switch from lower beam to upper beam automatically within the "dim" curve would constitute a void in sensitivity and shall be so identified.

4.4.4 VOLTAGE REGULATION—The "dim" sensitivity at H-V shall be determined with the voltage input to the device at 11 V $\pm$ 0.1 and at 15 V $\pm$ 0.1.

4.4.5 MANUAL OVERRIDE OF AUTOMATIC CONTROL—The test light shall be turned on to cause the device to be on lower beam. The manufacturer's instructions shall be followed to cause the device to override the test light and switch to upper beam. In a similar manner the test light shall be turned off to cause the device to be on upper beam. Again the manufacturer's instructions shall be followed to cause the device to switch to the lower beam.

4.4.6 WARMUP—The device shall be aimed on the H-V axis at a light source emitting 25 cd $\pm$ 0.5.

4.4.7 TEMPERATURE REGULATION—The device shall not be operated while being exposed for 1 h to an ambient temperature of 98°C $\pm$ 2 if the device is mounted in the passenger or engine compartment, or 65°C $\pm$ 2 if mounted elsewhere. After the high temperature exposure, the device shall be operated at the same conditions as initially adjusted in ambient temperatures of -30°C $\pm$ 2, 25°C $\pm$ 5, and 40°C $\pm$ 2 for 1 h each.

4.4.8 VIBRATION—The device shall not be operated while being subjected to sinusoidal vibration of 5 g $\pm$ 0.2 constant acceleration as follows:

a. The device shall be mounted in proper vehicle position and vibrated for 0.5 h in each of three directions: vertical, horizontal and parallel to the vehicle axis, and horizontal and normal to the vehicle axis.

b. The vibration frequency shall be varied from 30 to 200 Hz and back to 30 Hz over a period of approximately 1 min.

4.4.9 SUNLIGHT EXPOSURE—The device shall not be operated while being exposed for 1 h in bright noonday sunlight (54 000 lx minimum illumination with a clear sky) with the photounit aimed as it would be on a car and facing an unobstructed portion of the horizon in the direction of the sun. After resting for 1 h in normal room temperature, the device shall be operated at the same conditions as initially adjusted.

4.4.10 DURABILITY—The device shall be subjected to the following test:

a. The photounit shall be actuated by a light source which impresses 0.07 lx $\pm$0.01 (equivalent to approximately 60 cd $\pm$ 10 at 30 m) on the lens surface and which is cycled on and off four times per minute with a duty cycle of 50% on time.

b. The device shall be operated at 13 $\pm$ 0.V input for 90 min on and 30 min off for 200 h total time.

After resting for 2 h at room temperature in a lighted area of 500-1500 lx, the device shall be operated at the same conditions as initially adjusted.

4.4.11 RETURN TO UPPER BEAM TIME—An illumination of 1000 lx $\pm$ 100 intensity shall be impressed on the lens of the device for 10 s $\pm$ 1. The light shall then be extinguished.

5. Requirements—A device, when tested in accordance with the test procedures specified in Section 4, shall meet the following requirements:

5.1 Dust—After the dust test, the photounit lens shall be wiped clean. The device shall be operated at the same conditions as initially adjusted. The H-V "dim" sensitivity shall be between 8 and 25 cd.

5.2 Corrosion—After the test, the device shall be operated at the same conditions as initially adjusted. The H-V "dim" sensitivity shall be between 8 and 25 cd.

5.3 Sensitivity

5.3.1 The "dim" and "hold" sensitivities shall be within the limits of Table 1.

5.3.2 There shall be no sensitivity voids within the dim curve where

TABLE 1—OPERATING LIMITS
(candela at 30 m)

Test Position (deg)	Dim Intensity (cd)	Hold Intensity (cd)
H-V	15 - adjust	1.5 min to 3.75 max
H-2L	25 max	1.5 min
H-4L	40 max	1.5 min
H-6L	75 max	1.5 min
H-2R	25 max	1.5 min
H-5R	40 min to 150 max	1.5 min
1D-V	30 max	1.5 min
1U-V	30 max	1.5 min

the headlamps return to upper beam automatically.

5.4 Voltage Regulation—The H-V "dim" sensitivity shall be between 8 and 25 cd at 11 V $\pm$ 0.1 and 15 V $\pm$ 0.1.

5.5 Manual Override of Automatic Control—When the device is in the upper beam mode, the override shall be capable of switching to lower beam. When the device is in the lower beam mode, the override shall be capable of switching to upper beam.

5.6 Warmup—The warmup time after being energized to maintain lower beam shall not exceed 3 s.

5.7 Temperature Regulation—After a 1 h soak in each of the operating ambient temperatures, the H-V "dim" sensitivity shall be between 8 and 25 cd.

5.8 Vibration—At the conclusion of the test, the device shall be operated at the same conditions as initially adjusted. The H-V "dim" sensitivity shall be between 8 and 25 cd and the mechanical aim of the photounit shall not change more than 0.3 deg.

5.9 Sunlight Exposure—The H-V "dim" sensitivity shall be between 8 and 25 cd.

5.10 Durability—The H-V "dim" sensitivity shall be between 8 and 25 cd.

5.11 Return to Upper Beam Time—The time to return to upper beam shall not exceed 2 s.

6. Guidelines

6.1 Installation Requirements—The following requirements apply to the device as used on the vehicle and are not part of the laboratory test requirements and procedures.

6.1.1 LENS ACCESSIBILITY—The device lens shall be accessible for cleaning when the unit is mounted on a vehicle.

6.1.2 MOUNTING HEIGHT—The center of the device lens shall be mounted not less than 600 mm above the road surface.

6.1.3 MALFUNCTION OVERRIDE—In the event that there is a malfunction of the automatic control (light sensor) portion of the system, which would maintain the system on upper beam, means must be provided for manual switching to low beam. Malfunction of the automatic control portion of the system may be simulated by placing the photounit in darkness (light level below 0.001 lx) where the device should effectively be locked on high beam.

6.1.4 AUTOMATIC DIMMING INDICATOR—There shall be a convenient means of informing the driver when the device is controlling the headlights automatically. The manufacturer's instructions shall be followed to determine the means of indication.

6.1.5 UPPER BEAM INDICATOR—The device shall not affect the function of the upper beam indicator light.

6.1.6 SENSITIVITY CONTROL—A sensitivity control shall be provided for the driver.

6.2 Installation Recommendations—The following design parameters should be considered in mounting the light sensor portion of the device on the vehicle for satisfactory performance.

6.2.1 For optimum performance, the light sensor portion of the device should face forward and be located and mounted, whenever possible, to sense the equivalent perception of the driver's field of view ahead of the vehicle.

6.2.2 As a minimum mounting height, the light sensor portion of the device should be above the top edge of the highest mounted headlamp unit on the vehicle.

6.2.3 The lens of the light sensor portion of the device should be mounted for an unobstructed field of view ahead of the vehicle within 15 deg L, 10 deg R, 5 deg D, and 10 deg U, relative to the vehicle longitudinal axis.

6.3 Operating Instructions—A set of operating instructions shall be included to permit a driver to operate the device correctly. The following items shall be covered:

a. How to turn the automatic control on and off.

b. How to adjust sensitivity.

c. Any other instructions applicable to the particular device.

Report of Lighting Committee approved September 1950 and last revised June 1971. Editorial change October 1977.

1. Definition

1.1 A turn signal switch is that part of a turn signal system by which the operator of a vehicle causes the turn signal lamps to function.

1.2 A *Class A* turn signal switch may be used on any vehicle but is intended for use on multipurpose passenger vehicles, trucks, and buses that are 80 in. or more wide overall.

1.3 A *Class B* turn signal switch is intended for use in passenger cars, motorcycles, and multipurpose passenger vehicles, trucks, and buses of less than 80 in. overall width.

2. Reference Standards

2.1 The following sections from SAE J575f (April, 1975) are a part of this φ standard:

Section B—Samples for Test
Section C—Lamp Bulbs
Section D—Laboratory Facilities

2.2 Turn signal pilot indicators—See SAE J588e (September, 1970).

3. Temperature Test

3.1 To insure basic function, the switch shall be manually cycled for 10 cycles at design electrical load at: 75 ± 10 F (24 ± 5.5 C); $165 +0, -5$ F ($74 +0, -2.8$ C); $-25 +5, -0$ F ($-32 +2.8, -0$ C). This to be done after a 1 h exposure at each of these temperatures. The switch shall be electrically and mechanically operable during each of these cycles.

3.2 This same switch shall be used for the endurance test described in paragraph 4.

4. Endurance Test Setup

4.1 The switch shall be operated with the maximum design bulb load stated by the switch manufacturer with the flasher not included in the circuit. Failed bulbs shall be replaced during the test.

4.2 When the switch is provided with a self-canceling mechanism, the test equipment shall be arranged so that the switch can be turned off by the self-canceling mechanism. Provision shall also be made for manual canceling.

4.3 The test shall be set up to operate the switch for the prescribed number of cycles.

One cycle shall consist of the following sequence of positions: off, left turn, off, right turn, off.

The test requirement shall function within the following mechanical timing requirements at a cycle rate of 12-20 cycles/minute:

Travel time—0.1-0.5 s max (time from one position to the next position)
Dwell time—0.4 s min (in each position)

4.4 During the test the switch shall be operated at 6.4 V d-c for a 6 V system, 12.8 V d-c for a 12 V system, or 25.6 V d-c for a 24 V system, measured at the input termination of the switch. The power supply shall not generate any adverse transients not present in motor vehicles and shall comply with the following specifications:

(a) Output current—Capable of supplying a continuous output current of the design load and inrush currents as required by the bulb load complement.

(b) Regulation—

Dynamic—The output voltage shall not deviate more than 1.0 V from zero to maximum load (including inrush current) and should recover 63% of its maximum excursion within 5 ms.

Static—The output voltage shall not deviate more than 2% with changes in static load from zero to maximum (not including inrush current), and means shall be provided to compensate for static input line voltage variations.

(c) Ripple voltage—Maximum 300 mV, peak to peak.

5. Endurance Requirements

5.1 Class A turn signal switches shall be capable of meeting the following endurance requirements:

(a) 165,000 cycles at 75 ± 10 F (24 ± 5.5 C).

(b) When the switch is provided with a self-canceling mechanism it shall be tested as follows: 155,000 cycles of self-canceling followed by 10,000 cycles of manual canceling.

(c) If the turn signal switch includes stop lamp circuitry, the stop lamp circuit shall be fed electrically for the first 100,000 cycles only.

5.2 Class B turn signal switches shall be capable of meeting the following endurance requirements:

(a) 100,000 cycles at 75 ± 10 F (24 ± 5.5 C).

(b) When the switch is provided with a self-canceling mechanism it shall be tested as follows: 95,000 cycles of self-canceling followed by 5000 complete cycles of manual canceling.

(c) If the turn signal switch includes stop lamp circuitry, the stop lamp circuit shall be fed electrically for the first 50,000 complete cycles only.

5.3 If the turn signal switch includes cornering light circuitry which is fed from the headlight switch, the cornering light circuit shall be fed electrically for the first 50,000 cycles only.

5.4 The voltage drop from the input terminal of each circuit to the lamp terminal of each circuit shall be measured at the beginning of the test and at intervals of 25,000 cycles.

This voltage drop shall not exceed:

0.25 V for 2 lamp load (or less) per side
0.30 V for 3 lamp load per side
0.35 V for 4 lamp load per side
0.40 V for 5 lamp load (or greater) per side

before, during, and after the endurance test.

If wiring is an integral part of the switch, the voltage drop measurement is to be made including 3 in. of wire on each side of switch; otherwise, measurement is to be made at switch terminals. Care shall be taken not to include the voltage drop of other devices in the circuit.

6. Combination Turn Signal and Hazard Warning Signal Switches

6.1 The same combination switch shall be used for the test of each function. The turn signal switch function shall meet the requirements of this standard. The hazard warning signal switch function shall meet the requirements of SAE J910b (June, 1971). φ

6.2 The operating motion of the hazard warning signal switch function shall differ from the actuating motion of the turn signal switch function.

Report of the Lighting Committee approved March 1960 and completely revised July 1986. Rationale statement available. Revised by the SAE Flasher Task Force of the SAE Auxiliary Devices Standards Committee April 1993.

R) *Foreword*—The development of this SAE Standard was based on the premise that it described the requirements for all turn signal flashers regardless of the electrical load. Since this document was first introduced, the predominant load for passenger car use has been two lamp bulbs, one at the front and one at the rear of the vehicle and the vehicles have used fixed load flashers. The load for trucks can vary from two to as many as ten depending on the vehicle. Trucks with trailers generally use variable load flashers. Passenger cars with trailers should use a variable load flasher. Federal Motor Vehicle Safety Standard 108 requires vehicles to be equipped to indicate the loss of one or more turn signal lamps except when a variable load flasher is required.

R) *1. Scope*—This SAE Standard defines the test conditions, procedures, and minimum design requirements for nominal 6, 12, and 24 V turn signal flashers.

2. References

2.1 Applicable Documents—The following publications form a part of this specification to the extent specified herein. The latest issue of SAE publications shall apply.

2.1.1 SAE PUBLICATIONS—Available from SAE, 400 Commonwealth Drive, Warrendale, PA 15096-0001.

SAE J588—Turn Signal Lamps for Use on Motor Vehicles Less Than 2032 mm in Overall Width

SAE J759—Lighting Identification Code

SAE J823—Flasher Test

R) **2.2 Definition**—The flasher is a device installed in a vehicle lighting system which has the primary function of causing the turn signal lamps to flash when the turn signal switch is actuated. Secondary functions may include the visible pilot indication for the turn signal system (required by SAE J588) an audible signal to indicate when the flasher is operating, and an indication of turn signal lamp outage.

R) *3. Flasher Identification Code*—Flashers conforming to this document may be identified by the code J590 in accordance with SAE J759.

4. Tests

4.1 Test Equipment—The standard test equipment and circuitry for performing flasher tests shall conform with the specifications in SAE J823.

4.2 Test Procedures—All of the following tests shall be performed at 12.8 V (or 6.4 V and/or 25.6 V) at the bulbs unless otherwise specified.

R) 4.2.1 START TIME—The start time of a normally closed type flasher is the time to open the circuit after the voltage is applied, provided the closed circuit remains closed for a minimum of 0.10 s. If the closed circuit opens in less than 0.10 s, the flasher shall be considered a normally open type flasher for this test. The start time of a normally open type flasher is the time to complete one cycle (close the circuit then open the circuit) after voltage is applied. For a fixed-load flasher, the test shall be made with the specific ampere design load connected. For a variable-load flasher, the test shall be made with both the minimum and maximum ampere design load. The test shall be made in an ambient temperature of 24 °C ± 5 °C. The start time shall be measured and recorded for three starts, each of which is separated by a cooling interval of at least 5 min.

4.2.2 VOLTAGE DROP—The lowest voltage drop across the flasher shall be measured between the input and the load terminals at the flasher and during the "on" period. The voltage drop shall be measured and recorded during any three cycles after the flasher has been operating for five consecutive cycles. For fixed-load flashers, the voltage drop is measured with the specific ampere design load connected. For variable load flashers, the voltage drop shall be measured with

the maximum ampere design load connected. The test shall be made in an ambient temperature of 24 °C ± 5 °C.

4.2.3 FLASH RATE AND PERCENT CURRENT ON TIME—The flash rate and percent current on time shall be measured and recorded after the flasher has completed five consecutive cycles and shall be an average of at least three consecutive cycles at each of the following bulb voltages and ambient temperature conditions.

a. 12.8 V (or 6.4 V or 25.6 V) and 24 °C ± 5 °C
b. 12.0 V (or 6.0 V or 24.0 V) and -17 °C ± 3 °C
c. 15.0 V (or 7.5 V or 30.0 V) and -17 °C ± 3 °C
d. 11.0 V (or 5.5 V or 22.0 V) and 50 °C ± 3 °C
e. 14.0 V (or 7.0 V or 28.0 V) and 50 °C ± 3 °C

The flashers shall be temperature stabilized before each test. For a fixed load flasher, the test shall be made with the specific ampere design load connected. For a variable load flasher, the test shall be made with both the minimum and maximum ampere design load connected.

4.2.4 EXTREME TEMPERATURE—The flasher shall be subjected to ambient temperatures of 63 °C ± 3 °C and -32 °C ± 3 °C until stabilized. The start time and flash rate shall be measured and recorded at each extreme temperature. The flash rate measurement must be completed within the first minute of energization. Otherwise the procedure shall be as specified in 4.2.1 and 4.2.3a.

4.2.5 DURABILITY—The durability test shall be conducted near the following conditions:

a. 24 °C ± 5 °C ambient temperature
b. 14.0 V (7.0 V or 28.0 V) applied to the input terminals of the test circuit
c. Specific ampere design load for fixed load flashers and maximum specified ampere design load for variable load flashers
d. 100 h of intermittent flashing (15 s on, 15 s off) followed by 50 h of continuous flashing

5. Performance Requirements

5.1 Start Time—The average and maximum of the three start time measurements (see 4.2.1) for the flasher shall not exceed the values shown in Table 1.

TABLE 1—START TIME, s

Flasher Type	Average Time	Maximum Time
Normally closed	1.3	2.0
Normally open	1.5	2.0

5.2 Voltage Drop—The average of the three voltage drop measurements (see 4.2.2) for the flasher shall not exceed 0.5 V. No single measurement shall exceed 0.8 V.

5.3 Flash Rate and Percent Current On Time—The average flash rate and percent current on time shall fall within 60 to 120 flashes per minute and 30 to 75% on under all conditions of 4.2.3.

5.4 Extreme Temperature—At the extreme temperature conditions, start time shall not exceed 3 s and flash rate shall be 50 to 130 flashes per minute.

5.5 Durability—The flasher shall conform to 5.1, 5.2, and 5.3 (under test condition 4.2.3a only) at the start and conclusion of the test.

Report of Lighting Committee approved January 1965 and completely revised October 1988. Rationale statement available.

1. Scope—This standard defines the test conditions, procedures and performance specifications for 6, 12 and 24-V manually actuated hazard warning signal switch.

2. Definition—The hazard warning switch is an operator actuated device whose function is to cause at least one turn signal lamp on the left and right of the front, and left and right of the rear of the vehicle to flash simultaneously to indicate to the approaching driver the presence of a vehicular hazard.

2.1 Combination Turn Signal and Hazard Warning Signal

2.1.1 A combination switch is defined as a hazard warning switch combined in the same housing as the turn signal switch.

2.1.2 The operating motion of the hazard warning signal switch function shall differ from the actuating motion of the turn signal function.

3. Test Requirements

3.1 Test Equipment and Instrumentation

3.1.1 POWER SUPPLY—The power supply shall not generate any adverse transients not present in motor vehicles, and shall comply with the following specifications:

a. Output Current—The power supply shall be capable of supplying the continuous current of the design electrical load and the in-rush current, as required by the bulb load complement.

b. Output Regulation
Dynamic—The dynamic output voltage at the supply shall not deviate more than 1.0 V from zero to maximum load (including in-rush current) and shall recover 63% of its maximum excursion within 100 ms.
Static—The static output voltage at the supply shall not deviate more than 2% with changes in static load from zero to maximum (not including in-rush current), and means shall be provided to compensate for static input line voltage variations.

c. Ripple Voltage—The ripple output voltage shall be a maximum of 300 mV peak-to-peak.

3.1.2 VOLTMETER—A voltmeter with a 0-30 V maximum full scale deflection and ±1/2% accuracy should be used. NOTE: A digital meter having at least a 3-1/2 digit readout with an accuracy of ±1% plus 1 digit is recommended for mV readings.

3.1.3 AMMETER—Capable of carrying full system load current, with an accuracy of ±3%.

3.2 Test Procedures—It is essential to duplicate specific environmental conditions under which the device is expected to function.

3.2.1 ELECTRICAL LOADS

3.2.1.1 The design load applied to the switch is the electrical load specified by the quantity and type of bulbs (or other electrical load devices) to be operated by each circuit of the hazard warning signal switch.

3.2.1.2 The switch shall be operated with the maximum design bulb load stated by the switch manufacturer with the flasher not included in the circuit unless the flasher is an integral part of the assembly.

3.2.1.3 The switch shall be operated at 6.4 ± 0.2 V DC for a 6-V system, 12.8 ± 0.2 V DC for a 12-V system, or 25.6 ± 0.2 V DC for a 24-V system. These voltages shall be the open circuit voltage measured at the input termination on the switch.

3.2.2 TEMPERATURE TEST PROCEDURE

3.2.2.1 The switch shall be manually cycled after a 1-h exposure with no electrical load at each of these temperatures: 25 ± 5°C; 74 + 0, −3°C; −32 +3, −0°C. The switch shall be manually cycled at each temperature for 10 cycles at the designed loads.

3.2.2.2 The same hazard warning signal switch shall be used for the described endurance test described in paragraph 3.2.3.

3.2.3 ENDURANCE TEST PROCEDURE

3.2.3.1 The switch shall be electrically connected to operate its design load for 7500 cycles at a temperature of 25 ± 5°C, followed by a 1-h "on" at a temperature of 25 ± 5°C.

3.2.3.2 One complete cycle shall consist of sequencing it through each position (with dwell in each position): Off, On, Off.

3.2.3.3 The test equipment shall be arranged to provide the following switch operating time requirements:
Travel Time - 0.1–0.5 s (time from one position to next)
Dwell Time - 1.0–2.0 s (time in each position)
Make and Break Rate - 130–150 mm/s

3.2.4 VOLTAGE DROP TEST PROCEDURE

3.2.4.1 The voltage drop from the input terminals to the corresponding output terminals shall be measured at the beginning of the test and immediately after the endurance test. Cycling the switch three times prior to taking readings is permitted and the reading should be taken right after cycling. A total of five readings can be taken and the average reading will prevail.

3.2.4.2 If wiring is an integral part of the switch, the voltage drop measurement shall be made including 75 ± 6 mm of wire on each side of the switch; otherwise, the measurement shall be made at the switch terminals.

4. Performance Requirements

4.1 During and after each of the tests described in paragraphs 3.2.2 and 3.2.3, the switch shall be electrically and mechanically operable.

4.2 Combination Turn Signal and Hazard Warning—The same combination switch shall be used for the test of each function. The hazard warning switch shall meet the requirements of this standard. The turn signal switch shall meet the requirements of SAE J589.

4.3 The voltage drop shall not exceed 0.30 V.

(R) VEHICULAR HAZARD WARNING FLASHERS
—SAE J945 JUN93

SAE Standard

Report of the Lighting Committee approved February 1966 and completely revised June 1987. Rationale statement available. Completely revised by the Auxiliary Device Standards Committee and the Flasher Task Force of the SAE Lighting Coordinating Committee June 1993. Rationale statement available.

1. Scope—This SAE Standard defines the test conditions, procedures, and minimum design requirements for nominal 6, 12, and 24 V hazard warning flashers.

2. References

2.1 Applicable Documents—The following publications form a part of this specification to the extent specified herein. The latest issue of SAE publications shall apply.

2.1.1 SAE PUBLICATIONS—Available from SAE, 400 Commonwealth Drive, Warrendale, PA 15096-0001.

SAE J759—Lighting Identification Code
SAE J823—Flasher Test
SAE J910—Hazard Warning Signal Switch

2.2 Definition

2.2.1 The HAZARD WARNING FLASHER is a device installed in a vehicle lighting system which has the primary function of causing the turn signal lamps to flash when the hazard warning switch is actuated. Secondary functions may include the visible pilot indication for the hazard system (required by SAE J910) and an audible signal to indicate when the flasher is operating.

3. Flasher Identification Code—Flashers conforming to this document may be identified by the code J945 in accordance with SAE J759.

4. Tests

4.1 Test Equipment—The standard test equipment and circuitry for performing flasher tests shall conform with the specifications in SAE J823.

4.2 Test Procedures—All of the following tests shall be performed at 12.8 V (or 6.4 V or 25.6 V) at the bulbs unless otherwise specified.

4.2.1 START TIME—The start time of a normally closed type flasher is the time to open the circuit after the voltage is applied, provided the closed circuit remains closed for a minimum of 0.10 s. If the closed circuit opens in less than 0.10 s, the flasher shall be considered a normally open type flasher for this test. The start time of a normally open type flasher is the time to complete one cycle (close the circuit and then open the circuit) after the voltage is applied. For a fixed load flasher, the test shall be made with the specific ampere design load connected. For a variable load flasher, the test shall be made with both the minimum and maximum ampere design loads. The test shall be made in an ambient temperature of 24 °C ± 5 °C. The start time shall be measured and recorded for three starts, each of which is separated by a cooling interval of at least 5 min.

4.2.2 VOLTAGE DROP—The voltage drop across the flasher shall be measured between the input and the load terminals at the flasher and during the "on" period of each cycle. After the flasher has been operating for five consecutive cycles, the lowest voltage drop observed during each of three consecutive cycles

shall be measured and recorded. For a fixed load flasher, the test shall be conducted with the specific ampere design load connected. For a variable load flasher, the test shall be conducted with both the minimum and maximum ampere design loads. The test shall be conducted in an ambient temperature of 24 °C ± 5 °C.

4.2.3 FLASH RATE AND PERCENT CURRENT ON TIME—The flash rate and percent current on time shall be measured and recorded after the flasher has completed five consecutive cycles and shall be the average of at least three consecutive cycles at each of the following bulb voltages and ambient temperature conditions:

   a. 12.8 V (or 6.4 V or 25.6 V) and 24 °C ± 5 °C
   b. 11.0 V (or 5.5 V or 22.0 V) and -17 °C ± 3 °C
   c. 13.0 V (or 6.5 V or 26.0 V) and -17 °C ± 3 °C
   d. 11.0 V (or 5.5 V or 22.0 V) and 50 °C ± 3 °C
   e. 13.0 V (or 6.5 V or 26.0 V) and 50 °C ± 3 °C

The flashers shall be temperature stabilized before each test. For a fixed load flasher, the test shall be conducted with the specific ampere design load connected. For a variable load flasher, the test shall be conducted with both the minimum and maximum design loads connected.

4.2.4 EXTREME TEMPERATURE—The flasher shall be subjected to ambient temperatures of 63 °C ± 3 °C and -32 °C ± 3 °C until stabilized. The start time and flash rate shall be measured and recorded at each extreme temperature. The flash rate measurement must be completed within the first minute of energization. Otherwise, the procedure shall be as specified in 4.2.1 and 4.2.3a.

4.2.5 DURABILITY—The durability test shall be conducted under the following conditions:

   a. 24 °C ± 5 °C ambient temperature
   b. 13.0 V (6.5 V or 25.6 V) applied to the input terminals of the test circuit
   c. Maximum specified ampere design load
   d. Continuous flasher operation for 36 h

5. Performance Requirements

5.1 Start Time—The average of the three start time measurements (4.2.1) shall not exceed 1.5 s. No single measurement shall exceed 2.0 s.

5.2 Voltage Drop—The average of the three voltage drop measurements (4.2.2) shall not exceed 0.5 V. No single measurement shall exceed 0.8 V.

5.3 Flash Rate and Percent Current On Time—The average flash rate and percent current on time shall fall within 60 to 120 flashes per minute and 30 to 75% on time, respectively, under all conditions of 4.2.3.

5.4 Extreme Temperature—At the extreme temperature conditions, start time shall not exceed 3 s and flash rate shall be 50 to 130 flashes per minute.

5.5 Durability—The flasher shall conform to 5.1, 5.2, and 5.3 (under test condition 4.2.3a only) at the start and conclusion of the test.

Report of the Lighting Committee approved September 1973. Editorial change January 1977. Completely revised by the Auxiliary Devices Standards Committee October 1989. Rationale statement available. Revised by the Auxiliary Devices Standards Committee September 1994.

1. Scope—This SAE Recommended Practice defines the test conditions, procedures, and minimum design requirements for nominal 6, 12, and 24 V warning lamp alternating flashers.

2. References

2.1 Applicable Documents—The following publications form a part of this specification to the extent specified herein. The latest issue of SAE publications shall apply.

2.1.1 SAE PUBLICATIONS—Available from SAE, 400 Commonwealth Drive, Warrendale, PA 15096-0001.

SAE J595—Flashing Warning Lamps for Authorized Emergency,
Maintenance, and Service Vehicles

SAE J759—Lighting Identification Code

SAE J823—Flasher Test

SAE J887—School Bus Warning Lamps

2.2 Definition

2.2.1 FLASHER—A device installed in a vehicle lighting system which has the primary function of causing warning lamps to alternately flash when the system is activated. Secondary functions may include the visible pilot(s) indication for the warning system and an audible signal to indicate when the flasher is operating (recommended by SAE J887 and J595).

3. Flasher Identification Code—Flashers conforming to this document may be identified in accordance with SAE J759.

4. Tests

4.1 Test Equipment—The standard test equipment and circuitry for performing flasher tests shall conform with the specifications in SAE J823.

4.2 Test Procedures—All the following tests shall be performed at 12.8 V (or 6.4 V or 25.6 V) at the bulbs unless otherwise specified.

4.2.1 START TIME—The start time is the time to complete one cycle (both load circuits have been energized and de-energized) after voltage is applied to the flasher. For fixed-load flashers, the test shall be made with the specific ampere design loads connected. For variable-load flashers, the test shall be made with both the minimum and maximum ampere design loads connected. The test shall be made in an ambient temperature of 24 °C ± 5 °C. The start time shall be measured and recorded for three starts, each of which is separated by a cooling interval of at least 5 min at 24 °C ± 5 °C.

4.2.2 VOLTAGE DROP—The lowest voltage drop across the flasher shall be measured between the input and each load terminal at the flasher and during the "on" period. The test shall be made with the specific maximum ampere design load connected and in an ambient temperature of 24 °C ± 5 °C. The voltage drop shall be measured and recorded during any three cycles after the flasher has been operating for five consecutive cycles.

4.2.3 FLASH RATE AND PERCENT CURRENT ON TIME—The flash rate and percent current on time of each load terminal shall be measured and recorded

after the flasher has completed five consecutive cycles and shall be an average of at least three consecutive cycles at each of the following bulb voltages and ambient temperature conditions:

    a.   12.8 V (or 6.4 V or 25.6 V) and 24 °C ± 5 °C

    b.   12.0 V (or 6.0 V or 24.0 V) and -17 °C ± 3 °C

    c.   15.0 V (or 7.5 V or 30.0 V) and -17 °C ± 3 °C

    d.   11.0 V (or 5.5 V or 22.0 V) and 50 °C ± 3 °C

    e.   14.0 V (or 7.0 V or 28.0 V) and 50 °C ± 3 °C

The flashers shall be temperature stabilized before each test. The test shall be made with the specific ampere design load connected for each circuit.

4.2.4 EXTREME TEMPERATURE TESTS—The flasher shall be subjected to ambient temperatures of 63 °C ± 3 °C and -32 °C ± 3 °C until stabilized. The start time and flash rate shall be measured and recorded at each extreme temperature. The measurements must be completed within the first minute of energization, otherwise the procedure shall be as specified in 4.2.1 and 4.2.3a.

4.2.5 DURABILITY—The durability test shall be conducted under the following conditions:

    a.   24 °C ± 5 °C ambient temperature

    b.   13.0 V (6.5 V for 6.0 V nominal system or 26.0 V for 25.6 V nominal system) applied to the input terminal of the test circuit

    c.   Specific maximum ampere design load

    d.   100 h of intermittent flashing (15 s on, 15 s off) followed by 50 h of continuous flashing

5. Performance Requirements

5.1 Start Time—The average and maximum of the three start time measurements (4.2.1) for the flasher shall not exceed 1.5 and 2.0 s, respectively.

5.2 Voltage Drop—The average of the three voltage drop measurements (4.2.2) shall not exceed 0.5 V. No single measurement may exceed 0.8 V.

5.3 Flash Rate and Percent Current On Time—At each load terminal, the flash rate shall be a minimum of 60 and a maximum of 120 per minute and the percent current "on" time shall be a minimum of 30 and a maximum of 75. The total of the percent current "on" times for the two terminals shall be a minimum of 90 and a maximum of 110.

5.4 Extreme Temperature—At the extreme temperature conditions, start time shall not exceed 5 s and flash rate shall be not less than 30 nor more than 150 flashes per minute.

5.5 Durability—The flasher shall conform to 5.1, 5.2, and 5.3 (under test procedure 4.2.3a only) at the start and conclusion of test.

6. Notes

6.1 Marginal Indicia—The (R) is for the convenience of the user in locating areas where technical revisions have been made to the previous issue of the report. If the symbol is next to the report title, it indicates a complete revision of the report.

Report of Lighting Committee approved February 1974. Completely revised by the Auxiliary Devices Standards Committee March 1990. Rationale statement available.

1. Scope—This standard defines the test conditions, procedures and performance specification for 6, 12, and 24 V backup lamp switches which are intended for use in motor vehicles.

2. Definitions—The backup lamp switch is an operator activated device intended primarily to control the function of the backup lamps. There are three types:

2.1 Type "A"—A transmission mounted backup lamp switch is that device which is mounted in or on the transmission and actuated by a moving part within the transmission that energizes the backup lamps when the transmission is shifted into reverse.

2.2 Type "B"—A backup lamp switch performing the same function as Type "A", except that it is operated by a mechanism external of the transmission but not mounted in the passenger compartment.

2.3 Type "C"—A backup lamp switch performing the same function as Type "A" but mounted in the passenger compartment and actuated by movement of the shift mechanism or linkage.

3. Test

3.1 Test Equipment and Instrumentation:

3.1.1 Power Supply—The power supply shall comply with the following specifications:

a. Output current–capable of supplying the continuous and inrush currents of the design load (see 3.2.1.1).

b. Regulation:

(1) Dynamic—The output voltage at the supply shall not deviate more than 1.0 V from zero to maximum load (including inrush current) and should recover 63% of its maximum excursion within 100 ms.

(2) Static—The output voltage at the supply shall not deviate more than 2% with changes in static load from zero to maximum (not including inrush current), and means shall be provided to compensate for static input line variations.

c. Ripple Voltage–maximum 300 mV peak to peak.

3.1.2 Voltmeter—0–30 V maximum full scale deflection, accuracy ±1/2%.

Note: A digital meter having at least a 3-1/2 digit readout with an accuracy of ±1% plus 1 digit is recommended for mV readings.

3.1.3 Ammeter—Capable of carrying full system load current, accuracy ±3%.

3.2 Test Procedures— Environmental conditions have been selected for this document to help assure satisfactory operation under general customer use conditions. It is essential to duplicate specific environmental conditions under which the device is expected to function.

3.2.1 Electrical Loads

3.2.1.1 The design load applied to the switch is the electrical load specified by the number and type of lamp(s) or other electrical load device(s) to be operated by each circuit of the switch. For example, the design load for the backup lamp circuit may be two 1156 bulbs.

3.2.1.2 The switch shall be operated at 6.4 V DC ± 0.2 for a 6 V system, 12.8 V DC ± 0.2 V for a 12 V system, or 25.6 V DC ± 0.2 V for a 24 V system. These voltages shall be the open circuit voltage measured at the input termination on the switch.

3.2.2 Temperature Test Procedure

3.2.2.1 Type "A" and "B"—The switch shall be exposed for 1 h without electrical load to each of these temperatures: 25°C ± 5; 107 (+0°, -3°C); -32 (+3°C, -0°C). After each of the one h temperature exposures, the switch shall be manually cycled for ten cycles at the design electrical load to insure basic electrical and mechanical function at these temperatures.

3.2.2.2 Type "C"—The temperature test shall be conducted the same as for Type "A" and "B" except the ambient temperatures shall be 25°C ± 5°C; 74 (+0, -3°C); -32 (+3, -0°C).

3.2.2.3 This same switch shall be used for the endurance test described in 3.2.3.

3.2.3 Endurance Test Procedure

3.2.3.1 The switch shall be electrically connected to operate its design load (both primary and secondary circuit function design electrical loads) at a temperature of 25°C ± 5°C.

3.2.3.2 The switch shall be operated for a minimum of 30 000[1] cycles. One complete cycle shall consist of sequencing through each position (with dwell in each position) and return without dwelling in each of the intermediate positions to the initial position.

[1] 30 000 cycles represents 8 cycles of backup lamp switch operation every day for approximately 10 years, or one cycle for each 3.3 miles driven for 100 000 miles.

The test equipment shall be arranged to provide the following switch operating time requirements:

Travel Time: 0.1-0.5 s
                 (time from one position to the next)

Dwell Time: 0.5-2.0 s
                 (time in each position)

Make &
Break Rate: 130-150 mm per s

3.2.3.3 At the completion of the cycle testing, the switch shall be operated for 1 h in each detect position with the design load(s) connected.

3.2.4 Voltage Drop Test Procedure

3.2.4.1 The voltage drop from the input terminal(s) to the corresponding output terminal(s) shall be measured at design load before and after the completion of the endurance test and shall be the average of three consecutive readings. If wiring is an integral part of the switch, the voltage drop measurement shall be made including 75 mm ± 6 mm of wire on each side of the switch; otherwise the measurement shall be made at the switch terminals.

4. Performance Requirements

4.1 During and after each of the cycles described in 3.2.2 and 3.2.3, the switch shall be electrically and mechanically operable.

4.2 The voltage drop shall not exceed 0.3 V when measured as in 3.2.4, before and after completion of the tests described in 3.2.3.

| The Engineering Society For Advancing Mobility Land Sea Air and Space® INTERNATIONAL 400 Commonwealth Drive, Warrendale, PA 15096-0001 | SURFACE VEHICLE RECOMMENDED PRACTICE Submitted for recognition as an American National Standard | SAE J1690 |
| | | Issued 1996-08 |

FLASHERS

1. Scope—This SAE Recommended Practice defines the test conditions, procedures, and minimum design requirements for nominal 6, 12, and 24 V turn signal, hazard warning, warning lamp alternating, and combination flashers.

2. References

2.1 Applicable Documents—The following publications form a part of this specification to the extent specified herein. The latest issue of the SAE publications shall apply.

2.1.1 SAE PUBLICATIONS—Available from SAE, 400 Commonwealth Drive, Warrendale, PA 15096-0001.

SAE J595—Flashing Warning Lamps for Authorized Emergency, Maintenance and Service Vehicles
SAE J823—Flasher Test
SAE J887—School Bus Warning Lamps
SAE J910—Hazard Warning Signal Switch

2.2 Related Publications—The following publications are provided for information purposes only and are not a required part of this document.

2.2.1 FEDERAL PUBLICATION—Available from the Superintendent of Documents, U.S. Grovernment Printing Office, Washington, DC 20402.

FMVSS-108

2.2.2 ISO PUBLICATION—Available from ANSI, 11 West 42nd Street, New York, NY 10036-8002.

ISO 4082—Road vehicles—Motor vehicles flasher units

2.2.3 JIS PUBLICATION—Available from ANSI, 11 West 42nd Street, New York, NY 10036-8002.

JIS D 5707—Flasher Units for Automobiles

QUESTIONS REGARDING THIS DOCUMENT: (412) 772-8512 **FAX:** (412) 776-0243
TO PLACE A DOCUMENT ORDER: (412) 776-4970 **FAX:** (412) 776-0790

Printed in U.S.A.

3. Definitions

3.1 Turn Signal Flasher—A device installed in a vehicle lighting system which has the primary function of causing the turn signal lamps to flash when the turn signal switch is actuated. Secondary functions may include the visible pilot indication for the turn signal system (required by SAE J910) and an audible signal to indicate when the flasher is operating.

3.2 Hazard Warning Signal Flasher—A device installed in a vehicle lighting system which has the primary function of causing all of the turn signal lamps to flash when the hazard warning switch is actuated. Secondary functions may include the visible pilot indication for the hazard warning signal system (required by SAE J910) and an audible signal to indicate when the flasher is operating.

3.3 Combination Flasher—A device which satisfies all the turn signal and hazard warning requirements of this document. These devices are used on vehicles whose operation or mode of operation presents a variable electrical load to the flasher.

3.4 Warning Lamp Alternating Flasher—A device installed in a vehicle lighting system which has the primary function of causing warning lamps to alternately flash when the system is actuated. Secondary functions may include the visible pilot(s) indication for the warning system and an audible signal to indicate when the flasher is operating (recommended by SAE J887 and J595).

3.5 "Class A" Flashers—Flashers designed to perform in vehicles whose expected life or mode of operation requires a flasher with normal durability. Examples of these vehicles are passenger cars and light-duty trucks.

3.6 "Class B" Flashers—Flashers designed to perform in vehicles whose expected life or mode of operation requires a flasher with extended durability. Examples of these vehicles are heavy-duty trucks, buses, and taxicabs.

4. Flasher Identification Code—Flashers conforming to this document may be marked with the following information.

SAE J1690
Class designation
Application (i.e., Turn Signal Flasher)
Minimum and maximum ampere load rating

5. Tests

5.1 Test Equipment—The standard test equipment and circuitry for performing flasher tests shall conform with the specifications in SAE J823, Flasher Test Equipment.

5.2 Test Procedures—All of the following tests shall be performed at 12.8 V for nominal 12 V devices, 6.4 V for nominal 6 V devices and 25.6 V for nominal 24 V devices and at an ambient temperature of 24 °C ± 5 °C unless otherwise specified.

5.2.1 START TIME

5.2.1.1 Turn Signal, Hazard Warning Signal, and Combination Flashers—The start time of a normally closed type flasher is the time to open the circuit after the voltage is applied, provided the closed circuit remains closed for a minimum of 0.10 s. If the closed circuit opens in less then 0.10 s, the flasher shall be considered a normally open type flasher for this test. The start time of a normally open type flasher is the time to complete one cycle (close the circuit and then open the circuit) after the voltage is applied. For a fixed load flasher, the test shall be made with the specific ampere design load connected. For a variable load flasher, the test shall be made with the minimum and maximum ampere design loads for both the turn and hazard warning signal functions. The start time shall be measured and recorded for three starts, each of which is separated by a cooling interval of at least 5 min.

5.2.1.2 Warning Lamp Alternating Flashers—The start time is the time to complete one cycle (both load circuits have been energized and de-energized) after voltage is applied to the flasher. For fixed load flashers, the test shall be conducted with the specific ampere design loads connected. For a variable load flasher, the test shall be conducted with both the minimum and maximum ampere design loads connected. The start time shall be measured and recorded for three starts, each of which is separated by a cooling interval of at least 5 min.

5.2.2 VOLTAGE DROP

5.2.2.1 Turn Signal, Hazard Warning Signal, and Combination Flashers—The lowest voltage drop across the flasher shall be measured between the input and the load terminals at the flasher and during the "on" period. The voltage drop shall be measured and recorded during any three cycles after the flasher has been operating for five consecutive cycles. For a fixed load flasher, the test shall be made with the specific ampere design load connected. For a variable load flasher, the test shall be made with the maximum ampere design load connected.

5.2.2.2 Warning Lamp Alternating Flashers—The lowest voltage drop across the flasher shall be measured between the input and each load terminal at the flasher and during the "on" period. The voltage drop shall be measured and recorded during any three cycles after the flasher has been operating for five consecutive cycles. For fixed load flashers, the test shall be made with the specific maximum ampere design load connected. For a variable load flasher, the test shall be conducted with the maximum ampere design load connected.

5.2.3 FLASH RATE AND PERCENT CURRENT ON TIME—The flash rate and percent current on time shall be measured and recorded after the flasher has completed five consecutive cycles. The average of a minimum of three consecutive cycles shall be determined.

The flasher shall be temperature stabilized before each test. For a fixed load flasher, the test shall be made with the specific ampere design load connected. For a variable load flasher, the test shall be made with both the minimum and maximum ampere design loads.

5.2.3.1 Turn Signal Flashers and Warning Lamp Alternating Flashers—The test shall be conducted at each of the following bulb voltage and ambient temperature conditions:

a. 12.8 V (or 6.4 V or 25.6 V) and 24 °C ± 5 °C.
b. 12.0 V (or 6.0 V or 24.0 V) and –17 °C ± –3 °C.
c. 15.0 V (or 7.5 V or 30.0 V) and –17 °C ± –3 °C.
d. 11.0 V (or 5.5 V or 22.0 V) and 50 °C ± –3 °C.
e. 14.0 V (or 7.0 V or 28.0 V) and 50 °C ± –3 °C.

5.2.3.2 Hazard Warning Signal Flashers—The test shall be conducted at each of the following bulb voltages and ambient temperature conditions:

a.   12.8 V (or 6.4 V or 25.6 V) and 24 °C ± 5 °C.
b.   11.0 V (or 5.5 V or 22.0 V) and −17 °C ± −3 °C.
c.   13.0 V (or 6.5 V or 26.0 V) and −17 °C ± −3 °C.
d.   11.0 V (or 5.5 V or 22.0 V) and 50 °C ± −3 °C.
e.   13.0 V (or 6.5 V or 26.0 V) and 50 °C ± −3 °C.

5.2.3.3 Combination Flashers—The test shall be conducted at each of the bulb voltage and ambient temperature conditions listed in 5.2.3.1 and 5.2.3.2.

5.2.4 EXTREME TEMPERATURE—The flasher shall be subjected to extreme temperatures of 63 °C ± 3 °C and −32 °C ± 3 °C until stabilized.

The start time shall be measured and recorded at each extreme temperature per 5.2.1 of this document.

The flash rate and percent current on time shall be measured and recorded at each ambient temperature per 5.2.3 of this document. The flash rate measurement must be completed within the first minute of operation of the flasher.

5.2.5 DURABILITY—The durability test shall be conducted using the maximum specified ampere design load for the function tested.

5.2.5.1 Turn Signal Flashers and Warning Lamp Alternating Flashers

a.   Class A Flashers—The test sequence shall be:

  (1) Step 1—The test shall be conducted for 100 h of intermittent flashing (15 s on, 15 s off) followed by 50 h of continuous flashing with 14.0 V (7.0 V or 28.0 V) applied to the input terminals of the test circuit.
  (2) Step 2—Determine start time per 5.2.1.1 for turn signal flashers and 5.2.1.2 for warning lamp alternating flashers, voltage drop per 5.2.2.1 for turn signal flashers and 5.2.2.2 for warning lamp alternating flashers, flash rate and percent current on time per 5.2.3 and 5.2.3.1(a).

b.   Class B Flashers—The test sequence shall be:

  (1) Step 1—The test shall be conducted for 1000 h of continuous flashing with 14.0 V (7.0 V or 28.0 V) applied to the input terminals of the test circuit.
  (2) Step 2—Determine start time per 5.2.1.1 for turn signal flashers and 5.2.1.2 for warning lamp alternating flashers, voltage drop per 5.2.2.1 for turn signal flashers and 5.2.2.2 for warning lamp alternating flashers, flash rate and percent current on time per 5.2.3 and 5.2.3.1(a).

5.2.5.2 Hazard Warning Signal Flashers

a.   Class A Flashers—The test sequence shall be:

  (1) Step 1—The test shall be conducted for 36 h of continuous flashing with 13.0 V (6.5 V or 26.0 V) applied to the input terminals of the test circuit.

(2) Step 2—Determine start time per 5.2.1.1, voltage drop per 5.2.2.1, flash rate and percent current on time per 5.2.3 and 5.2.3.2(a).

b. Class B Flashers—The test sequence shall be:

(1) Step 1—The test shall be conducted for 360 h of continuous flashing with 13.0 V (6.5 V or 26.0 V) applied to the input terminals of the test circuit.
(2) Step 2—Determine start time per 5.2.1.1, voltage drop per 5.2.2.1, flash rate and percent current on time per 5.2.3 and 5.2.3.2(a).

5.2.5.3 Combination Flashers

a. Class A Flashers—The test sequence shall be:

(1) Step 1—100 h of intermittent flashing (15 s on, 15 s off) followed by 50 h of continuous flashing with 14.0 V (7.0 V or 28.0 V) applied to the input terminals of the test circuit with the turn signal load.
(2) Step 2—36 h of continuous flashing with 13.0 V (6.5 V or 26.0 V) applied to the input terminals of the test circuit with the hazard warning load.
(3) Step 3—Determine start time per 5.2.1.1, voltage drop per 5.2.2.1, flash rate and percent current on time per 5.2.3 , 5.2.3.1(a), and 5.2.3.2(a).

b. Class B Flashers—The test sequence shall be:

(1) Step 1—1000 h of continuous flashing with 14.0 V (7.0 V or 20.0 V) applied to the input terminals of the test circuit with the turn signal load.
(2) Step 2—360 h of continuous flashing with 13.0 V (6.5 V or 26.0 V) applied to the input terminals of the test circuit with the hazard warning load.
(3) Step 3—Determine start time per 5.2.1.1, voltage drop per 5.2.2.1, flash rate and percent current on time per 5.2.3, 5.2.3.1(a), and 5.2.3.2(a).

6. Peformance Requirements

6.1 Start Time—The average and maximum of the three start time measurements per 5.2.1 shall not exceed the values shown in Table 1.

TABLE 1—START TIME (SECONDS)

FLASHER TYPE	AVERAGE TIME	MAXIMUM TIME
Normally closed	1.3	2.0
Normally open	1.5	2.0

6.2 Voltage Drop—The average of the three voltage drop measurements per 5.2.2 shall not exceed 0.5 V. Any single measurement shall not exceed 0.0V.

6.3 Flash Rate and Percent Current On Time

6.3.1 TURN SIGNAL AND HAZARD WARNING SIGNAL FLASHERS—The average flash rate and percent current on time shall fall within 60 to 120 flashes per minute and 30 to 75% current on time, respectively, under all conditions of 5.2.3 and 5.2.3.1 for turn signal flashers and 5.2.3.2 for hazard warning signal flashers.

6.3.2 WARNING LAMP ALTERNATING FLASHERS—At each load terminal, the average flash rate and percent current on time shall fall within 60 to 120 flashes per minute and 30 to 75% current on time, respectively, under all conditions 5.2.3 and 5.2.3.1.

The total of the percent current on times for the two terminals shall be a minimum of 90 and a maximum of 110.

6.3.3 COMBINATION FLASHERS—The average flash rate and percent current on time shall fall within 60 to 120 flashes per minute and 30 to 75% current on time, respectively, under all conditions of 5.2.3 and 5.2.3.3.

6.4 Extreme Temperature

6.4.1 TURN SIGNAL, HAZARD WARNING SIGNAL, AND COMBINATION FLASHERS—At each of the extreme temperature conditions, start time shall not exceed 3 s and average flash rate shall be 50 to 130 flashes per minute. The percent current on time shall be between 25 and 80%.

6.4.2 WARNING LAMP ALTERNATING FLASHERS—At each of the extreme temperature conditions, start time shall not exceed 5 s and flash rate shall not be less than 30 or more than 150 flashes per minute.

6.5 Durability

6.5.1 TURN SIGNAL FLASHERS—At the start of the test, the flashers shall conform to the requirements of 6.1, 6.2, and 6.3.1. At the completion of Step 2 of 5.2.5.1, the flashers shall conform to the requirements of 6.1, 6.2, and 6.3.1 (only test condition "a" of 5.2.3.1 is required).

6.5.2 HAZARD WARNING SIGNAL FLASHERS—At the start of the test, the flashers shall conform to the requirements of 6.1, 6.2, and 6.3.1. At the completion of Step 2 of 5.2.5.2, the flashers shall conform to the requirements of 6.1, 6.2, and 6.3.1 (only test condition "a" of 5.2.3.2 is required).

6.5.3 WARNING LAMP ALTERNATING FLASHERS—At the start of the test, the flashers shall conform to the requirements of 6.1, 6.2, and 6.3.2. At the completion of Step 2 of 5.2.5.1, the flashers shall conform to the requirements of 6.1, 6.2, and 6.3.2 (only test condition "a" of 5.2.3.1 is required).

6.5.4 COMBINATION FLASHERS—At the start of the test, the flashers shall conform to the requirements of 6.1, 6.2, and 6.3.3. At the completion of Step 2 of 5.2.5.3, the flashers shall conform to the requirements of 6.1, 6.2, and 6.3.3 (only test condition "a" of 5.2.3.1 and test condition "a" of 5.2.3.2 are required).

7. *Notes*—The following international standards were used as reference for the extended durability requirements included in the document:

International Standard ISO 4082, Road vehicles—Motor vehicles flasher units.
Japanese Industrial Standard JIS D 5707, Flasher Units for Automobiles.

PREPARED BY THE SAE FLASHER TASK FORCE OF THE
SAE LIGHTING COORDINATING COMMITTEE

COMBINATION TURN SIGNAL HAZARD WARNING SIGNAL FLASHERS—SAE J2068 DEC94

SAE Recommended Practice

Report of the Auxiliary Devices Standards Committee approved January 1990. Rationale statement available. Revised by the Flasher Task Force of the SAE Auxiliary Device Standards Committee and the SAE Lighting Coordinating Committee December 1994. Rationale statement available.

1. Scope—This SAE Recommended Practice defines the test conditions, procedures, and minimum design requirements for nominal 6, 12, and 24 V flashers used for both turn signal and hazard warning signaling.

2. References

2.1 Applicable Documents—The following publications form a part of this specification to the extent specified herein. The latest issue of SAE publications shall apply.

2.1.1 SAE PUBLICATIONS—Available from SAE, 400 Commonwealth Drive, Warrendale, PA 15096-0001.

SAE J590—Turn Signal Flashers

SAE J759—Lighting Identification Code

SAE J823—Flasher Test

SAE J945—Vehicular Hazard Warning Signal Flasher

2.2 Definition—This flasher is a device installed in a vehicle lighting system, which has the primary functions of causing the turn signal lamps to flash when the turn signal switch is actuated and the hazard warning signal lamps to flash when the hazard warning switch is activated.

3. Flasher Identification Code—Flashers conforming to this document may be identified by the code SAE J590/J945 in accordance with SAE J759.

4. Tests

4.1 Test Equipment—The standard test equipment and circuitry for performing flasher tests shall conform with the specifications in SAE J823.

4.2 Test Procedures—All of the following tests shall be performed at 12.8 V (or 6.4 V or 25.6 V) at the bulbs and at ambient temperature of 24 °C ± 5 °C.

4.2.1 START TIME—The start time of a normally closed type flasher is the time to open the circuit after the voltage is applied, provided the closed circuit remains closed for a minimum of 0.10 s. If the closed circuit opens in less than

0.10 s, the flasher shall be considered a normally open type flasher for this test. The start time of a normally open type flasher is the time to complete one cycle (close the circuit and then open the circuit) after the voltage is applied. The test shall be made with the minimum and maximum ampere design loads for both the turn and hazard warning signal functions. The start time shall be measured and recorded for three starts, each of which is separated by a cooling interval of at least 5 min.

(R) *4.2.1.1 Turn Signal Test*—For a fixed-load flasher, the test shall be made with the specific ampere design load connected. For a variable-load flasher, the test shall be made with both the minimum and maximum ampere design load connected.

4.2.1.2 Hazard Warning Test—The test shall be made with both the minimum and maximum ampere design load.

4.2.2 VOLTAGE DROP—The lowest voltage drop across the flasher shall be measured between the input and the load terminals at the flasher and during the "on" period. The voltage drop shall be measured and recorded during any three cycles after the flasher has been operating for a minimum of five consecutive cycles but less than twenty cycles. The test shall be made in an ambient temperature of 24 °C ± 5 °C.

4.2.2.1 Turn Signal Test—For a fixed-load flasher, the voltage drop is measured with the specific ampere design load connected. For a variable-load flasher, the voltage drop shall be measured with the maximum ampere design load connected.

4.2.2.2 Hazard Warning Test—The voltage drop shall be measured with the maximum ampere design load connected.

(R) 4.2.3 FLASH RATE AND PERCENT CURRENT ON TIME—The flash rate and percent current on time shall be measured and recorded after the flasher has completed five consecutive cycles and shall be an average of at least three

187

consecutive cycles at each of the specified bulb voltage and ambient temperature conditions.

The flashers shall be temperature stabilized at the ambient temperature before each test.

4.2.3.1 *Turn Signal Tests:*
a. 12.8 V (or 6.4 or 25.6 V) and 24 °C ± 5 °C
b. 12.0 V (or 6.0 or 24.0 V) and −17 °C ± 3 °C
c. 15.0 V (or 7.5 or 30.0 V) and −17 °C ± 3 °C
d. 11.0 V (or 5.5 or 22.0 V) and 50 °C ± 3 °C
e. 14.0 V (or 7.0 or 28.0 V) and 50 °C ± 3 °C

For a fixed-load flasher, the test shall be made with the specific ampere design load connected. For a variable-load flasher, the test shall be made with both the minimum and maximum ampere design load.

4.2.3.2 *Hazard Warning Tests*
a. 12.8 V (or 6.4 or 25.6 V) and 24 °C ± 5 °C
b. 11.0 V (or 5.5 or 22.0 V) and −17 °C ± 3 °C
c. 13.0 V (or 6.5 or 26.0 V) and −17 °C ± 3 °C
d. 11.0 V (or 5.5 or 22.0 V) and 50 °C ± 3 °C
e. 13.0 V (or 6.5 or 26.0 V) and 50 °C ± 3 °C

The test shall be made with both the minimum and maximum ampere design load.

4.2.4 EXTREME TEMPERATURE—The flasher shall be subjected to ambient temperatures of 63 °C ± 3 °C and −32 °C ± 3 °C until stabilized. The start time and flash rate shall be measured and recorded at each extreme temperature. The flash rate measurement must be completed within the first minute of energization. Otherwise the procedure shall be as specified in 4.2.1.1 and 4.2.3.1(a) for turn signal and 4.2.1.2 and 4.2.3.2(a) for hazard warning.

4.2.5 DURABILITY—The durability test shall be conducted under the following conditions:

4.2.5.1 *Turn Signal Test Conditions:*
a. 24 °C ± 5 °C ambient temperature
b. 14.0 V (7.0 or 28.0 V) applied to the input terminals of the test circuit
c. Specific ampere design load for fixed-load flashers and maximum specified ampere design load for variable-load flashers

4.2.5.2 *Hazard Warning Test Conditions:*
a. 24 °C ± 5 °C ambient temperature

b. 13.0 V (6.5 or 26 V) applied to the input terminals of the test circuit
c. Maximum specified ampere design load

4.2.5.3 *Test Cycle:*
a. 50 h of intermittent flashing (15 s on, 15 s off) per 4.2.5.1
b. 8 continuous hours per 4.2.5.2
c. 50 h of intermittent flashing (15 s on, 15 s off) per 4.2.5.1
d. 8 continuous hours per 4.2.5.2
e. 50 continuous hours per 4.2.5.1
f. 20 continuous hours per 4.2.5.2

5. *Performance Requirements*

5.1 Start Time—The average and maximum of the three start time measurements (4.2.1, 4.2.1.1, 4.2.1.2) for the flasher shall not exceed the values shown in Table 1.

TABLE 1—START TIME, SECONDS

Flasher Type	Average Time	Maximum Time
Normally Closed	1.3	2.0
Normally Open	1.5	2.0

5.2 Voltage Drop—The average of the three voltage drop measurements (4.2.2) for the flasher shall not exceed 0.5 V. No single measurement shall exceed 0.8 V.

5.3 Flash Rate and Percent Current on Time—The average flash rate and percent current on time shall fall within 60 to 120 flashes/min and 30 to 75% on under all conditions of 4.2.3.

5.4 Extreme Temperature—At the extreme temperature conditions, start time shall not exceed 3 s and flash rate shall be 50 to 130 flashes/min.

5.5 Durability—The flasher shall conform to 5.1, 5.2, and 5.3 (under test conditions 4.2.3.1(a) and 4.2.3.2(a) only) at the start and conclusion of the test.

6. *Guidelines*

6.1 Turn signal secondary functions may include the visible pilot indication (required by SAE J588), an audible signal to indicate flasher operation, and indication of turn signal lamp outage.

6.2 Hazard warning secondary functions may include the visible pilot indicator required in hazard warning signal systems and an audible signal to indicate flasher operation. When included, the pilot function must operate under all hazard warning test conditions.

DOOR COURTESY SWITCH
—SAE J2108 DEC91

SAE Recommended Practice

Report of the SAE Circuit Protection and Switching Devices Standards Committee approved June 1991. Rationale statement available. Reaffirmed by the SAE Switch Task Force of the SAE Auxiliary Devices Standards Committee December 1991.

1. Scope—This SAE Recommended Practice defines the test conditions, procedures, and performance requirements for 6, 12, and 24 V Door Courtesy Switches which are intended for use in motor vehicles.

2. References

2.1 Applicable Documents—There are no referenced publications specified herein.

2.2 Definitions—The courtesy lamp switch is a door or door latch actuated device which controls the electrical operation of the courtesy lamp, ignition key alarm, and other related components.

2.3 Types

2.3.1 GROUNDED AND NON-GROUNDED—Grounded switches provide an electrical path to vehicle ground through their mounting attachment. Non-grounded switches have their electrical conductors insulated from vehicle ground.

2.3.2 SINGLE TERMINAL—Characterized by one wiring connection to the vehicle.

2.3.3 MULTI-TERMINAL—Any other terminal/connector configuration, other than single terminal.

2.3.4 SPECIAL—Switch types, which by their design, construction, and function, require separate definition.

2.4 Cycle—One cycle shall consist of allowing the actuation portion of the switch to move or be moved throughout its travel and to return to its initial position.

3. Test Requirements

3.1 Test Equipment and Instrumentation

3.1.1 POWER SUPPLY—The power supply shall comply with the following specifications:

3.1.1.1 *Output Current*—Capable of supplying the continuous and inrush currents of the design load (reference 3.2.1.1).

3.1.1.2 *Regulation*—Dynamic: The output voltage at the supply shall not deviate more than 1.0 V from zero to maximum load (including inrush current) and should recover 63% of its maximum excursion within 100 ms.

Static: The output voltage at the supply shall not deviate more than 2% with changes in static load from zero to maximum (not including inrush current), and means shall be provided to compensate for static input line variations.

3.1.1.3 *Ripple Voltage*—Maximum 300 mV peak-to-peak.

3.1.2 VOLTMETER—0 to 30 maximum full scale deflection, accuracy ± 1/2%. (Note: a digital meter having at least a 3 1/2 digit readout with an accuracy of ± 1% plus 1 digit is recommended for millivolt readings.)

3.1.3 AMMETER—Capable of carrying full system load current, accuracy ± 3%.

3.2 Test Procedures—Environmental conditions have been selected for this document to help assure satisfactory operation under general customer use conditions. It is essential to duplicate the specific environmental conditions under which the device is expected to function.

3.2.1 ELECTRICAL LOADS

3.2.1.1 The design load applied to the switch is the electrical load defined by the number and type of bulbs (or other electrical load devices) to be operated by each circuit of the switch. For example, the design load for the courtesy lamp circuit may be four 1156 bulbs.

3.2.1.2 The switch shall be operated at 6.4 V DC ± 0.2 V DC for a 6 V system, 12.8 V DC ± 0.2 V DC for a 12 V system, or 25.6 V DC ± 0.2 V DC for a 24 V system. These voltages shall be the open circuit voltage measured at the input terminations of the switch.

3.2.2 TEMPERATURE TEST PROCEDURE

3.2.2.1 The switch shall be exposed for 1 h without electrical load to each of the following temperatures: 25 °C ± 5 °C, 74 °C +0, –3, –32 °C +3, –0. The switch shall be cycled at each temperature for ten cycles at design load.

3.2.2.2 The same switch shall be used for the endurance test described in 3.2.3.

3.2.3 ENDURANCE TEST PROCEDURE

3.2.3.1 The switch shall be electrically connected to operate its design load (both primary and secondary circuit function design electrical loads) at a temperature of 25 °C ± 5 °C.

3.2.3.2 The switch shall be operated for a minimum of 50 000 cycles. The speed and the incident angle of actuation shall be representative of the point of application ("A" pillar, "B" pillar) in the vehicle. The test equipment shall be designed to provide this timing: Travel Time: 0.1 to 1.0 s (time to travel from one extreme position to the other). Dwell Time: 2.0 to 5.0 s (time spent stationary at an extreme position). Make and Break Rate Range:

"A" Pillar application: 30 to 300 mm/s.

"B" Pillar application: 0.3 to 3.0 m/s.

3.2.3.3 At the conclusion of the endurance testing, the switch shall be operated for 1 h in each of its positions with the design load connected.

3.2.4 VOLTAGE DROP TEST PROCEDURE

3.2.4.1 Voltage drop from the input terminal(s) to the corresponding output terminal(s) shall be measured at design load before and after the completion of the endurance test. Three consecutive readings shall be taken and the average recorded. If wiring is an integral part of the switch, the voltage drop measurement shall be made by including 75 mm ± 6 mm of wire on each side of the switch. Otherwise, the measurement shall be made at the switch terminals.

4. Performance Requirements

4.1 During and after each of the cycles described in 3.2.2 and 3.2.3, the switch shall operate without hesitation mechanically, e.g., not more than 1.0 s, and shall be within its electrical design specifications.

4.2 The voltage drop shall not exceed 0.3 V when measured as in 3.2.4, either before or after the tests described in 3.2.3.

Report of the Lighting Division, approved May 1942, completely revised by the Lighting Committee July 1983, and reaffirmed by the Lighting Coordination Committee December 1988. Completely revised by the SAE Test Methods and Equipment Standards Committee June 1992. Rationale statement available.

1. Scope—This SAE Recommended Practice provides standardized laboratory tests, test methods, and requirements applicable to many of the lighting devices and components covered by SAE Recommended Practices and Standards and is intended for reference for devices used on vehicles less than 2032 mm in width, regardless of length, or 7620 mm in length regardless of width. Tests for vehicles larger than 2032 mm in overall width are covered in J2139.

2. References

2.1 Applicable Documents—The following publications form a part of this specification to the extent specified herein. The latest issue of SAE publications shall apply.

2.1.1 SAE PUBLICATIONS—Available from SAE, 400 Commonwealth Drive, Warrendale, PA 15096-0001.

SAE J387—Terminology—Motor Vehicle Lighting

SAE J1330—Photometry Laboratory Accuracy Guidelines

SAE J2139—Test Methods and Equipment for Lighting Devices and Components for Use on Vehicles More than 2032 mm in Overall Width

2.1.2 ASTM PUBLICATIONS—Available from ASTM, 1916 Race Street, Philadelphia, PA 19103.

ASTM B 117-73—Method of Salt Spray (Fog) Testing

ASTM C 150-84—Specification for Portland Cement

ASTM E 308-85—Standard Practice for Spectrophotometry and Description of Color in CIE 1931 System

2.2 Definitions

2.2.1 LIGHTING DEVICES—An assembly (divisible or indivisible) which contains a bulb or other light source and generally an optical system such as a lens or a reflector, or both, and which provides a lighting function. Lighting device samples submitted for test shall be representative of the device as regularly manufactured and marketed, unless otherwise identified. Each sample shall be securely mounted on a test fixture in its designed operating position and shall include all accessory equipment necessary to operate the device in its normal manner.

2.2.2 BULB—An indivisible assembly which contains a source of light and which is normally used in a lamp. Unless otherwise specified, bulbs used in the tests shall be supplied by the test facility and shall be representative of bulbs in regular production. Where special bulbs are specified, they shall be submitted with the sample devices and the same or similar bulbs shall be used in the tests. Lighting devices designed for use in 6 V, 12 V, or 24 V systems shall be tested with 12 V bulbs.

2.2.3 TEST FIXTURE—A device specifically designed to support the lighting device in its designed operating position during laboratory testing. This fixture, when used for the vibration test, shall not have a resonant frequency in the 10 to 55 Hz range with the sample installed.

3. Test Descriptions—The following sections describe individual tests which need not be performed in any particular sequence. The completion of the tests may be expedited by performing the tests simultaneously on separately mounted samples. However, it is recommended that the design of each device be evaluated to determine if vibration or warpage tests might affect the results of other tests, in which case the vibration and/or warpage test(s) should be performed first.

3.1 Vibration Test—This test evaluates the ability of the sample device to resist damage from vibration induced stresses. This test is not intended to test the vibration resistance of bulb filaments or headlamp light source filaments.

3.1.1 VIBRATION TEST EQUIPMENT—A vibration test machine capable of linear frequency variation at a constant unidirectional excursion shall be used. The vibrator table shall be of sufficient size to completely contain the test fixture base with no overhang. If this is not possible, a transition table shall be used to mechanically interface the large test fixture base to the smaller vibrator table. Precautions shall be taken to minimize the introduction of extraneous responses in the test setup. The vibration machine output wave form shall be sinusoidal with a maximum permissible harmonic distortion as shown in Figure 1, when measured as follows:

3.1.1.1 *Distortion Measurement*—The test machine output wave form shall be measured with an accelerometer having a flat frequency response (±5%) from 5 to 2200 Hz, attached to the unloaded vibrator table or to the transition table, if used. The acceleration component measured shall be in the direction of table travel.

3.1.1.2 *Harmonic Distortion Analysis*—The percent distortion shall be measured directly or shall be computed by taking the ratio (×100) of the rms (root mean squared) voltage of the distortion components to the rms voltage of the total signal (distortion plus fundamental) of the accelerometer.

3.1.2 VIBRATION TEST PROCEDURE—A sample device as mounted on a test fixture shall be securely bolted to the table of the vibration test machine and subjected to vibration according to the following test parameters:

3.1.2.1 *Frequency*—Varied from 10 to 55 Hz and return to 10 Hz at a linear sweep period of 2 min/complete sweep cycle.

3.1.2.2 *Excursion*—1.0 + 0.1/- 0.0 mm peak to peak over the specified frequency range.

3.1.2.3 *Direction of Vibration*—Vertical axis of the device as it is mounted on the vehicle.

3.1.2.4 *Test Duration* 60 + 1/-0 minutes

3.2 Moisture Test—This test evaluates the ability of the sample device to resist moisture leakage from a water spray and determines the drainage capability of those devices with drain holes or other exposed openings in the device. This test is not intended to provide a complete test on the device seal (see Dust Exposure Test 3.3). A sample device as mounted on the test fixture shall be tested according to either Test 3.2.1 (Water Spray) or Test 3.2.3 (Water Submersion) as applicable. The purpose of the Water Submersion Test is to reduce the test time for sealed lighting devices. Devices which comply with the Water Submersion Test are considered to have complied with all requirements of the Moisture Test.

3.2.1 WATER SPRAY TEST EQUIPMENT—A water spray cabinet with the following characteristics shall be used:

3.2.1.1 *Cabinet*—The cabinet shall be equipped with a nozzle(s) which provides a solid cone water spray of sufficient angle to completely cover the sample device. The centerline of the nozzle(s) shall be directed downward at an angle of 45 degrees ± 5 degrees to the vertical axis of a rotating test platform.

3.2.1.2 *Rotating Test Platform*—Having a minimum diameter of 140 mm and rotating about a vertical axis in the center of the cabinet.

3.2.1.3 *Precipitation Rate*—The precipitation rate of the water spray at the device shall be 2.5(+ 1.6/-0) mm/min as measured with a vertical cylindrical collector centered on the vertical axis of the rotating test platform. The height of the collector shall be 100 mm and the inside diameter shall be a minimum 140 mm.

3.2.2 WATER SPRAY TEST PROCEDURE—The mounted sample device shall be subjected to a water spray as follows:

3.2.2.1 *Device Openings*—All drain holes and other openings shall remain open. Devices having a portion completely protected in service (i.e., trunk mounted lamps) shall have that part of the device covered to prevent moisture entry during the test. Drain wicks, when used, shall be tested in the device.

3.2.2.2 *Rotational Speed*—The device shall be rotated about its vertical axis at a rate of 4.0 ± 0.5 rpm.

3.2.2.3 *Test Duration*—The water spray test shall continue for 12 h.

3.2.2.4 *Drain Period*—The rotation and the water spray shall be turned off and the device allowed to drain for 1 h with the cabinet door closed.

3.2.2.5 *Sample Evaluation*—Upon completion of the drain period, the interior of the device shall be observed for moisture accumulation. If a standing pool of water has formed, or can be formed by tapping or tilting the device, the accumulated moisture shall be extracted and measured.

3.2.3 WATER SUBMERSION TEST PROCEDURE—The device shall be completely submerged under laboratory ambient temperature water at a depth of 150 to 175 mm as measured from the top of the device.

3.2.3.1 *Test Duration*—The device shall be submerged for 1 h.

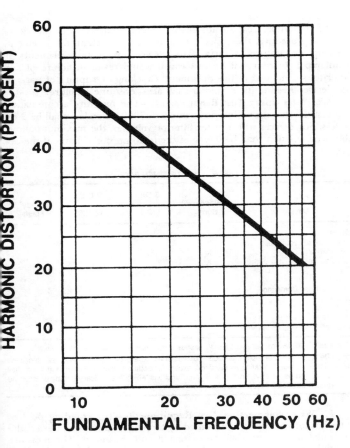

FIGURE 1—MAXIMUM PERMISSIBLE VIBRATION WAVE FORM
HARMONIC DISTORTION

3.2.3.2 *Sample Evaluation*—Immediately after the device is removed from submersion, the interior of the test device shall be observed for water accumulation.

3.3 Dust Exposure Test—This test evaluates the ability of the sample device to resist dust penetration which could significantly affect the photometric output of the lamp device. This test is not intended to provide a complete test on the device seals. A sample device shall be tested to either the Dust Exposure Test or Water Submersion Test. Devices which comply with the water submersion requirements are considered to have complied with all requirements of the Dust Exposure Test. If the device does not comply with the water submersion requirements, it may still comply with all requirements of the Dust Exposure Test.

3.3.1 DUST EXPOSURE TEST EQUIPMENT—The following equipment shall be used to test for dust exposure:

3.3.1.1 *Dust Exposure Test Chamber*—The interior of the test chamber shall be cubical in shape with measurements of 0.9 to 1.5 m per side. The bottom may be "hopper shaped" to aid in collecting the dust. The internal chamber volume, not including a "hopper shaped" bottom, shall be 2 m³ maximum and shall be charged with 3 to 5 kg of the test dust. The chamber shall have the capability of agitating the test dust by means of compressed air or blower fans in such a way that the dust is diffused throughout the chamber.

3.3.1.2 *Test Dust*—The test dust used shall be fine powdered cement in accordance with ASTM C 150-84.

3.3.2 DUST EXPOSURE TEST PROCEDURE—A sample device, mounted on a test fixture, with the initial maximum luminous intensity photometrically measured and recorded, shall be subjected to dust as follows:

3.3.2.1 *Device Openings*—All device openings shall be open. A device which has a portion completely protected in service (i.e., trunk mounted lamp) shall have that portion of the device covered to prevent dust entry during the dust exposure.

3.3.2.2 *Dust Exposure*—The mounted device shall be placed in the dust chamber no closer than 150 mm from a wall. Devices with a length exceeding 600 mm shall be horizontally centered in the test chamber. The test dust shall be agitated as completely as possible by compressed

air or blower(s) at intervals of 15 min for a 2 to 15 s period. The dust shall be allowed to settle between the agitation periods.

3.3.2.3 *Test Duration*—5 h.

3.3.2.4 *Sample Evaluation*—Upon completion of the dust exposure test, the lamp exterior shall be cleaned and the maximum luminous intensity measured.

3.4 Corrosion Test—This test evaluates the ability of the sample device to resist salt corrosion which would impair the functional characteristics of the device.

3.4.1 CORROSION TEST EQUIPMENT—A salt spray (fog) cabinet, operating at the conditions specified by ASTM B 117-73, shall be used.

3.4.2 CORROSION TEST PROCEDURE—A sample device as mounted on the test fixture shall be subjected to salt spray (fog) as follows:

3.4.2.1 *Device Openings*—All device openings shall remain open. If a portion of the device is completely protected in service (such as a trunk mounted lamp) that portion shall be covered to prevent salt fog entry during the salt exposure.

3.4.2.2 *Salt Exposure*—The device shall be placed in the salt spray chamber for a period of 48 h.

3.4.2.3 *Sample Evaluation*—After removal from the chamber and after a 1 h drying period, the device shall be visually examined for corrosion which could affect other tests contained in this document.

3.5 Photometry Test—This test measures luminous intensities at test points throughout the light distribution pattern as specified by the applicable SAE report for the sample device.

3.5.1 PHOTOMETRIC TEST EQUIPMENT—Unless otherwise specified, the following equipment shall be used to make the photometric measurements:

3.5.1.1 *Positioner*—The positioner (goniometer) configuration shall be capable of positioning the sample device at the test point positions specified in 3.5.2.4 and in the applicable SAE report. (The recommended configuration is shown in SAE J1330.) Other systems may be used to achieve equivalent positioning, but it may be necessary at compound angles greater than 5 degrees from H-V to calculate the position which is equivalent to that of the recommended goniometer.

3.5.1.2 *Photometer*—The photometer system consists of a sensor, amplifier, and indicator instrument. The system shall be capable of providing the luminous intensity readings (candela) of the output of the device being tested. The sensor shall be located at the distance from the device specified in the applicable SAE report and shall have the following characteristics:

3.5.1.2.1 Maximum Size—Unless otherwise specified, the maximum effective area of the sensor shall fit within a circle whose diameter is equal to 0.009 times the actual test distance from the light source of the sample device to the sensor. The sensor effective area is the actual area of intercepted light striking the detector surface of the photometer. For systems with lens(es) that change the diameter of the intercepted light beam before it reaches the actual detector surface, the maximum size requirements shall apply to the total area of the light actually intercepted by the lens surface. The sensor shall be capable of intercepting all direct illumination from the largest illuminated dimension of the sample device at the test distance.

3.5.1.2.2 Photopic Response—The color response of the photometer sensor shall be corrected to that of ASTM E 308-85.

3.5.2 PHOTOMETRY TEST PROCEDURE—The sample device shall be mounted on a test fixture and luminous intensity measurements made as follows:

3.5.2.1 *Bulbs*—Unless otherwise specified, accurate rated bulbs (selected per SAE J387) shall be used and shall be operated at their rated luminous flux output. Where special bulbs are used, they shall be seasoned per SAE J387 and operated at their rated luminous flux output.

3.5.2.2 *Test Voltage*—If the rated luminous flux output is not available, or not applicable, operate the bulb at its specified design voltage. If the luminous flux output of the bulb is intentionally modified from specifications for the device through internal or external circuitry, operate the bulb at its modified voltage, or with the voltage modification circuitry attached and with the specified design voltage applied to the input of the modification circuitry.

3.5.2.3 *Test Distance*—The luminous intensity measurements shall be made at a distance equal to, or greater than, the minimum test distance between the center of the light source (or the face of a reflex reflector) and the photometer sensor as specified in the SAE Technical Report applicable to the function of the sample device. If no test distance is specified, the distance shall be at least 10 times the largest illuminated dimension of the sample device.

3.5.2.4 *Test Point Positions*—Test point positions are specified in the applicable SAE Technical Report. The following nomenclature shall also

191

apply: The letters "V" and "H" designate the vertical and horizontal planes intersecting both the device light source (or center or a reflex reflector) and the goniometer axis. A device using a bulb with a major and minor light source shall be oriented with respect to its major light source. "H-V" designates the test point angle at the intersection of the H and V planes (H = O, V = O degrees). Unless otherwise specified, this intersection shall be parallel to the longitudinal axis of the vehicle in the case of the designed operating position of front or rear device functions and shall be horizontal and perpendicular to the longitudinal axis of the vehicle in the case of side function devices. The letters "U," "D," "L," and "R" (up, down, left, and right, respectively) designate the angular position in degrees from the H and V planes to the goniometer as viewed from a lamp, or to the source of illumination as viewed from a reflex reflector. This angular direction is defined as follows:

3.5.2.4.1 HORIZONTAL ANGLE (L AND R)—The angle between the vertical plane and the projection onto the horizontal plane of the ray from the center of the light source of the device to the center of the photometer sensor.

3.5.2.4.2 VERTICAL ANGLE (U AND D)—The true angle between the horizontal plane and the ray from the center of the light source of the device to the center of the photometer sensor.

3.5.2.4.3 The direction can be visualized where an observer stands behind the device and looks in the direction of the emanating light beam towards the photometer sensor when the device is properly aimed with respect to H-V. It should be noted that when rotating the device on a goniometer, it is necessary to move the aim of the device from the H-V point in the opposite direction of the test point being measured. For example, to read a 5U-V test point, the goniometer shall aim the device 5 degrees down. A similar reversal applies to the down (D), left (L), and right (R) test points.

3.5.2.5 *Photometric Measurements*—Photometric measurements shall be made with the light source(s) steady burning. The luminous intensity measurements, in candela, shall be recorded for each of the test points and zones specified for the function of the device being tested.

3.6 Warpage Test on Devices with Plastic Components—This test evaluates the ability of the plastic components of the sample device to resist damage due to ambient and light source heat.

3.6.1 WARPAGE TEST EQUIPMENT—A circulating air oven having a predominant air flow direction shall be used with the air flow inlet on one side of the interior test chamber and the exhaust air outlet on the opposite side of the chamber.

3.6.2 WARPAGE TEST PROCEDURE—A sample device as mounted on the test fixture shall be placed in the circulating air oven and tested to the following procedures:

3.6.2.1 *Oven Temperature*—The oven temperature shall be controlled between 46 to 49 °C.

3.6.2.2 *Sample Position*—The device shall be positioned at the center of the oven such that the predominant direction of air flow approximates that which the device will encounter in its installed position on the vehicle.

3.6.2.3 *Bulb Operation*—Unless otherwise specified, the light source(s) shall be operated at design voltage and cycled as specified in Table 1.

3.6.2.4 *Test Duration*—1 h.

3.6.2.5 *Sample Evaluation*—Upon completion of the test, the device shall be visually examined for warpage of the plastic components.

4. Test Requirements

4.1 Vibration Test Requirements—Upon completion of the vibration test procedure, there shall be no observed rotation, displacement, cracking, or rupture of parts of the device (except bulb filaments or headlamp light source filaments) which would result in failure of any other tests contained in this document. Cracking or rupture of parts of the device affecting its mounting shall also constitute a failure.

4.2 Water Spray Test Requirements—The moisture accumulation in a test device with an interior volume of 7000 ml or less shall be 2 ml or less. For devices with greater interior volumes, the maximum allowable accumulation shall be 0.03% of the total interior volume of the device.

TABLE 1—CYCLE TIMES (MIN)

Device	Steady Burn	5 On – 5 Off	3 On – 12 Off	Steady[1] Flash
License	X			
Clearance & Identification	X			
Side Marker	X			
Tail, Fog Tail	X			
Park	X			
Stop		X		
Back-up, Rear Cornering		X		
Cornering			X	
Turn Signal				X
Illuminating (Fog Lamp, Driving Lamp, etc)	X			

[1] Flash rate—90 flashes per minute ± 10 flashes per minute with a 50% ± 2% on time.

NOTE—Devices with multiple function combinations shall be tested with all functions simultaneously operating as specified, except for backup functions. Backup functions shall be tested separately. Stop-Turn Signal Functions which are optically combined shall be tested as a stop function only.

4.3 Water Submersion Test Requirements—If a standing pool of water has formed, or can be formed by tapping or tilting the device, the accumulated moisture shall be extracted and measured. The moisture accumulation in the device, regardless of the volume of the device, shall not exceed 1 ml.

4.4 Dust Exposure Test Requirements—The maximum luminous measured intensity after the dust exposure test shall be at least 90% of the initial maximum luminous intensity measured before the test.

4.5 Corrosion Test Requirements—If corrosion is found that could affect other tests in this document, the test(s) shall be performed on the corrosion sample to ensure compliance to that test requirement.

4.6 Photometry Design and Performance Requirements—Upon completion of the test procedure, the luminous intensities at the test points or zones shall be within the limits specified in the applicable SAE Technical Report for the function being tested.

4.6.1 Unless otherwise specified in the applicable SAE Technical Report, the minimum luminous intensity requirements between the specified test points shall be no less than 60% of the lower specified design requirement minimum values for any two adjacent test points on a horizontal or vertical line.

4.7 Warpage Test Requirements—If warpage is observed that could result in failure of other tests contained in this document, the test(s) shall be performed on the warpage sample to insure compliance to that test requirement.

PLASTIC MATERIALS FOR USE IN OPTICAL PARTS SUCH AS LENSES AND REFLEX REFLECTORS OF MOTOR VEHICLE LIGHTING DEVICES—SAE J576 JUL91

SAE Standard

Report of the Lighting and Nonmetallic Materials Committee approved January 1955, and revised by the Lighting Committee September 1986. Rationale statement available. Completely revised by the SAE Lighting Coordinating Committee and the Materials Standards Committee July 1991. Rationale statement available.

1. Scope—This SAE Recommended Practice provides test methods and requirements to evaluate the suitability of plastic materials intended for optical applications in motor vehicles. The tests are intended to determine physical and optical characteristics of the material only. Performance expectations of finished assemblies, including plastic components, are to be based on tests for lighting devices, as specified in SAE Standards and Recommended Practices for motor vehicle lighting equipment. Field experience has shown that plastic materials meeting the requirements of this document and molded in accordance with good molding practices will produce durable lighting devices.

2. References

2.1 Applicable Documents—The following publications form a part of this specification to the extent specified herein. The latest issue of SAE publications shall apply.

2.1.1 SAE PUBLICATIONS—Available from SAE, 400 Commonwealth Drive, Warrendale, PA 15096-0001.

SAE J578—Color Specification

2.1.2 ASTM PUBLICATIONS—Available from ASTM, 1916 Race Street, Philadelphia, PA 19103.

ASTM D 1003-61—Test for Haze and Luminous Transmittance of Transparent Plastics

ASTM D 4364—Standard Practice for Performing Accelerated Outdoor Weathering Using Concentrated Natural Sunlight Utilizing Night Cycle Water Spray

ASTM E 308-66—Recommended Practices for Spectrophotometry and Description Color in CIE 1931 System

2.2 Definitions

2.2.1 MATERIAL—The type and grade of plastics, composition, and manufacturer's designation (number) and color.

2.2.1.1 *Coated Materials*—A coated material is a material as defined in 2.2.1 which has a coating applied to the surface of the finished sample to impart some protective properties. Coating identification includes manufacturer's name, formulation designation (number), and recommendations for application.

2.2.2 MATERIAL EXPOSURE

2.2.2.1 *Exposed*—Material used in lenses or optical devices exposed to direct sunlight as installed on the vehicle.

2.2.2.2 *Protected*—Material used in inner lenses for optical devices where such lenses are protected from exposure to the sun by an outer lens made of materials meeting the requirements for exposed plastics.

2.2.3 WEATHERING EFFECTS

2.2.3.1 *Color Bleeding*—The migration of color out of a plastic part onto the surrounding surface.

2.2.3.2 *Crazing*—A network of apparent fine cracks on or beneath the surface of materials.

2.2.3.3 *Cracking*—A separation of adjacent sections of a plastic material with penetration into the specimen.

2.2.3.4 *Haze*—The cloudy or turbid appearance of an otherwise transparent specimen caused by light scattered from within the specimen or from its surface.

2.2.3.5 *Delamination*—A separation of the layers of a material including coatings.

3. Test Procedures

3.1 Materials to be Tested—Outdoor exposure tests shall be made on each material (as defined in 2.2.1 and 2.2.1.1) offered for use in optical parts employed in motor vehicle lighting devices. Concentrations of polymer components and additives such as plasticizers, lubricants, colorants, weathering stabilizers, and antioxidants in plastic materials and/or coatings may be changed without outdoor exposure testing if: the changes are within the limits of composition represented by higher and lower concentrations of these polymer components and additives have been tested in accordance with 3.3 and found to meet the requirements of Section 4.

3.2 Samples Required

3.2.1 GENERAL—Samples of plastic preferably should be injection molded into polished metal molds to produce test specimens with two flat and parallel faces. Alternative processing techniques may also be used to produce equivalent test specimens. Test specimen shape may vary, but each exposed surface should contain a minimum uninterrupted area of 32 cm² (5.0 in²).

3.2.2 THICKNESS—Samples shall be furnished covering the thickness range stated by the manufacturer. Recommended nominal thicknesses are: 1.6 mm (0.063 in); 3.2 mm (0.125 in); 6.4 mm (0.250 in). A 2.3 mm (0.090 in) sample is also suggested.

3.2.3 NUMBER OF SAMPLES REQUIRED—Outdoor Exposure Test—1 sample/each thickness/each site × 2 sites for each material = 2 samples/each thickness for each material. Control: 1 sample/each thickness for each material—1 sample each.

NOTE—The control sample must be kept properly protected from influences which may change its appearance and properties.

3.3 Outdoor Exposure Tests

3.3.1 EXPOSURE SITES—Florida (warm, moist climate) and Arizona (warm, dry climate).

3.3.2 SAMPLE MOUNTING—One sample of each thickness of each material at each test station shall be mounted so that the exposed upper surface of the samples is at an angle of 45 degrees to the horizontal facing south. The exposed surface of the sample shall contain a minimum uninterrupted area of 32 cm² (5.0 in²). The sample shall be mounted in the open no closer than 30 cm (11.8 in) to its background.

3.3.3 EXPOSURE TIME AND CONDITIONS—The time of exposure shall be as noted in 3.3.3.1 for each type of material exposed. During the exposure time the samples shall be cleaned once every three months by washing with mild soap or detergent and water, and then rinsing with distilled water. Rubbing shall be avoided.

3.3.3.1 *Exposure Time Based on Material Usage*—Exposed—(defined in 2.2.2.1): 3 years. Protected—(defined in 2.2.2.2): 6 consecutive months starting in May.

3.3.3.2 *Accelerated Weathering*—After establishing and documenting correlation between accelerated and SAE outdoor exposure tests (3.3) for the plastic material and colorant under consideration, accelerated weathering may be used to evaluate minor changes in concentrations of polymer components and additives (3.1) previously found to be acceptable in the outdoor exposure tests. These tests may be used to establish acceptable high and low concentrations of the components and additives pending completion of 3 year weathering tests. These tests will serve as an indication that the plastic materials are capable of meeting the performance requirements of Section 4.

3.4 Optical Measurements

3.4.1 LUMINOUS TRANSMITTANCE AND COLOR MEASUREMENTS—Measurements shall be made in accordance with ASTM E 308-66 (1973).

3.4.2 HAZE MEASUREMENTS—Measurements shall be made in accordance with ASTM D 1003-61 (1977).

4. Material Performance Requirements—A material in the range of thickness as stated by the material manufacturer, and defined in 2.2.1 or 2.2.1.1, shall conform to the following requirements:

4.1 Before Exposure to Any Tests—The chromaticity coordinates shall conform with the requirements of SAE J578 in the range of thickness stated by the material manufacturer.

4.2 After Outdoor Exposure

4.2.1 LUMINOUS TRANSMITTANCE—The luminous transmittance of the exposed samples using CIE Illuminant A (2856K) shall not have changed by more than 25% of the luminous transmittance of the unexposed control sample when tested in accordance with ASTM E 308.

4.2.2 CHROMATICITY COORDINATES—The chromaticity coordinates shall conform with the requirements of SAE J578 in the range of thickness stated by the material manufacturer.

4.2.3 HAZE—The haze of plastic materials used for lamp lenses shall not be greater than 30% as measured by ASTM D 1003 (1977). The haze of plastic materials used for reflex reflectors and/or exposed cover lens materials used in front of reflex reflectors shall not be greater than 7% as measured by ASTM D 1003. Plastic materials used for forward road illumination devices, excluding cornering lamps, shall show no deterioration.

4.2.4 APPEARANCE—The exposed samples when compared with the unexposed controls shall not show physical changes affecting performance such as color bleeding, delamination, crazing, or cracking.

5. Detection of Coatings—In order to test for the presence of a coating, a trace quantity (100 ppm maximum in wet state) of an optical brightener should be added to a coating formulation. This should be checked by ultraviolet inspection against a known coated sample. Additionally, coating suppliers have the option of providing coatings without optical brighteners if they can provide an industry accepted method to detect the coating.

(R) COLOR SPECIFICATION
—SAE J578 JUN95

SAE Standard

Report of the Lighting Committee approved January 1942 and completely revised May 1988. Rationale statement available. Completely revised by the SAE Emergency Warning Lamps And Devices Standards Committee and the SAE Lighting Coordinating Committee June 1995.

1. Scope—This SAE Standard defines and provides a means for the control of colors employed in motor vehicle external lighting equipment, including lamps and reflex reflectors. The document applies to the overall effective color of light emitted by the device in any given direction and not to the color of the light from a small area of the lens. It does not apply to pilot, indicator, or tell-tale lights.

2. References

2.1 Applicable Documents—The following publications form a part of this specification to the extent specified herein. The latest issue of SAE publications shall apply.

2.1.1 SAE PUBLICATIONS—Available from SAE, 400 Commonwealth Drive, Warrendale, PA 15096-0001.

SAE J578—Color Specification for Electric Signal Lighting Devices

SAE J774—Emergency Warning Device

SAE J943—Slow-Moving Vehicle Identification Emblem

SAE HS 34—SAE Ground Vehicle Lighting Standards Manual

2.1.2 FEDERAL PUBLICATIONS—Available from the Superintendent of Documents, U.S. Government Printing Office, Washington, DC 20402-9371.

FMVSS No. 125—Warning Devices, 39 FR 28636, Aug. 9, 1974 as amended at 40 FR4, Jan. 2, 1975

FMVSS 108

2.1.3 ASTM PUBLICATIONS—Available from American National Standards Institute, Inc., 11 West 42nd Street, New York, NY 10036-8002.

ASTM E 308-66—Method for Computing the Colors of Objects by Using the CIE System

3. Definitions

3.1 Chromaticity Coordinates—The fundamental requirements for color are expressed as chromaticity coordinates according to the CIE (1931) standard colorimetric system (see Figure 1). The following requirements shall apply when measured by the tristimulus or spectrophotometric methods.

3.1.1 RED—The color of light emitted from the device shall fall within the following boundaries:

y = 0.33 (yellow boundary)

y = 0.98 − x (purple boundary)

3.1.2 YELLOW AMBER—The color of light emitted from the device shall fall within the following boundaries:

y = 0.39 (red boundary)

y = 0.79 − 0.67x (white boundary)

y = x − 0.12 (green boundary)

3.1.2.1 Selective Yellow (See A-2 Appendix)—The color of light emitted from the device shall fall within the following boundaries:

y = 0.58x + 0.14 (red boundary)

y = 1.29x − 0.10 (green boundary)

y = 0.97 − x (white boundary)

3.1.3 WHITE (ACHROMATIC)— The color of light emitted from the device shall fall within the following boundaries:

x = 0.31 (blue boundary)

x = 0.50 (yellow boundary)

y = 0.15 + 0.64x (green boundary)

y = 0.05 + 0.75x (purple boundary)

y = 0.44 (green boundary)

y = 0.38 (red boundary)

3.1.3.1 White to Yellow—The color of light emitted from the device shall fall within one of the following areas:

a. That defined in 3.1.2 Yellow.

b. That defined in 3.1.2.1 Selective Yellow.

c. That defined in 3.1.3 White.

d. The area between Yellow, Selective Yellow, and White as shown by the dashed line in Figure 1.

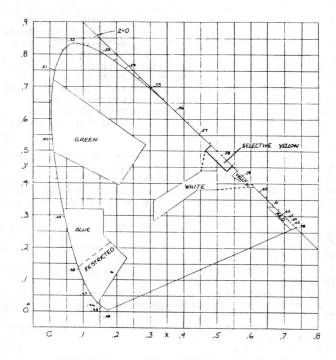

FIGURE 1—CHROMATICITY DIAGRAM

3.1.4 GREEN—The color of light emitted from the device shall fall within the following boundaries:

y = 0.73 − 0.73x (yellow boundary)

x = 0.63y − 0.04 (white boundary)

y = 0.50 − 0.50x (blue boundary)

3.1.5 BLUE—The color of light emitted from the device shall fall within the following boundaries:

3.1.5.1 Restricted Blue—This color should be elected when recognition of blue as such is necessary.

y = 0.07 + 0.81x (green boundary)

x = 0.40 − y (white boundary)

x = 0.13 + 0.60y (violet boundary)

3.1.5.2 Signal Blue—This color may be elected when, due to other factors, it is not always necessary to identify blue as such.

194

y = 0.32 (green boundary)

x = 0.16 (white boundary)

x = 0.40 − y (white boundary)

x = 0.13 + 0.60 (violet boundary)

3.2 Visual Method—When checking by the visual method of 4.1.1, the following subjective guidelines shall be considered:

3.2.1 RED—Red shall not be acceptable if it is less saturated (paler), yellower, or bluer than the limit standards.

3.2.2 YELLOW (AMBER)—Yellow shall not be acceptable if it is less saturated (paler), greener, or redder than the limit standards.

3.2.3 WHITE—White shall not be acceptable if its color differs significantly from that of a blackbody source operating at a color temperature between CIE Illuminant A (2854K) and CIE Illuminant B (5000K).

3.2.4 GREEN—Green shall not be acceptable if it is less saturated (paler), yellower, or bluer than the limit standards.

3.2.5 BLUE—Blue shall not be acceptable if it is less saturated (paler), greener, or redder than the limit standards.

4. Test Methods

4.1 Method of Color Measurement—One of the methods listed in 4.1.1, 4.1.2, or 4.1.3 shall be used to check the color of the light from the device or its optical components for compliance with the color specifications. The device shall be operated at the design test voltage. Components (bulbs, cap lenses, and the like) shall be tested in a fixture or in a manner simulating the intended application.

In measuring the color of reflex devices, precautions shall be made to eliminate the first surface reflections of the incident light.

Lighting devices that are covered with neutral density filters shall be tested for color with such filters in place.

4.1.1 VISUAL METHOD—In this method, the color of the emitted light from the device is visually compared to the light from a filter/source combination of known chromaticity coordinates. The filter/source combinations are generally chosen to describe the limits of chromaticity coordinates of the color being measured. The color of the filter/source combination is determined spectrophotometrically.

In making visual appraisals, the light from the device lights one portion of a comparator field and the filter/source standard lights an adjacent area. The two fields should be in close proximity to each other.

To make valid visual comparisons, the two fields to be viewed must be of near equal luminance (photometric brightness). A means of mechanically adjusting the filter/source standard is generally used to accomplish this. See Appendix A for measuring precautions.

4.1.2 TRISTIMULUS METHOD—In this method, photoelectric detectors with spectral responses that approximate the 1931 CIE standard spectral tristimulus values are used to make the color measurements. These measured tristimulus values are used to calculate the chromaticity coordinates of the color of emitted light from the device. The instrument used for this type of measurement is a colorimeter. These instruments are generally used for production control of color and are satisfactory if calibrated against color filters of known chromaticity coordinates.

Visual tristimulus colorimeters can also be used for color evaluation. See Appendix A for measuring precautions.

4.1.3 SPECTROPHOTOMETRIC METHOD—The standard CIE method of color measurement is computing chromaticity coordinates from the spectral energy distribution of the device. This method should be used as a referee approach when the commonly used methods produce questionable results.

Refer to ASTM E 308-66 for more details on spectrophotometric measurements (reprinted in the SAE Lighting Manual, HS-34).

APPENDIX A

A.1 Precautions—The following are applicable to all methods of determining the color of light:

a. Some devices may emit a different color of light in one direction than another. Measurements should be made in as many directions as required to define the color characteristic of emitted light.

Some instruments (tristimulus and spectroradiometric) use an integrating sphere at the inlet port of the device to integrate all the light from the device. Care should be taken to assure that the integrating sphere is not combining different color light emitted in different directions from the device and thereby providing an erroneous reading.

b. The lamp and optical components should be allowed to reach operating temperature before any measurements are made. Lamps should be operated at design voltage.

If visually the device does not appear to be emitting light with a uniform color, additional precautions should be taken.

c. The distance between the test instrument and the device under test should be great enough so that further increases in distance do not affect the results. The visual field of the instrument should view the entire lighted area of the device.

A.2 Color Application—Selective yellow is used on a limited basis primarily for fog lights and is not to be used in turn signal, parking, identification, clearance, sidemarker, and school bus warning lamps, or yellow reflex reflector applications as required by FMVSS 108.

A.3 Neutral Density—Filtering materials are sometimes used over existing lighting devices to reduce the light intensity but not to change the fundamental color requirements as detailed in SAE J578.

A.4 Orange Fluorescent Information Guideline—Definitions and Requirements for Orange Fluorescent color can be found in the appropriate SAE Recommended Practice or Standard. Refer to SAE J774, Emergency Warning Device, or SAE J943, Slow-moving Vehicle Identification Emblem or to FMVSS No. 125, Warning Devices, 39 FR 28636, Aug. 9, 1974 as amended at 40 FR4, Jan. 2, 1975.

A.5 Color Measurements of Gaseous Discharge Lighting Devices—Some laboratories cannot measure the color of light from the short pulses of lamps that use discharge tubes and, therefore, these lamps need a steady burning test source, operated at the color temperature of the gaseous discharge warning lamp. Use of CIE Illuminant C for strobe lights has been confirmed by independent testing laboratories.

A.6 Cited ASTM Report—ASTM E 308-66, Standard Practice for Spectrophotometry and Description of Color in CIE 1931 System. Reprinted in SAE Ground Vehicle Lighting Manual, HS-34.

(R) HEADLAMP AIM TEST MACHINES
—SAE J600 FEB93

SAE Recommended Practice

Report of the Lighting Committee approved December 1952, revised November 1963, editorial change May 1981. Rationale statement available. Completely revised by the SAE Road Illumination Devices Standards Committee February 1993. Rationale statement available.

1. Scope—This SAE Recommended Practice provides laboratory test procedures for testing headlamp aim test machines to determine their ability to aim or to check the aim of headlamps, fog lamps, and auxiliary driving and lower beam lamps. This report does not apply to aiming devices of the kind covered by SAE J602.

2. References

2.1 Applicable Documents—The following publications form a part of this specification to the extent specified herein. The latest issue of SAE publications shall apply.

2.1.1 SAE PUBLICATIONS—Available from SAE, 400 Commonwealth Drive, Warrendale, PA 15096-0001.

SAE J575—Tests for Motor Vehicle Lighting Devices and Components

SAE J599—Lighting Inspection Code

SAE J602—Headlamp Aiming Device for Mechanically Aimable Sealed Beam Headlamp Units

SAE J1383—Performance Requirements for Motor Vehicle Headlamps

2.2 Definitions

2.2.1 A headlamp aim test machine is an optical or photoelectric device used to aim or check the aim of forward lighting devices.

2.2.2 The H and V readings are located relative to the H-V axis as defined in paragraph 2.7 in SAE J1383. The H reading is located at H-2R and the V reading at V-1D.

3. Tests

3.1 Samples for Test

3.1.1 Headlamp aim test machines submitted for laboratory tests should be representative of the device as regularly manufactured and marketed, except that in the case of a machine using a track, an abbreviated section of track may be supplied for the test. Each sample shall include all accessory equipment for the device and necessary to its service operation and calibration. Full assembly and operating instructions shall be provided, including information on how to check accuracy and maintain the device in calibration.

3.1.2 Sample lamps for test shall include a group of upper (1A) and lower (2B) beam headlamp units which meet SAE specifications. Representative groups of fog lamps and auxiliary driving and lower beam lamps will be obtained in the same manner.

3.2 Laboratory Facilities—The laboratory shall be equipped with facilities to make physical and optical tests required in this report, in accordance with established laboratory practice. It will include a goniometer, a test screen located at 7.6 m from the goniometer and calibrated photocells or equivalent light-detecting devices.

3.3 Test Procedures

3.3.1 SYMMETRICAL BEAM—UPPER BEAM HEADLAMPS AND AUXILIARY DRIVING LAMPS

3.3.1.1 The sample lamp shall be mounted on a goniometer which meets the requirement of the Photometry Test in SAE J575.

3.3.1.2 The sample lamp should be operated at rated voltage and then kept burning through the end of test.

3.3.1.3 The headlamp aim test machine shall be positioned in front of the headlamp according to the manufacturer's instructions.

3.3.1.4 The headlamp shall be aimed according to the aim test machine manufacturer's instructions, using the goniometer to position the lamp.

3.3.1.5 Goniometer initial readings (Hi, Vi) shall be recorded.

3.3.1.6 The aim test machine shall be removed from its position in the front of the headlamp.

3.3.1.7 The headlamp upper beam shall then be photoelectrically balanced on the goniometer in accordance with the Beam Pattern Location Test for the upper beam in SAE J1383.

3.3.1.8 The final goniometer reading (Hf, Vf) shall be recorded.

3.3.2 ASYMMETRICAL BEAM—LOWER BEAM HEADLAMPS AND AUXILIARY LOWER BEAM LAMPS

3.3.2.1 The lower beam headlamps and auxiliary lower beam lamps shall be used to test the headlamp aim test machine in accordance with 3.3.1.1 through 3.3.1.8, substituting lower beam for upper beam.

3.3.3 FOG LAMPS

3.3.3.1 Fog lamps shall be used to test the aim test machine in accordance with 3.3.1.1 through 3.3.1.8, substituting fog lamp for upper beam.

4. Requirements

4.1 For Testing With Upper Beam Headlamps and Symmetrical Beam Auxiliary Driving Lamps

4.1.1 The headlamp aim test machine shall permit determination of the vertical and horizontal aim of the geometric center of the high intensity zone on the upper beam within specified limits.

4.1.2 The final goniometer aim reading (Hf, Vf), when compared to the initial aim reading (Hi, Vi) shall not vary from the initial reading in the vertical direction by more than 0.3 degrees (37 mm at 7.6 m) and in the horizontal direction by more than 0.6 degrees (75 mm at 7.6 m).

4.2 For Testing With Asymmetrical Beam Lower Beam Headlamps and Auxiliary Lower Beam Lamps

4.2.1 The headlamp aim test machine shall permit determination of the aim of the top and left edge cutoffs of the high intensity zone of the lower beam of headlamps and auxiliary lower beam lamps.

4.2.2 The final goniometer aim reading (Hf, Vf), when compared to the initial aim reading (Hi, Vi) shall not vary from the initial reading in the vertical direction by more than 0.3 degrees (37 mm at 7.6 m) and in the horizontal direction by more than 0.6 degrees (75 mm at 7.6 m).

4.3 For Testing With Fog Lamps

4.3.1 The headlamp aim test machine shall permit determination of the vertical aim of the top cutoff of the high intensity zone and the horizontal aim of the geometric center of the high intensity zone.

4.3.2 The final goniometer aim reading (Hf, Vf), when compared to the initial aim reading (Hi, Vi) shall not vary from the initial reading in the vertical direction by more than 0.3 degrees (37 mm at 7.6 m) and in the horizontal direction by more than 0.6 degrees (75 mm at 7.6 m).

4.4 General Requirements

4.4.1 The headlamp aim test machine shall incorporate a fixed track or equivalent for positioning the aiming device in front of the headlamps.

4.4.1.1 Means shall be provided in the device for compensating within ±0.05 for variation in the floor slope and the adjustment method shall be clearly explained in the operating instructions.

4.4.1.2 Means shall be provided in the device for lateral alignment within 0.1 degree with respect to the longitudinal axis of the vehicle.

4.4.2 Aim test machines using a photoelectric means to determine aim shall also have a visual screen or equivalent upon which the beam pattern is projected proportional to its appearance and aim on a screen at 7.6 m. Such visual screen or equivalent shall be plainly visible to the operator and should have horizontal and vertical reference lines to permit visual appraisal of the aim of the lamp.

4.4.3 Design of the headlamp aim test machine shall permit checking the aim of the lamps mounted at heights from 25 to 140 cm and spaced up to 130 cm from the center of the motor vehicle.

4.4.4 The device and/or the instructions shall provide a means for calibration and/or verification of calibration.

4.4.5 The spirit level or other means provided for indicating vertical aim shall be capable of indicating a deviation of at least 2.5 mm with a 0.2 degree (25 mm at 7.6 m) change in level.

4.4.6 A vertical aim scale shall be provided with numerical gradations in steps, each of which represents 25 mm at 7.6 m to provide for variations in aim at least 100 mm above level to 250 mm below level.

4.4.7 A lateral aim scale shall be provided with gradations in steps of not more than 50 mm at 7.6 m from straight ahead to at least 150 mm left and right.

4.4.8 The instructions covering use of the device shall include those items in the Preparation for Aiming Section of SAE J599.

4.4.9 Instructions furnished by the manufacturer for aiming lamps shall be such that the beam patterns when viewed on the screen will fall within the limits set in SAE J599.

4.4.10 Headlamp Aim Test Machines must be capable of operating accurately in service garages with a temperature range of 0 to 40 °C.

HEADLAMP AIMING DEVICE FOR MECHANICALLY AIMABLE HEADLAMP UNITS—SAE J602 DEC89

SAE Standard

Report of the Lighting Committee approved October 1957, revised October 1980. Completely revised by the Road Illumination Devices Standards Committee December 1989.

1. Scope—This document applies to the requirements of a device used in the field and inspection stations to aim and check aim of mechanically aimable headlamp units.

The purpose of this document is to provide a laboratory test procedure to determine whether the devices under test are capable of accurately positioning headlamp units from their aiming pads and maintaining their accuracy in service within the tolerances designated in this document.

2. Definitions

2.1 Headlamp Aiming Device—A device used to adjust and inspect the aim of mechanically aimable headlamp units consisting of one or more fixtures designed to seat against the three aiming pads (aiming plane) on mechanically aimable headlamp units installed on a vehicle to facilitate accurate aiming of such units, vertically and laterally.

2.2 Mechanically Aimable Headlamp Units—A unit having three pads on the face of the lens forming a mechanical aiming plane used to adjust and inspect the aim of the unit when installed on a vehicle.

2.3 Aiming Plane—A plane which is perpendicular to the longitudinal axis of the vehicle and tangent to the forward most aiming pad on the headlamp.

3. Samples For Test—Sample devices submitted for laboratory tests shall be representative of the devices as regularly manufactured and marketed. Each sample shall include all accessory equipment peculiar to the device. Full assembly and operating instructions shall be provided, including information on how to check accuracy and maintain the device in calibration.

4. Laboratory Facilities—The laboratory shall be equipped with all facilities necessary to make the tests in this document.

NOTE 1: All tests are to be made in air ambient temperature of 75°F ± 5 (24°C ± 3).

NOTE 2: If a vertical indication means other than a spirit level is used, equivalent accuracy shall be maintained.

5. Requirements

5.1 Design Requirements

5.1.1 The device shall be of such design that the seating portion will register only on the three aiming pads on the headlamp units as covered by SAE J1383.

5.1.2 No part of the device, except those parts (strings, sighting devices, scales, etc.) required for referencing lateral alignment between devices, shall extend beyond the dimensional limits of the headlamp aiming device locating plate (Figure 1, dimension C and Figures 2, 3, and 4, dimension 4.05 in (102.9 mm) maximum diameter).

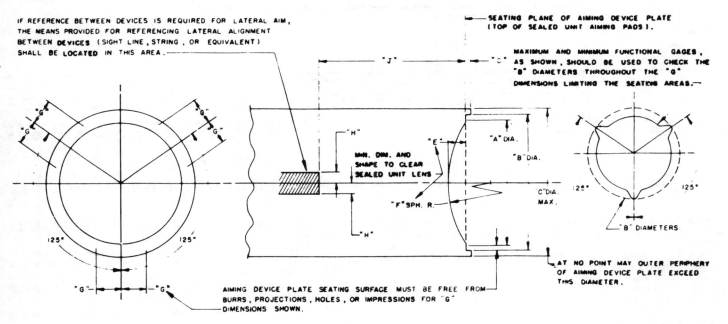

NOTE: There shall be no projections, tangs, lugs, etc. on this locating plate, which will permit locating the aiming device on any part of the headlamp other than the aiming pads on the mechanical headlamp unit.

Locating Plate	Unit of Measure	Dimensions										
		A		B		C	D		E	F	G	H	J
		Max	Min	Max	Min	Max	Max	Min	Ref	Ref	Min	Max	Min
5-3/4 in	in	4.830	4.770	5.375	5.345	5.700	0.165	0.145	0.70	4.40	0.70	1.00	9.50
(146 mm)	mm	122.7	121.2	136.5	135.8	144.8	4.19	3.68	17.8	111.8	17.8	25.4	241.3
7 in	in	6.140	6.080	6.710	6.680	7.031	0.180	0.160	0.96	5.60	0.70	1.00	10.25
(178 mm)	mm	156.0	154.4	170.4	169.7	178.6	4.57	4.06	24.4	142.2	17.8	25.4	260.4

FIG. 1—DIMENSIONAL SPECIFICATIONS FOR HEADLAMP AIMING DEVICE LOCATING PLATE

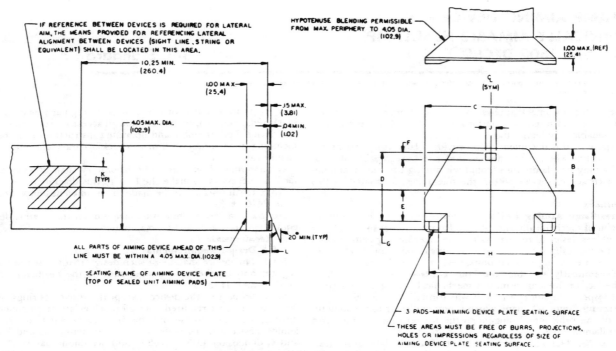

NOTE: There shall be no projections, tangs, lugs, etc. on this locating plate, which will permit locating the aiming device on any part of the headlamp other than the aiming pads on the mechanical headlamp unit.

ALL DIMENSIONS ENCLOSED (X.XX) ARE IN MM.

Locating Plate	Unit of Measure	Dimensions																						
		A		B		C		D		E		F		G		H		I		J		K		L	
		Max	Min	Max	Min	Max	Min	Max	Min	Max	Min	Max	Min	Max	Min	Max	Min	Max	Min	Max	Min	Max	Min	Max	Min
4 x 6½	in	3.935	3.925	1.975	1.953	6.001	5.991	3.320	3.300	1.550	1.540	0.370	0.350	0.330	0.310	5.088	5.018	—	5.421	—	0.400	1.000	—	0.080	0.060
100 x 165	mm	99.95	99.60	50.17	49.66	152.42	152.17	84.33	83.82	39.37	39.12	9.40	8.89	8.38	7.87	129.24	128.98	—	137.20	—	10.16	25.40	—	2.03	1.52

FIG. 2—DIMENSIONAL SPECIFICATIONS FOR HEADLAMP AIMING DEVICE LOCATING PLATE (100 × 165)

5.1.3 A device that uses adapters to fit more than one size headlamp unit shall meet all the requirements of this document with and without adapters.

5.1.4 The seating plane of the device shall meet the dimensions shown in Figures 1, 2, 3, and 4.

5.1.5 When aiming headlamp units spaced 90 in (2300 mm) apart, the torque exerted by the device at the aiming plane shall not exceed 18 lbf in (2.0 N·m) vertically and 12 lbf in (1.4 N·m) laterally.

5.1.6 The means of securing the device to the headlamp unit shall retain the device against the three aiming pads when an axially centered tensile force of 4.0 lb/ft (17.8 N·m) minimum is applied to the device.

5.1.7 The device shall be capable of being calibrated and shall have available for immediate use an independent calibration fixture and/or instructions to immediately recalibrate the device.

5.1.8 If a suction cup is used to retain the device to the headlamp unit, the effective diameter for 5—3/4 in (146 mm) and 7 in (178 mm) headlamps shall not exceed 3.5 in (90 mm) and the effective diameter for 4 × 6—1/2 in (100 × 165 mm) and 5 × 8 in (142 × 200 mm) headlamps shall not exceed 2.8 in (71 mm) when installed.

5.1.9 Means shall be provided in the device for compensating within ±0.1 deg through a slope range of ±1.5 deg from horizontal. The method for device compensation shall be clearly explained in the operating instructions.

5.1.10 If the horizontal aim is to be accomplished by reference between devices on opposite sides of the vehicle, the means provided for referencing lateral alignment between devices (sight line, string, or equivalent) shall be located as shown in Figures 1, 2, 3, and 4.

5.1.11 The spirit level or other means provided for indicating vertical aim shall be capable of showing at least a 0.1 in (2.5 mm) deviation with a 1 in (25 mm[1]) change in level.

5.1.12 A horizontal aim scale shall be provided with graduations in steps of not more than 2 in (51 mm) from straight ahead to at least 8 in (203 mm) left and right.

5.1.13 The instructions covering the use of the device shall include those items shown in Section 3 of SAE J599.

5.1.14 The vertical aim scale shall be marked 0 with the aiming plane vertical.

5.1.15 The vertical aim scale shall be provided with numerical graduations in steps, each of which represents 1 in (25 mm) to provide for variations in vertical aim from at least 8 in (203 mm) below 0.

5.2 Test Procedure—Assuming that the devices comply with the general requirements, they shall be considered acceptable if they comply with additional test requirements as follows:

5.2.1 With the aiming plane vertical and with the vertical scale on the device set at 0, the angle through which the aiming plane must be rotated vertically to center the bubble in the spirit level, or equivalent, shall not exceed 0.5 in (13 mm).

5.2.2 With the aiming planes in the same vertical plane and with the means provided for adjusting lateral aim in use, the angle through which the aiming plane must be rotated laterally to indicate straight ahead shall not exceed ±1 in (25 mm)[2] with the lamps 24 and 90 in (610 and 2300 mm) apart.

---

[1] Represents inches (millimeters) at 25 ft (7.6 m).
[2] Represents inches (millimeters) at 25 ft (7.6 m).

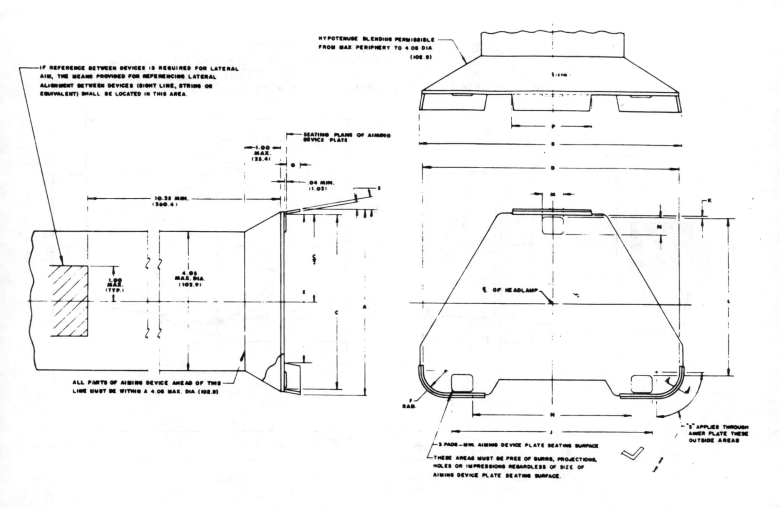

NOTE: There shall be no projections, tangs, lugs, etc. on this locating plate, which will permit locating the aiming device on any part of the headlamp other than the aiming pads on the mechanical headlamp unit.

ALL DIMENSIONS ENCLOSED (X.XX) ARE IN MM.

Unit of Measure	Dimensions														
	A ±0.010	B ±0.010	C ±0.005	D ±0.005	E ±0.010	F ±0.010	G ±0.010	H ±0.005	J ±0.005	K ±0.005	L ±0.005	M ±0.010	N ±0.010	P ±0.010	S
															±0° 30 ft
in	5.275	7.340	4.995	7.030	4.285	0.625	0.395	4.450	5.663	0.005	4.487	0.610	0.485	2.125	10° 0 ft
mm	133.98	186.43	126.87	179.07	108.83	15.87	10.03	113.03	143.84	0.12	113.97	15.49	12.31	53.97	

FIG. 3—DIMENSIONAL SPECIFICATIONS FOR HEADLAMP AIMING DEVICE LOCATING PLATE (142 × 200)

5.2.3 With the aiming planes initially in the same vertical plane and subsequently toed inward and outward 6 in (152 mm) and with the means provided for checking lateral aim in use, the error in reading shall not exceed ±1 in (25 mm) with the lamps 60 in (1520 mm) apart.

5.2.4 With the aiming plane vertical and with the vertical scale on the device set at 0, the level on the aimer shall be adjusted prior to each of the following tests to center the bubble in the spirit level or equivalent.

5.2.4.1 Each step on the vertical aim scale shall be checked and in no case shall the variation from the correct aim exceed ±0.5 in (13 mm).

5.2.4.2 A pair of devices shall be stabilized at 20°F ± 5 (−7°C ± 3) and then installed on a pair of unlighted headlamp units spaced 60 in (1520 mm) apart at the 20°F (−7°C) ambient temperature. After a period of 30 min, the seating portion of the device shall continue to register against the three headlamp unit aiming pads, and the variation from correct vertical aim shall not exceed ±0.5 in (13 mm) and the variation from correct lateral aim shall not exceed ±1 in (25 mm)[3].

5.2.4.3 They shall then be installed on the pair of unlighted headlamp units spaced 60 in (1520 mm) apart and the variation from

[3] Represents inches (millimeters) at 25 ft (7.6 m).

199

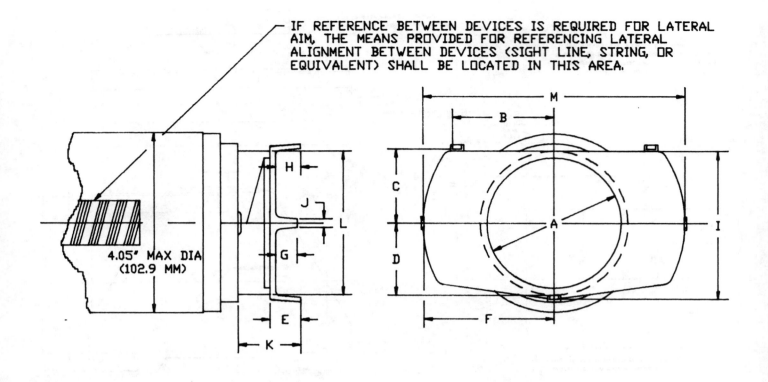

IF REFERENCE BETWEEN DEVICES IS REQUIRED FOR LATERAL AIM, THE MEANS PROVIDED FOR REFERENCING LATERAL ALIGNMENT BETWEEN DEVICES (SIGHT LINE, STRING, OR EQUIVALENT) SHALL BE LOCATED IN THIS AREA.

4.05" MAX DIA (102.9 MM)

Locating Plate	Unit of Measure	Dimensions												
		A	B	C	D	E	F	G	H	I	J	K	L	M
	Tolerance inches (mm)	±0.010 (±0.254)	±0.005 (±0.127)	±0.010 (±0.254)	±0.010 (±0.254)	±0.010 (±0.254)	±0.005 (±0.127)	±0.010 (±0.254)	±0.001 (±0.025)	±0.010 (±0.254)	±0.010 (±0.254)	±0.005 (±0.127)	±0.010 (±0.254)	±0.010 (±0.254)
92 x 150	inches (mm)	2.925 (74.295)	2.264 (57.506)	1.575 (40.005)	1.634 (41.504)	0.676 (17.170)	2.853 (72.466)	0.472 (11.989)	0.551 (13.995)	3.300 (83.820)	0.197 (5.004)	1.375 (34.925)	3.225 (81.915)	5.720 (145.288)

FIG. 4—DIMENSIONAL SPECIFICATIONS FOR HEADLAMP AIMING DEVICE LOCATING PLATE (92 × 150)

correct vertical aim shall not exceed ±0.5 in (13 mm) and the variation from correct lateral aim shall not exceed ±1 in (25 mm).[4]

5.2.4.4 A sample device shall be exposed to 35°F ± 5 (1.7°C ± 3) for 1 h and then immediately allowed to free fall onto a concrete floor three times from its normal operating position on a headlamp unit at a height of 40 in (1020 mm), after which it shall show no damage that would interfere with the proper calibration of the device. It shall then be installed in combination with its companion device on a pair of un-lighted headlamp units spaced 60 in (1520 mm) apart and the variation from correct vertical aim shall not exceed 1 in (25 mm)[5] and the variation from the correct lateral aim shall not exceed 1 in (25 mm)[6] . (This test applies only to devices that are supported by the headlamp unit.)

5.2.4.5 Using the calibration fixture and/or instructions required by 5.1.7, the device shall be calibrated and checked for compliance with 5.2.1 and 5.2.2.

[4] Represents inches (millimeters) at 25 ft (7.6 m).

[5] Represents inches (millimeters) at 25 ft (7.6 m).

[6] Represents inches (millimeters) at 25 ft (7.6 m).

Report of the Lighting Committee approved April 1962 and completely revised October 1987. Rationale statement available. Completely revised by the Flasher Task Force of the SAE Auxiliary Devices Standards Committee June 1991. Rationale statement available. Revised by the Flasher Task Force of the SAE Lighting Coordinating Committee and the SAE Auxiliary Devices Standards Committee January 1994. Rationale statement available.

1. Scope—This SAE Standard specifies the test procedure, test circuitry, and instruments required for measuring the performance of flashers used in motor vehicles.

2. References—There are no referenced publications specified herein.

3. Laboratory Facilities—The laboratory shall be equipped with all of the facilities required to make the tests in this document, in accordance with established laboratory practice, including the following:

3.1 Ambient Conditions—Means shall be provided to maintain ambient temperatures over the range from -32 to 63 °C within the tolerances specified for each test condition, in an air atmosphere.

3.2 Power Supply—Performance Tests—The power supply for testing performance requirements shall not generate any adverse transients not present in motor vehicles and shall comply with the following specifications:

3.2.1 OUTPUT VOLTAGE—Capable of supplying to the input terminals of the standard circuit 11 to 16 V DC for 12 V flashers or 5.5 to 8 V DC for 6 V flashers or 22 to 32 V DC for 24 V flashers.

3.2.2 OUTPUT CURRENT—Capable of supplying required design current(s) continuously and inrush currents as required by the design bulb load complement.

3.2.3 REGULATION

3.2.3.1 Dynamic—The output voltage shall not deviate more than 1.0 V from 0 to maximum load (including inrush current) and shall recover within the area generated by the equation $1.0\ V(1-e^{-t/T})$, T = 100 μs. The curve shall end at the maximum voltage deviation allowed for static regulation (see Figure 1).

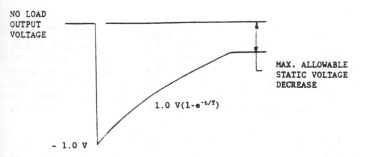

FIGURE 1—POWER SUPPLY—MAXIMUM DYNAMIC
REGULATION CURVE

3.2.3.2 Static—The output voltage shall not deviate more than 2% with changes in static load from 0 to maximum (not including inrush current) nor for static line voltage variations.

3.2.4 RIPPLE VOLTAGE—Maximum 75 mV, peak to peak, from 0 to maximum design bulb load.

3.3 Power Supply—Durability Tests—The power supply for the durability test requirements shall not generate any adverse transients not present in motor vehicles and shall comply with the following specifications:

3.3.1 OUTPUT VOLTAGE—Capable of supplying, as required, 14 and 13 V (7 and 6.5 V DC or 28 and 26 V), according to the flasher rating, to the input terminals of the standard test circuits shown in Figures 2 and 3.

3.3.2 OUTPUT CURRENT—Capable of supplying a continuous output current of the design load for one flasher times the number of flashers and inrush currents as required by the bulb load complement.

3.3.3 REGULATION

3.3.3.1 Dynamic—The output voltage shall not deviate more than 1.0 V from 0 to maximum load (including inrush current) and shall recover within the area generated by the equation $1.0\ V(1-e^{-t/T})$, T = 5 ms. The curve shall end at the maximum voltage deviation allowed for static regulation (see Figure 1).

3.3.3.2 Static—The output voltage shall not deviate more than 2% with changes in static load for 0 to maximum (not including inrush current), and means shall be provided to compensate for static line voltage variations.

3.3.4 RIPPLE VOLTAGE—Maximum 300 mV, peak to peak, from 0 to maximum design bulb load for one flasher times the number of flashers.

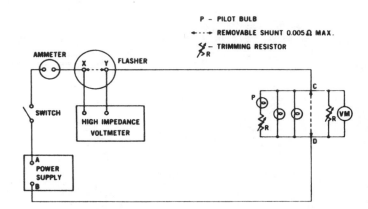

FIGURE 2—STANDARD TEST CIRCUIT—TURN SIGNAL
AND HAZARD WARNING FLASHERS

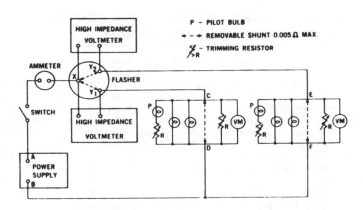

FIGURE 3—STANDARD TEST CIRCUIT—WARNING LAMP
ALTERNATING FLASHERS

4. Test Procedures

4.1 The flashers shall be mounted as specified by the manufacturer if special precautions are required.

4.2 The flashers shall be connected in a standard test circuit as shown in Figure 2 for turn signal and hazard warning flashers or Figure 3 for warning lamp alternating flashers using the design load(s) within 0.5% at 12.8 V (6.4 V or 25.6 V) specified by the flasher manufacturer.

4.3 A suitable high impedance measuring device connected to points X-Y in Figure 2, or to points X-Y$_1$ and to points X-Y$_2$ in Figure 3 shall be used for measuring flash rate, percent current "on" time, starting time, and voltage drop across the flasher. The measurement of these quantities shall not affect the circuit.

4.4 The resistance at A-B for each load circuit in Figure 2 or Figure 3 shall be measured with flasher and bulb loads at each shorted out with removable shunt resistances not to exceed 0.005 Ω each.

The effective series resistance in the total circuit (Figure 2) or in each of the parallel circuits (Figure 3) between the power supply and bulb sockets (excluding the flasher and bulb loads by using the removable shunt resistances) shall be 0.10 Ω ± 0.01 Ω.

(R) 4.5 The effective 0.10 Ω ± 0.01 Ω series resistance from A to B shall be distributed along the circuit wiring so that the sum of the voltage drops between A to X and between B and a flasher ground terminal, if required, shall not exceed 2.0 V when 12.8 V (or 6.4 V or 25.6 V) is applied to a load that is equal to 110% of the flasher maximum rating.

(R)   **4.6** Adjust the voltage at the bulbs to 12.8 V (6.4 V or 25.6 V) as required for testing at C-D in Figure 2 or C-D and E-F in Figure 3 with the flasher shorted out by an effective shunt resistance not to exceed 0.005 Ω. The load current shall be held to the rated value for the total flasher design load(s) within 0.5% at 12.8 V (6.4 V or 25.6 V) by simultaneously adjusting trimmer resistors, R.

(R)   **4.7** For testing fixed load flashers at other required voltages, adjust the power supply to provide required voltages at required temperatures at C-D in Figure 2 or C-D and E-F in Figure 3 without readjustment of trimming resistors, R.

(R)   **4.8** For testing variable load flashers, the circuit shall be first adjusted at 12.8 V (6.4 V or 25.6 V) at C-D in Figure 2 or C-D and E-F in Figure 3 with a minimum required bulb load and the power supply shall be adjusted to provide other required test voltages at required temperatures at C-D in Figure 2 or C-D and E-F in Figure 3 without readjustment of trimming resistors, R (each required test voltage shall be set with a minimum bulb load in place). The required voltage tests with a maximum bulb load shall be conducted without readjusting each corresponding power supply voltage previous set with minimum bulb load.

(R) PHOTOMETRY LABORATORY ACCURACY GUIDELINES—SAE J1330 JUN94

SAE Information Report

Report of the SAE Test Methods and Equipment Standards Committee approved June 1994. Rationale statement available.

1. Scope—The purpose of this SAE Information Report is to list and explain major equipment, instrumentation, and procedure variables which can affect inter-laboratory differences and repeatability of photometric measurements of various lighting devices listed in SAE Technical Reports. The accuracy guidelines listed in the report are for the purpose of controlling variables that are not a direct function of the lighting device being measured. The control of these individual variables is necessary to control the overall accuracy of photometric measurements. These accuracy guidelines apply to the measurement of the luminous intensities and reflected intensities of devices at the specified geometrically distributed test points and areas. These guidelines do not apply to photometric equipment used to measure license plate lamps.

2. References

2.1 Applicable Documents—The following publications form a part of this specification to the extent specified herein. The latest issue of SAE publications shall apply.

2.1.1 SAE PUBLICATIONS—Available from SAE, 400 Commonwealth Drive, Warrendale, PA 15096-0001.

    SAE J575—Test Methods and Equipment for Lighting Devices and Components for Use on Vehicles Less Than 2032 mm in Overall Width

    SAE J1889—LED Lighting Devices

    SAE J2009—Discharge Forward Lighting System

    SAE J2039—Tests for Lighting Devices, Reflective Devices, and Components Used on Vehicles 2032 mm or More in Overall Width

    SAE HS-34—Section IV. ASTM Reports—ASTM E 308-85[e2]

2.1.2 BIBLIOGRAPHY AND OTHER REFERENCES

I.E.S. Lighting Handbook, Sixth Edition, 1982, Illuminating Engineering Society

    Journal of I.E.S., October 1971—Practical Guide to Photometry

    Illuminating Engineering, March and April, 1955—I.E.S. General Guide to Photometry

3. Accuracy Guidelines and Limitations—The accuracy limit guidelines suggested in this report are intended as a reference guide to photometric laboratories of various accuracy parameters to help maintain correlation of photometric measurements between laboratories. The guidelines are not intended as specifications to be applied to all photometric equipment, test fixtures, and measurements. Actual photometric performance of various functions and the designs of lighting devices and test fixtures may vary considerably. The use of the guideline information in this report as rigid specifications applied to all types of photometric measurements would be impractical and in some cases would result in equipment with unnecessary accuracy restrictions. These guidelines should be used to aid laboratory personnel in their awareness of the major variables and to provide information on equipment, instrumentation, and procedure accuracies which may affect overall laboratory differences and repeatability.

3.1 Accuracy Guidelines for Mechanical Positioning

3.1.1 DEVICE POSITIONING—The lighting device to be photometered should be mounted on a rigid test fixture in a position corresponding to the design nominal operating position of the device on the vehicle. For devices designed for a specific vehicle, the designed nominal position should be determined from the vehicle manufacturer's specifications. For devices designed for multiple vehicle use, the designed nominal position should be determined from the device manufacturer's specifications or instructions. Multiple-use devices should be tested in each position in which they are designed for use, or the equivalent, by mathematically translating axis angles and test points.

One of the factors which can significantly affect the device mounting attitude is the torque used to fasten the device to the test stand. This is particularly important when the device floats on a compression-type gasket. Mounting torques should be specified for all devices, and these torques should be sufficient to compress the specified gaskets so that "floating" of parts does not occur unless certain parts are so designed as a means of absorbing shock and vibration.

3.1.2 TEST FIXTURE POSITIONING—Numerous factors affect the ability of the test fixture to position the test device in its designed nominal position. Some of these accuracy factors are the rigidity and flatness of the base, the rigidity of the test fixture structure, and the length of the machined alignment edge or the spacing between alignment pins. Each test fixture should be built from a manufacturer's test fixture design standard to minimize these errors. One suggested example of a test fixture design guide is shown in Appendix A. Other test fixture designs may be equally satisfactory (for example, specialized fixtures for sealed beam units) if they provide proper positioning accuracy.

3.1.3 POSITIONING TOLERANCE—Tolerance guidelines for positioning the device are listed as follows:

3.1.3.1 Lighting Devices Except Headlamp Units—The tolerance for positioning the device in the test fixture should be ±0.1 degree in each axis.

3.1.3.2 Headlamp Units—The positioning of headlamp units is generally more critical than other lighting devices. The tolerance for positioning of headlamp units in the test fixture should be ±0.05 degree in each axis.

3.2 Measurement of Spatial Distributions of Luminous Intensity—The photometric test point patterns specified in the SAE technical reports are based on measurement of luminous intensity as a function of angular position when using a Type A goniometer (as shown in Appendix B and recommended by SAE J575 and SAE J2039) to position the device with the configuration of horizontal rotation over elevation. The other goniometer configuration is elevation over horizontal rotation (Type B). The use of a Type B goniometer configuration may require the use of a conversion table as given in Appendix B. Methods other than a two-axis goniometer as described previously may be used. For example, a fixed test device with fixed photometer sensors mounted at every specified test point at some suitable distance, or other configurations of fixed and/or moveable sensors may be used. It should be noted that specified luminous intensity maximums or values between test points cannot be measured using fixed sensors with a fixed test device.

3.2.1 POSITIONER ACCURACY DETERMINATION—The accuracy of positioners or goniometers used to measure spatial distributions of luminous intensities can be determined by using a checking procedure such as outlined in Appendix C.

3.2.2 POSITIONER TOLERANCES—The repeatability of photometric measurements stated as a percent difference between laboratories when measuring the same device cannot be solely determined as a function of the accuracy of the Positioner system or goniometer. For example, a difference of 0.1 degree due to mounting/Positioner accuracy will result in no difference between measurements (other factors being equal) if the light distribution is uniform and does not vary significantly with angle in the area of interest. On the other hand, if the area of interest has a high gradient (rate of change of luminous intensity and angle), one system may, for example, measure 500 cd and another system with a difference of 0.1 degree may measure 550 to 600 cd. The percent difference between the two measurements could then be 10 to 20% even with the small difference in orientation. This example demonstrates that it is not possible to state a specific accuracy for a photometric measurement system as a function of angle accuracy alone, as both the Positioner angular accuracy and the luminous intensity gradient are involved.

Two axis goniometer are available with an accuracy of ±0.05 degree with a resolution of ±0.01 degree. However, in most photometric measurements, a Positioner system accuracy deviation of ±0.1 degree with a resolution of ±0.03 degree is considered adequate (see 3.1.3.2).

3.3 Power Supplies—Unless otherwise specified, a regulated DC power supply should be used for all photometric measurements. The following are suggested specifications for the DC power supply:

3.3.1 LINE REGULATION—±0.1%

3.3.2 RIPPLE AND NOISE—0.4% maximum

3.3.3 STABILITY—Any power supply that remains stable within ±0.1% during the photometric measurement period is satisfactory.

3.4 Voltage Measurements—A 4-1/2-digit digital voltmeter (DC) with a 10 megohm minimum impedance and with an accuracy of 0.05% of the reading is recommended for measurements up to at least 20 V. Voltage measurements should be taken as close to the device input terminations as practicable.

3.5 Current Measurements—A 4-1/2-digit digital voltmeter reading the output of a precision current shunt is recommended for measurements up to 100 W. The size of the shunt should be sufficient to prevent error due to excessive heat loading. The minimum accuracy of this system should be 0.09% of the value of the current being measured.

3.6 Accurate Rated Bulbs—Unless otherwise specified, accurate rated bulbs should be used for all photometric measurements. When applicable ratings are available, these bulbs should be rated at the current to produce the designed luminous flux (lumens) or mean spherical candela in the attitude in which they are intended to be used with respect to gravity (any attitude for vacuum bulbs). Yellow glass bulbs should also be rated for current to produce their designed luminous flux. Because there are several filament parameters in addition to those controlled in accurate rated bulbs such as coil length, pitch, diameter, and color temperature, some lighting devices may produce significantly different luminous intensity measurements with two different accurate rated bulbs, particularly lighting devices with exceptionally short focal lengths. The light source should be allowed sufficient warm-up period for the luminous flux to stabilize. Yellow glass bulbs should also have a sufficient warm-up period for any color change to stabilize.

3.6.1 NONREPLACEABLE LIGHT SOURCES—Devices employing LEDs or permanently sealed-in light sources should be operated at the voltage specified by the manufacturer and in the attitude they are intended to be used (any attitude for vacuum bulbs or LEDs). The appropriate comments noted in 3.5 should also be heeded. Additional information on testing LEDs is found in SAE J1889.

3.7 Sensor/Photometer System

3.7.1 COLOR RESPONSE—The spectral response of the photometer sensor system should be such that color corrections in the yellow color being tested are less than 2% between the yellow-green limit and the yellow-red limit. Likewise, the red correction should not exceed 3% from the red-yellow limit to medium red. One method to determine this color response requires a 2856 K (C.I.E. Illuminant A) standard lamp and a set of at least four glass color filters calibrated for transmittance at 2856 K. Suggested filters are shown in Table 1:

TABLE 1—SUGGESTED FILTERS

Color Region	Chromaticity Coordinate x	Chromaticity Coordinate y
SAE Yellow-Green Limit Area	0.56	0.44
SAE Yellow-Red Limit Area	0.61	0.39
SAE Red-Yellow Limit Area	0.67	0.33
Medium Red Area	0.69	0.31

In addition, blue filters can be used to check the blue response such as ones with 2856 K chromaticity coordinates of approximately x = 0.16, y = 0.13; and approximately x = 0.12, y = 0.30. Other methods for determinations of color response are acceptable. For example, a calibrated filter may be used whose color matches the color of the light emitted by the device(s) being measured. Special color response calibrations should be made when photometric measurements are made with light sources with high monochromatic output, such as LEDs, or on devices which have colors in spectral areas different than the color regions calibrated.

3.7.2 HIGH INTENSITY DISCHARGE SOURCES—High intensity discharge sources, or HID devices, can be measured as white light sources on systems employing proper photopic correction. (Reference IES Lighting Handbook and E 308-85^{e2} in Section IV of HS-34.) It should be noted that rotational movement of HID devices in the vertical plane by a goniometer can cause change in light output distribution and intensity of the light emitted from the discharge source. This change is negligible within a tilt range of 10 degrees up or down from the nominal design position. Photometric measurement accuracy beyond this range may be affected. In cases where extreme up/down angles must be measured (such as for headlight glare) alternative techniques may be used. It is recommended that any variations in measurement method be noted along with the photometric data obtained. Additional information on testing HID sources is found in SAE J2009.

3.7.3 RANGE LINEARITY—The linearity of the sensor/photometer system should be verified at least over the range of the luminous intensities used for the specific type of device being measured. A deviation from linear response over the range from the calibration level to the extreme luminous intensity value measured should not exceed 2.5%. Measurements made over a narrow range of intensities should have a smaller deviation from linear response.

3.7.4 PHOTOMETER SENSOR APERTURE SIZE—Since photometric measurements are allowed at various distances with different lighting device functions, the area of the photosensor aperture determines the intercepted solid angle of the light flux at the measured test point. Use of large diameter photodetectors should be avoided at shorter measurement distances. Unless otherwise specified, the actual effective area of the sensor used for making the photometric measurements should fit within a circle whose diameter is approximately 0.009 times the distance from the measured light source to the sensor. A 0.009 ratio is equivalent to a solid angle formed by a radius of 0.26 degree. At test distances greater than 5 or 10 m, it is common practice for sensor areas to be considerably smaller than the 0.009 maximum. Sensor ratios of 0.003 or less are recommended for the photometry of devices with higher gradients of luminous intensity such as headlamps and front fog lamps.

3.7.5 PHOTOMETER SYSTEM CALIBRATION—The preferred method of photometric calibration is with a calibrated photometric standard lamp. When a calibrating lamp is used for the procedure, it should be calibrated using standard lamps of a higher order of accuracy and be traceable to the National Institute of Science and Technology or other qualified laboratories, through no more than four steps. A minimum of three photometric standard lamps or calibrating lamps should be maintained by the testing laboratory. These lamps should be intercompared periodically and records of the results should be maintained by the laboratory.

3.8 Instrument Calibration—Maintenance of instrumentation calibration is necessary for the photometric laboratory to make measurements with consistent precision. The following are recommendations of calibration intervals on various instruments and standards.

3.8.1 GENERAL INSTRUMENTATION—All instruments including voltmeters, current shunts, standard lamps, and accurate rated bulbs should be recalibrated at least annually by comparison with standards of a higher order of accuracy whose calibration is traceable to the National Institute of Science and Technology or other national laboratories, or by comparison to other like calibrated instrumentation. Records of these checks should be maintained by the laboratory.

3.8.2 SENSOR/PHOTOMETER SYSTEM—The system should be checked for color response and linearity (see 3.7.1 and 3.7.3) at least annually. Records of these checks should be maintained by the laboratory.

3.8.3 STANDARD LAMPS AND BULBS—In addition to the annual recalibration, operating time records should be kept on standard lamps, calibrating lamps, and accurate rated bulbs. Secondary and working calibrating lamps should be recalibrated or replaced at the interval recommended by the calibrating laboratory.

3.9 Environmental Variables—The following environmental variables should be controlled so their effect on photometric measurement accuracy is minimal.

3.9.1 TEMPERATURE AND HUMIDITY—Temperature and humidity can have a significant influence on electrical and photometric measuring instrumentation. Unless special steps have been taken to negate the effects of these factors, such as temperature control (or compensation) and humidity protection on the sensors and amplifiers, the photometry test area should be maintained at a calibrated room temperature within a sufficient temperature and humidity range so as not to have a significant effect on the instrumentation. Typical acceptable tolerances are ±5 °C and a maximum of 80% relative humidity. Large temperature gradients and turbulent air can cause fluctuations in luminous intensity measurements over long test distances of 20 m or more. Uniform temperatures should be maintained in long, enclosed photometric tubes or tunnels. Likewise, high concentrations of smoke or dust in the atmosphere may also influence results.

3.9.2 CONDITIONING PERIODS—Injection-molded plastic optical components may tend to change dimensionally after molding. Final critical photometric measurements should be made after the parts have stabilized. Similar precautions should be taken with devices which have been exposed to extreme temperatures or humidity in shipping or storage. For maximum accuracy and repeatability, parts should be conditioned in the laboratory environment for a minimum of 24 h, immediately prior to testing.

APPENDIX A
TEST FIXTURE DESIGN GUIDE

To assist the photometric laboratory in using test fixtures which control the main factors influencing the overall positioning accuracy (see 3.2.1), an example of a test fixture design is shown in Figure A1. Other designs, suitable for specific devices such as sealed beam units or for multipurpose use, and sufficient to provide proper positioning accuracy, may be equally satisfactory.

APPENDIX B
GONIOMETER POSITION CONVERSIONS

To assist the laboratory in converting the test position settings from the recommended goniometer configuration in SAE J575 and SAE J2039 (Horizontal Rotation Over Elevation, Type A) to the alternate configuration (Elevation Over Horizontal Rotation, Type B), calculated equivalent positions are given in Table B1. Other positions, not given in the table may be calculated as follows in Equations 1 and 2:

$$V_B \text{ deg} = \tan^{-1} (\tan V_A \text{ deg}/\cos H_A \text{ deg}) \quad \text{(Eq.1)}$$
$$H_B \text{ deg} = \sin^{-1} [(\cos V_A \text{ deg})(\sin H_A \text{ deg})] \quad \text{(Eq.2)}$$

It should be noted that test position settings on both the horizontal and the vertical axes are identical for both goniometer configurations. Differences in the coordinates are also insignificant over a range of 5 degrees in any direction from H-V. Sketches of both goniometer configurations are shown in Figure B1.

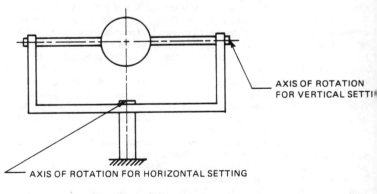

TYPE A GONIOMETER

HORIZONTAL ROTATION OVER ELEVATION

TYPE B GONIOMETER

ELEVATION OVER HORIZONTAL ROTATION

FIGURE B1—GONIOMETER CONFIGURATIONS

TABLE B1—GONIOMETER COORDINATE CONVERSIONS

Goniometer Configuration A[1] (Horizontal Rotation Over Elevation) V_A (U or D), deg	Goniometer Configuration A[1] (Horizontal Rotation Over Elevation) H_A (L or R), deg	Goniometer Configuration B (Elevation Over Horizontal Rotation) V_B (U or D), deg	Goniometer Configuration B (Elevation Over Horizontal Rotation) H_B (L or R), deg
5	5	5.02	4.98
	10	5.08	9.96
	20	5.32	19.92
	30	5.77	29.87
	45	7.05	44.78
10	5	10.04	4.92
	10	10.15	9.85
	20	10.63	19.68
	30	11.51	29.50
	45	14.00	44.14
15	5	15.05	4.83
	10	15.22	9.66
	20	15.92	19.29
	30	17.19	28.88
	45	20.75	43.08
20	5	20.07	4.70
	10	20.28	9.39
	20	21.17	18.75
	30	22.80	28.02
	45	27.24	41.64

[1] Recommended configuration in SAE J575.

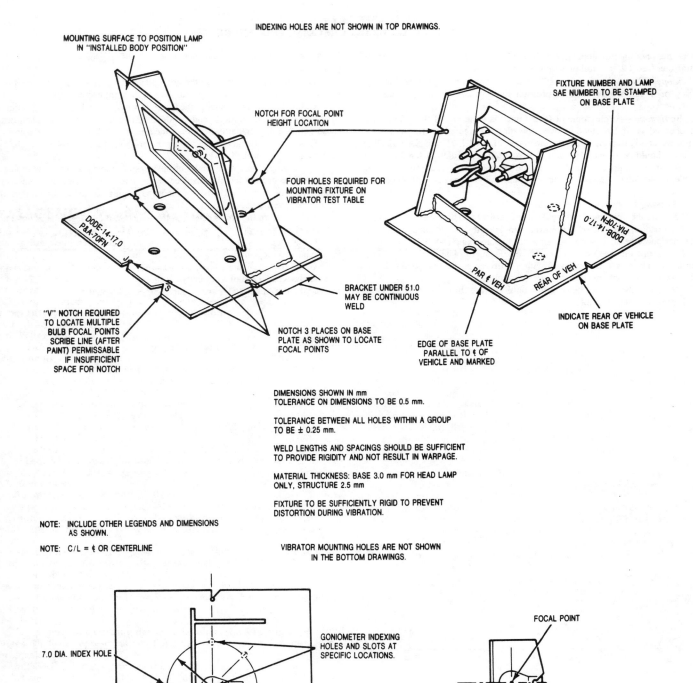

INDEXING HOLES ARE NOT SHOWN IN TOP DRAWINGS.

MOUNTING SURFACE TO POSITION LAMP
IN "INSTALLED BODY POSITION"

NOTCH FOR FOCAL POINT
HEIGHT LOCATION

FIXTURE NUMBER AND LAMP
SAE NUMBER TO BE STAMPED
ON BASE PLATE

FOUR HOLES REQUIRED FOR
MOUNTING FIXTURE ON
VIBRATOR TEST TABLE

D0DE-14-17.0
P&A-70FN

"V" NOTCH REQUIRED
TO LOCATE MULTIPLE
BULB FOCAL POINTS
SCRIBE LINE (AFTER
PAINT) PERMISSABLE
IF INSUFFICIENT
SPACE FOR NOTCH

BRACKET UNDER 51.0
MAY BE CONTINUOUS
WELD

NOTCH 3 PLACES ON BASE
PLATE AS SHOWN TO LOCATE
FOCAL POINTS

D0DB-14-17.0
PIA-70FN

PAR ₵ VEH

REAR OF VEH

EDGE OF BASE PLATE
PARALLEL TO ₵ OF
VEHICLE AND MARKED

INDICATE REAR OF VEHICLE
ON BASE PLATE

DIMENSIONS SHOWN IN mm
TOLERANCE ON DIMENSIONS TO BE 0.5 mm.

TOLERANCE BETWEEN ALL HOLES WITHIN A GROUP
TO BE ± 0.25 mm.

WELD LENGTHS AND SPACINGS SHOULD BE SUFFICIENT
TO PROVIDE RIGIDITY AND NOT RESULT IN WARPAGE.

MATERIAL THICKNESS: BASE 3.0 mm FOR HEAD LAMP
ONLY, STRUCTURE 2.5 mm

FIXTURE TO BE SUFFICIENTLY RIGID TO PREVENT
DISTORTION DURING VIBRATION.

NOTE: INCLUDE OTHER LEGENDS AND DIMENSIONS
AS SHOWN.

NOTE: C/L = ₵ OR CENTERLINE

VIBRATOR MOUNTING HOLES ARE NOT SHOWN
IN THE BOTTOM DRAWINGS.

7.0 DIA. INDEX HOLE

GONIOMETER INDEXING
HOLES AND SLOTS AT
SPECIFIC LOCATIONS.

FOCAL POINT

45 DEGREES
CORNERING LAMP ONLY

159.0 ± .5 DIA.

FOCAL POINT

7.0 X 8.0 SLOT

ALTERNATE LOCATION
FOR INDEXING PIN

6.0
6.5
DIA. INDEXING PIN

79.0 ± .5

159.0 ± .5

FIGURE A1—LAMP TEST FIXTURE DESIGN

205

APPENDIX C
GONIOMETER ACCURACY CHECKING PROCEDURE

To aid the photometric laboratory in determining the positioning deviation of a goniometer (see 3.2), the following procedure is presented.

C.1 Scope—The purpose of this procedure is to check the positioning accuracy of a goniometer used to position lighting devices for photometric measurements.

C.2 Equipment—A telescopic or laser transit is required. If the goniometer to be checked is of the rotation over elevation configuration (recommended goniometric configuration, Type A, referenced in SAE J575 and SAE J2039), the transit should be of the elevation over rotation configuration for the direct measurement of compound angles. If the proper configured transit is not available, the angular displacement for compound angles may be calculated (see Appendix B).

C.3 Checking Procedure

C.3.1 Set the goniometer to the 0 degree vertical and horizontal positions.

C.3.1.1 Position a laser so that its beam is located on the goniometer/photometer sensor or goniometer/projector lamp H-V axis.

C.3.1.2 Mount on the goniometer a precision angle plate (flat and square within 0.1 mm over a 150 mm span) with a mirrored surface perpendicular to the H-V axis of the goniometer.

C.3.1.3 Adjust the goniometer controls until the laser beam is reflected back on itself as precisely as possible.

C.3.1.4 Adjust the position indicators of the goniometer to read 0,0 if necessary.

C.3.2 Install the transit on the goniometer Positioner so that the rotational axes of the transit are on the rotational axes of the goniometer.

C.3.3 Set the goniometer to the 0 degree vertical and horizontal positions.

C.3.4 Align the optical center of the transit to the center of the photometer sensor, and set the angular indicators of the transit to 0 degree for both axes.

C.3.5 Rotate the goniometer along the horizontal or vertical axis to the test point angle to be checked.

C.3.6 Align the optical center of the transit to the center of the photometer sensor and record the angular displacement. The deviation of the goniometer angle from the actual angle is the recorded angular displacement minus the accuracy of the transit.

C.3.7 Return the goniometer and the transit to the 0 degree horizontal and vertical position.

C.3.8 Repeat steps C.3.5 and C.3.6 to check additional test pointer Positioner accuracy along the horizontal or vertical axes.

C.3.9 In a similar manner, the accuracy of compound angle test points may be checked by use of a correctly configured transit (see Section C.2) and by moving the Positioner and transit to the compound angle location.

PLASTIC MATERIALS AND COATINGS FOR USE IN OR ON OPTICAL PARTS SUCH AS LENSES AND REFLECTORS OF HIGH-INTENSITY DISCHARGE FORWARD LIGHTING DEVICES USED IN MOTOR VEHICLES—SAE J1647 MAR95

SAE Recommended Practice

Report of the SAE Materials Standards Committee and the SAE Lighting Coordinating Committee approved March 1995. Rationale statement available.

1. Scope—This SAE Recommended Practice provides test methods and requirements to evaluate the suitability of plastic optical materials for possible use in discharge forward lighting (DFL) devices in motor vehicles. These materials are typically used for lenses and reflectors.

Separate testing is required for each combination of material, industrial coating, DFL light source, and device focal length. The tests are intended to determine physical and optical characteristics of the materials and coatings. Performance expectations of finished assemblies, including plastic components, are to be based on tests for lighting devices, as specified in SAE Standards and Recommended Practices for motor vehicle lighting equipment. Optical components exposed to weathering should also be subject to SAE J576.

2. References

2.1 Applicable Documents—The following publications form a part of this specification to the extent specified herein. Unless otherwise specified, the latest issue of SAE publications shall apply.

2.1.1 SAE PUBLICATIONS—Available from SAE, 400 Commonwealth Drive, Warrendale, PA 15096-0001.

SAE J576 JUL91—Plastic Materials for Use in Optical Parts Such as Lenses and Reflex Reflectors of Motor Vehicle Lighting Devices

SAE J578 MAY88—Color Specification

2.1.2 ASTM PUBLICATIONS—Available from ASTM, 1916 Race Street, Philadelphia, PA 19103-1187.

ASTM D 1003-61 (1988)—Tests for Haze and Luminous Transmittance of Transparent Plastics

ASTM E 308-66 (1985)—Recommended Practice for Spectrophotometry and Description of Color in CIE 1931 System

2.1.3 CIE PUBLICATION—Available from U. S. National Committee, CIE, National Bureau of Standards, Gaithersburg, MD 20899.

CIE 1931 System

2.1.4 ISBN PUBLICATION—Available from ACGIH at 6500 Glenway Ave., Bldg. D-7, Cincinnati, OH 45211-4438.

ISBN:0936712-81-3—The Threshold Limit Values for Occupational Exposure to Ultraviolet Radiation Incident Upon Skin or Eye

3. Definitions

3.1 Material—A type and grade of plastic, distinguished by its composition, manufacturer's designation (number), and color.

3.2 Coated Material—A coated material is a material as defined in 3.1 which has a coating applied to the surface of the finished sample to impart some protective properties. Coating identification includes manufacturer's name, formulation designation (number), and recommendations for application.

3.3 Apparatus

3.3.1 HIGH-INTENSITY DISCHARGE LAMP—A sealed light source that produces light flux by means of an electrical discharge.

3.3.2 DISCHARGE FORWARD LIGHTING (DFL) SYSTEMS—A lighting system providing forward illumination, comprised of the light discharge source, ballast/starting system, and interconnecting wiring.

3.3.3 TEST CHAMBER—An aluminum box that provides an alternative to DFL system testing of materials. It is intended to simulate UV intensity and thermal conditions within a DFL device. Refer to Figure 1.

3.3.3.1 Test Chamber Design—The test chamber design is given in Figures 2, 3, 4, and 5. The ability of the chamber to simulate device environments is limited to distances "d" of 44 to 64 mm. It is made of clear anodized 3.2 mm thick aluminum. The assembled test chamber is tight fitting, but not hermetically sealed. The lamp is mounted in compliance with the manufacturer's recommendations and positioned so that the arc discharge

coincides with the geometric center of the test chamber. Sample holders are placed a distance "d" from center, on opposite sides of the lamp. The distance "d" determines the UV intensity at the sample. It is nominally twice the focal length of the intended DFL system. There are two sample holders. One sample holder contains PYREX and the other contains the material to be tested. A 38 mm x 76 mm PYREX window is built into the top of the test chamber to allow the escape of excess thermal radiation. For d < 50 mm, the window should be covered with an aluminum plate. Thermal equilibrium is reached in an open air environment.

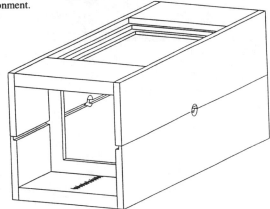

FIGURE 1—SAE HID TEST CHAMBER—ASSEMBLED—FULL SCALE

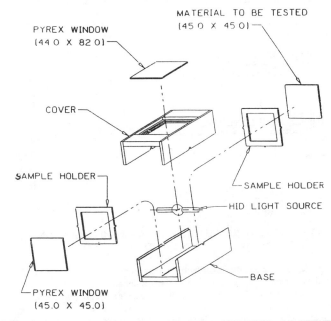

FIGURE 2—SAE HID TEST CHAMBER—PERSPECTIVE—1/2 SCALE

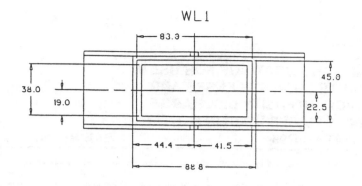

WL1

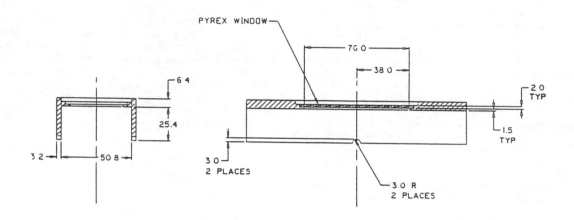

PYREX WINDOW

FIGURE 3—SAE HID TEST CHAMBER—COVER

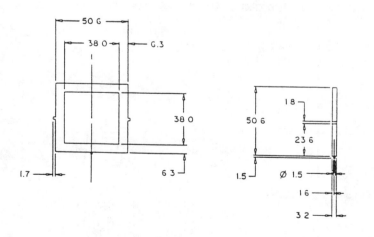

FIGURE 4—SAE HID TEST CHAMBER—SAMPLE HOLDER—2
REQUIRED

At its discretion, the manufacturer may perform the recommended tests using the actual DFL system rather than the test chamber.

3.3.3.2 Safety—The threshold limit values for occupational exposure to ultraviolet radiation incident upon skin or eye defined by the American Conference of Governmental Industrial Hygienist should not be exceeded during testing.

The values are found in ISBN:0936712-81-3.

3.4 Surfaces

3.4.1 EXPOSED SURFACES—Those surfaces of the material, coated or uncoated, exposed to the irradiation of a DFL light source.

3.4.2 INNER SURFACE—The side of the material, coated or uncoated, closest to the DFL light source.

3.4.3 OUTER SURFACE—The side of the material, coated or uncoated, farthest from the DFL light source.

3.5 Exposure Effects

3.5.1 COLOR BLEEDING—The migration of color out of a plastic part onto the surrounding surface.

3.5.2 CRAZING—A network of fine cracks on or beneath the surface of the material with penetration below the surface of the substrate.

3.5.3 CRACKING—A separation of adjacent sections of a plastic material with penetration into the specimen.

3.5.4 HAZE—The cloudy or turbid appearance of an otherwise transparent specimen caused by light scattered from within the specimen or from its surface.

3.5.5 DELAMINATION—A separation of the layers of a material including coatings.

4. Test Procedure

4.1 Materials to be Tested—Exposure tests shall be made on each material (as defined in 3.1 and 3.2) used in optical parts employed in DFL motor vehicle lighting devices. Concentrations of polymer components and additives such as plasticizers, lubricants, colorants, weathering stabilizers, and anti-oxidants in plastic materials and/or coatings may be changed without retesting if: the changes are within the limits of composition represented by higher and lower concentrations of these polymer components and additives which have been tested in accordance with Section 4 and found to meet the requirements of Section 5.

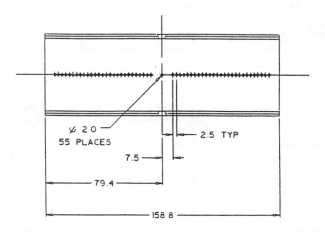

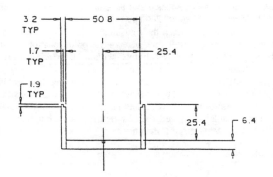
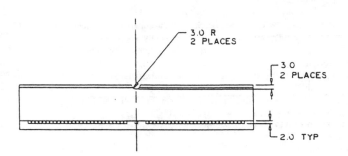

FIGURE 5—SAE HID TEST CHAMBER—BASE

4.2 Samples Required

4.2.1 GENERAL—Samples of plastic shall be injection molded into polished metal molds to produce test specimens with two flat and parallel faces. Alternative processing techniques may also be used to produce equivalent test specimens. Both inner and outer surfaces shall be prepared as in the intended application.

4.2.2 NUMBER—A minimum of two test samples and one control sample of each material is required, for each thickness to be tested.

4.2.3 SIZE—Test specimen size shall be 45 mm x 45 mm.

4.2.4 THICKNESS—The thickness of the sample shall be equal to the minimum thickness of the component in the device. Additionally, the performance limitations of the material can be determined by testing over the thickness range recommended by the manufacturer. Recommended nominal thicknesses are: 1.6 mm, 3.2 mm, 6.4 mm, and 2.3 mm.

4.3 Light Source—A production sample of the DFL light source that will be used in the device, or a representative prototype, shall be used as the light source.

4.4 Chamber and Sample Setup

4.4.1 SAMPLE MOUNTING—The sample and PYREX shall be mounted in the sample holders using spring clips or alternative means. The holders shall be mounted at a distance "d" from the DFL light source. The distance "d" is twice the focal length of the HID device under consideration. If the material, in the application, is located closer to the DFL light source than twice the focal length, the material should be tested at the closer distance.

4.4.2 DURATION—The test shall last for 2200 continuous hours.

4.4.3 WATTAGE—The DFL light source shall be energized to its maximum low beam rated wattage specified by the manufacturer. Means for monitoring the lamp input power are recommended.

4.4.4 TEST ENVIRONMENT—The testing shall be conducted in a laboratory environment. The internal temperature of the test chamber shall be allowed to develop without any forced heating or cooling.

4.4.5 OUTDOOR EXPOSURE—The outer surface of the lamp material shall be tested to and meet the requirements of SAE J576 (1991).

4.5 Optical Measurements

4.5.1 LUMINOUS TRANSMITTANCE AND COLOR—Measurements shall be made in accordance with ASTM E 308-66 (1973).

4.5.2 HAZE—Measurements shall be made in accordance with ASTM D 1003-61 (1977).

4.5.3 CHROMATICITY (COLOR)—The chromaticity coordinates shall conform with the requirements of SAE J578 (1988) in the range of thickness stated by the material manufacturer.

5. Upon completion of the test procedure, the following requirements apply:

5.1 Luminous Transmittance—The luminous transmittance of the exposed samples using CIE Illuminant A (2856K) shall not have changed by more than 25% (15% for a headlamp that is also used as a daytime running lamp) of the luminous transmittance of the unexposed control sample when tested in accordance with ASTM E 308.

5.2 Chromaticity Coordinates—The chromaticity coordinates shall conform with the requirements of SAE J578 in the range of thickness stated by the material manufacturer.

5.3 Haze—The haze of plastic materials used for road illuminating and signaling and marking lamp lenses shall not be greater than 30% as measured by ASTM D 1003-61 (1977).

5.4 Appearance—The exposed samples when compared with the unexposed controls shall not show physical changes affecting performance, such as color bleeding, delamination, crazing, or cracking, as defined in 3.4.

6. *Guidelines*—In order to test for the presence of coatings, trace quantities (100 ppm maximum in the wet state) of an optical brightener should be added to the coating formulation. This should be checked by ultraviolet inspection against a known sample. Additionally, coating suppliers have the option of providing coatings without optical brighteners if they can provide a method to detect the coating.

SAE MINIATURE BULB VIBRATION TEST
—SAE J1765 MAY95

Report of the SAE Road Illumination Devices Standards, Test Methods, and Equipment Committee approved by the SAE Lighting Coordinating Committee, May 1995. Rationale statement available.

1. Scope—This SAE Recommended Practice was designed to be an accelerated vibration test that subjects bulbs to critical vibration/shock loading typically observed in normal vehicle service and can be employed for conformance of production (COP) testing. The test was designed for external vehicle applications.

2. References

2.1 Applicable Documents—The following publications form a part of this specification to the extent specified herein. The latest issue of SAE publications shall apply.

2.1.1 SAE PUBLICATIONS—Available from SAE, 400 Commonwealth Drive, Warrendale, PA 15096-0001.

SAE J573—Miniature Lamp Bulbs

SAE J759—Lighting Identification Code

2.2 Related Publications—The following publications are provided for information purposes only and are not a required part of this document.

2.2.1 SAE PUBLICATIONS—Available from SAE, 400 Commonwealth Drive, Warrendale, PA 15096-0001.

SAE J575—Tests for Motor Vehicle Lighting Devices and Components

SAE J1455—Joint SAE/TMC Recommended Environmental Practices for Electronic Equipment Design (Heavy-Duty Trucks)

2.2.2 FMVSS PUBLICATIONS—Available from the National Highway Traffic Safety Administration, 400 Seventh Street SW, Washington, DC 20024-0002.

FMVSS108—Lamps, Reflective Devices, and Associated Equipment (Available as 49 CFR 571.108)

2.2.3 IEC PUBLICATIONS—Available from American National Standards Institute, Inc., 11 West 42nd Street, New York, NY 10036.

IEC 810—Lamps for Road Vehicles—Performance Requirements

3. Definitions

3.1 Power Spectral Density (PSD)—The product of the real and imaginary Fourier coefficients of a signal divided by the frequency interval. The square root of the integral of PSD over all measured frequencies will yield the root-mean-square acceleration (Grms).

3.2 Wide Band Random—Random vibration whose power spectral density has a relatively broad frequency range. All frequencies in the test range are excited simultaneously as opposed to the "narrow-band" where only a small portion of the frequencies in the test frequency range are excited at any one time.

3.3 Filament Mount Structure—The filament mount structure consists of the filament, electrical lead wires, clamps or welds, and any filament or lead supports that comprise the active structure inside the bulb.

3.4 Closed-Loop Dynamic Vibration Equipment—A laboratory test system consisting of an electromagnetic exciter (shaker), a feedback transducer (accelerometer), and a control unit with necessary power amplifiers capable of reproducing, within prescribed statistical limits, a predetermined vibration profile for the purpose of performing environmental stress screening. See Figure 1.

3.5 Natural Frequency—A vibration frequency of a mechanical system when the system is allowed to freely oscillate following an initial displacement. Real mechanical systems have numerous natural frequencies corresponding to distinct natural modes of vibration. Natural frequencies are inherent properties of a mechanical system, determined by the distribution of mass and stiffness of the system, and by boundary conditions imposed upon the system.

3.6 Resonant Frequency—A frequency at which the ratio of the steady-state response amplitude (at the point of excitation) to harmonic excitation magnitude reaches a relative maximum. Resonant frequencies closely (but not necessarily exactly) coincide with natural frequencies.

Resonant frequencies are dependent upon the type and location of harmonic excitation (e.g., force, displacement, or velocity), as well as the mechanical properties and boundary conditions of the mechanical system. For example, displacement resonance and velocity resonance occur at different frequencies for any system with damping. (Ordinarily the difference is not significant.) A system will not exhibit a resonant frequency corresponding to a particular natural frequency if the point of excitation is at a node of the modeshape for the natural frequency; however, an antiresonance will be exhibited at that frequency (i.e., zero vibration amplitude at the point of excitation).

3.7 Grms—The root-mean-square acceleration equivalent as a ratio with respect to gravity.

4. Lighting Identification Codes, Markings, and Notices

4.1 Bulbs identified for use in vehicle exterior applications listed in SAE J759 (except H, HH, and HR headlamps) shall meet this document.

5. Test Procedure—See Figure 1.

5.1 Seasoning—Bulbs are seasoned as specified in SAE J573 prior to being subjected to testing.

5.2 Voltage—Test shall be conducted at the voltage specified in SAE J573 Section 2.2 or as specified by the manufacturer.

5.3 Test Equipment—The test equipment shall be closed-loop dynamic vibration equipment and controller (or equivalent) capable of vibrating in random modes, produce variable vibration from 10 to 2000 Hz with a tolerance of ±4 dB and a minimum of 500 pounds force.

5.4 Test Fixture Mounting—The bulb shall be fastened rigidly to a fixture on the vibration table. This may be achieved by clamping, soldering, or embedding. Electrical connections shall be made such that the connection is assured during the whole test.

Fixtures shall be designed such that their natural frequencies (fully loaded or unloaded) do not occur below 1200 Hz.

5.5 Control Point—Attach the transducer used to measure and maintain the specified vibration characteristics at a control point location as close to the test bulb as possible on the test fixture without interfering with the bulb resonance frequencies.

5.6 Axis of Vibration—With the filament mounting structure horizontal, a direction of excitation normal to the filament(s) axis is used for testing.

5.7 Test Conditions—The test shall last for a period of 6 h total. This is to include periods of 2 h unlighted, then 2 h lighted, then 2 h unlighted again.

  a. Vibration—Wide Band Random
  b. Duration— 2 h Cold (Unlighted)
        2 h (Lighted)
        2 h Cold
        6 Total
  c. Frequency Range—50 to 1000 Hz
  d. Acceleration Levels— 0.08 g^2/Hz (50 to 400 Hz)
        0.0025 g^2/Hz (600 to 1000 Hz)
  e. Total Grms—5.75

6. Requirements

6.1 Upon completion of the 6-h test specified in Section 5, bulb shall be functional and meet the requirements of SAE J573 or as specified by the manufacturer.

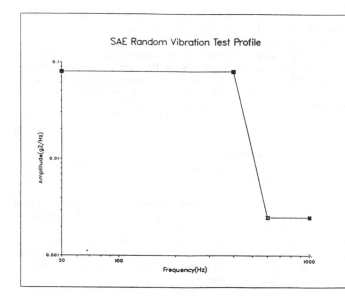

FIGURE 1—SAE RANDOM VIBRATION TEST PROFILE

RETROREFLECTIVE MATERIALS FOR VEHICLE CONSPICUITY—SAE J1967 MAR91

SAE Recommended Practice

Report of the SAE Truck and Bus Conspicuity Subcommittee of the Truck and Bus Electrical and Electronics Committee March 1991.

1. Scope—This SAE Recommended Practice shall apply to nonexposed lens retroreflective materials which may be used solely for conspicuity purposes on vehicles of any size or type. This is a specification for materials only, and does not mandate the use of any such materials.

1.1 Purpose—This document establishes test procedures and related requirements for identifying and evaluating retroreflective materials intended for use in passive devices used to enhance the conspicuity of vehicles at nighttime. The specifications in this document are not intended to apply, in any way, to materials used for commercial identification, advertising, or similar graphics. Their use is outside the scope of this document.

2. References

2.1 Applicable Documents—The following publications form a part of this specification to the extent specified herein. The latest issue of SAE publications shall apply.

2.1.1 SAE PUBLICATIONS—Available from SAE, 400 Commonwealth Drive, Warrendale, PA 15096-0001.

SAE J575—Tests for Motor Vehicle Lighting Devices and Components

SAE J576—Plastic Materials for Use in Optical Parts Such as Lenses and Reflectors of Motor Vehicle Lighting Devices

2.1.2 ASTM PUBLICATIONS—Available from ASTM, 1916 Race Street, Philadelphia, PA 19103.

ASTM B 117—Method of Salt Spray (Fog) Testing

ASTM D 4956—Standard Specification for Retroreflective Sheeting for Traffic Control

ASTM E 97—Standard Test Method for Directional Reflectance Factor

ASTM E 308—Broad Band Filter Photometry

ASTM E 810-81—Standard Test Method for Coefficient Retroreflection of Retroreflective Sheeting

ASTM E 1164—Standard Practice for Obtaining Spectrophotometric Data for Object-Color Evaluating

ASTM G-23-81—Recommended Practice for Operating Light and Water Exposure Apparatus (Carbon-Arc Type) for Exposure of Non-Metallic Materials

2.1.3 GOVERNMENT PUBLICATIONS—Available from the Superintendent of Documents, U. S. Government Printing Office, Washington, DC 20402.

DOT-HS-806-098—(Department of Transportation)—Improved Vehicle Conspicuity and Signalling Systems; Task II, Vector Research

Federal Specification L-S-300C—Sheeting and Tape, Reflective, Non-Exposed Lens

Federal Standard 141—Paint, Varnish, Lacquer and Related Materials; Methods of Inspection, Sampling and Testing

2.1.4 OTHER PUBLICATIONS

CIE 39-2 (TC-1.6)—(Commission Internationale de L'Eclairage/International Commission on Illumination) Recommendations for Surface Colours for Visual Signalling

Austin & Forrester; Visibility Characteristics of Large Vehicle Conspicuity Marking, October, 1988 (unpublished)

AASHTO M268-84—(American Association of State Highway Transportation Officials)—Standard Specification for Retroreflective Sheeting for Traffic Control

2.2 Definitions

2.2.1 CONSPICUITY—The ability of an object to be noticed and recognized without confusion or ambiguity.

2.2.2 DAYTIME—The period when an object is illuminated primarily by natural sunlight, either direct or diffused by weather or clouds; the period when headlamps are not required for road illumination.

2.2.3 GRAPHICS—Markings, illustrations, or other identifying devices on observable surfaces of a vehicle.

2.2.4 PASSIVE DEVICES—Devices which require no electrical power or internal illumination, but which are instead made visible by retroreflection from external light sources.

2.2.5 NIGHTTIME—The period when an object is illuminated solely or primarily by artificial light, such as the headlamps of the vehicle of the observer. The period when headlamps are required to be illuminated.

2.2.6 RETROREFLECTION—The process by which illumination is returned by an object directly or generally back to the source of that illumination; reflection characterized by the flux in an incident beam being returned in directions close to the direction from which it came, this effect occurring over a wide range of incidence angles.

2.2.7 REFLECTANCE FACTOR (CAP Y)—Ratio of flux reflected from a specimen to the luminous flux reflected from the standard surface identified in ASTM E 97, under the same geometric conditions of measurement. Cap Y is one of the three tristimulus values (XYZ) of the CIE system used to identify and assign measurable values to color and light, as used in Figure 3—"Chromaticity Regions for the Colours of Retroreflecting Materials" of CIE 39-2 (TC-1.6). It is used in conjunction with the CIE color coordinates (x,y) to give the "lightness value" associated with the specific color so identified.

3. Test Procedures

3.1 Introduction—Whenever possible, existing test procedures have been referenced in establishing performance requirements. However, for certain of the desired material characteristics no existing tests were found to be appropriate to evaluate the performance of some of the newer materials under consideration. In such instances, specific tests were developed.

3.2 Test Procedures

3.2.1 REFLECTANCE FACTOR (CAP Y)

3.2.1.1 *Preparation*—Sample to be evaluated shall be placed on a flat substrate which shall be capable of being rotated through 360 degrees. Other preparations shall be in accordance with ASTM E-97.

3.2.1.2 *Test Procedure*—Testing in accordance with ASTM E 308 and ASTM E 1164, the Cap Y value for the retroreflective material shall be determined in two ways: by the average value and the highest measured value, when the sample is rotated through 360 degrees. The average shall be determined by taking a sufficient number of data points at equal degrees of rotation, such that the average shall not change significantly ($\pm$ 3%) with the addition or subtraction of data points.

3.2.2 SALT SPRAY RESISTANCE TEST

3.2.2.1 *Preparation*—Test Panels measuring 152 mm x 152 mm (6 in × 6 in) shall be prepared by applying retroreflective materials to smooth 0.51 mm (0.020 in) minimum thickness aluminum, degreased and acid etched, using recommended procedures, and conditioned for 24 h under standard conditions as specified in Federal Standard 141.

3.2.2.2 *Test Procedure*—The test panels shall be subjected to 150 h of exposure to a 5% concentration salt spray at 35 °C (95 °F) in accordance with ASTM B 117.

3.2.3 SOLVENT AND FLUID RESISTANCE TEST

3.2.3.1 *Test Fluids*
a. Reference fuel (85% mineral spirits and 15% Xylene).
b. Diesel Fuel (ASTM −2D)
c. Car wash detergent (TSP or equivalent).

3.2.3.2 *Preparation*—Prepare and condition test panels as specified in 3.2.2.1.

3.2.3.3 *Test Procedure*—Immerse each test panel into all fluids, each for 10 s, 10 times, with a 20 s evaporation period between each dip.

3.2.4 WEATHERING TESTS—To determine that weathering characteristics will be at acceptable levels after a period of extended use, conspicuity materials must pass Test 1, and either Test 2a or Test 2b herein. Before the material can be used, it must pass Test 1. Thereafter, materials being tested under either Test 2a or Test 2b may be used for a period of 4 years from the initiation of marketing of the material. The manufacturer will make available test results upon successful completion of either Test 2a or Test 2b.

3.2.4.1 *Test 1*—Materials shall be exposed for 2200 h in accordance with the procedures in AASHTO 268-84.

3.2.4.2 *Test 2a*—Conspicuity materials shall be subjected to the exposure procedures in SAE J576 Sections 2.2 and 3.3.

3.2.4.3 *Test 2b*—The manufacturer shall arrange for samples to be mounted on one or more vehicles. The samples will be tested for 3 years. They will be mounted on vehicles that meet the following conditions during the entire period of the test:
a. Each vehicle shall be in regular service for the full 3-year period.
b. Each vehicle shall be domiciled out of doors.
c. Each vehicle shall operate south of interstate route I-80 for at least 50% of the 3-year test period.

3.2.4.3.1 *Application*—Two strips of the retroreflective tape to be tested shall be mounted on the vehicle, one strip on each side for the full length of the vehicle body. The surfaces on which the test strips are to be mounted shall be undamaged. These surfaces shall be cleaned and the test strips mounted in accordance with the directions of the manufacturer of the retroreflective tape being tested.

3.2.4.3.2 *Procedure*—At the end of the 3-year test period, the test strips shall be cleaned. The retained brightness and retroreflective photometric values of both of the clean test strips shall be measured at zero and 90 degrees orientation, at five places, approximately equally spaced along their length. The values so obtained shall be averaged. Measured areas of strips shall show no evidence of damage.

The day colors of the retroreflective material shall be tested in accordance with ASTM E 308 with exception of Cap-Y values for white material which shall be tested according to the procedure in Section 3. The photometric values shall be measured with a portable retroreflectometer at 0.2 degrees observation angle and minus 4 degrees entrance angle

3.2.5 IMPACT RESISTANCE TEST—The materials shall be subjected to the impact resistance test procedures in AASHTO M268-84.

3.2.6 ADHESION TEST

3.2.6.1 *Application*—This test is applicable to either mechanical or adhesive attachment systems for materials thicker than 25 mils. Materials 25 mils thick or less shall be tested to Federal Specification L-S-300C.

3.2.6.2 *Preparation*—Apply the retroreflective material specimen to smooth panels of aluminum alloy 6061-T6 or 5053-H38. The panels must be sufficiently thick to withstand the load of the test without deforming more than ± 0.025 mm (0.001 in) from "flat." Degrease and acid etch the panel prior to application. Apply the specimen to the panel in accordance with the recommendations of the retroreflective material manufacturer. Condition the bonded specimen at a temperature between 21 to 23 °C (70 to 75 °F) and 50% ± 5% relative humidity for 24 h prior to testing.

3.2.6.3 *Test Procedure*—Apply a load of 1.7 N for each square centimeter (2.5 lb for each square inch) of retroreflective area, in two different directions, for 1 min each. First, the load shall be applied in tension, or perpendicular to the mounting surface; then in shear, or parallel to the mounting surface.

3.2.7 MOISTURE TEST—The material specimen shall be tested in accordance with the moisture test specified in SAE J575, Section 4.2.

3.2.8 COEFFICIENT OF RETROREFLECTION—The coefficient of retroreflection of the specimen material shall be determined in accordance with the test procedures in ASTM E 810. The values shall be specified in units of candelas per lux per square meter (candelas per foot-candle per square foot).

3.2.9 TEST FOR COLOR—Conformance to color requirements shall be determined spectrophotometrically in accordance with ASTM E 1164, with instruments using either 45/0 or 0/45 illumination/viewing conditions and tolerances as described in ASTM E 1164. CIE tristimulus values for the 2 degree observer and illuminant C shall be calculated in accordance with ASTM E 308.

4. Requirements

4.1 Reflectance Factor (Cap Y)—When tested according to 3.2.1, the highest measured Cap Y value shall not be less than 20.0. The rotational average Cap Y value shall not be less than 12.0.

4.2 Salt Spray Resistance—The retroreflective materials must show no loss of adhesion, discoloration or blistering after exposure to the test in 3.2.2.

4.3 Solvent Resistance—After immersion in each of the test fluids indicated in 3.2.3, the materials shall show no noticeable softening, dulling, color change, or loss of adhesion.

4.4 Weathering

4.4.1 TEST 1—After completion of the accelerated weathering test described in 3.2.4.1, materials shall retain 80% of the photometric values indicated in Table 1.

4.4.2 TEST 2A—After being subjected to SAE J576, Sections 2.2 and 3.3 as described in 3.2.4.2, materials shall retain 50% of the photometric values indicated in Table 1.

4.4.3 TEST 2B—After being subjected to three years actual weathering as described in 3.2.4.3, retroreflective materials shall retain 80% of the photometric values in Table 1.

4.4.4 COLOR—After the weathering tests described in 3.2.4.1 and 3.2.4.2 or 3.2.4.3, materials shall meet the color requirements of 4.9.

TABLE 1—MINIMUM REFLECTIVE INTENSITY (cd/lx/m²)

Entrance Angle	Observation Angle 0.2 degrees White	Observation Angle 0.2 degrees Red	Observation Angle 0.5 degrees White	Observation Angle 0.5 degrees Red
−4 degrees	300	75	65	16
45 degrees	60	15	16	4

4.5 Impact Resistance—Impact resistance of the materials shall meet the requirements specified in AASHTO M268-84.

4.6 Adhesion

4.6.1 Retroreflective sheeting materials of 25 mils thickness or less shall conform to the requirements for initial adhesion in Federal Specification L-S-300C when so tested.

4.6.2 Retroreflective materials thicker than 25 mils shall maintain adhesion when subjected to the test procedures in 3.2.6.1.

4.7 Moisture—Retroreflective materials shall meet the moisture requirements specified in SAE J575 Section 4.2.

4.8 Reflective Intensity

4.8.1 The minimum reflective intensity for white (silver-white) as the primary or sole color used, and red used as a contrasting color, shall be as indicated in Table 1.

TABLE 2—COLOR TABLE

Color	Chromaticity Coordinates Corner Points 1 x/y	Cromaticity Coordinates Corner Points 2 x/y	Chromaticity Coordinates Corner Points 3 x/y	Cromaticity Coordinates Corner Points 4 x/y	Reflectance Limits (%Y) Min.	Reflectance Limits (%Y) Max.
White	0.303/0.287	0.368/0.353	0.340/0.380	0.274/0.316	—	—
Red	0.613/0.297	0.708/0.292	0.636/0.364	0.558/0.352	2.5	15.0

4.8.2 The ratio of the luminous intensities of white and another color shall not be less than 4:1 nor greater than 15:1.

4.9 Color Requirements

4.9.1 Any colored retroreflective materials may be deemed suitable for use in conspicuity devices provided they meet the contrast ratio and minimum brightness of 4.8.

4.9.2 Materials selected to conform to specifications calling for white and/or red retroreflective materials, shall comply with the chromaticity coordinates of the CIE diagram, as shown in Table 2.

4.10 Photometric Values—After completion of salt spray resistance and solvent resistance tests, samples shall be tested for coefficient of retroreflection as specified in 4.8 and color requirements as specified in 4.9. Cap Y values shall be those specified in 4.1.

TESTS FOR LIGHTING DEVICES AND COMPONENTS USED ON VEHICLES 2032 mm OR MORE IN OVERALL WIDTH—SAE J2139 JAN94

SAE Recommended Practice

Report of the SAE Heavy-Duty Lighting Standards Committee approved January 1994. Rationale statement available.

1. Scope—This SAE Recommended Practice provides standardized laboratory tests, test methods, and performance requirements applicable to lighting devices and components used on vehicles 2032 mm or more in overall width.

2. References

2.1 Applicable Documents—The following publications form a part of this specification to the extent specified herein. The latest issue of SAE publications shall apply.

2.1.1 SAE PUBLICATIONS—Available from SAE, 400 Commonwealth Drive, Warrendale, PA 15096-0001.

SAE J387—Terminology—Motor Vehicle Lighting

SAE J575—Tests for Motor Vehicle Lighting Devices and Components for Use on Vehicles Less than 2032 mm in Overall Width

SAE J577—Vibration Test Machine

SAE J1330—Photometry Laboratory Guidelines

2.1.2 ASTM PUBLICATIONS—Available from ASTM, 1916 Race Street, Philadelphia, PA 19103-1187.

ASTM B 117—Method of Salt Spray (Fog) Testing

ASTM C 150-84—Specification for Portland Cement

ASTM E 308-85—Standard Method for Computing the Colors of Objects by Using the CIE System

2.2 Definitions

2.2.1 LIGHTING DEVICES

2.2.1.1 Sample—Samples submitted for test shall be representative of the device as regularly manufactured and marketed. Each sample shall be securely mounted on the test fixture in its design position and shall include all accessory equipment necessary to operate the device in its normal manner.

2.2.2 FIXTURE

2.2.2.1 Test Fixture—A fixture specifically designed to support the device in its designed operating position during a laboratory test.

2.2.2.2 Vibration Test Fixture—A fixture specifically designed to support the device in its operating position during the vibration test. The fixture shall not have a resonant frequency in the test range.

3. Tests—The following sections describe the individual tests which need not be performed in any particular sequence, except as noted in the test procedure. The completion of the tests may be expedited by performing the tests simultaneously on separately mounted samples.

However, it is recommended that the design of each device be evaluated to determine if the vibration test or the warpage test affect other tests, in which case, those tests shall be performed first.

3.1 Vibration Test—This test evaluates the ability of the sample device to resist damage from vibration-induced stresses. This test is not intended to test the vibration resistance of bulb filaments, but may be used to evaluate the effects of vibration-induced stresses on shock-mounted devices.

3.1.1 VIBRATION TEST EQUIPMENT

3.1.1.1 See SAE J577 JUN73 for details of vibration test machine (1979 Handbook).

3.1.2 VIBRATION TEST PROCEDURES

3.1.2.1 A sample device, as mounted on the support supplied, shall be bolted to the anvil end of the table of the vibration test machine and vibrated at 750 cpm through a distance of 3 mm. The table shall be spring mounted at one end and fitted with steel calks on the underside of the other end. These calks are to make contact with the steel anvil once during each cycle at the completion of the fall. The rack shall be operated under a spring tension of 27.2 kg to 31.7 kg.

3.1.2.2 Test duration, 60 +1/-0 min.

3.2 Moisture Test

3.2.1 WATER-SPRAY MOISTURE TEST—This test procedure shall be used to test devices with replaceable light sources.

The test evaluates the ability of the device to resist moisture leakage into the device from a water spray and to determine the drainage capability of the device with drain holes or other exposed openings in the device.

3.2.2 WATER-SPRAY MOISTURE TEST EQUIPMENT

3.2.2.1 The water-spray cabinet shall be equipped with a nozzle which provides a solid cone of water spray of sufficient included angle to completely cover the sample device. The centerline of the nozzle shall be directed

downward at an angle of 45 degrees ± 5 degrees to the vertical axis of the rotating test platform.

3.2.2.2 The precipitation rate of the water spray at the device shall be 2.5 +1.6/-0.0 mm/min as measured with a vertical cylindrical collector centered on the vertical axis of rotation. The collector shall be 100 mm high and the inside diameter shall be a minimum of 140 mm.

3.2.2.3 The device shall rotate about its vertical axis at a rate of 4.0 rpm ± 0.5 rpm.

3.2.3 WATER-SPRAY MOISTURE TEST PROCEDURES

3.2.3.1 The device shall be mounted and tested in the design position (as mounted on the vehicle) and in accordance with the manufacturer's instructions.

3.2.3.2 All drain holes, slots, and other openings shall remain open during the test.

3.2.3.3 Devices which have a portion protected in service may have that portion of the exterior surface of the device protected in the same manner during the test.

3.2.3.4 The test duration shall be 12 h.

3.2.3.5 The device shall be lighted for the first 5 min of each hour.

When multiple function lamps are tested:

a. The major filament or major light source only shall be lighted.

b. If more than one light source is used in the device then the major filament or major light source only of each shall be lighted.

c. For 6 V systems, use 6.4 V

   For 12 V systems, use 12.8 V

   For 24 V systems, use 25.6 V

3.2.3.6 At the end of the water-spray test period, the rotation, the electrical supply, and the water spray shall be turned off and the device allowed to drain for 1 h in the closed cabinet.

3.2.3.7 Upon completion of the drain period, the interior of the device shall be observed for moisture accumulation. If a standing pool of water has formed, or can be formed by tapping or tilting the device, the accumulated moisture shall be extracted and measured.

3.2.3.8 Alternate Method for Determining Moisture Accumulation Within the Device—The device before testing shall be weighed and the weight in grams recorded. Upon the completion of the drain period the device shall be wiped dry of any exterior moisture and the device reweighed.

3.2.4 WATER-SUBMERSION MOISTURE TEST—This test procedure shall be used to test devices designed and marketed as sealed devices, without drain holes, vents, wicks, or other openings. The test evaluates the ability of the device to resist moisture leakage into the device.

3.2.4.1 Water-Submersion Moisture Test Equipment

3.2.4.1.1 A tank large enough to completely submerge the test sample to a depth of 50 mm measured from the top of the device is required.

3.2.4.1.2 The tank shall be filled with a mixture of water and wetting agent. The concentration of the mixture shall be sufficient to eliminate air bubble formation on the surface of the device.

3.2.4.2 Water-Submersion Moisture Test Procedures

3.2.4.2.1 The device shall be maintained at ambient room temperature until conditions have stabilized before testing.

3.2.4.2.2 The device shall be completely submerged to a depth of not less than 50 mm measured from the top of the device.

3.2.4.2.3 Test duration shall be 1 min.

3.2.4.2.4 The device shall be observed for air bubbles forming or escaping from the sealed portion of the device.

3.2.4.2.5 Throughout the test the tank temperature shall be maintained at a constant temperature 45 °C ± 3 °C above the stabilized device temperature.

3.3 Dust Test—This test evaluates the ability of the device to resist dust penetration which could significantly affect the photometric output of the sample device.

Devices meeting the requirements of the Water-Submersion Moisture Test need not be subjected to the dust test.

3.3.1 DUST TEST EQUIPMENT

3.3.1.1 The interior of the test chamber shall be cubical in shape with measurements of 0.9 to 1.5 m per side. The bottom may be hopper shaped to aid in collecting the dust.

3.3.1.2 The internal chamber volume, not including a hopper-shaped bottom, shall be 2 m^3 maximum and shall be charged with 3 to 5 kg of the test dust.

3.3.1.3 The chamber shall have the capability of agitating the test dust by means of compressed air or blower fans in such a way that the dust is diffused throughout the chamber.

3.3.1.4 The test dust used shall be fine-powdered cement in accordance with ASTM C 150-84.

3.3.2 DUST TEST PROCEDURES

3.3.2.1 The device shall be mounted and tested in the design position(s) (as mounted on the vehicle) and in accordance with the manufacturer's instruction.

3.3.2.2 All drain holes, slots, and other openings shall remain open during the test.

3.3.2.3 Devices which have a portion protected in service may have that portion of the exterior surface of the device protected in the same manner during the test.

3.3.2.4 Before the dust test, the luminous intensity at H-V shall be measured and the intensity recorded.

3.3.2.5 The mounted device shall be placed no closer than 150 mm from a wall of the dust chamber. Devices with a length exceeding 600 mm shall be horizontally centered in the test chamber.

3.3.2.6 The test dust shall be agitated as completely as possible by compressed air or blower(s) for 2 to 15 s at intervals of 15 min. The dust shall be allowed to settle between agitation periods.

3.3.2.7 The test duration is 5 h.

3.3.2.8 The device shall be lighted for the first 5 min of each hour.

When multiple function lamps are tested:

a. The major filament or major light source only of each shall be lighted.

b. If more than one light source is used in the device then the major filaments or major light source only of each shall be lighted.

c. For 6 V systems, use 6.4 V
   For 12 V systems, use 12.8 V
   For 24 V systems, use 25.6 V

3.3.2.9 Upon completion of the dust test, the exterior of the lamp shall be cleaned and the luminous intensity at H-V measured.

3.4 Corrosion Test—This test evaluates the ability of exterior-mounted devices to resist salt corrosion which would impair the functional characteristics of the device.

3.4.1 CORROSION TEST EQUIPMENT

3.4.1.1 A salt-spray (fog) cabinet, operating at the conditions specified by ASTM B 117 shall be used.

3.4.2 CORROSION TEST PROCEDURES

3.4.2.1 The device shall be mounted and tested in the design position(s) (as mounted on the vehicle) and in accordance with the manufacturer's instructions.

3.4.2.2 All drain holes, slots, and other openings shall remain open during the test.

3.4.2.3 Devices which have a portion protected in service may have that portion of the exterior surface of the device protected in the same manner during the test.

3.4.2.4 The test duration shall be 96 h.

3.4.2.5 The device shall be lighted for the first 5 min of each hour.

When multiple function lamps are tested:

a. The major filament or major light source only shall be lighted.

b. If more than one light source is used in the device then the major filament or major light source shall be lighted.

c. For 6 V systems, use 6.4 V
   For 12 V systems, use 12.8 V
   For 24 V systems, use 25.6 V

3.4.2.6 At the end of the corrosion test, the electrical supply shall be turned off and the device removed from the test cabinet and allowed to dry for 1 h.

3.5 Photometry Test—This test measures the luminous intensities at test points throughout the light distribution pattern as specified by the applicable SAE Technical Report for the sample device.

3.5.1 PHOTOMETRIC TEST EQUIPMENT

3.5.1.1 The positioner (goniometer) configuration shall be capable of positioning the sample device at the test point position specified in the applicable SAE Technical Report. The recommended goniometer configuration is specified as Type A as shown in Figure B1 of SAE J1330. Other systems may be used to achieve equivalent positioning, but it will be necessary at compound angles greater than 5 degrees from "H-V" to calculate the position which is equivalent to that of the recommended goniometer.

3.5.1.2 The photometer system shall consist of a sensor, amplifier, and indicator instrument. The system shall be capable of providing the luminous intensity reading (candela) of the output of the device being tested.

3.5.1.3 The sensor, unless otherwise specified, shall have a maximum effective area that will fit within a circle whose diameter is equal to 0.009 times the actual test distance from the light source of the device to the sensor. The sensor effective area is the actual area of intercepted light striking the detector surface of the photometer. For systems with lens(es) that change the diameter of the intercepter light beam before it reaches the actual detector surface, the maximum size requirements shall apply to the total area of light actually intercepted by the lens surface. The sensor shall be capable of intercepting all direct illumination from the largest illuminated dimension of the sample device at the test distance.

3.5.1.4 The color response of the photometer sensor shall be corrected to that of the 1931 CIE Standard observer (2 degree) Photopic Response Curve (ASTM E 308-85).

3.5.2 PHOTOMETRIC TEST PROCEDURE

3.5.2.1 The device shall be mounted and tested in the design position(s) (as mounted on the vehicle) and in accordance with the manufacturer's instruction.

3.5.2.2 Unless otherwise specified, accurate, rated bulbs shall be used. They shall be selected for accuracy as specified in SAE J387 and shall be operated at their design mean spherical candlepower.

3.5.2.3 Where special bulbs are used, they shall be aged in accordance with SAE J387 and operated at their design mean spherical candlepower.

3.5.2.4 If the design value of the mean spherical candlepower is not available, operate the light source at its specified design voltage.

3.5.2.5 If the design mean spherical candlepower of the bulb is intentionally modified from specifications for a device through internal or external circuitry, operate the bulb with the voltage-modification circuitry attached and with the specified design voltage applied to the input of the modification circuitry.

3.5.2.6 The test distance for measuring the luminous intensity shall be made at equal to, or greater than, the minimum test distance between the center of the light source (or the face of a reflex reflector) and the photometer sensor as specified in the SAE Technical Report applicable to the function of the sample device.

3.5.2.7 The locations of test points are specified in the applicable SAE Technical Report. The following nomenclature shall apply:

3.5.2.7.1 The letters "V" and "H" designate the vertical and horizontal planes intersecting both the center of the device light source (or center of a reflex reflector) and the goniometer axis.

3.5.2.7.2 A device using a bulb that has a major and a minor light source shall be oriented with respect to its major light source.

3.5.2.7.3 "H-V" designates the zero test point angle at the intersection of the "H" and "V" planes. Unless otherwise specified, this intersection shall be parallel to the longitudinal axis of the vehicle in the case of front and rear function devices and shall be horizontal and perpendicular to the longitudinal axis of the vehicle in the case of side function devices. The letters "U," "D," "L," and "R" (up, down, left, and right, respectively) designate the angular position in degrees from the H-V planes to the goniometer as viewed from a lamp or to the source of illumination as viewed from a reflex reflector.

3.5.2.7.4 The horizontal angle of the test point ("L" left and "R" right) is the angle between the vertical plane and the projection of the light ray from the device onto the horizontal plane.

3.5.2.7.5 The vertical angle of the test point ("U" up and "D" down) is the true angle between the horizontal plane and the light ray from the device.

3.5.2.7.6 The direction of an angular test point can be visualized when an observer stands behind the device and looks in the direction of the emanating light beam towards the photometer sensor when the device is properly aimed with respect to H-V.

It should be noted that when rotating the device on a goniometer, it is necessary to move the aim of the device from the H-V point in the opposite direction of the test point being measured. For example, to read a 5U-V test point, the goniometer shall aim the device 5 degrees down. A similar reversal applies to the down "D," left "L," and right "R" test points.

3.5.2.8 Photometric measurements shall be made with the light source(s) steady burning. The luminous intensity measurements, in candela, shall be recorded for each of the test points and zones specified for that function of the device being tested. Also, determine the minimum luminous intensity value between the two closest adjacent test points on a horizontal and vertical line.

3.6 Warpage Test for Devices With Plastic Components—This test evaluates the ability of the plastic components of the sample device to resist warpage due to ambient heat and heat from the light source.

3.6.1 WARPAGE TEST EQUIPMENT

3.6.1.1 A circulating air oven having a predominant direction of air flow shall be used with the air-flow inlet on one side of the interior test chamber and the exhaust air outlet on the opposite side of the chamber.

3.6.2 WARPAGE TEST PROCEDURE

3.6.2.1 The sample device shall be mounted and tested in the design position (as mounted on the vehicle) and in accordance with the manufacturer's instructions.

3.6.2.2 The oven temperature shall be maintained between 46 °C to 49 °C throughout the test.

3.6.2.3 The device shall be positioned at the center of the oven with the predominant direction of air flow parallel to the longitudinal axis of the vehicle for front and rear functioning devices and shall be horizontal and perpendicular to the longitudinal axis of the vehicle for side functioning devices.

3.6.2.4 Unless otherwise specified, the light source(s) shall be operated at design voltage and cycled as specified.

3.6.2.4.1 Cycle Times (minutes)—See Table 1.

TABLE 1—CYCLE TIMES (MINUTES)

Device	Steady Burn	5 On — 5 Off	Steady Flash
Clearance	x		
Identification	x		
Side Marker	x		
Tail	x		
Stop		x	
Front and Rear Turn Signal			x
Side Turn Signal			x
Illuminating	x		
High-Mounted Stop		x	
Back Up		x	
License Plate	x		

3.6.2.5 Test duration is 1 h.

3.6.2.6 The flash rate shall be between 80 and 100 flashes per minute with a 50% ± 2% on time.

3.6.2.7 Devices with multiple functions shall be tested with all functions simultaneously operating as specified, except for the backup function, which shall be tested separately. Stop and turn signal lamp combinations shall be tested as a stop lamp function only.

4. Performance Requirements

4.1 Vibration Requirements

4.1.1 Upon completion of the test, the device shall be examined. Any device showing evidence of material physical weakness, lens or reflector rotation, displacement or rupture of parts except bulb filament failures, shall be considered to have failed, except that rotation of lens or reflector shall not be considered as a failure when tests show compliance with specification despite such rotation.

4.2 Moisture

4.2.1 WATER-SPRAY REQUIREMENTS

4.2.1.1 For devices with an interior volume of 7000 mL or less, the accumulation of moisture shall not exceed 2.0 mL.

4.2.1.2 For devices with an interior volume greater than 7000 mL, the accumulation of moisture shall not exceed 0.03% of the total interior volume of the test device.

4.2.1.3 Alternate Method

4.2.1.3.1 For devices with an interior volume of 7000 mL or less, the increase in weight from the accumulation of moisture shall not exceed 2.0 g.

4.2.1.3.2 For devices with an interior volume greater than 7000 mL, the increase in weight from the accumulation of moisture shall not exceed 0.0003 g/mL of interior volume.

4.2.2 WATER SUBMERSION REQUIREMENTS

4.2.2.1 A device producing a steady flow of air bubbles, or the formation of three or more air bubbles in any 10 s period from anywhere on or around the device, is considered a failure.

4.3 Dust Requirements

4.3.1 The luminous intensity of the test lamp shall not be less than 90% of the lamp intensity before the test.

4.4 Corrosion Requirements

4.4.1 After removal from the Salt-Spray Cabinet and after the 1 h drying period, the device shall be visually examined for corrosion which could affect other tests contained in this document. If such corrosion is found, the affected test(s) shall be performed on the corroded sample to insure compliance.

4.5 Photometric Requirements

4.5.1 The luminous intensity values shall be within the limits specified in the applicable SAE Technical Report for the function being tested.

4.6 Warpage Requirements

4.6.1 Upon completion of the test, the device shall be visually examined for warpage of plastic components. If warpage is observed that could result in failure of other tests contained in this document, the test(s) shall be performed on the warped sample to insure compliance.

5. Notes

5.1 As a matter of information, attention is called to the following: SAE J1330, SAE J387, SAE J575, SAE J577, ASTM C 150-84, ASTM B 117-73, and ASTM E 308-85.

PHOTOMETRIC GUIDELINES FOR INSTRUMENT PANEL DISPLAYS THAT ACCOMMODATE OLDER DRIVERS —SAE J2217 OCT91

SAE Information Report

Report of the SAE Mature Driver Standards Committee approved October 1991.

1. Scope—Physical parameters that influence the legibility of an instrument panel display include letter/graphic size, the luminance and color difference between graphics and background, the observer's luminance adaptation level, and the level of glare present. Several aspects of visual functioning deteriorate as part of the normal aging process. These include a reduction in luminance and color contrast sensitivity, an increase in sensitivity to glare, a reduction in visual accommodation capacity, and a reduction in the sensitivity to light. This SAE Information Report provides introductory information that should be considered when setting photometric guidelines for instrument panel displays that are designed to accommodate the older driver. More detailed information is provided in Section 2 of this document.

2. References

2.1 Applicable Documents—The following publications form a part of this specification to the extent specified herein.

1. Wyszecki, G., and Stiles, W.S. (1982), *Color Science: Concepts and Methods, Quantitative Data and Formula* (2nd edition), New York: John Wiley and Sons.
2. Poynter, D. (1988), "The Effects of Aging on Perception of Visual Displays," SAE 881754, Warrendale, PA.
3. Poynter, D. (1991), "Contrast Sensitivity and English Letter Recognition," *Proceedings of the 1991 Human Factors Society Annual Meeting*, September 2-6, San Francisco, CA.
4. Blackwell, H.R. (1959), "Specification of interior illumination levels," *Journal of the Illuminating Engineering Society*, June, 317-353
5. Blackwell, O.M., and Blackwell, H.R. (1971), "Visual performance data for 156 normal observers of various ages," *Journal of the Illuminating Engineering Society*, October, 3-13.
6. Blackwell, O.M., and Blackwell, H.R. (1980), "Individual responses to lighting parameters for a population of 235 observers of varying ages," *Journal of the Illuminating Engineering Society*, July, 205-232.
7. Snyder, H.L., Lynch, E.F., Abernathy, C.N., Green, J.M., Helander, M.G., Hirsh, R.S., Hunt, S.R., Korell, D.D., Kroemer, K.H.E., Murch, G.M., Palacios, N.P., Palermo, S.A., Rinalducci, E.J., Rupp, B.A., Smith W., Wagner, G.N., Williams, R.D., Zwahlen, H.T. (1988), "American National Standard for Human Factors Engineering of Visual Display Terminal Workstations," The Human Factors Society Inc., Santa Monica, CA, ANSI/HFS 100-188.
8. Boynton, R.M., Rinalducci, E.J., and Sternheim, C. (1969), "Visibility losses produced by transient adaptational changes in the range from 0.4 to 4000 footlamberts," *Illuminating Engineering*, 217-227.
9. Osaka, N. (1985, July), "The effects of VDU color on visual fatigue in the fovea and periphery of the visual field," *Displays*, 138-140.
10. Matthews, M.L. (1987), "The influence of colour on CRT reading performance and subjective comfort under operational conditions," *Applied Ergonomics*, 18.4, 323-328.
11. Galer, M.D., and Simmonds, G.R.W. (1985), "The lighting of car instrument panels—drivers' responses to five colours," SAE 850328, Warrendale, PA.
12. Uchikawa, K., Uchikawa, H., and Kaiser, P.K. (1984), "Luminance and saturation of equally bright colors," *Color Research and Application*, 9(1), 5-14.
13. Poynter, D. (1988), "Variability in brightness matching of colored lights," *Human Factors*, 30(2), 143-151.

2.2 Terminology—The spectral power distribution of a light source can be described as a location in any one of several three-dimensional color spaces [1].[1] In most of these spaces, two of the dimensions correspond to the perceived color of the light. The third dimension (luminance) corresponds to the perceived intensity of the light. The luminance dimension can be thought of as representing perceptual brightness, although other factors aside from luminance can affect how bright a light source appears to be (e.g., the size of the source).

"Luminance Contrast" is a measure of the difference between the luminance of a display letter/graphic and the luminance of its spatially contiguous background. There are several commonly used indices of luminance contrast. The one used in this document is as in Equation 1:

$$\frac{L_{max} - L_{min}}{L_{min}} \qquad \text{(Eq. 1)}$$

where:

L_{max} and L_{min} are the larger and smaller of stimulus and background luminance, respectively.

The term *"Color Contrast"* refers to the difference in color between the letter/graphic and its background. There are several ways to quantify color contrast. One of the most common indices is the distance in color space between the coordinates for the letter/graphic and the coordinates for the background. In this document, luminance contrast and color contrast are considered separately; therefore the term color contrast refers to a two-dimensional distance across a plane in color space perpendicular to the luminance dimension.

Finally, the term *"Adaptation Luminance"* refers to the level of light that the driver's visual system is adapted to. In an automobile, for example, the adaptation luminance will most often be the average luminance of the driver's field of view through the windshield. During daytime driving, the adaptation luminance will typically be many times higher than the luminance of displays in the interior of the automobile.

3. Photometric Guidelines for IP Displays

3.1 Luminance Contrast—The minimum value of luminance contrast required to ensure display legibility is not a constant. It depends upon the amount of color contrast present, the size of letters/graphics, display luminance, adaptation luminance, driver age, and other contextual factors. For example, the studies of references [2,3] show that changing the height of display letters from 0.15 degrees to 0.3 degrees can reduce contrast requirements by a factor of 3. Contrast requirements for relatively dark ambient conditions (less than 0.1 cd/m²) can be 20 times greater than contrast requirements for moderate to bright conditions (greater than 50 cd/m²) [4,5,6]. Adding a color difference between letters and background also has a strong impact on minimum luminance contrast. For example, a distance between letters and background of 0.10 in the 1976 u′ v′ color plane can reduce luminance contrast requirements to 0.0. The effect of color contrast on legibility depends upon letter size and display luminance [3,7]. Color contrast improves legibility the most when letters/graphics are relatively large and display luminance is relatively high.

The presence of glare sources, and a difference between display luminance and adaptation luminance, can both increase contrast requirements dramatically [6,8]. Older drivers are much more sensitive to glare than are younger drivers.

Although there is no single value of contrast that is optimal for all viewing contexts, the fact that older drivers as a group require much higher contrast than younger drivers is well documented [2,3,5,6]. On average, drivers over 60 years old will require at least twice as much contrast as drivers under 30 years of age. This is true for daytime and nighttime visibility, but the differences between young and old are more dramatic at night.

3.2 Color Usage—When the background of a display letter/graphic is not black (i.e., when it has some perceivable luminance level), colors should be chosen for graphic and background that are distant from one another in color space. This will help to ensure adequate legibility.

Spectrally pure (i.e., monochromatic) blues and reds should be avoided for light emitting displays. Different wavelengths require different levels of visual accommodation (i.e., lens refractive indices). Using pure red and blue symbols within the same display can result in frequent refocusing of the eye, leading to visual fatigue and blurry images. Such color combinations can also produce a distance illusion in which one color appears to be closer than the other. These effects are more pronounced when letters/graphics are relatively high in luminance and placed against a low luminance background. Because visual accommodation is more difficult for the aging eye, using pure blues and reds (especially together on the same display) is more of a problem for the mature driver.

For CRT displays, red-blue phosphor combinations should also be

---

[1] The brackets represent the references.

avoided for letters and graphics. The eye sometimes focuses preferentially on one of these colors (usually red). The result, a fuzzy "halo" effect around the image (usually blue), can be visually annoying and can make the image hard to resolve.

3.3 Color Preference — In general, older drivers should find yellow and green colors easier to focus on than reds and blues, and most studies seem to indicate that older drivers prefer the mid-spectrum colors [2,9,10,11]. However, it is important to remember that spectral purity and intensity are very important factors that influence the acceptability of a display color for older drivers. Stating that designers should avoid blue altogether would therefore be inappropriate. Very pure, end-of-the-spectrum blue should be avoided for graphic colors, however. These wavelengths are hard to focus on, the older eye is relatively insensitive to them, and fine detail is especially difficult to resolve when illuminated with these wavelengths.

In general, the broader the spectral power distribution of the light emitted by the display, the less concerned designers need to be about the effects of color on display legibility.

3.4 Brightness Preference — Because the older eye scatters light more than the younger eye, older drivers are more sensitive to glare from instrument panel lighting during night driving. As a result, older drivers may actually prefer lower brightness levels for display lighting than younger drivers, despite the fact that the older eye is generally less sensitive to light than the younger eye [2]. To avoid discomfort glare problems for the older driver, allow the driver control over instrument panel light levels.

Also consider that the perceived brightness of display colors is not always consistent with the luminance of the color. Perceived brightness varies with the size of the display graphics, the predominant hue and the saturation of the color [2,12,13].

3.5 Gloss — For displays that may be exposed to bright ambient lighting (e.g., heater and air-conditioning control buttons, radio and wiper controls, etc.), the gloss of the display graphics and their backgrounds can have significant effects on display legibility. If the graphic color is lighter than the background color (e.g., a white graphic on a gray background) and the gloss of the background material is higher than that for the graphic, legibility of the display can be greatly reduced when viewed at specular angles. This legibility problem can be eliminated by making the graphic gloss higher than the background gloss. The background should be glossier than the graphic if the graphic color is darker than the background color.

FLASHING WARNING LAMPS FOR AUTHORIZED EMERGENCY, MAINTENANCE AND SERVICE VEHICLES—SAE J595 JAN90

SAE Recommended Practice

Report of the Lighting Committee, approved December 1948, completely revised August 1983. Rationale statement available. Reaffirmed by the Emergency Warning Devices Standards Committee January 1990.

1. Scope—This document provides design guidelines, test procedure references, and performance requirements for flashing incandescent warning lamps. It is intended to apply to, but is not limited to, surface land vehicles.

2. Purpose—The purpose of this document is to establish general requirements for flashing warning lamps for use on authorized emergency, maintenance, and service vehicles.

3. Definition—A flashing warning lamp is a lamp in which the light source is turned on and off by circuit interruption producing a repetitive flash of light which is directionally aimed and will project a flashing beam signal over a minimum area from 20 deg right to 20 deg left on a horizontal plane and from 10 deg up to 10 deg down on a vertical plane.

4. Test Procedures—The following sections of SAE J575, are a part of this document:

Section 2.1—Lighting Devices
Section 2.2—Bulbs
Section 2.3—Test Fixture
Section 3—Laboratory Facilities
Section 4.1—Vibration Test
Section 4.2—Moisture Test
Section 4.3—Dust Test
Section 4.4—Corrosion Test
Section 4.5—Color Test (See SAE J578)
Section 4.6—Photometry Test

Photometric measurements shall be made with the device mounted in its normal operating position and all luminous intensity measurements shall be made with the incandescent filament of the signal lamp 3 m or more from the photometer screen. The lamp shall be mounted so that the horizontal and vertical plane through the photometer axis also passes through the center of the test bulb filament. Photometry shall be done with the filament burning continuously.

Section 4.8—Warpage Test on Devices with Plastic Components:
A sample device shall be mounted in its normal operating position, operating at a flash rate of 1.50 Hz ± 0.17 with a 50% ± 2 current,

on time and at the voltage recommended by the bulb manufacturer in a circulating air oven for 1 h within a temperature range of 46 to 49°C.

5. Dimensional Requirements—The effective projected luminous area measured on a plane at right angles to the axis of the lamp shall be not less than 60 cm^2 .

6. General Requirements

6.1 Photometric Design Guidelines—Design guidelines are listed in Table 1—Photometric Design Guidelines.

6.2 Lighting Identification Code—The lighting identification code should be "W" in accordance with SAE J759.

7. Performance Requirements

7.1 Lighting Devices—Sample devices submitted for laboratory tests shall be representative of devices as regularly manufactured and marketed.

7.2 Bulbs—Requirements are based on laboratories using accurately rated bulbs operated at their designed mean spherical luminous intensity. Sealed units shall be seasoned (lighted) at 12.8 V for 1% of their rated average laboratory life or 10 h maximum prior to photometry and then operated at their design voltage. (For units designed to operate on other than a 12-V circuit, check manufacturer for proper seasoning schedule.)

7.3 Vibration—Upon completion of the test, there shall be no observed rotation, displacement, cracking, or rupture of parts of the test device (except bulb(s) and sealed beam unit internal components) that would result in failure of any other tests contained in Section 4 of SAE J575. Cracking or rupture of parts of the device affecting its mounting shall also constitute a failure.

7.4 Moisture—Upon completion of the test, the moisture accumulation in the test device shall be 2 mL or less. For devices with an interior volume greater than 7000 mL, the maximum allowable moisture ac-

TABLE 1—PHOTOMETRIC DESIGN GUIDELINES

Test Points, deg	Luminous Intensity, Candela		
	White	Yellow	Red
5L	80	40	20
10U-V	200	100	50
5R	80	40	20
20L	80	40	20
10L	200	100	50
5L	400	200	100
5U-V	600	300	150
5R	400	200	100
10R	200	100	50
20R	80	40	20
20L	120	60	30
10L	300	150	75
5L	800	400	200
H-V	1200	600	300
5R	800	400	200
10R	300	150	75
20R	120	60	30
20L	80	40	20
10L	200	100	50
5L	400	200	100
5D-V	600	300	150
5R	400	200	100
10R	200	100	50
20R	80	40	20
5L	80	40	20
10D-V	200	100	50
5R	80	40	20

TABLE 2—PHOTOMETRIC REQUIREMENTS

Zones	Test Points deg	Luminous Intensity, Candela		
		White Zone Total	Yellow Zone Total	Red Zone Total
1	5U-10L 5U-20L H-20L 5D-20L 5D-10L	600	300	150
2	10U-5L 10U-V 10U-5R	320	160	80
3	5U-5L H-10L 5D-5L	1000	500	250
4	5U-V H-5L H-V H-5R 5D-V	3600	1800	900
5	5U-5R H-10R 5D-5R	1000	500	250
6	10D-5L 10D-V 10D-5R	320	160	80
7	5U-10R 5U-20R H-20R 5D-20R 5D-10R	600	300	150

cumulation in the test device shall be 0.03% of the total interior volume of the test device.

7.5 Dust—On completion of the test, the test device shall be considered to have met all the requirements of the dust test when complying with either of the following requirements:

7.5.1 No dust shall be found on the interior surface of the test device, or

7.5.2 The ratio of the maximum luminous intensities (exterior only cleaned to exterior and interior cleaned) shall be a minimum of 0.9.

7.6 Corrosion—On completion of the test, there shall be no observed corrosion that would result in the failure of any other test contained in Section 4 of SAE J575.

7.7 Color—The color of the light emitted from the flashing warning lamps shall be white, yellow, or red as specified in SAE J578.

7.8 Photometry—The lamp shall meet the zonal photometric requirements of Table 2.

7.8.1 For the device to comply with the photometric performance requirements, the summation of the luminous intensity values shall meet the values specified in Table 2.

7.8.2 The measured luminous intensity at each test point shall be not less than 60% of the values specified in Table 1.

7.8.3 An adjustment in lamp orientation from the design position may be made in determining compliance to the performance photometric requirements, provided such adjustment does not exceed 3 deg in any direction. All zone totals must comply after reaim.

7.9 Warpage—Upon completion of the test, there shall be no observed warpage of plastic components of the test device that would result in the failure of any other test contained in Section 4 of SAE J575.

8. Plastic Material—Plastic materials used in optical parts shall comply with the requirements of SAE J576.

9. General Installation Recommendations—These general recommendations apply to the device as used on the vehicle and are not part of the performance requirements.

9.1 Front and rear warning lamps should be mounted as high and as far apart as practicable. The location of front warning lamps should be such that they can be clearly distinguished when the headlamps are lighted on the lower beam.

9.2 Visibility of the warning lamps should be unobstructed by any part of the vehicle 10 deg above to 10 deg below the horizontal and from 45 deg to the right to 45 deg to the left of the centerline of the vehicle.

9.3 There should be a visible or audible means of giving a clear and unmistakable indication to the driver when the warning lamps are turned "on."

9.4 To improve the efficiency of the signal, it is recommended that, where practical, the area surrounding the lamp should be black.

9.5 Flash Rate—The flash rate when observed from a fixed position shall be between 1.0–2.0 Hz—when operated at the voltage recommended by the manufacturer. The "on" period of the lamp shall be as specified in SAE J945 and/or SAE J1054.

APPENDIX A

Appendix A contains additional information considered useful in application to this document.

Attention is called to SAE J567, for requirements and gages to be used in socket design.

EMERGENCY WARNING DEVICE (TRIANGULAR SHAPE)—SAE J774 DEC89

SAE Standard

Report of Lighting Committee approved June 1961 and last revised January 1971. Completely revised by the Heavy Duty Lighting Standards Committee December 1989. Rationale statement available.

1. Scope—This document provides test procedures, performance requirements and guidelines for emergency warning devices (triangular shape) that are designed to be carried in motor vehicles and intended for highway use.

2. References

SAE J575 DEC88, Tests for Motor Vehicle Lighting Devices and Components

SAE J576 SEP86, Plastic Materials for Use in Optical Parts Such as Lenses and Reflectors of Motor Vehicle Lighting Devices

SAE J578 MAY88, Color Specification

SAE J594 MAY89, Reflex Reflectors

SAE J759 DEC87, Lighting Identification Code

SAE J774c revised January 1971 for information on "TYPE 2, DOT over DOT" Flare design

Federal Motor Vehicle Safety Standard 125

Federal Highway Administration Parts and Accessories Necessary for Safe Operation Subpart "H", 393.95, Emergency Equipment

3. Definitions

3.1 Emergency Warning Device—A triangular shaped device placed on the highway to warn the driver of an approaching vehicle of a stationary hazard (disabled vehicle) by reflection of light from the headlamps of the approaching vehicle at night or by a fluorescent area in the daytime.

3.2 Fluorescent—The property of emitting visible light due to the absorption of radiation of a shorter wavelength which may be outside the visible spectrum.

4. Identification Code

4.1 Emergency warning devices (triangular shape) may be identified by the code W4 in accordance with SAE J759.

5. Tests

5.1 Emergency warning device (triangular shape) sample submitted for test shall be representative of the device as regularly manufactured and marketed.

5.2 SAE J575 is a part of this document. The following tests are applicable with the modifications as detailed. All tests shall be run on a single device in the order listed. At the conclusion of all tests, the device shall be photometered and shall meet the specified photometric values.

5.2.1 VIBRATION TEST—The complete device in its opaque container shall be tested in the stored position. If a means is not provided to attach the device securely to the vehicle, the device in its container shall be vibration tested in a metal box on the test equipment with a clearance of 25 mm (1 in) to the closest surface of the device when the device is at rest.

5.2.2 DUST TEST—The device shall be tested in its functional position. All units shall be subjected to this test whether sealed or not sealed.

5.2.3 MOISTURE TEST—The device shall be tested in its functional position.

5.2.4 CORROSION TEST—The device shall be tested in its functional position.

5.2.5 PHOTOMETRIC TEST

5.2.5.1 Submit the warning device to the following conditioning sequence, returning the device after each step in the sequence to ambient air at 20°C (68°F) for at least 2 h.

5.2.5.1.1 Low Temperature Test—The device in its functional position shall be conditioned at −40°C ± 3 (−40°F ± 5) for 16 h in a circulating air chamber using ambient air, which would have not less than 30% and not more than 70% relative humidity at 20°C (70°F).

5.2.5.1.2 High Temperature Test—The device in its functional position shall be conditioned at 65°C ± 3 (150°F ± 5) for 16 h in a circulating air chamber using ambient air, which would have not less than 30% and not more than 70% relative humidity at 20°C (70°F).

5.2.5.1.3 Humidity Test—The device in its functional position shall be conditioned at 38°C (100°F) and 90% relative humidity for 16 h.

5.2.5.1.4 Immersion Test—The device in its functional position shall be immersed for 2 h in water at a temperature of 38°C (100°F).

5.2.5.2 *Reflex Reflector Area*—Prevent the orange fluorescent material from affecting the photometric measurements of the reflectivity of the reflex reflector by masking.

The device shall be tested in its functional position in accordance with SAE J594, except that the candela return for each side and at each test point shall be not less than the values specified in Table 1. The total area for each side of the device shall be photometered either in whole or in parts with particular caution regarding beam uniformity.

TABLE 1—PHOTOMETRIC REQUIREMENTS FOR THE RED REFLEX REFLECTOR AREA, EACH SIDE OF THE EMERGENCY WARNING DEVICE

Obs. Angle	Ent. Angle	Minimum Candela Per Incident Footcandle	Minimum Milli-Candela Per Incident Lux
0.2	V-10U	80	7430
	H-30L	8	745
	H-20L	40	3715
	H-V	80	7430
	H-20R	40	3715
	H-30R	8	745
	V-10D	80	7430
1.5	V-10U	0.8	74
	H-30L	0.08	7
	H-20L	0.4	37
	H-V	0.8	74
	H-20R	0.4	37
	H-30L	0.08	7

5.2.5.3 *Fluorescent Area*—Prevent the red reflex reflective material from affecting the photometric measurement of the luminance of the orange fluorescent material by masking.

Using a 150 watt high pressure xenon compact arc lamp as the light source, illuminate the test sample at an angle of incidence of 45 deg and an angle of observation of 90 deg. Measure the luminance of the material at a perpendicular viewing angle with no ray of the viewing beam more than 5 deg from the perpendicular to the specimen.

Repeat the procedure for a flat magnesium oxide surface, and compute the quotient (percentage) of the luminance of the material relative to that of the magnesium oxide surface.

5.3 Stability Test (Wind Test)—The device in its functional position shall be placed on a horizontal brushed concrete surface both with and against the brush marks and subjected to a horizontal wind of 65 km/h (40 mph). The wind shall be directed for 3 min in each position; perpendicular to the device face, first on one side and then the other side and then at three intermediate positions.

5.4 Color

5.4.1 REFLEX REFLECTOR AREA—The test sample may be either the reflex reflector or a disc of the same material, technique of fabrication, and dye formulation as the reflex reflector. If a disc is used, the thickness shall be twice the thickness of the reflector as measured from the face of the reflector to the apexes of the reflecting elements.

5.4.2 FLUORESCENT MATERIAL AREA—A 150 watt high pressure xenon compact arc lamp shall illuminate the sample using the unmodified spectrum at an angle of incidence of 45 deg and an observation of 90 deg.

6. Requirements

6.1 Material Requirements—The plastic material used in optical parts shall meet the requirements of SAE J576.

6.2 Performance Requirements—The device when tested in accordance with the test procedures of SAE J575 and with the modifications detailed in this document shall meet the following requirements:

6.2.1 VIBRATION—The reflex reflector sections shall show no evidence of surface abrasion at the conclusion of the test.

6.2.2 MOISTURE—There shall be no visible moisture within the device at the conclusion of the test.

6.2.3 PHOTOMETRIC

6.2.3.1 *Reflex Reflector*—Both before and after the device has been conditioned the intensity for each side shall be not less than the values specified in Table 1.

6.2.3.2 *Fluorescent*—Both before and after the device has been conditioned the relative luminance shall not be less than 25% of a flat magnesium oxide surface and a minimum product of that relative luminance and width in inches of 44.

6.2.4 COLOR

6.2.4.1 *Reflex Reflector Area*—The color of the reflected light shall be red, as specified in SAE J578.

6.2.4.2 *Fluorescent Area*—The fluorescent material shall be orange and shall have the following characteristics when the source of illumination is a 150 watt high pressure xenon compact arc lamp, expressed in terms of the International Commission on Illumination (CIE) 1931 standard colorimetric observer system. The chromaticity coordinates of the orange fluorescent material shall lie within the region bounded by the spectrum locus and the lines on the diagram defined by the following:

YELLOW	$y = 0.49x + 0.17$
WHITE	$y = 0.93 - x$
RED	$y = 0.35$

6.2.5 STABILITY TEST (WIND TEST)—No part of the device shall slide more than 75 mm (3 in) from its initial position.

The triangular portion shall not tilt to a position that is more than 10 deg from vertical.

The device shall not turn through a horizontal angle of more than 10 deg in either direction from the initial position.

6.2.6 DURABILITY—After all testing has been completed, the device shall be functional and no part of the device shall be warped or separated from the rest of the device.

6.3 Design Requirements

6.3.1 The emergency warning device (triangular shape) shall form an equilateral triangle and each side shall display both a daytime and a nighttime warning area. The device shall stand in a plane not more than 10 deg from the vertical, with the lower base of the triangle horizontal and not less than 25 mm (1 in) above the road surface.

6.3.2 The daytime warning shall be an orange fluorescent area meeting the color and luminance requirements specified.

6.3.3 The nighttime warning shall be a red retroreflective area meeting the color and photometric requirements specified.

6.3.4 Each of the three legs of the triangular portion of the warning device shall not be less than 430 mm (17 in) and not more than 560 mm (22 in) and not more than 75 mm (3 in) wide. See Figure 1.

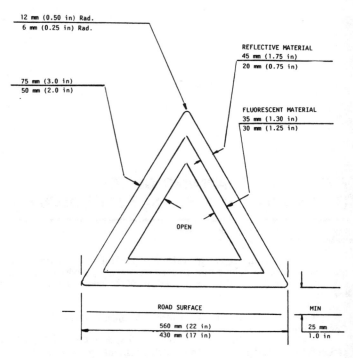

FIG. 1—DIMENSIONS OF THE EMERGENCY WARNING DEVICE (TRIANGULAR SHAPE)

6.3.5 Each face of the triangular portion of the warning device shall have an outer border of red reflex reflective material of uniform width not less than 20 mm (0.75 in) and not more than 45 mm (1.75 in) wide and an inner border of orange fluorescent material of uniform width not less than 30 mm (1.25 in) and not more than 35 mm (1.30 in) wide.

6.3.6 Each vertex of the triangular portion of the device shall have a radius of not less than 6 mm (0.25 in) and not more than 13 mm (0.5 in).

6.3.7 Each device shall have instructions for its erection and display. The instructions shall be either indelibly printed on the warning device or attached in such a manner that they cannot be easily removed.

6.3.8 The instructions shall include a recommendation that the driver activate the vehicular hazard warning signal lamps before leaving the vehicle to erect the warning devices.

6.3.9 Instructions shall include an illustration indicating the recommended positioning of the warning device on the highway. See Figure 2.

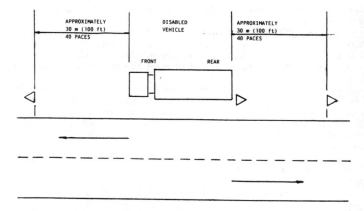

FIG. 2—RECOMMENDED WARNING DEVICE POSITIONING ON THE ROADWAY

360 DEGREE WARNING DEVICES FOR AUTHORIZED EMERGENCY, MAINTENANCE, AND SERVICE VEHICLES — SAE J845 MAR92   SAE Recommended Practice

Report of the Lighting Committee, approved January 1963, completely revised January 1984. Completely revised by the SAE Lighting Coordinating Committee and the SAE Emergency Warning Lamp and Devices Standards Committee March 1992. Rationale statement available.

1. Scope—This SAE Recommended Practice provides test procedures, requirements, and guidelines for single color, 360 degree warning devices.

2. References

2.1 Applicable Documents—The following publications form a part of this specification to the extent specified herein. The latest issue of SAE publications shall apply.

2.1.1 SAE PUBLICATIONS—Available from SAE, 400 Commonwealth Drive, Warrendale, PA 15096-0001.

SAE J575—Tests for Motor Vehicle Lighting Devices and Components

SAE J576—Materials for Use in Optical Parts Such as Lenses and Reflectors of Motor Vehicle Lighting Devices

SAE J578—Color Specification of Electric Signal Lighting Devices

SAE J590—Turn Signal Flashers

2.1.2 OTHER PUBLICATIONS

National Bureau of Standards Special Publication 480-16—Emergency Vehcle Warning Lights: State of the Arts

2.2 Definitions

2.2.1 360 DEGREE WARNING DEVICE—A device that projects light in a horizontal 360 degree arc. It will appear to project a regularly repeating pattern of flashes to an observer positioned at a fixed location. Its function is to inform other highway users to stop, yield right-of-way, or indicate the existence of a hazardous situation.

2.2.2 ROTATING SIGNAL DEVICE—A warning device in which the beam or beams rotate either because one or more lamps rotate around fixed axes or because one or more lenses, reflectors, or mirrors rotate around fixed 360 degree light sources projecting light through a 360 degree arc.

2.2.3 OSCILLATING SIGNAL DEVICE—A warning device in which the beam or beams oscillate (turn back and forth) through fixed angles, either because one or more lamps oscillate around fixed axes or because one or more lenses, reflectors, or mirrors oscillate around fixed 360 degree light sources projecting light though a 360 degree arc.

2.2.4 FLASHING SIGNAL DEVICE—A warning device in which the light source is turned on and off through circuit interruption producing repetitive flashes of light to all points on a 360 degree arc.

2.2.5 PRIMARY WARNING DEVICE—Devices or groups of devices that are intended to provide the primary visual warning signal as called out in each service class. Unless prohibited by law or regulation, a Class 1 device may be used in place of Class 2 device and a Class 1 or 2 device in place of Class 3 device.

2.2.6 SECONDARY WARNING DEVICES—Devices or groups of devices of lower performance that can be used to provide supplemental warning to that provided by the primary warning device or devices.

2.2.7 CLASS 1 WARNING DEVICES—Primary warning devices for use on authorized emergency vehicles responding to emergency situations. These devices are utilized to capture the attention of motorists and pedestrians and warn of a potentially hazardous activity or situation.

2.2.8 CLASS 2 WARNING DEVICES—Primary warning devices for use on authorized maintenance or service vehicles to warn of traffic hazards such as a lane blockage or slow moving vehicle.

2.2.9 CLASS 3 WARNING DEVICES—Primary warning devices for use on vehicles authorized to display a warning device for identification only.

3. Lighting Identification Code—360 Degree warning devices may be identified by the codes:

a. W3-1, Class 1

b. W3-2, Class 2

c. W3-3, Class 3

in accordance with SAE J759.

4. Tests

4.1 SAE J575 is a part of this report. The following tests are applicable with the modifications as indicated.

All tests are to be made at 12.8 V dc for devices intended for operation on 12.8 V systems and 25.6 V dc for 24 V systems.

4.1.1 VIBRATION TEST

4.1.2 MOISTURE TEST

4.1.3 DUST TEST

4.1.4 CORROSION TEST

4.1.5 PHOTOMETRY—In addition to the test procedures in SAE J575, the following apply:

4.1.5.1 *Flash Energy Method for Measuring Photometric Performance*—For 360 degree warning devices producing flashes of 0.125 s or less duration, photometric performance can be determined by measuring flash energy. The flash rate shall be measured and recorded at the end of the test.

4.1.5.1.1 *Alternate Method of Measuring Photometric Performance*—For 360 degree warning devices with a flash rate of 2 Hz or less, photometric performance can be determined by measuring the luminous intensity of the steady on light source (not flashing).

4.1.5.2 *Devices Flashed by Current Interruption*—Photometric measurements shall be made with the device mounted in its normal operating position and all measurements shall be made with the incandescent filament of the device at least 18 m from the photometer. The device shall be mounted so that the horizontal plane through the photometer axis passes through the center of the light source. The vertical axis through the center of the light source shall be perpendicular to this horizontal plane. The device shall be turned about its vertical axis until the photometer indicates minimum reading. This shall be the H-V point.

4.1.5.3 *Devices Flashed by Rotation or Oscillation*—Photometric measurements shall be made with the device mounted in its normal operating position and all measurements shall be made with the incandescent filament of the device at least 18 m from the photometer. The device shall be mounted so that the horizontal plane through the photometer axis passes through the center of the light source of the rotating element. The vertical axis through the center of rotation shall be perpendicular to this horizontal plane. The rotating element shall be turned about its vertical axis until the photometer indicates the maximum reading.

For a device with a symmetrical lens, filter, or lamp filament orientation, this shall be the H-V point.

For a device with an asymmetrical lens, filter, or lamp filament orientation, the H-V point shall be determined as previously stated after rotating the device about its vertical axis to determine the point of lowest photometric performance.

4.1.6 WARPAGE TEST FOR PLASTIC COMPONENTS

4.2 Color Test—SAE J578 is a part of this report.

4.3 Additional Tests

4.3.1 HIGH TEMPERATURE FLASH RATE TEST—The device shall be subjected to an ambient temperature of 50 °C ± 3 °C for a period of 6 h. The device shall be off (not operating) during the first hour and shall operate continuously for the next 5 h of the test. The flash range shall be measured before the test, not less than 3 min nor more than 4 min after the beginning of the second hour of the test, and not less than 3 min nor more than 4 min after the end of the test.

4.3.2 LOW TEMPERATURE FLASH RATE TEST—The device shall be subjected to an ambient temperature of -30 °C ± 3 °C for a period of 6 h. The device shall be off (not operating) during the first 5 h and shall operate continuously for the last hour of the test. The flash rate shall be measured before the test, not less than 3 min nor more than 4 min after the beginning of the last hour of the test, and not less than 3 min nor more than 4 min after the end of the test.

4.3.3 DURABILITY TEST—The device shall be operated continuously for 200 h at an ambient temperature of 25 °C ± 3 °C in cycles consisting of 50 min on and 10 min off. The flash rate shall be measured before the test and not more than 3 min after the last off period at the end of the test.

5. Requirements

5.1 Performance Requirements—A device, when tested in accordance with the test procedures specified in Section 4, shall meet the following requirements.

5.1.1 VIBRATION—SAE J575

5.1.2 MOISTURE—SAE J575

5.1.3 DUST—SAE J575

5.1.4 CORROSION—SAE J575

5.1.5 PHOTOMETRY—SAE J575

5.1.5.1 *Flash Energy*—The device shall meet the photometric requirements contained in Tables 1, 2, or 3, and Tables 4, 5, or 6, Photometric Requirements and their footnotes. The summation of the flash energy measurements at the specified test points in a zone shall be at least the value shown.

5.1.5.2 *Alternate Method*—The device shall meet the photometric requirements contained in Tables 7, 8, or 9 and Tables 10, 11, or 12, Photometric Requirements and their footnotes. The summation of the luminous intensity measurements at the specified test points in a zone shall be at least the value shown.

The steady-state totals for warning devices shown in the referenced Tables (7, 8, or 9, and 10, 11, or 12) apply to devices where two or more lamps, lenses, reflectors or mirrors rotate or oscillate around fixed axes.

5.1.5.3 For warning devices having only one lamp, lens, reflector or mirror, the steady-state zone totals and design guidelines shall be twice those shown in these Tables.

TABLE 1—PHOTOMETRIC REQUIREMENTS—CLASS 1 WARNING LAMPS

Zone	Test Points Degrees	Minimum Flash Energy Candela Seconds White	Minimum Flash Energy Candela Seconds Yellow	Minimum Flash Energy Candela Seconds Red	Minimum Flash Energy Candela Seconds Signal Blue
1	5U-V 2.1/2U-V H-V 2.1/2D-V 5D-V	396	198	99	99

Notes:

1. A one-time adjustment in lamp orientation from design position may be made in determining compliance to Tables 1 and 4, provided each adjustment does not exceed 1 degree in any direction. The same shall comply after this one time, final reaim.

2. The measured value at each test point shall not be less than 60% of the minimum values in Table 4.

TABLE 2—PHOTOMETRIC REQUIREMENTS—CLASS 2 WARNING LAMPS

Zone	Test Points Degrees	Minimum Flash Energy Candela Seconds White	Minimum Flash Energy Candela Seconds Yellow	Minimum Flash Energy Candela Seconds Red	Minimum Flash Energy Candela Seconds Signal Blue
1	5U-V 2.1/2U-V H-V 2.1/2D-V 5D-V	99	49.5	25	25

Notes:

1. A one-time adjustment in lamp orientation from design position may be made in determining compliance to Tables 2 and 5, provided such adjustment does not exceed 1 degree in any direction. The zone shall comply after this one time, final reaim.

2. The measured value at each test point shall not be less than 60% of the minimum values in Table 5.

5.1.6 WARPAGE—SAE J575

5.1.7 COLOR—The color of light emitted shall be white, yellow, red, or signal blue as specified in SAE J578.

5.2 Material Requirements—Plastic materials used in optical parts shall meet the requirements of SAE J576.

5.3 Additional Requirements

5.3.1 HIGH TEMPERATURE—There shall be no evidence of operating conditions which would result in failure to comply with Section 5 of this document. The flash rate at each of the required measurements shall be not less than 0.8 Hz nor more that 133% of the flash rate measured per 4.1.5.1.

However, if photometric performance was determined using the Alternate Method in 4.1.5.1.1, the flash rate at each of the required measurements shall be not less than 0.8 Hz nor more that 2.2 Hz.

5.3.2 LOW TEMPERATURE—There shall be no evidence of operating conditions which would result in failure to comply with Section 5 of this document. The flash rate at each of the required measurements shall be not less than 0.8 Hz nor more than 133% of the flash rate measured per 4.1.5.1.

However, if photometric performance was determined using the Alternate Method in 4.1.5.1.1, the flash rate at each of the required measurements shall be not less than 0.8 Hz nor more than 2.2 Hz.

5.3.3 DURABILITY—There shall be no evidence of operating conditions which would result in failure to comply with Section 5 of this document. The flash rate at each of the required measurements shall be not less than 1 Hz nor more than 133% of the flash rate measured in 4.1.5.1 up to a maximum of 4 Hz.

However, if photometric performance was determined using the Alternate Method in 4.1.5.2, the flash rate at each of the required measurements shall be not less than 1 Hz nor more than 2 Hz.

6. Guidelines

6.1 Photometric

6.1.1 FLASH ENERGY—For devices tested in accordance with 4.1.5.1, the Photometric Design Guidelines are contained in Tables 4, 5, or 6.

6.1.2 ALTERNATE METHOD—For devices tested in accordance with 4.1.5.1.1, the Photometric Design Guidelines are contained in Tables 10, 11, or 12.

6.2 Installation Guidelines—The following guidelines apply to 360 degree warning lamps as used on the vehicle and shall not be considered part of the requirements.

6.2.1 MOUNTING—The vertical axis of the device shall be installed normal to the longitudinal axis of the vehicle.

6.2.2 VISIBILITY—Visibility of the 360 degree warning lamp should be unobstructed by any part of the vehicle 5 degrees above to 5 degrees below the horizontal and provide a flashing light throughout a 360 degree circle.

6.2.3 INDICATOR—There should be a visible or audible means of giving a clear and unmistakable indication to the driver when the warning lamps are turned on and functioning normally.

6.2.4 "ON" TIME—For current interrupted devices the on period of the lamp shall be as specified in SAE J590.

APPENDIX A

Following the procedure outlined in the National Bureau of Standards Special Publication 480-16 entitled, Emergency Vehicle Warning Lights: State of the Arts, it is possible to directly calculate the flash energy produced by the sealed beam lamp typically used in rotating warning lights and which is used as the basis for the steady-state photometry tables.

In section 10.6 NBS demonstrates that the effective intensity (I_e) of a 360 degree warning lamp utilizing two sealed beam lamps having a 4.5 degree wide by 11 degree tall beam spread producing 90 fpm (45 rpm) is equal to 4.4% of the peak steady-state intensity (I).

Current definition of effective intensity (I_e) is:

$$I_e = \max_{t_1, t_2} \frac{\int_{t_1}^{t_2} I(t)dt}{0.2 + (t_2 - t_1)} \qquad \text{(Eq. A1)}$$

where:

I_e = the effective intensity of the flashing light

$I(t)$ = the instantaneous actual intensity of the light at the time (t) during the course of a single flash

t_1 and t_2 = the beginning and ending times of the useful, higher intensity portion of the flash

0.2 = constant

$\max_{t_1, t_2}$ = the maximum value obtainable through variation of both t_1 and t_2

TABLE 3 — PHOTOMETRIC REQUIREMENTS — CLASS 3 WARNING LAMPS

Zone	Test Points Degrees	Minimum Flash Energy Candela Seconds White	Minimum Flash Energy Candela Seconds Yellow	Minimum Flash Energy Candela Seconds Red	Minimum Flash Energy Candela Seconds Signal Blue
1	5U-V 2.1/2U-V H-V 2.1/2D-V 5D-V	40	20	10	10

Notes:

1. A one-time adjustment is lamp orientation from design position may be made in determining compliance to Tables 3 and 6, provided such adjustment does not exceed 1 degree in any direction. The zone shall comply after this one time, final reaim.

2. The measured value at each test point shall not be less than 60% of the minimum values in Table 6.

TABLE 4 — PHOTOMETRIC DESIGN GUIDELINES — CLASS 1 WARNING LAMPS

Zone	Test Points Degrees	Minimum Flash Energy Candela Seconds White	Minimum Flash Energy Candela Seconds Yellow	Minimum Flash Energy Candela Seconds Red	Minimum Flash Energy Candela Seconds Signal Blue
1	5U-V	10	9	4.5	4.5
	2.1/2U-V	90	45	22.5	22.5
	H-V	180	90	45	45
	2.1/2D-V	90	45	22.5	22.5
	5D-V	10	9	4.5	4.5

TABLE 5 — PHOTOMETRIC DESIGN GUIDELINES — CLASS 2 WARNING LAMPS

Zone	Test Points Degrees	Minimum Flash Energy Candela Seconds White	Minimum Flash Energy Candela Seconds Yellow	Minimum Flash Energy Candela Seconds Red	Minimum Flash Energy Candela Seconds Signal Blue
1	5U-V	4.5	2	1	1
	2.1/2U-V	22.5	11.5	6	6
	H-V	45	22.5	11	11
	2.1/2D-V	22.5	11.5	6	6
	5D-V	4.5	2	1	1

TABLE 6 — PHOTOMETRIC DESIGN GUIDELINES — CLASS 3 WARNING LAMPS

Zone	Test Points Degrees	Minimum Flash Energy Candela Seconds White	Minimum Flash Energy Candela Seconds Yellow	Minimum Flash Energy Candela Seconds Red	Minimum Flash Energy Candela Seconds Signal Blue
1	5U-V	1	1	0.5	0.5
	2.1/2U-V	9	4.5	2	2
	H-V	18	9	5	5
	2.1/2D-V	9	4.5	2	2
	5D-V	1	1	0.5	0.5

TABLE 7 — PHOTOMETRIC REQUIREMENTS (ALTERNATE METHOD) — CLASS 1 WARNING LAMPS

Zone	Test Points Degrees	Minimum Luminous Intensity Zone Totals Candela White	Minimum Luminous Intensity Zone Totals Candela Yellow	Minimum Luminous Intensity Zone Totals Candela Red	Minimum Luminous Intensity Zone Totals Candela Signal Blue
1	5U-V 2.1/2U-V H-V 2.1/2D-V 5D-V	39 600	19 800	9 900	9 900

Notes:

1. A one-time adjustment in lamp orientation from design position may be made in determining compliance to Tables 7 and 10 provided such adjustment does not exceed 1 degree in any direction. The zone shall comply after this one time, final reaim.

2. The measured value of each test point shall not be less than 60% of the minimum values in Table 10.

TABLE 8 — PHOTOMETRIC REQUIREMENTS (ALTERNATE METHOD) — CLASS 2 WARNING LAMPS

Zone	Test Points Degrees	Minimum Luminous Intensity Zone Totals Candela White	Minimum Luminous Intensity Zone Totals Candela Yellow	Minimum Luminous Intensity Zone Totals Candela Red	Minimum Luminous Intensity Zone Totals Candela Signal Blue
1	5U-V 2.1/2U-V H-V 2.1/2D-V 5D-V	9 900	4 950	2 475	2 475

Notes:

1. A one-time adjustment in lamp orientation from design position may be made in determining compliance to Tables 8 and 11 provided such adjustment does not exceed 1 degree in any direction. The zone shall comply after this one time, final reaim.

2. The measured value at each test point shall not be less than 60% of the minimum values in Table 11.

TABLE 9 — PHOTOMETRIC REQUIREMENTS (ALTERNATE METHOD) — CLASS 3 WARNING LAMPS

Zone	Test Points Degrees	Minimum Luminous Intensity Zone Totals Candela White	Minimum Luminous Intensity Zone Totals Candela Yellow	Minimum Luminous Intensity Zone Totals Candela Red	Minimum Luminous Intensity Zone Totals Candela Signal Blue
1	5U-V 2.1/2U-V H-V 2.1/2D-V 5D-V	3 960	1 980	990	990

Notes:

1. A one-time adjustment in lamp orientation from design position may be made in determining compliance to Tables 9 and 12 provided such adjustment does not exceed 1 degree in any direction. The zone shall comply after this one time, final reaim.

2. The measured value of each test point shall not be less than 60% of the minimum values in Table 12.

TABLE 10 — PHOTOMETRIC DESIGN GUIDELINES (ALTERNATE METHOD) — CLASS 1 WARNING LAMPS

Zone	Test Points Degrees	Minimum Luminous Intensity Steady-State Beam Candela White	Minimum Luminous Intensity Steady-State Beam Candela Yellow	Minimum Luminous Intensity Steady-State Beam Candela Red	Minimum Luminous Intensity Steady-State Beam Candela Signal Blue
1	5U-V	1 000	900	450	450
	2.1/2U-V	9 000	4 500	2 250	2 250
	H-V	18 000	9 000	4 500	4 500
	2.1/2D-V	9 000	4 500	2 250	2 250
	5D-V	1 000	900	450	450

TABLE 11—PHOTOMETRIC DESIGN GUIDELINES (ALTERNATE METHOD)—CLASS 2 WARNING LAMPS

Zone	Test Points Degrees	Minimum Luminous Intensity Steady-State Beam Candela White	Minimum Luminous Intensity Steady-State Beam Candela Yellow	Minimum Luminous Intensity Steady-State Beam Candela Red	Minimum Luminous Intensity Steady-State Beam Candela Signal Blue
	5U-V	250	225	113	113
	2.1/2U-V	2 250	1 125	562	562
1	H-V	4 500	2 250	1 125	1 125
	2.1/2D-V	2 250	1 125	562	562
	5D-V	250	225	113	113

TABLE 12—PHOTOMETRIC DESIGN GUIDELINES (ALTERNATE METHOD)—CLASS 3 WARNING LAMPS

Zone	Test Points Degrees	Minimum Luminous Intensity Steady-State Beam Candela White	Minimum Luminous Intensity Steady-State Beam Candela Yellow	Minimum Luminous Intensity Steady-State Beam Candela Red	Minimum Luminous Intensity Steady-State Beam Candela Signal Blue
	5U-V	180	90	45	45
	2.1/2U-V	900	450	225	225
1	H-V	1 800	900	450	450
	2.1/2D-V	900	450	225	225
	5D-V	180	90	45	45

In this equation, $\int_{t_1}^{t_2} I(t)\,dt$ is the flash energy contained in the signal from one lamp, candela seconds.

Following the NBS sample calculation 4.5 degree beam spread lamp rotating at 45 rpm (90 fpm) has a flash interval of:

$$\frac{4.5 \text{ degrees} \times 60 \text{ s/min}}{360\ \frac{\text{deg}}{\text{rev}} \times 45\ \frac{\text{rev}}{\text{min}}} = 0.0167 \text{ s} \qquad \text{(Eq. A2)}$$

Thus, for a 20 000 cd lamp having a beam spread of 4.5 degree wide and rotating at 45 rpm (90 fpm), the flash energy (candela seconds) can be calculated as follows in equation A3:

Flash Energy (candela second)

$$\text{Flash Energy} = \int_{t_1}^{t_2} I(t)dt \qquad \text{(Eq. A3)}$$
$$= I_e \times [0.2 + (t_2 - t_1)]$$

$$= \frac{I_e}{I_o} \times I \times [0.2 + (t_2 - t_1)]$$
$$= (0.044)(20\ 000)(0.2 + 0.0167) = 190.7 \text{ cd s}$$

Rounding this value to 200 cd s yields the relationship of flash energy being numerically equal to 1% of peak intensity for the typical sealed beam lamp traditionally used in 360 degree rotating warning lamps, having a beam spread of 4.5 degree horizontal by 11 degree vertical and flashing at 90 fpm.

R) SCHOOL BUS WARNING LAMPS
—SAE J887 MAY96

Report of the Lighting Committee approved July 1964, and completely revised August 1987. Rationale statement available. Completely revised by the SAE Emergency Warning Devices Standards Committee of the SAE Lighting Coordinating Committee May 1996. Rationale statement available.

1. Scope—This SAE Standard provides test procedures, requirements, and guidelines for red and yellow school bus warning lamps.

2. References

2.1 Applicable Documents—The following publications form a part of this specification to the extent specified herein. Unless otherwise specified, the latest issue of SAE publications shall apply.

2.1.1 SAE PUBLICATIONS—Available from SAE, 400 Commonwealth Drive, Warrendale, PA 15096-0001.

SAE J575—Test Methods and Equipment for Lighting Devices and Components for Use on Vehicles Less Than 2032 mm in Overall Width

SAE J576—Plastic Materials for Use in Optical Parts Such as Lenses and Reflectors of Motor Vehicle Lighting Devices

SAE J578—Color Specification

SAE J602—Headlamp Aiming Device for Mechanically Aimable Headlamp Units

SAE J759—Lighting Identification Code

SAE J760a—Dimensional Specifications for General Service Sealed Lighting Units

SAE J1054—Warning Lamp Alternating Flashers

SAE J1383—Performance Requirements for Motor Vehicle Headlamps

3. Definitions

3.1 School bus red warning lamps are lights alternately flashing at 1 to 2 Hz per lamp, mounted horizontally both front and rear, intended to inform other users of the highway that such vehicle is stopped on highway to take on or discharge school children.

3.2 School bus yellow warning lamps are lights alternately flashing at 1 to 2 Hz per lamp, mounted horizontally both front and rear, intended to inform other users of the highway that such vehicle is about to stop to take on or discharge school children.

4. Lighting Identification Code—Lamps conforming to this document may be identified with the code W2 in accordance with SAE J759.

5. Tests

5.1 SAE J575 is part of this document. The following tests are applicable with the modifications as indicated:

5.1.1 VIBRATION TEST

5.1.2 MOISTURE TEST

5.1.3 DUST TEST

5.1.4 CORROSION TEST

5.1.5 PHOTOMETRY TEST

5.1.5.1 All photometric measurements shall be made with the filament of the lamp at a distance of at least 3 m from the photometric screen. The lamp axis shall be taken as the horizontal line through the light source parallel to what would be the longitudinal axis of the vehicle, if the lamp were mounted in its normal position on the vehicle.

5.1.5.2 The school bus warning lamp shall be operated at design voltage.

5.1.5.3 An optional alternate measure of photometric performance can be made using flash energy.

5.1.5.3.1 The device shall be allowed to operate for 15 min prior to making photometric measurements. In all instances where a device is required to be operated during a test specified in this document, the voltage applied to the input wires or terminals of the device shall be 12.8 V for nominal 12 V electrical systems and 25.6 V for nominal 24 V electrical systems.

5.1.5.3.2 Photometric luminous intensity measurements (candela seconds) shall be taken as the average of ten consecutive flash cycles. There shall be an off time before each flash of at least 50% of the total flash cycle time.

5.1.6 Warpage test on device with plastic components.

5.2 SAE J578—Color Specification is a part of this document.

5.3 Sealed Units as described in SAE J760a and SAE J1383 designed for use as school bus warning lamps, when tested without the other parts of the lamp assembly, need only be tested to 5.1.1 and 5.1.5.

6. Requirements

6.1 Performance Requirements—A device, when tested in accordance with the test procedures specified in Section 5, shall meet the following requirements. Sealed units, as described in SAE J760a and SAE J1383 when tested without the other parts of the lamp assembly, need only comply with 6.1.1, 6.1.5, and 6.1.6.

6.1.1 VIBRATION—SAE J575.

6.1.2 MOISTURE—SAE J575.

6.1.3 DUST—SAE J575.

6.1.4 CORROSION—SAE J575.

6.1.5 PHOTOMETRY—SAE J575.

6.1.5.1 The lamp under test shall meet the photometric performance requirements contained in Table 1 and its footnotes. The summation of the luminous intensity measurements at the specified test points in a zone shall be at least the value shown.

6.1.5.2 Alternate Method—The lamp under test shall meet the photometric performance requirements contained in Table 3 and its footnotes. The summation of the flash energy measurements at the specified test points in a zone shall be at least the value shown.

6.1.6 WARPAGE—SAE J575.

6.1.7 COLOR—The lamp shall comply with the red or yellow requirements specified in SAE J578.

6.2 Material Requirements—Any plastic materials used in optical parts shall comply with the requirements in SAE J576.

6.3 Design Requirements

6.3.1 The functional lighted lens area of a school bus warning lamp shall not be less than 120 cm^2.

6.3.2 Sealed units if used shall comply dimensionally with SAE J1383 for sealed beam lamps.

6.3.3 AIMING PROVISIONS—The lamp shall be equipped with aiming pads, as described in SAE J760a or SAE J1383 on the lens face suitable for use with mechanical headlamp aimers as described in SAE J602. The lamp shall be designed so that with the aiming plane normal to the photometric axis, the beam shall meet the photometric specifications of Table 1.

7. *Guidelines*—The mounting and use of school bus warning lamps are specified by various legal agencies. The following guidelines, if followed, will enhance performance of the system and uniformity in use throughout the various jurisdictional agencies. They are not part of the test provisions, specifications, requirements, or procedures.

7.1 Photometric Design Guidelines for School Bus Warning Lamps, when tested in accordance with 5.1.5 of this document, are contained in Tables 2 and 4.

7.2 The yellow lamps should be automatically deactivated and the red lamps activated when the vehicle is stopped to take on or discharge school children.

7.3 For circuit interrupted incandescent filament devices, see SAE J1054. The "on" period of the flasher should be long enough to permit a bulb filament to approach full brightness.

7.4 There should be a visible or an audible means of giving a clear and unmistakable indication to the driver when the warning lamps are activated.

7.5 Front and rear warning lamps should be spaced as far apart laterally as practical with the yellow lamps mounted inboard of the red lamps. In no case should the spacing between the inboard lamps be less than 1000 mm, as measured from the nearest edge of the lens.

TABLE 1—PHOTOMETRIC PERFORMANCE REQUIREMENTS SCHOOL BUS WARNING LAMPS

Zone	Test Point Degree	Test Point Degree	Minimum Total Zonal Luminous Intensity (Candela) Red	Minimum Total Zonal Luminous Intensity (Candela) Yellow
	H	30L		
	5D	30L		
1	5U	20L	590	1475
	H	20L		
	5D	20L		
	10U	5L		
2	10U	V	90	225
	10U	5R		
	5U	10L		
	5U	5L		
3	5U	V	1500	3750
	5U	5R		
	5U	10R		
	H	10L		
	H	5L		
4	H	V	2400	6000
	H	5R		
	H	10R		
	5D	10L		
	5D	5L		
5	5D	V	1950	4875
	5D	5R		
	5D	10R		
	10D	5L		
6	10D	V	120	300
	10D	5R		
	5U	20R		
	H	20R		
7	5D	20R	590	1475
	H	30R		
	5D	30R		

NOTES

a. For the lamp to conform to the photometric zonal performance requirements, the summation of the candela measurements at the specific test points in a zone shall meet or exceed the value specified for that zone in Table 1.

b. The measured candela at each test point shall not be less than 60% of the requirements specified in Table 2.

c. An adjustment in lamp aim from design position may be made, provided that such adjustment does not exceed 3 degrees. All zones shall comply after final re-aim.

d. See Figure 1 for a graphical description of the zonal boundaries.

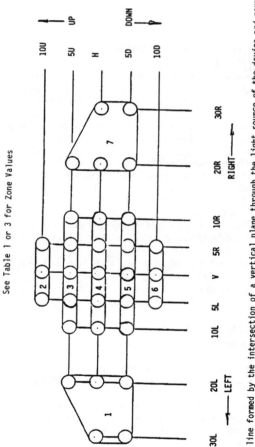

FIGURE 1—GRAPHICAL DESCRIPTION OF THE ZONAL BOUNDARIES

See Table 1 or 3 for Zone Values

The line formed by the intersection of a vertical plane through the light source of the device and normal to the test screen is designated V. The line formed by the intersection of a horizontal plane through the light source and normal to the test screen is designated H. The point of intersection of these two lines is designated H-V. The other points on the test screen are measured in terms of degree from these two lines. Degrees to the right (R) and to the left (L) are regarded as being to the right and left of the vertical line when the observer stands behind the lighting device and looks in the direction of the emanating light beam when the device is properly aimed for photometry with respect to the H-V point. Similarly, the upward angles designated as U and the downward angles designated D, refer to light emanating at angles above and below the horizontal line, respectively.

TABLE 2—PHOTOMETRIC DESIGN GUIDELINES
SCHOOL BUS WARNING LAMPS

Test Point Degree	Test Point Degree	Minimum Luminous Intensity (Candela) Red	Minimum Luminous Intensity (Candela) Yellow
	5L	20	50
10U	V	50	125
	5R	20	50
	20L	150	375
	10L	300	750
	5L	300	750
5U	V	300	750
	5R	300	750
	10R	300	750
	20R	150	375
	30L	30	75
	20L	180	450
	10L	400	1000
	5L	500	1250
H	V	600	1500
	5R	500	1250
	10R	400	1000
	20R	180	450
	30R	30	75
	30L	30	75
	20L	200	500
	10L	300	750
	5L	450	1125
5D	V	450	1125
	5R	450	1125
	10R	300	750
	20R	200	500
	30R	30	75
	5L	40	100
10D	V	40	100
	5R	40	100

NOTES

a. An adjustment in lamp aim from design position may be made provided that such adjustment does not exceed 3 degrees. The lamp should meet or exceed the values specified in Table 2 after final re-aim.

b. See Figure 2 for a graphical description of photometric design guidelines.

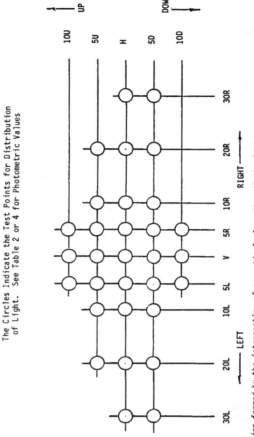

The Circles Indicate the Test Points for Distribution of Light. See Table 2 or 4 for Photometric Values

The line formed by the intersection of a vertical plane through the light source of the device and normal to the test screen is designated V. The line formed by the intersection of a horizontal plane through the light source and normal to the test screen is designated H. The point of intersection of these two lines is designated H-V. The other points on the test screen are measured in terms of degree from these two lines. Degrees to the right (R) and to the left (L) are regarded as being to the right and left of the vertical line when the observer stands behind the lighting device and looks in the direction of the emanating light beam when the device is properly aimed for photometry with respect to the H-V point. Similarly, the upward angles designated as U and the downward angles designated D, refer to light emanating at angles above and below the horizontal line, respectively.

FIGURE 2—GRAPHICAL DESCRIPTION OF THE PHOTOMETRIC GUIDELINES

7.6 The warning lamps should be mounted on the same horizontal centerline as high as practical at the front above the windshield and on the same horizontal centerline as high as practical at the rear so that the lower edge of the lenses is not lower than the top line of the side window openings.

7.7 The visibility of the front warning lamps to the front, and of the rear warning lamps to the rear, should be unobstructed by any part of the vehicle from 10 degrees above to 10 degrees below horizontal and from 30 degrees to the right to 30 degrees to the left of the centerline of the lamps.

7.8 To improve the effectiveness of the signal, the area of the vehicle immediately surrounding the warning lamp extending outward approximately 70 mm should be painted black.

7.9 The lamps should be mounted on the school bus with their aiming plane vertical and normal to the vehicle longitudinal axis. If lamps are aimed or inspected with a mechanical headlamp aimer, the graduation settings for aim should be 0 down and 0 sideways. The limits for inspection should be from 5 up to 5 down and from 10 right to 10 left.

8. Test Equipment Guidelines—The following guidelines apply to photometric test equipment and are not part of the technical requirements for the lamps:

8.1 A pulse integrating photometer or other accepted means of measuring pulsed light signals should have the following:

a. Response Time—1 μs or less.

b. Sensor Response—Sensor should be corrected to that of the 1931 C.I.E. standard observer (2 degrees) photopic response curve. Sensor should be calibrated for the color of the light being measured.

c. Range Linearity—Linearity of the sensor and photometer system should be verified over the range of the luminous intensities being tested. Linearity deviation should not exceed 2.5% from the calibration level to the extreme luminous intensity values measured.

8.2 The regulated DC power supply should have the following minimum requirement:

a. Line regulations: ±0.1%

b. Load regulation: ±0.1%

c. Ripple voltage: ±1.4%

d. Stability: ±0.1% during test

TABLE 3—PHOTOMETRIC PERFORMANCE REQUIREMENTS (ALTERNATE METHOD)
SCHOOL BUS WARNING LAMPS

Zone	Test Point Degree	Test Point Degree	Minimum Total Zonal Flash Energy (Candela Seconds) Red	Minimum Total Zonal Flash Energy (Candela Seconds) Yellow
1	H	30L		
	5D	30L		
	5U	20L	141	351
	H	20L		
	5D	20L		
2	10U	5L		
	10U	V	22	54
	10U	5R		
3	5U	10L		
	5U	5L		
	5U	V	360	890
	5U	5R		
	5U	10R		
4	H	10L		
	H	5L		
	H	V	571	1426
	H	5R		
	H	10R		
5	5D	10L		
	5D	5L		
	5D	V	465	1157
	5D	5R		
	5D	10R		
6	10D	5L		
	10D	V	30	72
	10D	5R		
7	5U	20R		
	H	20R		
	5D	20R	141	351
	H	30R		
	5D	30R		

NOTES

a. For the lamp to conform to the photometric zonal performance requirements, the summation of the flash energy measurements at the specific test points in a zone shall meet or exceed the value specified for that zone in Table 3.

b. The measured flash energy at each test point shall not be less than 60% of the requirements specified in Table 4.

c. An adjustment in lamp aim from design position may be made, provided that such adjustment does not exceed 3 degrees. All zones shall comply after final re-aim.

d. See Figure 1 for a graphical description of the zonal boundaries.

TABLE 4—PHOTOMETRIC DESIGN GUIDELINES
SCHOOL BUS WARNING LAMPS

Test Point Degree	Test Point Degree	Minimum Flash Energy (Candela Seconds) Red	Minimum Flash Energy (Candela Seconds) Yellow
10U	5L	5	12
	V	12	30
	5R	5	12
5U	20L	36	89
	10L	72	178
	5L	72	178
	V	72	178
	5R	72	178
	10R	72	178
	20R	36	89
H	30L	7	18
	20L	43	107
	10L	95	238
	5L	119	297
	V	143	356
	5R	119	297
	10R	95	238
	20R	43	107
	30R	7	18
5D	30L	7	18
	20L	48	119
	10L	72	178
	5L	107	267
	V	107	267
	5R	107	267
	10R	72	178
	20R	48	119
	30R	7	18
10D	5L	10	24
	V	10	24
	5R	10	24

NOTES

a. An adjustment in lamp aim from design position may be made provided that such adjustment does not exceed 3 degrees. The lamp should meet or exceed the values specified in Table 2 after final re-aim.

b. See Figure 2 for a graphical description of photometric design guidelines.

Report of the Lighting Committee approved April 1976, and completely revised April 1984. Rationale statement available. Completely revised by the Lighting Coordinating Committee July 1989. Rationale statement available. Completely revised by the Emergency Warning Devices Standards Committee of the SAE Lighting Coordinating Committee May 1996. Rationale statement available.

1. Scope—This SAE Recommended Practice provides test procedures, requirements, and guidelines for school bus stop arms.

2. References

2.1 Applicable Documents—The following publications form a part of this specification to the extent specified herein. Unless otherwise specified, the latest issue of SAE publications shall apply.

2.1.1 SAE PUBLICATIONS—Available from SAE, 400 Commonwealth Drive, Warrendale, PA 15096-0001.

SAE J575—Tests for Motor Vehicle Lighting Devices and Components

SAE J576—Plastic Materials for Use in Optical Parts Such as Lenses and Reflectors of Motor Vehicle Lighting Devices

SAE J578—Color Specification

SAE J759—Lighting Identification Code

SAE J887—School Bus Warning Lamps

SAE J1054—Warning Lamp Alternating Flashers

3. Definition

3.1 A **school bus stop arm** is an auxiliary device used to signal that a school bus has stopped to load or discharge passengers. It supplements devices specified by SAE J887.

4. Lamps for use on school bus stop arms may be identified by the code "W6" in accordance with SAE J759.

5. Tests

5.1 SAE J575 is a part of this document. The following tests are applicable, with the modifications indicated:

5.1.1 VIBRATION TEST

5.1.2 MOISTURE TEST

5.1.3 DUST TEST

5.1.4 CORROSION TEST

5.1.5 PHOTOMETRY—In addition to the test procedures in SAE J575, the following apply:

5.1.5.1 Photometric measurements shall be made with the light source(s) of the lamp(s) at least 18 m from the photometer. The H-V axis shall be taken as parallel to the longitudinal axis of the vehicle.

5.1.5.2 Photometric measurements shall be made with the bulb filament steadily burning.

5.1.5.3 An optional alternate measure of photometric performance can be made using flash energy.

5.1.5.3.1 Photometric measurements shall be made with the device in its normal operating position and all flash energy measurements shall be made with the light source at least 18 m from the photometer sensor. The H-V axis shall be taken as parallel to the longitudinal axis of the vehicle.

5.1.5.3.2 The voltage applied to the input wires or terminals of the device shall be 12.8 V for nominal 12 V electrical systems and 25.6 V for nominal 24 V electrical systems.

5.1.5.3.3 Photometric luminous intensity measurements (candela seconds) shall be taken as the average of ten consecutive flash cycles.

5.1.6 WARPAGE TEST FOR DEVICES WITH PLASTIC COMPONENTS

5.2 Color Test—SAE J578 is a part of this document.

5.3 Durability—The device shall be subjected to a test of 45 000 cycles at a rate not to exceed 0.2 Hz and at a temperature of 25 °C ± 3 °C. A cycle shall consist of movement from the parked or retracted position to the fully extended position and return to the parked position.

6. Requirements

6.1 Performance Requirements—A device, when tested in accordance with the test procedures specified in Section 5, shall meet the following requirements:

6.1.1 VIBRATION—SAE J575

6.1.2 MOISTURE—SAE J575

6.1.3 DUST—SAE J575

6.1.4 CORROSION—SAE J575

6.1.5 Photometry—In addition to the requirements of SAE J575, the school bus stop arm lamps shall meet the following photometric performance requirements:

6.1.5.1 The summation of the luminous intensity readings of the specific test points in a zone shall meet the values in Table 1.

TABLE 1—PHOTOMETRIC PERFORMANCE REQUIREMENTS

Zone	Test Points (degrees)	Minimum Total Zonal Luminous Intensity (cd)
1	10U-5L 5U-20L 5D-20L 10D-5L	52
2	5U-10L H-10L 5D-10L	100
3	5U-V H-5L H-V H-5R 5D-V	380
4	5U-10R H-10R 5D-10R	100
5	10U-5R 5U-20R 5D-20R 10D-5R	52

NOTES

1. For the lamp to conform to the photometric zonal performance requirements, the summation of the candela measurements at the specific test points in a zone shall meet or exceed the values specified for that zone in Table 1.
2. When calculating the zone total, the measured candela for a test point shall not be less than 60% of the value specified for that test point in Table 2.
3. See Figure 1 for a graphical description of the Zonal Boundaries.

6.1.5.2 When calculating the zone total, the measured luminous intensity for a test point shall not be less than 60% of the value specified for that test point in Table 2.

6.1.5.3 Alternate Method—The lamp under test shall meet the photometric performance requirements contained in Table 3. The summation of the flash energy measurements at the specified test points in a zone shall be at least the value shown. When calculating the zone total, the measured flash energy for a test point shall not be less than 60% of the value specified for that test point in Table 4.

6.1.6 WARPAGE—SAE J575

6.1.7 COLOR—The color of light emitted from the school bus stop arm lamps shall be red as specified in SAE J578.

6.1.8 DURABILITY—Failure of the device to operate in the intended electrical or mechanical manner during or at the conclusion of the test shall constitute a failure. Internal bulb failure shall not be considered a failure of the device.

6.1.9 FLASH RATE

6.1.9.1 For circuit-interrupted incandescent devices, the two lamps on each face shall flash alternately with the rate and percent "on" time as required in SAE J1054.

6.1.9.2 For gaseous discharge lamps, the two lamps on each face shall flash alternately with the flash rate not less than 0.80 Hz nor more than 2.2 Hz. There shall be an off time before each flash of at least 50% of the total flash cycle time.

6.2 Material Requirements—Plastic materials used in the optical parts shall meet the requirements of SAE J576.

6.3 Design Requirements

6.3.1 A school bus stop arm shall have on both the front and rear the word "STOP" in letters which are at least 150 mm in height and have a stroke width of at least 20 mm.

6.3.2 School bus stop arms shall have a minimum of two lamps to the front and two lamps to the rear, or two double-faced lamps may be used.

6.3.3 Lamps shall be activated at the commencement of the stop arm extension cycle and deactivated when the stop arm is retracted.

6.3.4 The functional lighted lens area of each lamp shall not be less than 75 cm² (12 in²).

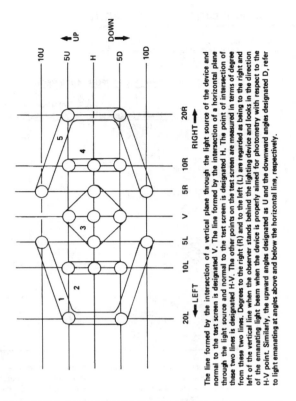

GRAPHICAL DESCRIPTION OF THE ZONAL BOUNDARIES

The line formed by the intersection of a vertical plane through the light source of the device and normal to the test screen is designated V. The line formed by the intersection of a horizontal plane through the light source and normal to the test screen is designated H. The point of intersection of these two lines is designated H-V. The other points on the test screen are measured in terms of degree from these two lines. Degrees to the right (R) and to the left (L) are regarded as being to the right and left of the vertical line when the observer stands behind the lighting device and looks in the direction of the emanating light beam when the device is properly aimed for photometry with respect to the H-V point. Similarly, the upward angles designated as U and the downward angles designated D, refer to light emanating at angles above and below the horizontal line, respectively.

FIGURE 1—GRAPHICAL DESCRIPTION OF THE ZONAL BOUNDARIES

TABLE 2—PHOTOMETRIC DESIGN GUIDELINES

Test Points (degrees)		Minimum Luminous Intensity (cd)
10U, 10D	5L, 5R	16
	V	70
5U, 5D	10L, 10R	30
	20L, 20R	10
	V	80
H	5L, 5R	80
	10L, 10R	40

NOTES

1. Any photometric measurements that fall below 60% of the test point value given in Table 2 shall not be used in the calculation of zone totals.
2. The luminous intensity values (candela) specified in Table 2 have been established by empirical and field evaluation techniques for lighting devices to perform their intended function in field service.
3. See Figure 2 for a graphical description of Photometric Design Guidelines.

7. Guidelines

7.1 Photometric design guidelines for lamps used on school bus stop arms, when tested in accordance with 5.1.5, are contained in Table 2 or in Table 4.

7.2 Installation Guidelines—The following apply to school bus stop arms as used on the vehicle, and shall not be considered part of the requirements.

7.2.1 The school bus stop arm should be installed on the left outside of the bus body and be mounted so as to be seen readily by motorists approaching from either the front or rear of the bus.

7.2.2 If the device is operated by a manual switch, that switch shall be located so as to be easily accessible to the driver.

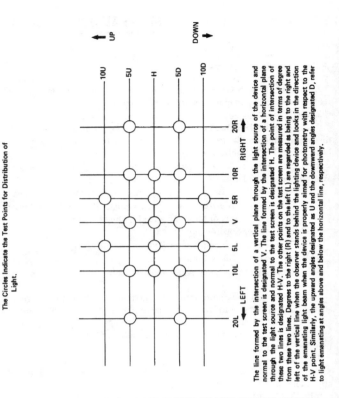

The Circles Indicate the Test Points for Distribution of Light.

The line formed by the intersection of a vertical plane through the light source of the device and normal to the test screen is designated V. The line formed by the intersection of a horizontal plane through the light source and normal to the test screen is designated H. The point of intersection of these two lines is designated H-V. The other points on the test screen are measured in terms of degree from these two lines. Degrees to the right (R) and to the left (L) are regarded as being to the right and left of the vertical line when the observer stands behind the lighting device and looks in the direction of the emanating light beam when the device is properly aimed for photometry with respect to the H-V point. Similarly, the upward angles designated as U and the downward angles designated D, refer to light emanating at angles above and below the horizontal line, respectively.

FIGURE 2—GRAPHICAL DESCRIPTION OF THE PHOTOMETRIC GUIDELINES

7.3 Design Guidelines

7.3.1 The lamps should be located in the extreme top and bottom portions of the stop arm, one above the other.

7.3.2 It is recommended that the word "STOP" be displayed as white letters against a red background, and that the stop arm have the shape of a regular octagon which is at least 450 x 450 mm. The octagon should have a white border at least 12 mm wide. The maximum extension should not exceed 560 mm beyond the left side of the vehicle. The school bus stop arm may also optionally be reflectorized.

7.3.3 The two lamps on each face should flash alternately with a flash rate of 1 to 2 Hz.

8. Test Equipment Guidelines—The following apply to photometric test equipment and is not part of the technical requirements:

8.1 A pulse integrating photometer or other accepted means of measuring pulsed light signals should have the following:

a. Response Time—1 μs or less.

b. Sensor Response—Sensor should be corrected to that of the 1931 CIE standard observer (2 degrees) photopic response curve. Sensor should be calibrated for the color of the light being measured.

c. Range Linearity—Linearity of the sensor and photometer system should be verified over the range of the luminous intensities being tested. Linearity deviation should not exceed 2.5% from the calibration level to the extreme luminous intensity values measured.

8.2 The regulated DC power supply should have the following minimum requirements:

a. Line Regulation: ±0.1%

b. Load Regulation: ±0.1%

c. Ripple Voltage: ±1.4%

d. Stability: ±0.1% during test

TABLE 3—PHOTOMETRIC PERFORMANCE REQUIREMENTS

Zone	Test Points (degrees)	Minimum Total Zonal Flash Energy Candela-Second
1	10U-5L 5U-20L 5D-20L 10D-5L	14
2	5U-10L H-10L 5D-10L	26
3	5U-V H-5L H-V H-5R 5D-V	96
4	5U-10R H-10R 5D-10R	26
5	10U-5R 5U-20R 5D-20R 10D-5R	14

NOTES

1. For the lamp to conform to the photometric zonal performance requirements, the summation of the candela-second measurements at the specific test points in a zone shall meet or exceed the values specified for that zone in Table 3.
2. When calculating the zone total, the measured candela-second for a test point shall not be less than 60% of the value specified for that test point in Table 4.
3. See Figure 1 for a graphical description of the Zonal Boundaries.

TABLE 4—PHOTOMETRIC DESIGN GUIDELINES

Test Points (degrees)		Minimum Flash Energy Candela-Second
10U, 10D	5L, 5R	4
5U, 5D	V 10L, 10R 20L, 20R	18 8 3
H	V 5L, 5R 10L, 10R	20 20 10

NOTES

1. Any photometric measurements that fall below 60% of the test point value given in Table 4 shall not be used in the calculation of zone totals.
2. The flash energy values (candela-seconds) specified in Table 4 have been established by empirical and field evaluation techniques for lighting devices to perform their intended function in field service and calculations.
3. See Figure 2 for a graphical description of Photometric Design Guidelines.

GASEOUS DISCHARGE WARNING LAMP FOR AUTHORIZED EMERGENCY, MAINTENANCE, AND SERVICE VEHICLES—SAE J1318 APR86

SAE Recommended Practice

Report of the Lighting Committee approved April 1986. Rationale statement available.

1. Scope—This SAE Recommended Practice provides test procedures, requirements, and guidelines for single color gaseous discharge warning lamps.

2. Definitions

2.1 Light Pulse—A sudden emission of light of short duration and high intensity.

2.2 Light Flash—A single light pulse or a train of pulses. In order to be considered a flash all pulse peaks must occur within 100 ms.

2.3 Gaseous Discharge Warning Lamp—A device that produces a regularly repeating pattern of light flashes when electrical current is discharged periodically through an ionized gas.

2.4 360 Deg Warning Lamp—A lamp that projects a light in a horizontal 360 deg arc. It will appear to project a regularly repeating pattern of flashes to an observer positioned at a fixed location. Its function is to inform other highway users to stop, yield right-of-way, or to indicate the existence of a hazardous situation.

2.5 Directional Warning Lamp—A lamp that produces a repetitive flash of light which is directionally aimed and will project a flashing beam signal over a minimum area from 20 deg right to 20 deg left on a horizontal plane and from 10 deg up to 10 deg down on a vertical plane.

2.6 Primary Warning Lamps—Lamps or groups of lamps that are intended to provide the primary visual warning signal as called out in each service class.

2.7 Secondary Warning Lamps—Lamps or groups of lamps that can be used to provide a supplemental warning signal for each service class.

2.8 Class 1 Warning Lamps—Primary warning lamps for use on authorized emergency vehicles responding to emergency situations. These lamps are utilized to capture the attention of motorists and pedestrians and to warn of a potentially hazardous activity or situation.

2.9 Class 2 Warning Lamps—Primary warning lamps for use on authorized maintenance and service vehicles to warn of traffic hazards such as an accident, slow moving service truck, etc.

2.10 Class 3 Warning Lamps—Primary warning lamps for use on vehicles that are authorized to display flashing warning lamps for identification only.

2.11 Flash Energy—Flash energy is the total luminous energy per unit solid angle contained in the entire flash in candela seconds.

$$\text{candela-second} = \int_{t_1}^{t_2} I\, dt$$

where: I = Instantaneous intensity (candela)

t_1 = Time at start of flash (seconds)

t_2 = Time at end of flash (seconds)

$(t_2 - t_1)$ = Flash Duration (seconds)

2.12 Light Center—The light center of a gaseous discharge warning lamp is the geometric center of the light emitting element (arc or light source) of the lamp.

2.13 Flash Cycle—A sequence of light flashes and dark intervals which, with regular repetition, constitutes the complete output cycle of a flashing lamp. For a simple flashing lamp, the full cycle consists of a single on-off sequence.

3. Lighting Identification Code—Gaseous discharge warning lamps may be identified in accordance with SAE J759, Lighting Identification Code, by the codes:

360 deg gaseous discharge lamps

(W5–1)—Class 1

(W5–2)—Class 2

(W5–3)—Class 3

Directional gaseous discharge lamps

(W5)—

4. Tests

4.1 SAE J575, Tests for Motor Vehicle Lighting Devices and Components, is a part of this report. The following tests are applicable with modifications as indicated:

4.1.1 VIBRATION TEST

4.1.2 MOISTURE TEST

4.1.3 DUST TEST

4.1.4 CORROSION TEST

4.1.5 PHOTOMETRY—In addition to the photometric test procedures in SAE J575, the following apply:

4.1.5.1 The device shall be allowed to operate for 15 min prior to making photometric measurements. In all instances where a device is required to be operated during a test specified in this report, the voltage applied to the input wires or terminals of the device shall be 12.8 V for nominal 12 V electrical systems and 25.6 V for nominal 24 V electrical systems.

4.1.5.2 *Photometric Measurement for 360 Deg Gaseous Discharge Warning Lamps*—Photometric measurements shall be made with the device mounted in its normal operating position and all flash energy measurements shall be made with the light source of the signal lamp at least 18 m from the photometer sensor. The lamps shall be mounted so that the horizontal plane through the photometer axis passes through the center of the light source. The vertical axis through the center of light source shall be perpendicular to this horizontal plane.

The lamp shall be turned about its vertical axis until the photometer indicates minimum flash energy. This shall be the H-V point.

4.1.5.3 *Photometric Measurement for Directional Gaseous Discharge Warning Lamps*—Photometric measurements shall be made with the device mounted in its normal operating position and all flash energy measurements shall be made with the light source of the warning lamp at least 18 m from the photometer sensor. The lamps shall be mounted so that the horizontal plane through the photometer sensor axis passes through the center of the light source. The vertical axis through the center of the light source shall be perpendicular to this horizontal plane.

4.1.5.4 Photometric luminous intensity measurements (candela seconds) shall be taken as the average of ten consecutive flash cycles. There shall be an off time before each flash of at least 50% of the total flash cycle time.

4.1.6 Warpage Test on Device with Plastic Components—The test described in paragraph 4.8.3.3 of SAE J575 shall be omitted and the following test conducted:

4.1.6.1 *Flash Tube Operation*—Unless otherwise specified, the gaseous discharge device shall be operated at design voltage and in a steady on, flashing operation.

4.2 Color Test—SAE J578, Color Specification for Electric Signal Lighting Devices, is a part of this report. Devices shall be tested with the light source normally supplied with the lamp. When it is not feasible to make measurements with this light source, a steady burning CIE Illuminant C (6774 K) light source shall be substituted.

4.3 Additional Tests

4.3.1 High Temperature Flash Rate Test—The device shall be subjected to an ambient temperature of 50 ± 3°C for a period of 6 h. The device shall be off during the first hour and shall operate continuously for the next 5 h at 12.8 V for a nominal 12 V system and 25.6 V for a nominal 24 V system. The flash rate shall be measured before the test, not less than 3 min nor more than 4 min after the beginning of the second hour of the test, and not less than 3 min nor more than 4 min after the end of the test.

4.3.2 Low Temperature Flash Rate Test—The device shall be subjected to an ambient temperature of −30 ± 3°C for a period of 6 h. The device shall be off during the first 5 h and shall operate continuously for the last hour of the test at 12.8 V for a nominal 12 V system and 25.6 V for a nominal 24 V system.

The flash rate shall be measured before the test, not less than 3 min nor more than 4 min after the beginning of the last hour of the test, and not less than 3 min nor more than 4 min after the end of the test.

4.3.3 Durability Test—The device shall be operated continuously for 200 h at an ambient temperature of 25 ± 3°C in cycles of 50 min on and 10 min off at 12.8 V for a nominal 12 V system and 25.6 V for a nominal 24 V system. The flash rate shall be measured before the test and not more than 3 min after the last off period at the end of the test.

5. Requirements

5.1 Performance Requirements—A device when tested in accordance with the test procedures specified in Section 4 shall meet the following requirements in SAE J575:

5.1.1 Vibration
5.1.2 Moisture
5.1.3 Dust
5.1.4 Corrosion
5.1.5 Photometry—The lamp under test shall meet the photometric performance requirements contained in Tables 1, 2, 3, and 4. The summation of the flash energy measurements at the specified test points in a zone shall be at least the value shown.
5.1.6 Warpage—Shall meet the requirements of paragraph 4.8.4 of SAE J575.
5.1.7 Color—The color of the light emitted shall be white, yellow, red, or signal blue as specified in SAE J578.

5.2 Material Requirements—Plastic materials used in optical parts shall meet the requirements of SAE J576, Plastic Material for Use in Optical Parts such as Lenses and Reflectors of Motor Vehicle Lighting Devices.

5.3 Additional Requirements

5.3.1 High Temperature—There shall be no evidence of operating conditions which would result in failure to comply with Section 5. After the unit has been allowed to operate for 3 min after the high temperature test, the flash rate shall not be less than 0.80 Hz nor more than 2.2 Hz.

5.3.2 Low Temperature—There shall be no evidence of operating conditions which would result in failure to comply with Section 5. The lamp must flash and continue to flash within 20 s after the current is turned on or it is considered a failure. After the unit has been allowed to operate for 3 min after the low temperature test, the flash rate shall not be less than 0.80 Hz nor more than 2.2 Hz.

5.3.3 Durability—There shall be no evidence of operating conditions which would result in failure to comply with Section 5. The flash rate shall be measured before the test and not more than 3 min after the last off period at the end of the test. The flash rate shall be not less than 1 Hz nor more than 2 Hz.

TABLE 2

PHOTOMETRIC REQUIREMENTS CLASS 2
360 DEG GASEOUS DISCHARGE WARNING LAMPS

Minimum Flash Energy Requirements
Zone Totals (Candela-Seconds)

Zone	Test Point Degree	Flash Energy—Candela Seconds			
		White	Yellow	Red	Signal Blue
#1	5U–V 2.5U–V H–V 2.5D–V 5D–V	99	49.5	25	12.5

Notes:
a. A one time adjustment in lamp orientation from design position may be made in determining compliance to Tables 5, 6, 7, and 8 provided such adjustment does not exceed 1 deg in any direction. The zone shall comply after this one time, final reaim.
b. When calculating zone totals, the measured value at each test point shall not be less than 60% of the minimum values in Tables 5, 6, 7, and 8.

TABLE 1

PHOTOMETRIC REQUIREMENTS CLASS 1
360 DEG GASEOUS DISCHARGE WARNING LAMPS

Minimum Flash Energy Requirements
Zone Totals (Candela-Seconds)

Zone	Test Point Degree	Flash Energy—Candela Seconds			
		White	Yellow	Red	Signal Blue
#1	5U–V 2.5U–V H–V 2.5D–V 5D–V	396	198	99	*

* Not Recommended.

Notes:
a. A one time adjustment in lamp orientation from design position may be made in determining compliance to Tables 5, 6, 7, and 8 provided such adjustment does not exceed 1 deg in any direction. The zone shall comply after this one time, final reaim.
b. When calculating zone totals, the measured value at each test point shall not be less than 60% of the minimum values in Tables 5, 6, 7, and 8.

TABLE 3

PHOTOMETRIC REQUIREMENTS CLASS 3
360 DEG GASEOUS DISCHARGE WARNING LAMPS

Minimum Flash Energy Requirements
Zone Totals (Candela-Seconds)

Zone	Test Point Degree	Flash Energy—Candela Seconds			
		White	Yellow	Red	Signal Blue
#1	5U–V 2.5U–V H–V 2.5D–V 5D–V	40	20	10	5

Notes:
a. A one time adjustment in lamp orientation from design position may be made in determining compliance to Tables 5, 6, 7, and 8 provided such adjustment does not exceed 1 deg in any direction. The zone shall comply after this one time, final reaim.
b. When calculating zone totals, the measured value at each test point shall not be less than 60% of the minimum values in Tables 5, 6, 7, and 8.

TABLE 4

PHOTOMETRIC REQUIREMENTS CLASS 1
DIRECTIONAL, GASEOUS DISCHARGE WARNING LAMPS

Minimum Flash Energy Requirements
Zone Totals (Candela-Seconds)

Zone	Test Point Degree	Flash Energy—Candela Seconds			
		White	Yellow	Red	Signal Blue
#1	5U–10L 5U–20L H–20L 5D–20L 5D–10L	108	54	27	*
#2	10U–5L 10U–V 10U–5R	56	28	14	*
#3	5U–5L H–10L 5D–5L	184	92	46	*
#4	5U–V H–5L H–V H–5R 5D–V	664	332	116	*
#5	5U–5R H–10R 5D–5R	184	92	46	*
#6	10D–5L 10D–V 10D–5R	56	28	14	*
#7	5U–10R 5U–20R H–20R 5D–20R 5D–10R	108	54	27	*

* Not Recommended.

NOTES:
a. A one time adjustment in lamp orientation from design position may be made in determining compliance to Tables 5, 6, 7, and 8 provided such adjustment does not exceed 1 deg in any direction. The zone shall comply after this one time, final reaim.
b. When calculating zone totals, the measured value at each test point shall not be less than 60% of the minimum values in Tables 5, 6, 7, and 8.

TABLE 5

PHOTOMETRIC DESIGN GUIDELINES
360 DEG GASEOUS DISCHARGE WARNING LAMPS

Minimum Design Flash Energy Guidelines
Class 1 Warning Lamps

Test Point Degree	Flash Energy—Candela-Seconds			
	White	Yellow	Red	Signal Blue
5U–V	18	9	4.5	*
2.5U–V	90	45	22.5	*
H–V	180	90	45	*
2.5D–V	90	45	22.5	*
5D–V	18	9	4.5	*

* Not Recommended.

TABLE 6

PHOTOMETRIC DESIGN GUIDELINES
360 DEG GASEOUS DISCHARGE WARNING LAMPS

Minimum Design Flash Energy Guidelines
Class 2 Warning Lamps

Test Point Degree	Flash Energy—Candela-Seconds			
	White	Yellow	Red	Signal Blue
5U–V	4.5	2	1	0.5
2.5U–V	22.5	11.5	6	3
H–V	45	22.5	11	5.5
2.5D–V	22.5	11.5	6	3
5D–V	4.5	2	1	0.5

TABLE 7

PHOTOMETRIC DESIGN GUIDELINES
360 DEG GASEOUS DISCHARGE WARNING LAMPS

Minimum Design Flash Energy Guidelines
Class 3 Warning Lamps

Test Point Degree	Flash Energy—Candela-Seconds			
	White	Yellow	Red	Signal Blue
5U–V	2	1	0.5	0.25
2.5U–V	9	4.5	2	1
H–V	18	9	5	2.5
2.5D–V	9	4.5	2	1
5D–V	2	1	0.5	0.25

TABLE 8

PHOTOMETRIC DESIGN GUIDELINES
DIRECTIONAL, GASEOUS DISCHARGE WARNING LAMPS

Minimum Flash Energy Guidelines
Warning Lamps

Test Point Degree	Flash Energy—Candela-Seconds			
	White	Yellow	Red	Signal Blue
10U–5L	12	6	3	*
10U–V	32	16	8	*
10U–5R	12	6	3	*
5U–20L	12	6	3	*
5U–10L	32	16	8	*
5U–5L	68	34	17	*
5U–V	100	50	25	*
5U–5R	68	34	17	*
5U–10R	32	16	8	*
5U–20R	12	6	3	*
H–20L	20	10	5	*
H–10L	48	24	12	*
H–5L	132	66	33	*
H–V	200	100	50	*
H–5R	132	66	33	*
H–10R	48	24	12	*
H–20R	20	10	5	*
5D–20L	12	6	3	*
5D–10L	32	16	8	*
5D–5L	68	34	17	*
5D–V	100	50	25	*
5D–5R	68	34	17	*
5D–10R	32	16	8	*
5D–20R	12	6	3	*
10D–5L	12	6	3	*
10D–V	32	16	8	*
10D–5R	12	6	3	*

* Not Recommended.

6. Guidelines

6.1 Photometric Guidelines—Photometric design guidelines for 360 deg and directional gaseous discharge warning lamps, when tested in accordance with Section 4.1.5 of this report, are contained in Tables 5, 6, 7, and 8.

6.2 Installation Guidelines—The following guidelines apply to 360 deg and directional gaseous discharge warning lamps as used on the vehicle and shall not be considered part of the requirements:

6.2.1 MOUNTING—The vertical axis of the lamp should be installed normal to the longitudinal axis of the vehicle.

6.2.2 VISIBILITY—Visibility of the 360 deg warning lamp should be unobstructed by any part of the vehicle 5 deg above to 5 deg below the horizontal and provide a flashing light throughout a 360 deg circle. Additional primary warning lamps may be used whenever vehicle size or design prevents a single primary warning lamp from projecting 360 deg of a full strength warning signal. These additional warning lamps shall be mounted so that the 360 deg of full strength signal is obtained around the vehicle.

Directional warning lamps should be mounted as high as practical and if mounted in pairs, as far apart as practical. Visibility to the front and to the rear of the vehicle should be unobstructed by any part of the vehicle from 10 deg up to 10 deg below horizontal and from 45 deg left to 45 deg right of the centerline of the vehicle. To improve the efficiency of the signal it is recommended that when practical, the area surrounding the lamps should be black.

6.2.3 INDICATOR—There should be a visible or audible means of giving a clear and unmistakable indication to the driver when the warning lamps are turned on and functioning normally.

7. *Test Equipment Guidelines*—The following guidelines apply to photometric test equipment and are not part of the technical requirements:

7.1 A pulse integrating photometer or other accepted means of measuring pulsed light signals shall have the following:

Response Time—1 μs or less

Sensor Response—Sensor shall be corrected to that of the 1931 C.I.E. standard observer (2 deg) photopic response curve. Sensor shall be calibrated for the color of the light being measured.

Range Linearity—Linearity of the sensor and photometer system shall be verified over the range of the luminous intensities being tested. Linearity deviation shall not deviate more than 2.5% from the calibration level to the extreme luminous intensity values measured.

7.2 The regulated D.C. power supply shall have the following minimum requirements:

Line regulations	±0.1%
Load regulation	±0.1%
Ripple voltage	±0.4%
Stability	±0.1% during test

References

ISO 4148, Road Vehicles—Special Warning Lights—Dimensions (1978).

NBS No. 480-3, Sirens and Emergency Warning Lights (June 1977).

NBS No. 480-36, Some Psychophysical Tests of the Conspicuities of Emergency Vehicle Warning Lights (July 1979).

NBS No. 480-37, Emergency Vehicle Warning Systems (May 1981).

SAE J595 AUG83.

SAE J845 JAN84.

EMERGENCY VEHICLE SIRENS—SAE J1849 AUG95   SAE Recommended Practice

Report of the Lighting Coordinating Committee approved July 1989. Rationale statement available. Revised by the Emergency Warning Devices Standards Committee and the SAE Lighting Coordinating Committee August 1995.

1. Scope—This SAE Recommended Practice provides test procedures, requirements, and guidelines for electronic and electromechanical sirens for use on authorized emergency vehicles. It is based on the performance of state-of-the-art devices that have proven effective in emergency service. However, it is important for the user to understand that such devices will not necessarily be heard by the drivers of every vehicle under all conditions in time to permit all drivers to take appropriate action.

Sound levels high enough to be heard at reasonable distances in soundproofed automobiles with operating air-conditioners and stereo sound systems are so high as to be environmentally unacceptable. The siren is a useful warning device for calling for the right-of-way by an emergency vehicle but must always be used in conjunction with effective visual warning devices and operated only by properly trained personnel.

2. References

2.1 Applicable Documents—The following publications form a part of this specification to the extent specified herein. The latest issue of SAE publications shall apply.

2.1.1 SAE PUBLICATIONS—Available from SAE, 400 Commonwealth Drive, Warrendale, PA 15096-0001.

SAE J184—Qualifying a Sound Data Acquisition System

SAE J336—Sound Level for Truck Cab Interior

SAE J575—Test Methods and Equipment for Lighting Devices and Components for Use on Vehicles Less Than 2032 mm in Overall Width

SAE J759—Lighting Identification Code

2.1.2 ANSI PUBLICATIONS—Available from ANSI, 11 West 42nd Street, New York, NY 10036-8002.

ANSI S1.4-1983—Sound Level Meters, Specification for

ANSI S1.13-1971—Sound Pressure Levels, Methods for the Measurement of

3. Definitions

3.1 Siren—A device for producing standardized acoustical signals which have become recognized as the call for the right-of-way by an emergency vehicle.

3.1.1 ELECTROMECHANICAL SIREN—A device consisting of a motor and a rotor within a stator. When electrically energized, air is pumped through the rotor. The discharge of air is modulated by a number of ports that open and close at varying rates thereby altering the pitch of the siren.

3.1.2 ELECTRONIC SIREN AMPLIFIER—A device intended to convert direct current into an alternating current of varying frequency but constant voltage for the purpose of supplying energy to the electronic siren speaker.

3.1.3 ELECTRONIC SIREN SPEAKER—A transducer intended to radiate acoustical energy into the air with an acoustical waveform equivalent to the input electrical waveform. The electronic siren speaker shall include the electrical to mechanical transducer plus any and all mechanisms or housings required to couple and control transducer acoustical output.

3.1.4 ELECTRONIC SIREN SYSTEM—An assembly of matched devices including an electronic siren speaker, an electronic siren amplifier, and such controls as are necessary to operate the system.

The number, wattage, and nominal impedance of electronic siren speakers are determined by the design of the amplifier and so specified on the nameplate of the electronic siren amplifier.

3.2 Siren Signals

3.2.1 WAIL—A tonal pattern of slow automatic increases and decreases in frequency at the rate of 10 to 30 cpm. This signal can be produced by both electronic and electromechanical sirens. The frequency of this signal shall not fall below 650 Hz for electronic siren systems nor rise above 2000 Hz for either system and shall encompass a range from high to low of at least 850 Hz.

3.2.2 YELP—A tonal pattern of rapid automatic increases and decreases in frequency at a rate of 150 to 250 cpm. This signal is usually produced only by electronic siren systems. The frequency of this signal shall not fall below 650 Hz for electronic siren systems nor rise above 2000 Hz for either system and shall encompass a range from high to low of at least 850 Hz.

3.2.3 MANUAL WAIL—Intermittently operated wail by a push button or other control means.

3.2.4 AUXILIARY SIGNALS—Any signal other than wail, yelp, or manual wail. While such signals may have legitimate uses in nonemergency situations and may be included as a part of an electronic siren system, it is recommended that only wail, yelp, or manual wail is used as a call for the right-of-way by an emergency vehicle.

3.3 Anechoic Chamber—An acoustical device testing room in which all six of the surfaces absorb at least 99% of the incident acoustic energy over the frequency range of interest. The chamber shall be in compliance with ANSI S1.13-1971 (3).

3.4 Sound Pressure Level—A quantity in decibels read from a sound level meter or other acoustical instrumentation system that fulfills the requirements of ANSI S1.4-1983-Type 1 (1) that is switched to the "Flat" or "Unweighted" network. The sound pressure level (Lp) is defined by $Lp = 20 \log 10\ (p/po)$, where "p" is the sound pressure and "po" is the reference sound pressure.

3.5 "A" Weighted Sound Level—The setting on an acoustical instrumentation system that adds a filter network to modify the reading of sound pressure level. The "A" weighting network discriminates against the lower frequencies according to a relationship approximately equivalent to the auditory sensitivity of the human ear at moderate sound levels.

3.6 Electronic Siren Output Voltage—A potential expressed in V AC rms that is required to produce the sound pressure levels as defined by this document when applied to an electronic siren speaker.

3.7 Nominal Impedance—The impedance expressed in Ohms of an electronic siren speaker over the range of frequencies of interest. This nominal impedance for the purposes of this document shall be that of the speaker at 1000 Hz.

4. Identification Code and Marking

4.1 Identification Code

4.1.1 Devices conforming to this document which are intended to be mounted in the interior of the vehicle including the trunk or any other dry compartment designed for mounting equipment shall be identified with the code EVS1 in accordance with SAE J759.

4.1.2 Devices conforming to this document which are intended to be mounted outside the vehicle or in any other wet location (except under hood) shall be identified with the code EVS2 in accordance with SAE J759.

4.1.3 Devices conforming to this document which are intended to be mounted under hood shall be identified with the code EVS3 in accordance with SAE J759.

4.2 Markings—All markings shall be 3.0 mm or greater in height, permanently affixed to the device.

4.2.1 ELECTROCHEMICAL SIRENS—The name of the manufacturer, the model number, the intended input voltage, operating amperage, mounting orientation, and the SAE identification code indicating mounting location shall be shown.

4.2.2 ELECTRONIC SIREN SPEAKERS—The name of the manufacturer, the model number, the nominal impedance, operating wattage, mounting orientation, and the SAE identification code indicating mounting location shall be shown.

If two or more speakers are used as an array, the exact geometry in which the array was tested must be specified. Approval of an array of speakers is valid only when mounted on a vehicle in exact conformance with the specified geometry.

4.2.3 ELECTRONIC SIREN AMPLIFIERS AND ASSOCIATED CONTROLS—The name of the manufacturer, the model number, the nominal impedance, operating wattage, and number of speaker(s) to which the device is intended to be connected, the intended input voltage, output voltage, and the SAE identification code indicating mounting location shall be shown.

If the amplifier and controls are separate components, each component shall be identified as to the system of which it was intended to be a part and the SAE identification code indicating mounting location shall be shown.

The controls for all functions shall be clearly identified and visible during operation both day and night.

4.2.4 SYSTEMS WHICH HAVE BEEN TESTED AS A WHOLE WITHOUT THE USE OF THE STANDARD SIGNAL GENERATOR/AMPLIFIER OR STANDARD RESISTIVE LOAD—The components of such a system shall be marked to indicate that they are approved only when used with each other and should not be interchanged with components or other systems.

5. Tests

5.1 General Information—Because siren systems can be composed of a single device or multiple, interconnected devices mounted in various locations inside or outside the vehicle, the tests required for any specific device or component are determined by its type, function, and intended mounting location.

To permit assembly of electronic siren systems using devices manufactured by more than one manufacturer, electronic siren speakers and electronic siren amplifiers may be independently certified in accordance to the requirements of this documents.

5.1.1 ELECTRONIC SIREN SPEAKERS—In conformance with the requirements and procedures of this document, all tests of electronic siren speakers may be made using a standard signal source. For typical electronic siren speakers having 11 Ω impedance referenced at 1000 Hz, the input test voltage "E" is defined as shown in Equation 1:

$$E = \sqrt{11\ W \times \text{rated wattage of the siren speaker}} \qquad \text{(Eq.1)}$$

Thus, the input voltage for testing an 11 Ω/100 W speaker shall be 33.0 V rms ± 0.5 V rms.

Alternatively, the input test voltage for speakers of any impedance or wattage may be determined by applying a constant frequency signal of 1000 Hz to the speaker through a wattmeter and increasing the voltage until the nameplate wattage of the speaker is reached. This voltage shall then be the test voltage.

When multiple siren speakers are tested connected in parallel, the input test voltage shall be 90% of voltage determined by either of the previously mentioned methods. This reduced voltage is necessary to approximate the internal losses within a typical electronic siren amplifier and the external wiring when additional electronic siren speakers are connected.

5.1.2 ELECTRONIC SIREN AMPLIFIERS—In conformance with the requirements and procedures of this document, all tests of electronic siren amplifiers may be made using a standard, noninductive resistive load per 5.2.6. This load shall have a resistance of 11.0 Ω ± 0.2 Ω (equivalent to the impedance of the typical electronic siren speaker referenced at 1000 Hz).

To test the performance of the amplifier if two such speakers are connected in parallel, the resistance shall be 5.5 Ω ± 0.1 Ω.

Electronic siren amplifiers designed to operate with nontypical electronic siren speakers (other than 11 Ω nominal impedance) may be tested using a noninductive, resistive load of the size matching the nominal impedance of the speaker intended for use.

5.1.3 FAMILY APPROVALS—Manufacturers of electronic siren amplifiers who market multiple variations of these amplifiers may elect to group such devices into product families. Representative models may be tested to obtain family wide approval as long as:

a. Model numbers or identification codes are arranged to define such families and,

b. The amplification and signal generation circuitry are identical in the family and,

238

c. The test report shall list each specific model variation and the manufacturer shall have on record the details of each variation, and state that the performance of the tested and untested members of the family are the same.

5.1.4 ELECTRONIC SIREN SYSTEMS—While it is permissible to test an electronic siren system as a whole (siren amplifier connected to a siren speaker) without the use of the standard signal source and the standard resistive load, the devices comprising a system so tested, cannot be interchanged with any other devices or used as a part of any other system. The testing of a siren system as a whole shall be in conformance with the requirements and procedures of this document.

5.1.5 ELECTROMECHANICAL SIRENS—In conformance with the requirements and procedures of this document, all tests of electromechanical sirens shall be made using a timer to automatically operate a relay of sufficient current carrying capacity to energize and de-energize the siren motor at a rate of 10 to 30 times per minute.

Electromechanical sirens whose acoustical performance substantially exceeds the requirements of this document (6.1.4) are exempted from this requirement and may be tested by automatic operation at any convenient rate.

5.2 Test Equipment and Instrumentation

5.2.1 TEST VOLTAGE—Unless otherwise specified, the test voltage shall be 13.6 V DC ± 0.2 V DC for devices intended for operation on 12 V systems and 27.2 V DC ± 0.2 V DC for devices intended for operation on 24 V systems.

5.2.2 ACOUSTICAL TEST FIXTURE—A test base approximately 30 x 30 x 2.5 cm shall be used to mount the device. The support shall be capable of being rotated by a turntable from 0 to ±50 degrees and shall position the acoustic axis of the device(s) at a height of at least 1.5 m. The axial positions shall contain no reflective surfaces with dimensions greater than 2.5 cm within 1.5 m of the siren or speaker(s) unless the design of the system incorporates external surfaces for proper operation. Such requirements, if any, shall be fully defined in the reports.

5.2.3 DIRECT CURRENT POWER SUPPLY—The power supply shall be regulated to ±0.1 V with a maximum ripple of 75 mV peak-to-peak. Output current capacity must be at least 1.5 times the rated current for the device under test. The output voltage shall be adjustable to provide the voltage required for specific tests.

Electromechanical sirens may be tested using an automotive battery of the correct nominal voltage for the siren provided the battery shall have a minimum cranking rate of –18 °C of 450 A for 30 s and a reserve capacity of 100 min at a discharge rate of 25 A. A power supply as defined may be used during the test to maintain the battery charge.

5.2.4 INTEGRATING WATTMETER—The integrating wattmeter used for measuring the electronic siren speaker input power shall be of adequate capacity to record peak wattage and have a range from 100 Hz to 20 kHz with ±1% accuracy.

5.2.5 SOUND METERING SYSTEM—The sound metering system shall meet the requirements of SAE J184.

5.2.6 STANDARD NONINDUCTIVE, RESISTIVE LOAD—The noninductive resistor shall be of adequate size to dissipate the heat produced during the test. The resistor shall have a value of 11 Ω ± 0.2 Ω if being used in place of a typical electronic siren speaker or 5.5 Ω ± 0.1 Ω if used in place of two typical speakers connected in parallel.

If the amplifier under test is designated by the manufacturer for use with nontypical siren speakers, the resistance values specified by the manufacturer shall be used.

5.2.7 STANDARD SIGNAL SOURCE—The signal generator/amplifier shall be capable of generating square wave signals at the required voltage from at least 500 to 2000 Hz into reactive loads with impedances at low as 4 Ω with rise and fall times of no more than 20 μs from 10 to 90% and 90 to 10% of the maximum waveform value. The amplifier shall remain stable regardless of the reactive nature of the load.

5.2.8 VOLTMETER FOR MEASURING ELECTRONIC SIREN AMPLIFIER OUTPUT—The voltmeter shall be capable of measuring the true AC rms value of nonsinusoidal waveforms with crest factors of up to 10 with a bandwidth of at least 10 Hz to 20 kHz. Accuracy over this entire bandwidth shall be ±1%.

5.3 Test Procedures

5.3.1 TEST SEQUENCE—The sequence of tests shall be:
a. The tests under 5.3.2.1 in any order
b. The tests under 5.3.2.2 in any order
c. The test under 5.3.4 or 5.3.5 as required
d. The test under 5.3.3

To reduce the time to test, two identical devices may be used. One device may be used for performing the entire test sequence except 5.3.3. The second device may be used to simultaneously run test 5.3.3.

NOTE—To determine whether or not an electromechanical siren is exempt from compliance with the cyclic rate requirement, it shall be necessary to run test 5.3.5 before the start of the test sequence. Regardless of the outcome, this test shall be performed again in the required sequence.

5.3.2 ENVIRONMENTAL TESTS

5.3.2.1 Tests from SAE J575 with Modifications as Indicated
a. Vibration test
b. Moisture test
c. Dust test
d. Corrosion test
Devices intended only for interior mounting in the vehicle do not need to be tested per b, c, and d.

5.3.2.2 Additional Environmental Tests
5.3.2.2.1 High Temperature Operating Test for All Devices Other Than Those Designed for Under Hood Mounting—The device shall be subjected to an ambient temperature of 50 °C ± 3 °C for a period of 6 h. The device shall be connected to any other components necessary to form an operable system and shall be off during the first hour and shall then operate continuously for the next 5 h.

Other components may be mounted in the test chamber if they are to be tested or outside the chamber if they are not under test. The device shall operate before the start of the test in the normal fashion. If the siren produces more than one siren signal, the setting of the unit shall be changed periodically to reasonably test all siren signals.

The measurements shall be made before the test, not less than 3 min or more than 4 min after the beginning of the second hour of operation, and not less than 3 min or more than 4 min after the end of the test. At each required measurement:
a. Electromechanical sirens shall have the maximum input amperage measured using an ammeter per 5.3.6.1 and the cyclic rate recorded.
b. Electronic siren amplifiers shall have the output voltage determined per 5.3.6.2 and the cyclic rate (cpm) of wail and yelp (if present) shall be measured and recorded.
c. Electronic siren speakers shall have their input wattage measured in accordance with 5.3.6.3.

5.3.2.2.2 High Temperature Test for Devices Designated by the Manufacturer as Permissible for Under Hood Mounting, i.e., In the Engine Compartment—Such devices shall be tested in accordance with 5.3.2.2.1 except at a temperature of 90 °C ± 3 °C.

5.3.2.2.3 Low Temperature Operating Test—All devices shall be subject to an ambient temperature of –30 °C ± 3 °C for 6 h. The device shall be connected to any other components necessary to form an operable system and shall be turned off (not operating) during the first 5 h of the test and then turned on and operated during the last hour of the 6 h test.

Other components may be mounted in the test chamber if they are to be tested or outside the chamber if they are not under test. The device shall operate before the start of the test in the normal fashion. If the siren produces more than one siren signal, the setting of the unit shall be changed periodically to reasonably test all siren signals. At each required measurement:
a. Electromechanical sirens shall have the maximum input amperage measured using an ammeter per 5.3.6.1 and the cyclic rate recorded.
b. Electronic siren amplifiers shall have the output voltage determined per 5.3.6.2 and the cyclic rate (cpm) of wail and yelp (if present) shall be measured and recorded.
c. Electronic siren speakers shall have their input wattage measured in accordance with 5.3.6.3.

The measurements shall be made before the test, not less than 3 min nor more than 4 min after the beginning of the last hour of operation, and not less than 3 min nor more than 4 min after the end of the test.

5.3.3 DURABILITY TEST—The device shall be connected to any other components necessary to form an operable system and the device shall be operated continuously for 200 h at an ambient temperature of 25 °C ± 3 °C in cycles consisting of 30 min on and 30 min off. The device shall operate in the normal fashion before the start of the test. If the siren produces more than one siren signal, the setting of the unit shall be changed periodically to reasonably test all siren signals.

At each required measurement:
a. Electromechanical sirens shall have the maximum input amperage measured using an ammeter per 5.3.6.1 and the cyclic rate recorded.

b. Electronic siren amplifiers shall have the output voltage determined per 5.3.6.2 and the cyclic rate (cpm) of wail and yelp (if present) shall be measured and recorded.

c. Electronic siren speakers shall have their input wattage measured in accordance with 5.3.6.3.

The measurements shall be made before the test, and not less than 3 min nor more than 4 min after the end of the test.

5.3.4 PERFORMANCE TEST FOR ELECTRONIC SIREN AMPLIFIERS—The electronic siren amplifier shall be connected to a DC power supply per 5.2.3 and to a load with a voltmeter conforming to 5.2.8 connected between the amplifier output terminals connected to the load.

The amplifier shall be allowed to operate for 5 min and output voltage readings taken per 5.3.6.2 for all siren signals. The frequency range and cyclic rate will also be determined for the siren tones of wail and yelp (if present).

The input voltage shall then be increased to 15.0 V DC for devices intended to operate on 12 V systems or 30 V for devices intended to operate on 24 V systems, and the procedure mentioned repeated.

5.3.5 ACOUSTICAL PERFORMANCE TEST—Electromechanical sirens and electronic siren speakers shall be tested in conformance with the following procedures:

5.3.5.1 General—Acoustical tests shall be conducted at a temperature of 25 °C ± 3 °C.

With the device under test mounted on the acoustical test fixture per 5.2.2 in an anechoic chamber, the microphone shall be positioned in line with the device at a distance of 3.0 m ± 0.01 m from the edge of the device. The microphone shall be mounted at normal incidence to the device axis, in line with the device axis and at the same height as the device axis.

The device shall be located as far away from the walls of the anechoic chamber as possible. There shall be no significant reflecting surfaces within 1.5 m of the microphone used to measure the generated signal or within 1.5 m of the path between the device and the microphone. Position the device at 0 degrees and connect the microphone to the instrument system.

Without changing the setup, adjust the measuring instrumentation to measure the "A-weighted" sound level. Adjust the response characteristic of the system to provide a time constant of 0.02 s. Operate the device for 1 min and record the maximum and minimum "A-weighted" sound pressure level at the 0 degree point. At the 0 degree point, determine the minimum and maximum fundamental frequency of sound produced by the device. The cyclic rate of wail and yelp (if present) shall also be measured and recorded.

Repeat the procedure by indexing the turntable until readings are obtained from 50 degrees left to 50 degrees right at 10 degrees ± 0.5 degree intervals. Sound pressure readings should be recorded to the nearest 0.5 dB. Frequency and cyclic rate readings need be taken only at the 0 degree point.

During the test, technicians and observers shall remain outside the chamber. The instrumentation shall be calibrated using a piston phone or calibrator before and after each period of use and at intervals not exceeding 2 h when the measuring instrumentation is used for a period longer than 2 h. The air temperature and pressure in the chamber shall be recorded during the test.

A record shall be kept of the calibration during the test period and any changes in calibration noted. The test shall be considered invalid if changes in calibration exceed 1 dB. All calibration equipment used during the performance of the measurements shall be operating correctly and traceable to the National Institute of Standards and Technology.

5.3.5.2 Electronic Siren Speaker(s)—Siren speakers shall be securely mounted to the test fixture and connected to the signal generator/amplifier per 5.2.7. A signal of the appropriate test voltage varying in frequency from 650 to 2000 Hz at a rate of 10 to 30 cpm (approximating wail) shall be applied to the terminals of the device and the acoustical measurements made according to the general procedure.

The tests shall then be repeated using the same signal but increasing the rate to 150 to 250 cpm (approximating yelp).

If testing a complete system per 5.1.4, the electronic siren amplifier is used as the signal source and operated in the wail and yelp modes.

NOTE—If multiple siren speakers are tested, the exact geometry of the array must be reported and the test results applied only to mountings which conform to this geometry.

5.3.5.3 Electromechanical Sirens—The siren shall be securely mounted on the test fixture and the device connected to a power supply through a relay of adequate size. A timer shall be used to energize the relay to achieve a rate of 10 to 30 cpm. The periods of on and off need not be the same and can be set to maximize the performance of the siren.

Acoustical measurements are then made in accordance with the general procedure and the cyclic rate recorded.

5.3.6 SECONDARY TEST PROCEDURES USED IN PERFORMING THE ENVIRONMENTAL, PERFORMANCE, AND DURABILITY TESTS

5.3.6.1 Input Amperage Test—An ammeter of appropriate size shall be connected to the electromechanical siren between the device and the power supply. The maximum input amperage of the device shall be determined at an operating voltage of 13.6 V ± 0.2 V at the terminals of the siren (27.2 V ± 0.2 V if intended for 24 V operation).

5.3.6.2 Output Voltage Test—Amplifiers for electronic sirens shall be connected to any other components necessary to form an operable system and a voltmeter per 5.7.8 installed between the output terminals of the amplifier connected to the load. The output voltage of the amplifier shall be determined at 13.6 V ± 0.2 V input voltage to the amplifier (27.2 V ± 0.2 V if intended for 24 V operation) or such other voltage as called for in the test.

5.3.6.3 Input Wattage Test—An integrating wattmeter per 5.2.4 shall be connected between the output terminals of the signal generator/amplifier and the input terminals of the electronic siren speaker.

6. Requirements—These requirements apply to new, undamaged production units selected at random. The device shall be tested in accordance with the test procedures in Section 5.

6.1 Performance Requirements

6.1.1 When tested in accordance with 5.3.2, the device shall meet the requirements of SAE J575, with modifications as indicated.

6.1.1.1 Vibration

6.1.1.2 Moisture

6.1.1.3 Dust

6.1.1.4 Corrosion—Any device which when tested fails the test or shows signs of change that would cause failure under any of the tests is to be considered a failure.

6.1.2 ADDITIONAL ENVIRONMENTAL AND DURABILITY REQUIREMENTS— When tested according to 5.3.2.2 and 5.3.3, any device or component which fails to operate at any of the required measurements shall be considered a failure.

Also considered failures are:

a. Electromechanical sirens that require more than 125% of nameplate amperage at any required measurement or that were tested at a cyclic rate other than from 10 to 30 cpm. However, electromechanical sirens producing sound pressure levels 2 dB(A) or greater than the required values at all required measurements in 6.1.4, can be tested at any cyclic rate.

b. Electronic siren amplifiers that produce at any required measurement—At 13.6 V (or 27.2 V) input, less than 92% or more than 108% of the nameplate voltage.

A wail signal at a cyclic rate other than from 10 to 30 cpm.

A yelp signal (if present) at a cyclic rate other than from 150 to 250 cpm.

c. Electronic siren speakers that when operated at the test voltage draw at any required measurement—More than 108% of the nameplate wattage.

6.1.3 When tested in conformance to 5.3.4, an electronic siren amplifier shall be considered a failure if when operated at an input voltage of 13.6 V ± 0.2 V (or 27.2 V ± 0.2 V), at any required measurement:

The output voltage is less than 92% or more than 108% of the nameplate output voltage.

A wail signal is measured at a cyclic rate other than from 10 to 30 cpm or at a frequency of less than 650 Hz or more than 2000 Hz or had a range of high to low of less than 850 Hz.

A yelp signal (if present) is measured at a cyclic rate other than from 150 to 250 cpm at a frequency of less than 650 Hz or more than 2000 Hz or had a range of high to low of less than 850 Hz.

The amplifier is also considered a failure if when operated at an input voltage of 15.0 V (or 30 V), at a required measurement:

The output voltage is more than 125% of the nameplate voltage.

A wail signal is measured at a cyclic rate other than from 10 to 30 cpm or at a frequency of less than 650 Hz or more than 2000 Hz or had a range of high to low of less than 850 Hz.

A yelp signal (if present) is measured at a cyclic rate other than from 150 to 250 cpm or at a frequency of less than 650 Hz or more than 2000 Hz or had a range of high to low of less than 850 Hz.

6.1.4 ACOUSTICAL PERFORMANCE—When measured in accordance with 5.3.5, the wail signal and the yelp signal (if present in the system) when operating within the required cycle rates shall produce at least the following sound pressure levels as shown in Table 1.

The sound pressure at each point must equal or exceed the value shown in Line A during some portion of each wail and yelp cycle (if yelp is present) except that up to three points may fall 1 dB(A) below the value shown so long as the total of all points exceeds 1262.

The sound pressure at each point must not fall below the value shown in Line B during any portion of each wail and yelp cycle (if yelp is present) except that up to three points may fall 1 dB(A) below the value shown so long as the total of all points exceeds 1191.

The exemption for electromechanical sirens applies only if the measured sound pressure level exceeds the table of values by 2 or more dB(A) at all points in both Line A and Line B.

TABLE 1—ACOUSTICAL PERFORMANCE

	Measurement Location in Degrees from Center	Measurement Location in Degrees from Center	Measurement Location in Degrees from Center	Measurement Location in Degrees from Center	Measurement Location in Degrees from Center	Measurement Location in Degrees from Center
	0	±10	±20	±30	±40	±50
Line A dB(A) SPL	118	117	116	115	113	111
Line B dB(A) SPL	111	110	109	108	107	106

6.2 Effect of Failure of a Given Test—The failure of any device or component at any point in the required test sequence shall constitute a failure of the entire sequence. The entire test sequence including the tests that were passed shall be considered void and the entire test sequence shall be repeated using a new device or component or the original device or component after repair.

Failure of a component which is included in order to have an operable system but which is not itself under test shall have no effect on the test sequence. Such a component may be replaced with a similar component and the test sequence continued.

6.3 Matching of Components in Electronic Siren Systems—In accordance with their respective nameplates, only properly matched electronic siren speaker(s) and electronic siren amplifiers shall be interconnected. The number, wattage, and nominal impedance of connected electronic siren speakers shall be in accordance with the requirements presented on the nameplate of the electronic siren amplifier.

7. *Guidelines*

7.1 General—Proper installation is vital to the performance of the siren and the safe operation of the emergency vehicle. It is important to recognize that the operator of the emergency vehicle is under psychological and physiological stress caused by the emergency situation. The siren system should be installed in such a manner as to:

a. Not reduce the acoustical performance of the system
b. Limit as much as practical the noise level in the passenger compartment of the vehicle
c. Place the controls within convenient reach of the operator so that he can operate the system without losing eye contact with the roadway

7.2 Mounting and Wiring—All devices should be mounted in accordance with the manufacturer's instructions and securely fastened to vehicle elements of sufficient strength to withstand the forces applied to the device.

All wiring should conform to the minimum wire size and other recommendations of the manufacturer and be protected from moving parts and hot surfaces. Looms, grommets, cable ties, and similar installation hardware should be used to anchor and protect all wiring.

Fuses or circuit breakers should be located as close to the power takeoff points as possible and properly sized to protect the wiring and devices.

Particular attention should be paid to the location and method of making electrical connections and splices to protect these points from corrosion and loss of conductivity. Ground terminations should be only made to substantial chassis components.

(R) 7.3 Placement of Electrochemical Sirens and Electronic Siren Speakers—The sound projecting opening should be pointed forward, parallel to the ground, and not obstructed or muffled by structural components of the vehicle. Concealed or under hood mounting will result in a dramatic reduction in performance and is not recommended.

To minimize potential hearing loss, it is recommended that a maximum sound pressure level not exceed 85 dB(A) in the passenger area when the vehicle is in motion with the siren operating. Manufacturers and users of emergency vehicles should measure the actual sound pressure levels per SAE J336 at each riding position.

Electromechanical sirens and electronic siren speakers should be mounted as far from the occupants as possible using acoustically insulated compartments and isolation mountings to minimize the transmission of sound into the vehicle. It may be helpful to mount the device on the front bumper, engine cowl or fender, heavily insulate the passenger compartment, and operate the siren only with the windows closed.

Each of these approaches may cause significant operational problems including loss of siren performance from road slush, increased likelihood of damage to the siren in minor collisions, and the inability to hear the sirens on other emergency vehicles. Appropriate training of vehicle operators is recommended to alert them to these problems and minimize the effect of these problems on operations.

7.4 Electronic Amplifiers and Siren Controls—Devices should be mounted only in locations that conform to their SAE identification code. Devices for interior mounting should not be placed under hood, etc.

Controls should be placed within the convenient reach of the driver or, if intended for two man operation, the driver and/or the passenger. In some vehicles, multiple control switches may be necessary for convenient operation from two positions.

Convenient reach is defined as the ability of the operator of the siren system to manipulate the controls from his normal driving/riding position without excessive movement away from the seat back or loss of eye contact with the roadway.

φLIGHTING AND MARKING OF AGRICULTURAL EQUIPMENT ON HIGHWAYS—SAE J137 JUN89

SAE Standard

Report of the Tractor Technical Committee, approved February 1970, completely revised by the Agricultural Tractor Technical Committee June 1989.

1. Purpose and Scope—This standard provides specifications for lighting and marking of agricultural equipment whenever such equipment is operated or traveling on a highway.

2. Definitions

2.1 Agricultural Equipment—Refer to SAE J1150 for definitions of terms.

2.2 Highway—The entire width between the boundary lines of every way publicly maintained, when any part thereof is open to the use of the public for purposes of vehicular travel (Uniform Vehicle Code).

2.3 Reflectors—Reflex reflectors as described in SAE J594 or reflective material that shall be visible at night from all distances within 183-31 m (600-100 ft) when directly in front of lawful lower beams of headlamps. Reflective material shall meet the durability requirements for such materials as specified in SAE J943.

2.4 Lamp Locations—Dimensions in this standard, unless specified otherwise, are based on measurements to the lamp filament.

3. Lighting and Marking Requirements

3.1 Lighting and marking of tractors and self-propelled machines shall be as follows:

3.1.1 At least two headlamps generally conforming to SAE J975 shall be mounted at the same height and spaced laterally as widely as practicable. Headlamps or the low beams of headlamps, if so equipped, shall be aligned such that measured at 7.5 m (25 ft) from the lamp, the horizontal line separating the upper edge of the lit zone (the line where the intensity is decreased to 10% or less of the peak intensity) is 0.1 x H minimum below the center of the lamp where H is the height of the lamp from the ground. The headlamp beams shall be centered laterally. (See Fig. 1.) Flood lamps or general service lamps shall be aimed downward to provide illumination close to the machine.

3.1.2 At least one red tail lamp conforming to SAE J585 shall be mounted to the rear of the machine and positioned less than 1.5 m (5 ft) to the left of the machine center. If two tail lamps are used, the second shall be placed to the right of the machine center and should be symmetrical with the left lamp location.

3.1.3 At least two amber flashing warning lamps conforming to SAE J974 shall be symmetrically mounted and as widely spaced laterally as practicable, visible from both front and rear, mounted at least 1 m (39 in) high. Lamps shall flash in unison at a rate of 60-85 flashes per minute.

3.1.3.1 On machines over 4 m (13 ft) wide, at least two amber flashing warning lamps conforming to SAE J974 visible from the front and rear shall be provided. The lamps shall be placed a minimum of 1 m (39 in) high and within 400 mm (16 in) of the lateral extremities of the machine and shall flash in unison with warning lamps described in paragraph 3.1.3. The extremity dimension includes such items as dual wheels, wide axles, headers, etc. These lamps may be used in addi-

tion to, or in place of, the lamps prescribed in paragraph 3.1.3.

3.1.4 When turn indicators are provided, the amber flashing warning lamps shall be used as the turn indicators. When a turn is to be signaled, the flashing lamp(s) opposite the direction of turn shall become steady burning until the turn signal is cancelled. The flashing lamp(s) in the direction of turn shall increase in flashing rate a minimum of 20 flashes per minute, but shall not exceed 110 flashes per minute.

3.1.5 At least two red reflectors visible to the rear and mounted to indicate, as nearly as practicable, the extreme left and extreme right projections. Reflectors may be incorporated as part of the lensing in tail lamps described in paragraph 3.1.2.

3.1.6 One SMV (slow moving vehicle) identification emblem as described in SAE J943 or means for mounting the SMV emblem such as a mounting socket described in SAE J725.

3.1.7 One seven-terminal receptacle conforming to SAE J560 shall be mounted on the machine and located as shown in Fig. 2. Tractors and self-propelled machines not primarily used with agricultural implements described in paragraphs 3.3.1 and 3.3.2 are excluded.

3.1.7.1 As a minimum, the receptacle terminals, numbers 1, 3, 5 and 6 (ground, flashing and turn signals, and tail lights), shall be wired for service.

3.1.7.2 The circuit designations for the breakaway connector defined in paragraph 3.1.7 are listed below:

TRACTOR RECEPTACLE

Conductor Identification	Wire Color	Terminal Number	Circuit
Wht	White	1	Ground
Blk	Black	2	Work lights
Yel	Yellow	3	Left-hand flashing and turn signals
Red	Red	4	Auxiliary
Grn	Green	5	Right-hand flashing and turn signals
Brn	Brown	6	Tail lamp
Blu	Blue	7	Auxiliary

3.2 Marking of agricultural implements shall be as follows:

3.2.1 Implements extending more than 1.2 m (4 ft) to the left of the center of the propelling machine shall have at least one amber reflector visible to the front and positioned to indicate as nearly as practicable the extreme left projection of the implement.

3.2.2 Implements extending more than 10 m (33 ft) behind the hitch point shall have amber reflectors visible from the left and right sides. The reflectors shall be spaced at intervals of 5 m (16.4 ft) maximum on both sides measuring from the transport hitch point. The rear most reflector shall be positioned as far rearward as practicable.

3.2.3 Implements extending more than 1.2 m (4 ft) to the rear of the hitch point of the propelling machine or more than 1.2 m (4 ft) to the right or left of the centerline of the propelling machine shall have at least two red reflectors visible to the rear and mounted to indicate, as nearly as practicable, the extreme left and extreme right projections.

3.2.4 Implements that obscure the SMV emblem on the propelling machine, or extend more than 10 m (33 ft) to the rear of the hitch point, shall be equipped with one SMV emblem as described in SAE J943 or means for mounting the SMV emblem, such as a mounting socket as described in SAE J725.

3.3 Lighting of agricultural implements shall be as follows:

3.3.1 Implements which obscure the effective illumination of any flashing warning lamp or extremity lamp on the propelling machine shall have lighting as described in paragraphs 3.3.3 and 3.3.4. If the tail lamps on the propelling machine are obscured, at least one tail lamp conforming to SAE J585 shall be mounted to the rear of the implement and positioned to the left of the implement center. If two tail lamps are used, the second shall be placed to the right of the implement center and should be symmetrical with the left tail lamp location.

3.3.2 Implements that 1) are more than 4 m (13 ft) wide or extend over 2 m (79 in) to the left or right of the centerline and beyond the left or right extremity of the propelling machine, or 2) extend more than 10 mm (33 ft) to the rear of the hitch point shall have lighting as described in paragraphs 3.3.3 and 3.3.4.

3.3.3 At least two amber flashing warning lamps conforming to SAE J974 visible from the front and rear shall be provided. The lamps shall be spaced to within 400 mm (16 in) of the lateral extremities of the machine, preferably mounted at least 1 m (39 in) but not over 3 m (10 ft) in height, and shall flash in unison with warning lamps described in paragraph 3.1.3. On nonsymmetrical implements extending only to the left or right such as moldboard plows or windrowers, one flashing warning lamp shall be provided spaced laterally to within 400 mm (16 in) of the left or right extremity.

3.3.4 When turn signals are provided on the propelling machine, the amber flashing warning lamps of the implement shall be used as turn indicators as described in paragraph 3.1.4.

3.3.5 A seven-terminal plug conforming to SAE J560 shall be provided for operating remote flashing warning lamps, turn indicators, and tail lamp(s). The plug location and cable length shall be compatible with the location of the seven terminal receptacle on the tractor or self-propelled machine (reference 3.1.7 as shown in Fig. 2).

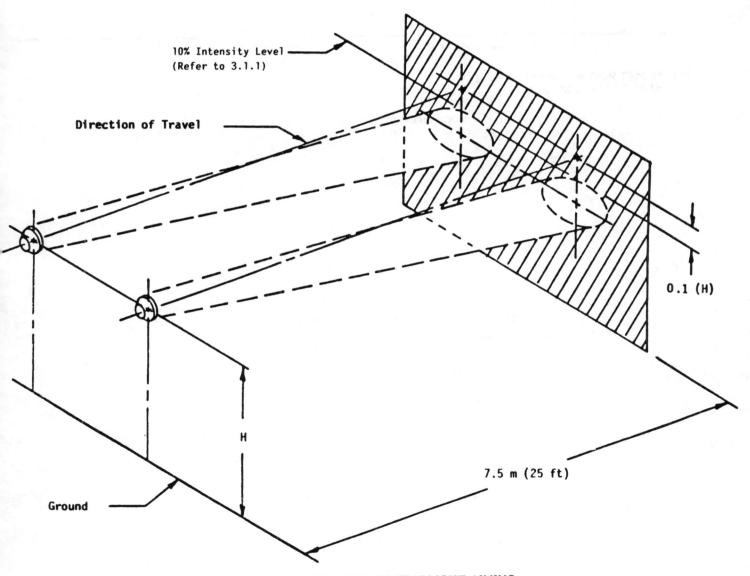

10% Intensity Level
(Refer to 3.1.1)

Direction of Travel

0.1 (H)

H

Ground

7.5 m (25 ft)

FIG. 1—ILLUSTRATION OF HEADLIGHT AIMING
PROCEDURE

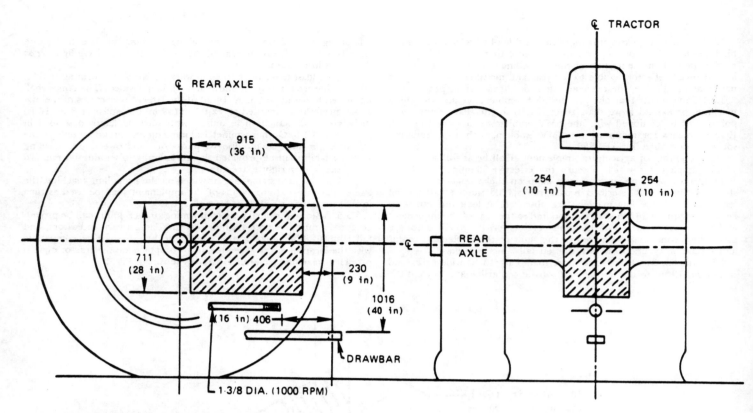

NOTE: SOCKET MUST BE LOCATED TO THE
REAR OF TRACTOR AXLE

FIG. 2—LOCATION ZONE FOR SEVEN-TERMINAL
CONNECTOR

MOUNTING BRACKETS AND SOCKET FOR WARNING LAMP AND SLOW-MOVING VEHICLE (SMV) IDENTIFICATION EMBLEM—SAE J725 MAR91

SAE Standard

Report of the Tractor Technical Committee, approved January 1954, last revised January 1972, reaffirmed without change, Agricultural Tractor Technical Committee, November 1984. Completely revised by the SAE Agricultural Tractor Technical Committee March 1991. Rationale statement available.

1. Scope

1.1 The bracket shown in Figure 1 is intended for fixed attachment to the SMV emblem and to provide, through the tapered portion, a means of detachably mounting the emblem assembly in cooperation with the socket shown in Figure 2.

1.2 The bracket shown in Figure 3 is intended for fixed attachment to the warning lamp and to provide, through the tapered portion, a means of detachably mounting the warning lamp assembly in cooperation with the socket shown in Figure 2.

1.3 The socket shown in Figure 2 is intended for fixed attachment to accommodate the tapered portion of brackets shown in Figures 1 and 3.

1.4 Purpose—This SAE Standard defines mounting devices for use with warning lamps and SMV emblems.

2. References

There are no referenced publications specified herein.

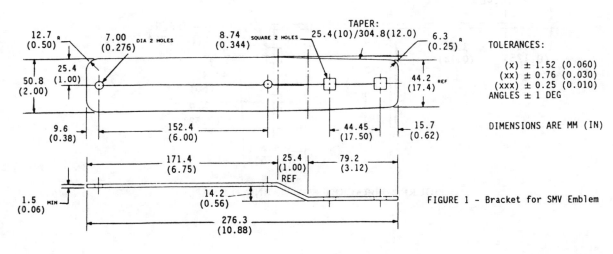

FIGURE 1—BRACKET FOR SMV EMBLEM

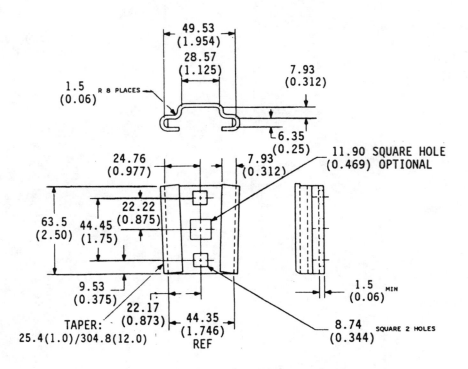

FIGURE 2—SOCKET

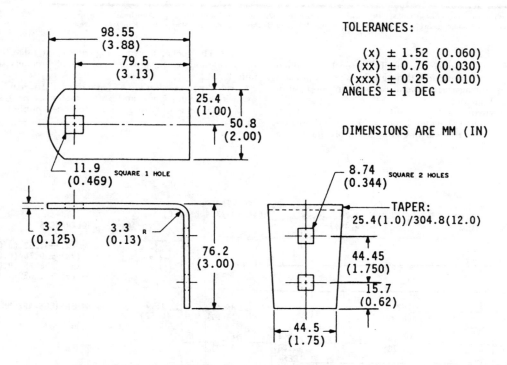

TOLERANCES:

(x) ± 1.52 (0.060)
(xx) ± 0.76 (0.030)
(xxx) ± 0.25 (0.010)
ANGLES ± 1 DEG

DIMENSIONS ARE MM (IN)

FIGURE 3—BRACKET FOR WARNING LAMP

SLOW-MOVING VEHICLE IDENTIFICATION EMBLEM
—SAE J943 JUN93

SAE Standard

Report of the Tractor Technical Committee approved June 1966. Revised by the Agricultural Tractor Technical Committee September 1983, and reaffirmed June 1988 and June 1993.

Foreword—This reaffirmed document has been changed only to reflect the new SAE Technical Standards Board format.

1. Scope

1.1 This SAE Standard establishes emblem dimensional specifications, performance requirements, related test procedures, and mounting requirements.

1.2 This unique identification emblem shall be used only on machines which are designed for and travel at rates of speed less than 40 km/h (25 mph).

1.3 The identification emblem shall supplement but not replace warning devices such as tail lamp regulators or flashing lights and shall not be used to identify stationary objects or stopped vehicles and/or machines.

1.4 The dimensions and color patterns of the emblem have been established as a unique identification and shall not be altered to permit advertising or other markings on the face of the emblem, except as permitted in 3.2.

1.5 Purpose—The purpose of this document is to establish specifications which define a unique identification emblem to be used only for slow-moving vehicles when operated or traveling on highways.

2. References

2.1 Applicable Documents—The following publications form a part of this specification to the extent specified herein. The latest issue of SAE publications shall apply.

2.1.1 SAE PUBLICATIONS—Available from SAE, 400 Commonwealth Drive, Warrendale, PA 15096-0001.

SAE J575—Tests for Motor Vehicle Lighting Devices and Components

SAE J594—Reflex Reflectors

2.1.2 ASAE PUBLICATION—Available from ASAE, 2950 Niles Road, St. Joseph, MI 49085-9659.

247

ASAE S277—Mounting Brackets and Socket for Warning Lamps and Slow-Moving Vehicle (SMV) Identification Emblem

2.1.3 ASTM PUBLICATIONS—Available from ASTM, 1916 Race Street, Philadelphia, PA 19103-1187.

ASTM D 1014—Conducting Exterior Exposure Tests of Paints on Steel

ASTM D 1788—Specifications for Rigid Acrylonitrile-Butadiene Styrene (ABS) Plastics

ASTM D 2794—Test for Resistance of Organic Coatings to the Effects of Rapid Deformation (Impact)

2.1.4 OTHER PUBLICATION

Handbook of Chemistry and Physics, 51st Ed.

2.2 Definitions

2.2.1 HIGHWAY—The entire width between the boundary lines of every way publicly maintained when any part thereof is open to the use of the public for purposes of vehicular travel.

2.2.2 PERMANENT-MOUNTED EMBLEM—A yellow-orange triangle with a dark red border as illustrated in Figure 1 and securely affixed to a machine.

2.2.3 PORTABLE EMBLEM—A yellow-orange triangle with a dark red border as illustrated in Figure 1 securely affixed to a backing material as illustrated in Figure 2 and displayed on a machine.

3. Description

3.1 The identification emblem, Figure 1, consists of a fluorescent, yellow-orange equilateral triangle with a dark red retroreflective border positioned with a point of the triangle up. The yellow-orange fluorescent triangle provides for daylight identification. The reflective border defines the shape of the fluorescent color in daylight and appears as a hollow red triangle in the path of motor vehicle headlights at night. The emblem may be permanently mounted or portable as defined in 2.2.2 and 2.2.3.

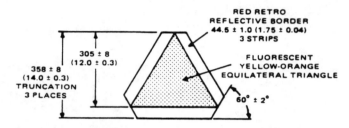

DIMENSIONS ARE IN MILLIMETERS WITH INCH EQUIVALENTS IN PARENTHESES.

NOTE: EMBLEM MUST BE MOUNTED WITH THE POINT UPWARD.

FIGURE 1—SLOW-MOVING VEHICLE IDENTIFICATION EMBLEM

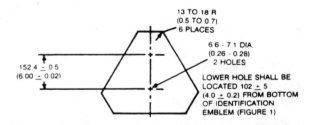

DIMENSIONS ARE IN MILLIMETERS WITH INCH EQUIVALENTS IN PARENTHESES.
BACKING MATERIAL SHALL BE AS LARGE AS OR LARGER THAN THE
IDENTIFICATION EMBLEM (FIGURE 1)

FIGURE 2—BACKING MATERIAL FOR PORTABLE SLOW-MOVING VEHICLE IDENTIFICATION EMBLEM

3.2 The emblem manufacturer shall place his name and address on the emblem, and may state that the emblem meets the requirements of this document. This information shall be clearly and permanently marked on the face of the emblem. It shall appear only in the lower center or lower right-hand corner of the emblem. On portable emblems, the information may be located on the reverse side of the backing material. When the information is located on the face of the emblem, it shall not include trademarks, symbols, or other types of promotional communications, and the total area used for such information on the face of the emblem shall not exceed 6.5 cm² (1 in²).

4. Performance Requirements

4.1 Visibility—The emblem shall be entirely visible in daylight and at night from all distances between 183 and 30 m (600 and 100 ft) from the rear when directly in front of the lawful upper beam of headlamps.

4.2 Emblem Dimensional Requirements—The size of the emblem shall be as shown in Figure 1.

4.3 Backing Material Dimensional Requirements—The size of the backing material for portable emblems shall be as shown in Figure 2.

4.4 Emblem Material—The reflective and fluorescent materials shall be tough, flexible, and of sufficient thickness and strength to meet the requirements of Sections 4 and 5. After the durability test, 5.2, the fluorescent and reflective materials shall show no appreciable cracking, crazing, blistering, loss of durable bond, or dimensional change, and reflective material shall show no appreciable discoloration.

4.4.1 FLUORESCENT MATERIAL—The yellow-orange color, purity, luminance, and peak reflectance of the fluorescent material shall be within the values shown in Table 1 before and after durability tests specified in 5.2. The test procedure for measuring fluorescent material is specified in 5.6.

4.4.2 REFLECTIVE MATERIAL—The dark red reflective material shall have minimum intensity values at each of the angles listed in Table 2 before and after durability tests specified in 5.2. The test procedure for measuring the reflective intensity values is specified in 5.5.

TABLE 1—FLUORESCENT VALUES

	Before Exposure Test	After Outdoor Exposure Test
Dominant wavelength, nm	602-610	585 min
Purity, percent	84 min	77 min
Luminance, percent	28 min	50 max
Peak reflectance observable at wavelength nearest dominant, percent	over 100	75 min

TABLE 2—MINIMUM REFLECTIVE LUMINANCE VALUES, R

Observation Angle, deg	Entrance Angle, deg (±)	Before Exposure Test	After Exposure Test
0.2	4	12.0	9.5
0.2	15	9.0	7.0
0.2	30	5.0	4.0
0.5	4	6.0	4.5
0.5	15	4.0	3.0
0.5	30	2.0	1.5

4.5 Backing Material for Portable Identification Emblems

4.5.1 Backing material for portable identification emblems shall be equivalent to 1.0 mm (0.04 in) minimum thickness aluminum; 22-gage, 0.8 mm (0.03 in) minimum thickness mill-galvanized or coated sheet steel; or 2.0 mm (0.08 in) minimum thickness ABS plastic as specified in ASTM D 1788.

4.5.2 The backing material shall be weatherable, semi-rigid, and have a surface receptive to a durable bond. The edges of the backing material shall be shaped to minimize personal injury during handling and when mounted on a machine. These backing materials shall withstand a minimum of 14 J (10 ft·lbf) using the falling dart procedure as described in 5.4.

4.6 All of these requirements are minimal and do not preclude the use of materials having superior performance.

5. Test Procedure

5.1 The emblem shall be tested in conformance with the following sections from SAE J575:

Paragraph 2.2—Definitions
Paragraph 3.1—Vibration Test
Paragraph 3.4—Corrosion Test (pertains to face of emblem only)

5.2 **Durability Test**—Samples mounted on backing material specified in 4.5.1 shall be exposed to the sun at an angle of 45 degrees to horizontal, facing upward and south, in nonmetallic racks, per ASTM D 1014. After the durability test (Table 3), the emblem material shall show no appreciable discoloration, cracking, crazing, blistering, loss of adhesion, or dimensional change, and shall meet the requirements set forth in 4.4.1 for fluorescent material, 4.4.2 for reflective materials, and the visibility requirements of 4.1.

TABLE 3—DURABILITY TEST

Location	Minimum Test Periods, Months Fluorescent Material	Minimum Test Periods, Months Reflective Material
Outside in South Florida	12	12

5.3 **Drop Test**—A portable emblem shall be dropped from a height of 1.8 m (6 ft) to a smooth hard surface equivalent to rigid metal or concrete. Each portable emblem shall be submitted to three drop tests; corner drop, edge drop, and flat surface drop. Failure shall be considered to have occurred when the emblem or the backing material will no longer meet the requirements of this document. The drop tests shall be conducted at both 24 °C (75 °F) and -23 °C (-10 °F).

5.4 **Impact Resistance of Backing Material**—This test procedure provides the means of determining the force required to fracture backing materials by a free-falling metal cylinder dropped vertically. The impact hammer shall be 15.88 mm (0.625 in) diameter and have a 15.88 mm (0.625 in) nose radius. The base shall be 31.8 mm (1.25 in) diameter, and the test specimen shall be a minimum of 102 mm (4 in) square. Test conditions shall be

at room temperature of 24 °C ± 2 °C (75 °F ± 3 °F), and failure will be any evidence of fracture or rupture of the backing material (see ASTM D 2794).

5.5 **Minimum Reflective Luminance Values, R**—Measurements shall be conducted in accordance with photometric testing procedures for reflex-reflectors as specified in SAE J594, except reference to area limitations need not be followed as long as area is greater than 6452 mm^2 (10 in^2). The maximum dimension of the test surface shall not be greater than 1.5 times the minimum dimension. The reflective luminance is computed from Equation 1:

$$R = \frac{(Lr)\left(d^2\right)}{(Ls)(A)} \qquad \text{(Eq.1)}$$

where:

R = Reflective luminance, candelas per square meter per incident lux (candle power per square foot per incident foot-candle)
Lr = Illumination incident upon the receiver at observation point, lux (foot-candles)
Ls = Illuminance incident upon a plane perpendicular to the incident ray at the test specimen position, lux (foot-candles)
d = Distance from test specimen to observation point, meters (feet)
A = Area of test surface, square meters (square feet)

5.6 **Fluorescent Color and Peak Reflectance**—The spectrophotometric color values of the fluorescent material shall be determined by using a Signature Model D-1, Color-Eye Spectrophotometer (Instrument Development Laboratories Division of Killmorgan Corporation) per Method "C" of instruction manual #4001-A or an equivalent spectrophotometer. Luminance shall be compared to that of barium sulfate under the International Commission of Illumination CIE Standard source C illuminant.

NOTE—"Vitrolite" standard plate calibrated by the National Bureau of Standards may be substituted for the barium sulfate standard.

If Signature Model D-1 is used, this procedure shall be followed. Barium sulfate standard and the specular insert shall be used. X, X', Y, and Z shall be determined, and the values for x and y shall be calculated as shown in 5.7. The dominant wavelength and purity shall be determined using x and y from CIE diagrams. The values for Y shall be the luminance factor recorded as percent. The peak reflectance obtained shall be recorded as the peak reflectance. If the peak reflectance is too high to be measured with the microdial, reverse the microdial, reverse the positions of the sample and standard so standard is at the rear and sample in front. Then take a new set of readings. The new reciprocal readings may be converted to peak reflectance by using the Reciprocal Table on page F247-1 270 in the "Handbook of Chemistry and Physics" 51st edition. The peak reflectance must be no lower than the values shown in 4.4.1. For other instruments, use the manufacturer's recommended procedures.

5.7 **Calculation Procedure for Fluorescent Material**

Reflectance measurements: Illuminant C—Barium sulphate as a standard

$X_{CIE} = 0.783 (X_{Color-Eye}) + 0.197 (X'_{Color-Eye})$
$Y_{CIE} = Y_{Color-Eye}$
$Z_{CIE} = 1.180 (Z_{Color-Eye})$

Transmittance measurements: Illuminant C—Either white Vitrolite or barium sulphate as a standard

$X_{CIE} = 0.783 (X_{Color-Eye}) + 0.197 (X'_{Color-Eye})$
$Y_{CIE} = Y_{Color-Eye}$
$Z_{CIE} = 1.180 (Z_{Color-Eye})$

The coefficients in the reflective formulae have been integrated from spectrophotometric curves on a General Electric recording spectrophotometer. In the transmittance formulae, the actual values of the glass coefficients do not enter the formula. Having obtained X, Y, Z (CIE), the coordinated x, y, and luminosity Y_{CIE} may be obtained as follows:

$$x = \frac{X}{X + Y + Z_{CIE}} \qquad \text{(Eq.2)}$$

$$y = \frac{Y}{X + Y + Z_{CIE}} \qquad \text{(Eq.3)}$$

$$Y_{CIE} = Y_{CIE}$$

When making measurements on CIE basis, the light source must be operated at calibrated voltage and the sphere must be clean. One method of comparison on the CIE basis is to compute the factors x, y, Y in the CIE system for sample and standard. The values for the standard will give the approximate location in the CIE diagram to determine the size of unit tolerance ellipses.[1]

6. Mounting

6.1 Both the permanently mounted emblem and the portable emblem shall be mounted with a point of the triangle upward (see Figure 1).

6.2 Emblems shall be mounted in a plane perpendicular, ±10 degrees, to the direction of travel and visible from the rear of a machine in accordance with Section 4.

6.3 The emblem shall be displayed as near to the rear and centered, or as near to the left of center of the machine or equipment as practicable. It shall be located 0.6 to 1.8 m (2 to 6 ft) above the ground measured from lower edge of the emblem.

6.4 The emblem shall be securely and rigidly affixed to the equipment. Portable emblems may be mounted by using the socket and identification emblem bracket specified in ASAE S277 or by other means that provide secure and rigid attachment.

6.5 The effective reflectivity and fluorescence of the emblem shall be unobscured to the extent that the triangular shape is readily identifiable both day and night.

6.6 When more than one machine is being operated or transported in a train or series, the emblem may be mounted on either the first machine or attached implement as long as the emblem is visible and identifiable from the rear of machines involved as described in 6.5.

---

[1] For CIE color difference work, reference is made to "Handbook of Colorimetry" by A. C. Hardy for descriptive information and CIE graphs, and "Colorimetry" by D. B. Judd for ellipse and other information.

FLASHING WARNING LAMP FOR AGRICULTURAL
EQUIPMENT—SAE J974 JUN93

SAE Standard

Report of the Tractor Technical Committee approved June 1967, editorial change April 1973. Reaffirmed by the SAE Agricultural Tractor Technical Committee January 1988, and again June 1993. Rationale statement available.

Foreword—This reaffirmed document has been changed only to reflect the new SAE Technical Standards Board format.

1. Scope—This SAE Standard covers the general requirements and the test requirements for a flashing warning lamp for agricultural equipment.

2. References

2.1 Applicable Documents—The following publications form a part of this specification to the extent specified herein. The latest issue of SAE publications shall apply.

2.1.1 SAE PUBLICATIONS—Available from SAE, 400 Commonwealth Drive, Warrendale, PA 15096-0001.

SAE J567—Lamp Bulb Retention System

SAE J575—Test Methods and Equipment for Lighting Devices and Components for Use on Vehicles Less than 2032 mm in Overall Width

SAE J578—Color Specification

SAE J588—Turn Signal Lamp for Use on Motor Vehicles Less than 2032 mm in Overall Width

2.2 Definition—This flashing warning lamp is a lighting device to indicate both forward and rearward the presence of agricultural equipment which normally travel at rates of speed below that of other traffic.

3. General Requirements

3.1 The lamp shall comply in both the forward and rearward direction with the candlepower requirements of a Class A turn signal, SAE J588, Table 1. In addition, the lamp shall project at least 4 cp on both sides at 90 degrees to the lamp axis.

3.2 The color of the light from the warning lamp shall be amber in accordance with SAE J578.

3.3 The lamp shall be flashed at least 60 fpm (flashes per minute) but not more than 120 fpm when it is operating.

3.4 The effective projected illuminated area measured on a plane at right angles to the axis of the lamp shall not be less than 77.5 cm^2 (12 in^2).

3.5 The bulb sockets shall comply with SAE J567.

4. Test Requirements—The flashing warning lamp shall be tested according to the following sections of SAE J575:

Section B—Samples for Test

Section C—Lamp Bulbs

Section D—Laboratory Facilities

Section E—Vibration Test

Section F—Moisture Test

Section G—Dust Test

Section H—Corrosion Test

Section J—Photometric Test—All beam candlepower measurements shall be made with the filament of the signal lamp at least 3 m (10 ft) from the photometer screen. The lamp axis is the horizontal line through the filament parallel to what would be the longitudinal axis of the vehicle if the lamp were mounted in its normal position on the vehicle.

Section L—Warpage Test on Devices with Plastic Lenses

HEADLAMPS FOR AGRICULTURAL EQUIPMENT
—SAE J975 JUN93

SAE Standard

Report of the Tractor Technical Committee approved June 1967 and reaffirmed by the SAE Agricultural Tractor Technical Committee January 1988, and again June 1993. Rationale statement available.

Foreword—This reaffirmed document has been changed only to reflect the new SAE Technical Standards Board format.

1. Scope—This SAE Standard provides performance and general design requirements and related test procedures for headlamps for use on agricultural equipment that may be operated on public roads.

2. References

2.1 Applicable Documents—The following publications form a part of this specification to the extent specified herein. The latest issue of SAE publications shall apply.

2.1.1 SAE PUBLICATIONS—Available from SAE, 400 Commonwealth Drive, Warrendale, PA 15096-0001.

SAE J572—Requirements for Sealed Lighting Unit for Construction and Industrial Machines

SAE J573—Miniature Lamp Bulbs

SAE J575—Test Methods and Equipment for Lighting Devices and Components for Use on Vehicles Less Than 2032 mm in Overall Width

SAE J598—Sealed Lighting Unit for Construction, Industrial, and Forest Machinery

SAE J760—Dimensional Specifications for General Service Sealed Lighting Units

2.2 Definition—A headlamp for agricultural equipment is a lighting device used to provide general illumination ahead of the vehicle.

3. General Requirements—The following sections from SAE J575 are part of this document:

Section B—Samples for Test

Section D—Laboratory Facilities

Section I—Color Tests—The color of the light from the lighting device shall be white.

Section J—Photometry—The photometric test shall be made with the photometer at a distance of at least 18.3 m (60 ft) from the lamp.

4. Dimensional Requirements—The headlamp shall conform to the dimensional requirements of either SAE J572 or SAE J760.

5. Electrical and Life Requirements—The headlamp shall conform to the appropriate requirements of either Table 2 of SAE J573 or Table 5 of SAE J598.

6. Beam Aim on Vehicle (Reference for photometric requirements only)

6.1 General Service Lamp (Trapezoidal)—The unit shall be aimed so that the top of the beam is at least 1 degree below lamp center level but not more than 4 degrees below lamp center level and centered laterally.

6.2 General Service Floodlamp—The unit shall be positioned with the lamp axis aimed downward to provide illumination close to the vehicle.

7. Photometric Requirements

7.1 General Service Lamp (Trapezoidal)—The unit shall comply with the photometric requirements of Table 3 of SAE J598.

7.2 General Service Floodlamp—The unit shall comply with the photometric requirements of Table 4 of SAE J598.

HEADLAMPS FOR INDUSTRIAL EQUIPMENT— SAE J95 MAR86

Report of the Construction and Industrial Machinery Technical Committee, approved May 1973, reaffirmed by the Off-Road Machinery Technical Committee, March 1986.

1. Scope—This SAE Standard provides performance and general design requirements and related test procedures for headlamps for use on industrial wheeled equipment that may be operated on public roads.

2. Definitions

2.1 Industrial wheeled equipment is defined as that class of tractors and associated equipment used in operations such as landscaping, construction services, loading, digging, grounds keeping, and highway maintenance.

2.2 A headlamp for industrial equipment is a lighting device used to provide general illumination ahead of the vehicle.

3. General Requirements—The following sections from SAE J575 are part of this standard:

Section B—Samples for Test

Section D—Laboratory Facilities

Section I—Color Tests—The color of the light from the lighting device shall be white.

Section J—Photometry—The photometric test shall be made with the photometer at a distance of at least 60 ft (18.3 m) from the lamp.

4. Dimensional Requirements—The headlamp shall conform to the dimensional requirements of either SAE J571, SAE J572, or SAE J760.

5. Electrical and Life Requirements—The headlamp shall conform to the appropriate requirements of either Table 2 of SAE J573 or Table 5 of SAE J598.

6. Beam Aim on Machine (Reference for photometric requirements only)

6.1 General Service Lamp (Trapezoidal)—The unit shall be aimed so that the top of the beam is at least 1 deg below lamp center level but not more than 4 deg below lamp center level and centered laterally.

6.2 General Service Floodlamp—The unit shall be positioned with the lamp axis aimed downward to provide illumination close to the vehicle.

7. Photometric Requirements

7.1 General Service Lamp (Trapezoidal)—The unit shall comply with the photometric requirements of Table 3 of SAE J598.

7.2 General Service Floodlamp—The unit shall comply with the photometric requirements of Table 4 of SAE J598.

8. Optional Headlamps—Optional with this specification, 7 in (178 mm) sealed beam units, or 5¾ in (146 mm) Type 1 and 5¾ in (146 mm) Type 2 sealed beam units meeting the requirements of SAE J579 may be used.

FLASHING WARNING LAMP FOR INDUSTRIAL EQUIPMENT—SAE J96 MAR86

Report of Construction and Industrial Machinery Technical Committee approved May 1973, reaffirmed by the Off-Road Machinery Technical Committee, March 1986.

1. Scope—This SAE Standard covers the general requirements and the test requirements for a flashing warning lamp for industrial wheeled equipment.

2. Definitions

2.1 Industrial wheeled equipment is defined as that class of tractors and associated equipment used in operations such as landscaping, construction services, loading, digging, grounds keeping, and highway maintenance.

2.2 This flashing warning lamp is a lighted device to indicate both forward and rearward the presence of industrial equipment which normally travel at rates of speed below that of other traffic.

3. General Requirements

3.1 The lamp shall comply in both the forward and rearward direction with the candela requirements of a turn signal lamp, SAE J588, Table 1. In addition, the lamp shall project at least 4 cd on both sides at 90 deg to the lamp axis.

3.2 The color of the light from the warning lamp shall be amber in accordance with SAE J578.

3.3 The lamp shall be flashed at least 60 fpm (flashes per minute) but not more than 120 fpm when it is operating.

3.4 The effective projected illuminated area measured on a plane at right angles to the axis of the lamp shall not be less than 12 in² (77.5 mm²).

3.5 The bulb sockets shall comply with SAE J567.

4. Test Requirements—The flashing warning lamp shall be tested according to the following sections of SAE J575:

Section B—Samples for Test

Section C—Lamp Bulbs

Section D—Laboratory Facilities

Section E—Vibration Test

Section F—Moisture Test

Section G—Dust Test

Section H—Corrosion Test

Section J—Photometric Test—All beam candela measurements shall be made with the filament of the signal lamp at least 10 ft (3 m) from the photometer screen. The lamp axis is the horizontal line through the filament parallel to what would be the longitudinal axis of the vehicle if the lamp were mounted in its normal position on the vehicle.

Section L—Warpage Test on Devices with Plastic Lenses

LIGHTING AND MARKING OF INDUSTRIAL EQUIPMENT ON HIGHWAYS—SAE J99 MAR86

SAE Standard

Report of the Construction and Industrial Machinery Technical Committee, approved May 1973, reaffirmed by the Off-Road Machinery Technical Committee, March 1986, and currently under revision by Subcommittee 5, Electrical Equipment.

1. Purpose—To provide specifications for lighting and marking of industrial wheeled equipment whenever such equipment is operated or traveling on a highway.

2. Definitions

2.1 Industrial Wheeled Equipment is defined as that class of tractors and associated equipment used in operations such as landscaping, construction services, loading, digging, grounds keeping, and highway maintenance.

2.2 Propelling Machines—Tractors or self-propelled units.

2.3 Towed, Semimounted, and Mounted Equipment—Equipment used in conjunction with propelling machines defined in paragraphs 2.1 and 2.2.

2.4 Highway—The entire width between the boundary lines of every way publicly maintained, when any part thereof is open to the use of the public for purposes of vehicular travel (Uniform Vehicle Code).

2.5 Reflectors—In this standard, reflectors are defined as reflex reflectors (SAE J594) or reflective material that shall be visible at night from all distances within 600 to 100 ft (182.9 to 30.5 m), when directly in front of lawful lower beams of headlamps. Reflective material shall meet the durability requirements for such material as specified in SAE J943.

3. Lighting and Marking Requirements

3.1 Lighting and marking for equipment defined in paragraph 2.3 shall include the following:

3.1.1 At least two headlamps conforming to SAE J95 and mounted at the same level and as widely spaced laterally as practicable. Lamps projecting a trapezoidal light pattern and mounted at a height of 7 ft (2.1 m) or less shall be aimed so that the top of the beam is at least 1 deg below lamp center level but not more than 4 deg below lamp center level, and centered laterally. Such lamps mounted above 7 ft (2.1 m) high shall be aimed so that the top of the beam is at least 6 deg below lamp center level and centered laterally. Lamps projecting a general flood pattern of light shall be aimed downward to provide illumination close to the machine.

3.1.2 At least one red tail lamp, conforming to SAE J94 or the test specification section of SAE J585, mounted to the rear of the machine as far to the left as practicable.

3.1.3 At least two amber flashing warning lamps, conforming to SAE J96, as widely spaced laterally as practicable, visible from both front and rear and mounted at the same level, and at least 42 in (1067 mm) high as measured to the lamp axis. Lamps shall flash in unison.

3.1.4 The flashing warning lamps may be used as turn indicators. When a turn is to be signaled, the flashing light opposite the direction of the turn shall become steady burning until such time that the turn signal is cancelled.

3.1.5 At least two red reflectors visible to the rear and mounted to indicate as nearly as practicable, the extreme left and extreme right projections. Reflectors may be incorporated as part of lensing in tail lamps described in paragraph 3.1.2.

3.1.6 One SMV (slow moving machine) emblem as described in SAE J943 or means for mounting the SMV emblem, such as a mounting socket as described in SAE J725. The SMV emblem or mounting facility shall be affixed as near to the rear and center of the machine as practicable.

3.2 Marking for equipment defined in paragraphs 2.1 and 2.2, and extending more than 4 ft (1.2 m) to the left of the center of the propelling machine, shall be as follows:

3.2.1 At least one amber reflector visible to the front and positioned to indicate, as nearly as practicable, the extreme left projection of the equipment.

3.3 Marking for equipment defined in paragraph 2.3, and (1) extending more than 4 ft (1.2 m) to the rear of the hitch point of the propelling machine, or (2) more than 4 ft (1.2 m) to the right or left of the centerline of the propelling machine, or (3) obscuring any rear lights on the propelling machine, shall be as follows:

3.3.1 At least two red reflectors visible to the rear and mounted to indicate, as nearly as practicable, the extreme left and extreme right projections.

3.4 Marking for equipment defined in paragraph 2.3, of such size as to obscure the SMV emblem on the propelling machine shall be as follows:

3.4.1 One SMV (slow moving machine) emblem as described in SAE J943 or means for mounting the SMV emblem, such as a mounting socket as described in SAE J725. The SMV emblem or mounting facility shall be affixed as near to the rear and center of the machine as practicable.

REQUIREMENTS FOR SEALED LIGHTING UNIT FOR CONSTRUCTION AND INDUSTRIAL MACHINES—SAE J572 MAY93   SAE Standard

Report of the Construction and Industrial Machinery Technical Committee and Lighting Committee, approved May 1951, revised by the Off-Road Machinery Technical Committee May 1986. Rationale statement available. Reaffirmed by the SAE Off-Road Machinery Technical Committee SC5—Electrical Equipment May 1993. Rationale statement available.

Foreword—This reaffirmed document has been changed only to reflect the new SAE Technical Standards Board format.

1. *Scope*—This SAE Standard applies to 145 mm nominal headlamp and floodlamp units.

1.1 Purpose—To define the dimensional requirements for sealed lighting units and assure their interchangeability.

2. *References*—There are no referenced publications specified herein.

3. *Requirements*—See Table 1 and Figure 1.

TABLE 1—DIMENSIONS FOR SEALED LIGHTING UNIT

Letter	mm	Letter	mm	Letter	mm	Letter	mm	Letter	mm
A	$144.78 \; ^{+0}_{-2.54}$	F	66.04	L	0.76	Q	0.88	U	23.36
B	$138.17 \; ^{+0}_{-1.01}$	G	$11.17 \; ^{+0}_{-0.63}$	M	$13.58 \; ^{+0}_{-1.77}$	R	$3.68 \; ^{+0.76}_{-0}$	V	$1.98 \; ^{+1.57}_{-0}$
C	130.04	H	$17.01 \; ^{+0.88}_{-0}$	N	$3.04 \; ^{+0.25}_{-0}$	S	126.52 ±3.04	W	6.35
D	$133.73 \; ^{+0}_{-0.76}$	J	0.88	P	$7.72 \; ^{+0.40}_{-0}$	T	13.46 ±1.01	X	$8.76 \; ^{+152}_{-0}$
E	1.52	K	0.76 +0.05						

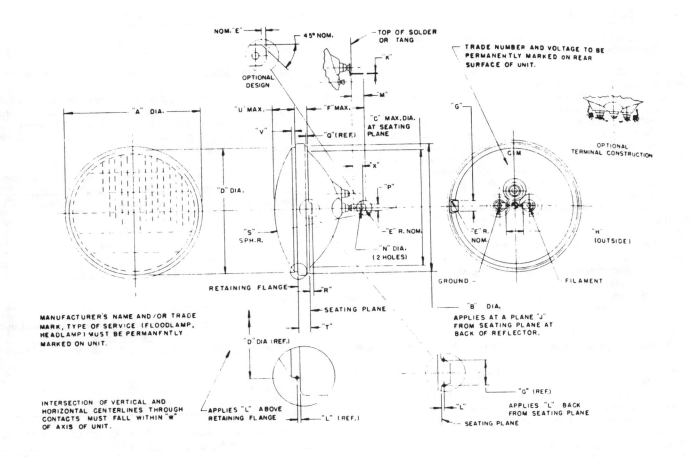

NOM. "E"

45° NOM.

TOP OF SOLDER OR TANG

"K"

"M"

TRADE NUMBER AND VOLTAGE TO BE PERMANENTLY MARKED ON REAR SURFACE OF UNIT.

"G"

OPTIONAL TERMINAL CONSTRUCTION

OPTIONAL DESIGN

"A" DIA.

"U" MAX.

"F" MAX.

"C" MAX. DIA. AT SEATING PLANE

"V"

"Q" (REF.)

"X"

"P"

"D" DIA.

C M

"S" SPH. R.

"E" R. NOM.

"E" R. NOM.

"N" DIA. (2 HOLES)

"H" (OUTSIDE)

RETAINING FLANGE

"R"

GROUND

FILAMENT

SEATING PLANE

"T"

"B" DIA.

MANUFACTURER'S NAME AND/OR TRADE MARK, TYPE OF SERVICE (FLOODLAMP, HEADLAMP) MUST BE PERMANENTLY MARKED ON UNIT.

"D" DIA (REF.)

APPLIES AT A PLANE "J" FROM SEATING PLANE AT BACK OF REFLECTOR.

INTERSECTION OF VERTICAL AND HORIZONTAL CENTERLINES THROUGH CONTACTS MUST FALL WITHIN "W" OF AXIS OF UNIT.

APPLIES "L" ABOVE RETAINING FLANGE

"L" (REF.)

"G" (REF.)

"L"

APPLIES "L" BACK FROM SEATING PLANE

SEATING PLANE

FIGURE 1—REQUIREMENTS

255

SEALED LIGHTING UNITS FOR CONSTRUCTION, INDUSTRIAL, AND FOREST MACHINERY
—SAE J598 JUN94

SAE Recommended Practice

Report of the Construction and Industrial Machinery Technical Committee and Lighting Committee approved February 1959. Completely revised by the Off-Road Machinery Technical Committee May 1987. Rationale statement available. Reaffirmed by the SAE Off-Road Machinery Technical Committee SC5—Electrical Equipment, June 1994.

Foreword—This reaffirmed document has been changed only to reflect the new SAE Technical Standards Board format.

1. Scope—This SAE Recommended Practice applies to floodlamp, headlamp, and general service lamp units intended for use on off-road self-propelled work machines classified as construction (1.1 and 1.2), general purpose industrial (2), and forestry machines (4), as noted in SAE J1116. Construction and Industrial Machinery is normally operated off highways; therefore, this document is not intended to be used as a basis for regulations by those having authority over motor vehicles used on public highways. Other performance and dimensional information is contained in SAE J572 and J760.

2. References

2.1 Applicable Documents—The following publications form a part of this specification to the extent specified herein. The latest issue of SAE publications shall apply.

2.1.1 SAE PUBLICATIONS—Available from SAE, 400 Commonwealth Drive, Warrendale, PA 15096-0001.

SAE J572—Requirements for Sealed Lighting Unit for Construction and Industrial Machines

SAE J575—Test Methods and Equipment for Lighting Devices and Components for Use on Vehicles Less Than 2032 mm in Overall Width

SAE J578—Color Specifications

SAE J760—Dimensional Specifications for General Service Sealed Lighting Units

SAE J1116—Categories of Off-Road Self-Propelled Work Machines

2.2 Definitions

2.2.1 FLOODLAMP (TRADE NO. 4078, 4478, 4578—145 MM (5-3/4 IN) NOMINAL DIAMETER; 4406, 4410, 4593, 4752—114 MM (4-1/2 IN) NOMINAL DIAMETER)—Recommended for general illumination of area close to the machine.

Typical usage—Track type machine, front and rear lamps

Wheeled tractor scraper, front lamp

Scraper bowl illumination

Motorgrader illumination

Tractor shovel bucket illumination

Off-highway truck backup illumination

2.2.2 GENERAL SERVICE LAMP (TRAPEZOIDAL BEAM) (TRADE NO. 4411, 4589—114 MM (4-1/2 IN) NOMINAL DIAMETER)—Recommended for general illumination.

Typical usage—Wheeled tractor shovel, front lamp

Motorgrader, front lamp

2.2.3 HEADLAMP (TRADE NO. 4080, 4480, 4880, 4813—145 MM (5-3/4 IN) NOMINAL DIAMETER; 4750—114 MM (4-1/2 IN) NOMINAL DIAMETER)—The headlamp has a single beam with a sharp cutoff at the top to reduce glare to other vehicles and to minimize reflection from dust.

2.2.4 HEADLAMP (TRADE NO. 4814—145 MM (5-3/4 IN) NOMINAL DIAMETER)—This headlamp has a concentrated beam for high-speed operation.

3. Laboratory Requirements

3.1 The following sections of SAE J575 are a part of this document.

3.1.1 SECTION 2.2—DEFINITIONS

3.1.2 SECTION 3.5—PHOTOMETRY TEST—The photometric test shall be made with the photometer at a distance of at least 18.3 m (60 ft) from the lamp. The unit shall be operated at its design voltage during the tests. For test values, see Tables 1 to 6. A tolerance of ±1/4 degree shall be allowed for any test point. Beam aim during photometric test shall be as follows:

1. Floodlamp and General Service Lamp Units—Visually center the beam vertically and horizontally on the photometer axis.
2. Headlamp Unit—Visually center the beam laterally on the photometer axis with the top cutoff of the beam 1 degree below photometer axis.
3. High-Speed Driving Lamp—Visually center the beam laterally on the photometer axis with the center of the high intensity zone 1/2 degree down from the lamp center level.

3.2 Color Test—The color of the light from the lighting device shall be white, as defined in SAE J578.

4. Physical Dimensions—Table 7 lists dimensional data for the lamps referred to in Tables 1 to 6.

5. Additional Specifications—Table 7 lists electrical and life specifications.

6. Additional Information—The units whose characteristics are shown in Tables 3 and 4 are also widely used for purposes other than construction and industrial machinery lighting. The tables are presented to facilitate lamp application and machine design.

TABLE 1—TEST POINT VALUES FOR FLOODLAMP[1] 145 MM (5-3/4 IN) NOMINAL DIAMETER (TRADE NO. 4078, 4478, 4578)

Position, degrees	Min cd	Position, degrees	Min cd
10U-V	750	H-20R and 20L	500
10U-10R and 10L	500	5D-V	1000
10U-20R and 20L	250	5D-10R and 10L	750
5U-V	1000	5D-20R and 20L	500
5U-10R and 10L	750	10D-V	750
5U-20R and 20L	500	10D-10R and 10L	500
H-V	1000	10D-20R and 20L	250
H-10R and 10L	750		

[1] The extremities of the beam should be diffused.

TABLE 2—TEST POINT VALUES FOR HEADLAMP, 145 MM (5-3/4 IN) NOMINAL DIAMETER (TRADE NO. 4080, 4480, 4880)

Position, degrees	Max cd	Min cd	Position, degrees	Max cd	Min cd
1U-10R and 10L	500	—	3D-10R and 10L	—	3000
H-10R and 10L	1000	—	3D-15R and 15L	—	1500
1-1/2D-V	—	3000	5D-V	—	3000
1-1/2D-10R and 10L	—	1500	5D-15R and 15L	—	750
1-1/2D-15R and 15L	—	1000	8D-V	—	1000
3D-V	—	6000	8D-10R and 10L	—	600

TABLE 3—TEST POINT VALUES FOR GENERAL SERVICE LAMP, 114 MM (4-1/2 IN) NOMINAL DIAMETER (TRADE NO. 4411, 4589)

Position, degrees	Min cd	Position, degrees	Min cd
10U-V	1500	H-8R and 8L	650
10U-5R	1200	10D-V	500
H-V	1000	10D-12R and 12L	300

TABLE 4—TEST POINT VALUES FOR GENERAL SERVICE FLOODLAMP, 114 MM (4-1/2 IN) NOMINAL DIAMETER (TRADE NO. 4406, 4410, 4593)

Position, degrees	Min cd	Position, degrees	Min cd
15U-V	250	H-40R and 40L	175
15U-40R and 40L	125	15D-V	250
H-V	400	15D-40R and 40L	125

TABLE 5—TEST POINT VALUES FOR HEADLAMP, 145 MM (5-3/4 IN) NOMINAL DIAMETER (TRADE NO. 4813, 90W, SINGLE BEAM HEADLAMP UNIT

Position, degrees	Max cd	Min cd	Position, degrees	Max cd	Min cd
1U-10R and 10L	500	—	3D-10R and 10L	—	5000
H-10R and 10L	1000	—	3D-15R and 15L	—	2000
1-1/2D-V	—	5 000	5D-V	—	5000
1-1/2D-10R and 10L	—	2 000	5D-15R and 15L	—	450
1-1/2D-15R and 15L	—	500	8D-V	—	500
3D-V	—	10 000	8D-10R and 10L	—	300

TABLE 6—TEST POINT VALUES FOR HEADLAMP, 145 MM (5-3/4 IN) NOMINAL DIAMETER (TRADE NO. 4814, 90W, HIGH-SPEED DRIVING LAMP UNIT)

Position, degrees	Max cd	Min cd	Position, degrees	Max cd	Min cd
1U-10R and 10L	600	—	3D-10R and 10L	—	400
H-10R and 10L	1500	—	3D-15R and 15L	—	100
1-1/2D-V	—	20 000	5D-V	—	3500
1-1/2D-10R and 10L	—	700	5D-15R and 15L	—	100
1-1/2D-15R and 15L	—	100	8D-V	—	500
3D-V	—	12 000	8D-10R and 10L	—	100

7. Installation Recommendations—(These recommendations are not a part of the test specification.)

7.1 The units recommended have been evaluated for lighting performance with satisfactory results in average job situations when used as suggested under definitions.

7.2 Dimensional interchangeability among types and voltages make it possible for the equipment designer or operator to choose units to suit the wide variety of lighting tasks met in service.

7.3 These units have been selected with special emphasis on light for working conditions and lamp durability which are best provided by units producing only a single beam. Because machines that travel on construction haul roads often encounter traffic similar to highway conditions, careful aiming of the lighting units is required. Headlamp systems composed of these single beam types have been made that restrict glare to acceptable limits, while maintaining adequate illumination for the work areas. This approach avoids the necessity of using dimming switches. Systems employing four or more units, combining headlamps and floodlamps, without dimming switches, have been devised which provide a marked improvement in operating efficiency.

7.4 Good results from a construction and industrial machinery lighting system require ample provision for individual adjustment of the lamp unit aim, depending on the particular lighting task. Some applications have been used to advantage with vertical aims from 30 degrees below to 15 degrees above the horizontal and with lateral aims from 15 degrees left to 15 degrees right.

7.5 Service life or units may be materially prolonged by mountings properly designed to cushion the unit from shock and vibration loading inherent in construction machinery. Where space permits, it is recommended that the 145 mm (5-3/4 in) nominal diameter units be specified to obtain maximum illumination.

TABLE 7—SEALED UNITS FOR CONSTRUCTION AND INDUSTRIAL MACHINES

Type of Service[1]	Trade No.	Design Watts	Design Volts	Rated Average Lab Life Hr at V	Max AMP of Design Volts	Filament Type	Bulb Size	Maximum Diameter mm	Maximum Diameter in	Max Overall Length mm	Max Overall Length in	Dimensional Specification	Terminal
							6 V CIRCUITS						
1	4078	50	6.4	500 at 7	8.2	C-6	PAR 46	144.78	5.70	101.6	4	Figure 1[2]	Lug
2	4080	60	6.4	500 at 7	8.2	C-6	PAR 46	144.78	5.70	101.6	4	Figure 1[2]	Lug
							12 V CIRCUITS						
1	4406	35	12.8	300 at 14	2.93	C-6	PAR 36	113.28	4.46	69.85	2-3/4	Figure 2[3]	Screw
1	4410	35	12.8	300 at 14	2.93	C-6	PAR 36	113.28	4.46	69.85	2-3/4	Figure 2[3]	Screw
3	4411	35	12.8	300 at 14	2.93	C-6	PAR 36	113.28	4.46	69.85	2-3/4	Figure 2[3]	Screw
1	4478	60	13	800 at 14	4.9	2-C6 in Ser.	PAR 46	144.78	5.70	101.6	4	Figure 1[2]	Lug
2	4480	60	13	800 at 14	4.9	2-C6 in Ser.	PAR 46	144.78	5.70	101.6	4	Figure 1[2]	Lug
							24 V CIRCUITS						
1	4578	60	28	800 at 28	2.3	2-C6 in Ser.	PAR 46	144.78	5.70	101.6	4	Figure 1[2]	Lug
3	4589	50	28	400 at 28	1.95	CC-6	PAR 36	113.28	4.46	69.85	2-3/4	Figure 2[3]	Screw
1	4593	50	28	400 at 28	1.95	CC-6	PAR 36	113.28	4.46	69.85	2-3/4	Figure 2[3]	Screw
2	4750	60	28	800 at 28	2.3	2-C6 in Ser.	PAR 36	113.28	4.46	69.85	2-3/4	Figure 2[3]	Screw
1	4752	60	28	800 at 28	2.3	2-C6 in Ser.	PAR 36	113.28	4.46	69.85	2-3/4	Figure 2[3]	Screw
2	4813	90	28	800 at 28	3.4	2-C6 in Ser.	PAR 46	144.78	5.70	101.6	4	Figure 1[2]	Lug
4	4814	90	28	800 at 28	3.4	2-C6 in Ser.	PAR 46	144.78	5.70	101.6	4	Figure 1[2]	Lug
2	4880	60	28	800 at 28	2.3	2-C6 in Ser.	PAR 46	144.78	5.70	101.6	4	Figure 1[2]	Lug

NOTE—Service life of construction machine light units might not equal laboratory life because of vibration, shock, and variations in vehicle voltage.

[1] Numbers designate type of service
    1—Floodlamp
    2—Headlamp
    3—General Service Lamp
    4—High-Speed Driving Lamp
[2] See SAE J572
[3] See SAE J760

LIGHTING AND MARKING OF CONSTRUCTION AND INDUSTRIAL MACHINERY—SAE J1029 MAR86

SAE Recommended Practice

Report of the Construction and Industrial Machinery Technical Committee, approved March 1974, reaffirmed by the Off-Road Machinery Technical Committee, March 1986. This report is currently under revision by Subcommittee 5, Electrical Equipment, of the Off-Road Machinery Technical Committee.

(Construction and industrial machinery is normally operated off-highways, therefore, this SAE Recommended Practice is not intended to be used as a basis for regulations by those having authority over motor vehicles used on public highways.)

1. Purpose—The purpose of this recommended practice is to establish the minimum requirements for lighting and marking construction and industrial machinery.

2. Scope

2.1 The following types of machinery are within the scope of this specification:

Track type—Tractors and end loaders.

Rubber tired—Pusher-dozers, end loaders, tractor scrapers, trucks, motor graders, and wagons.

Roller compactors—Self-propelled.

2.2 This specification applies to the mounted lights and markers required for forward illumination when the machine is traveling up to its maximum rated speed, illuminating the work area close to the machine when working at low speed, and identifying the machine when it is operating at its normal work site.

3. Forward Lighting

3.1 This section applies to the lighting requirements for illuminating the area ahead of the machine when operated in its normal direction of travel at its maximum rated speed.

3.2 At least two headlamps or two floodlamps conforming to SAE J598 shall be used. They shall be symmetrically mounted and located so both are visible from the entire length of a line located 50 ft (15.2 m) in front of, and extending 25 ft (7.6 m) to, either side of the centerline of the machine.

3.3 Forward lighting shall provide adequate illumination for a distance that exceeds the machine stopping distance. Stopping distance from the machine maximum rated speed shall include the distance traveled during the operator reaction time interval added to the braking distance.

The distance traveled during a 1.5 s operator reaction time interval can be computed by the formulas:

$$D(ft) = 2.2 \times mph$$
$$D(m) = 0.4167 \times km/h$$

Braking distance from machine maximum rated speed shall be established using the procedure described in the latest revision of SAE J166, J319, J236, and J237. These procedures shall be used as reference in establishing the braking distances for lighting purposes for types of vehicles not covered in the minimum braking specifications.

3.4 Various combinations of head and floodlamps conforming to SAE J598 have been developed for use in earthmoving applications. Table 1 can be used to select units that will fulfill the forward lighting requirements.

4. Work Area Lighting

4.1 The construction and industrial machinery applicable to this specification, as listed in paragraph 2.1, is operated over a wide variety of speeds, terrains, and climatic conditions. Numerous types of mounted or drawn work tools are available for performing a multitude of different work assignments. Much of this work is done at slow speeds and/or under hazardous conditions with many directions of travel. Thus, it is not always possible to predict accurately the lighting needs for the life of the machine at the time of manufacture. The following guidelines should be used by the manufacturer, distributor, and user to select lamps for properly illuminating the work areas for the intended machine work applications.

4.2 Floodlamp—Trade Nos. 4078, 4478, 4578, 4406, 4410, 4593 are recommended for general illumination of area close to the machine.

TABLE 1

Stopping Distance from Maximum Machine Rated Speed		Lamp Units[a]		Recommended Aiming Instructions
ft	m	24V	12V	
Up to 100	Up to 30.5	Two 4578	Two 4478 or Two 4406 or Two 4410	Center of beam horizontal
Up to 200	Up to 61	—	Two 4411	High intensity portion of beam horizontal
Up to 250	Up to 76	Two 4880 or Four 4880 or Two 4813	Two 4480 or Four 4480	Top of beam cut off horizontal
Up to 350	Up to 107	Two 4813[b] and Two 4880	—	Top of beam cut off 1 deg above horizontal / Top of beam cut off horizontal
Up to 500	Up to 152	Two 4814[b] and Two 4813	—	Top of beam cut off 1 deg above horizontal / Top of beam cut off horizontal

[a] Lamp unit numbers shown are industry numbers.
[b] To restrict glare to acceptable limits, provisions for dimming are recommended.

4.2.1 TYPICAL USAGE—Track-type vehicle front and rear lamp, scraper bowl lamp, motor grader blade lamp, tractor shovel bucket lamp, off-highway truck backup lamp, ripper lamp.

4.3 General Service Lamp—Trade Nos. 4411, 4480, 4880, 4589 are recommended for general illumination of areas a moderate distance from machine.

4.3.1 TYPICAL USAGE—Rubber-tired end loader front lamp, motor grader front lamp.

5. Lighting Equipment for Rear of Machine

5.1 This section specifies the types of lighting equipment and reflectors to be used to identify the machine when it is working at its normal job site. Lighting equipment should have performance equal to or greater than the applicable specifications.[1]

5.2 Rubber-Tired End Loader and Pusher Dozer, Self-Propelled Compactor—Two stop lamps, two tail lamps, and backup lamp for after-dark operation. Two stop lamps for daylight operation.

5.3 Rubber-Tired Truck—Two tail lamps for night operation. Two stop lamps for day or night operation. One backup for day or night operation.

5.4 Rubber-Tired Motor Grader—Two tail lamps for night operation. Two stop lamps for night operation.

---

[1] Stop lamps conforming to SAE J585.

Tail lamps conforming to SAE J586 (except that 24 V lighting equipment will be considered acceptable if it complies with 75% of the minimum photometric values shown.)

Backup lamps conforming to SAE J598.

ALL-TERRAIN VEHICLE HEADLAMPS
—SAE J1623 FEB94

SAE Recommended Practice

Report of the SAE Special Purpose Vehicle Committee approved February 1994.

1. Scope—This SAE Recommended Practice provides test procedures and performance requirements for all-terrain vehicle headlamps.

2. References

2.1 Applicable Document—The following publication forms a part of this specification to the extent specified herein.

2.1.1 SAE PUBLICATION—Available from SAE, 400 Commonwealth Drive, Warrendale, PA 15096-0001.

SAE J575 JUL83—Tests for Motor Vehicle Lighting Devices and Components

2.2 Definitions

2.2.1 ALL-TERRAIN VEHICLE (ATV)—An all-terrain vehicle is any motorized off-highway vehicle 1270 mm (50 in) or less in overall width, with an unladen dry weight of 275 kg (600 lb) or less, designed to travel on four low-pressure tires, having a seat designed to be straddled by the operator and handlebars for steering control, and intended for use by a single operator and no passenger. Width and weight shall be exclusive of accessories and optional equipment.

2.2.2 ALL-TERRAIN VEHICLE (ATV) HEADLAMP—An all-terrain vehicle headlamp is one or more lamps used as the major lighting device to provide general illumination ahead of an all-terrain vehicle.

3. General Requirements

3.1 If multiple headlamps are used to meet this document, the combination of lamps, as mounted on the ATV, shall meet the requirements when treated as one lamp.

3.2 The following sections from SAE J575 JUL83 are a part of this document:

a. Section 2—Samples for Tests
b. Section 2.2—Bulbs
c. Section 3—Laboratory Facilities
d. Section 4.2—Moisture Test
e. Section 4.3—Dust Test
f. Section 4.4—Corrosion Test
g. Section 4.6—Photometry Test
h. Section 4.8—Warpage Test on Devices With Plastic Components

4. Vibration Test

4.1 Scope—This test evaluates the ability of the sample device to resist damage from vibration-induced stresses. This test is not intended to test the vibration resistance of bulbs or the internal components of sealed-beam units.

4.2 Test Equipment—Illustrations giving the essential arrangement and dimensions for a test machine is satisfactory for the vibration test required are shown in Figure 1. Any vibration test machine which provides the displacement and frequency specified may be used.

4.3 Test Procedure—A sample unit shall be mounted to a vibration test machine and vibrated 12.5 Hz through a distance of 3.2 mm.

4.4 Test Duration—The test shall be continuous for 1 h.

4.5 Requirements—Upon completion of test procedure 4.3 and 4.4, any unit showing evidence of material physical weakness, lens or reflector rotation, displacement, cracking or rupture of parts except bulb failure(s), shall be considered to have failed. Any rotation of a lens or reflector that occurs does not constitute failure of the test if the device still meets the photometric requirements with the component(s) in their rotated, post-vibration test position.

259

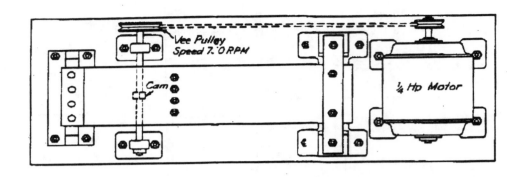

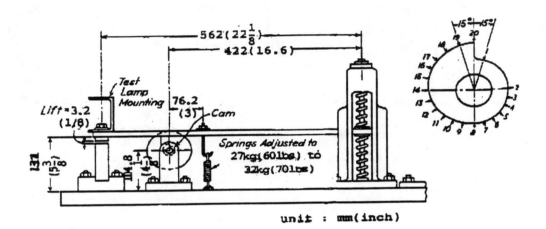

unit : mm(inch)

CAM PROFILE RADII

Point	Radius mm (in)	Point	Radius mm (in)	Point	Radius mm (in)	Point	Radius mm (in)
1	12.70 (0.5000)	6	13.98 (0.5504)	11	15.96 (0.6284)	16	17.94 (0.7064)
2	12.70 (0.5000)	7	14.38 (0.5660)	12	16.36 (0.6440)	17	18.34 (0.7220)
3	12.92 (0.5088)	8	14.77 (0.5816)	13	16.75 (0.8596)	18	18.74 (0.7376)
4	13.19 (0.5192)	9	15.17 (0.5972)	14	17.15 (0.6752)	19	18.96 (0.7466)
5	13.58 (0.5348)	10	15.57 (0.6128)	15	17.55 (0.6908)	20	19.05 (0.7500)

The cam width is to be between 12.70 mm (1/2 in) and 25.40 mm (1 in).

FIGURE 1—VIBRATION TEST MACHINE

5. Photometric Test

5.1 Scope—This test evaluates the ability of the headlamp or headlamps to meet the applicable luminous intensity requirements in Tables 1 and 2.

5.2 Beam Aim—If the test unit is equipped with upper- and lower-beam patterns, the upper beam shall be aimed so that the center of the zone of highest intensity falls at 1/2D-V. If the test unit has a single beam, the beam shall be aimed so that the zone of highest intensity falls at 1-1/2D-V. The center of the zone of highest intensity shall be established by the intersection of a horizontal plane passing through the point of maximum intensity, and the vertical plane established by balancing the photometric values at 3 degrees left and 3 degrees right.

5.3 Requirements—The headlamp shall be operated at its designed voltage during the photometric test. When treated as one lamp, the beam or beams from the headlamp shall be designed to conform to the applicable luminous intensity requirements in Tables 1 and 2, measured by a photometer positioned at least 18 m from the headlamp. A tolerance of 0.25 degree in location may be allowed for any test point.

6. Installation Requirements—The following requirements apply to the devices as used on the vehicle and are not part of laboratory test requirements and procedures.

260

TABLE 1—UPPER BEAM	
Test Point (degrees)	Intensity (cd)
H-V	3000 min
1/2D-V	10 000 min
1/2D-3L & R	3000 min
1/2D-6L & R	750 min
1D-V	5000 min
2D-V	2500 min
3D-V	1500 min
3D-6L & R	400 min
4D-V	5000 max
Any	75 000 max

TABLE 2—LOWER BEAM OR SINGLE BEAM	
Test Point (degrees)	Intensity (cd)
1/2U-2L & R	2500 max
1/2U-4L & R	2000 max
2D-V	2500 min
3D-4L & R	1500 min
3D-6L & R	750 min

6.1 A means shall be provided to adjust the optical axis of the headlamp a minimum of ±2 degrees in the vertical direction.

6.2 If the ATV is equipped with a headlamp having both upper and lower beams, switching between the upper and lower beams should be by means of a switch located so that it may be operated conveniently by the operator's hand or foot.

REQUIREMENTS FOR COMPOSITE LIGHTING ASSEMBLIES USED ON CONSTRUCTION AND INDUSTRIAL MACHINERY—SAE J2121 APR95

SAE Standard

Report of the SAE Off-Road Machinery Technical Committee SC5—Electrical Equipment approved April 1995. Rationale statement available.

1. Scope—This SAE Standard provides general design performance requirements and related test procedures for composite lighting unit assemblies, other than signaling and marking devices, used on construction and industrial machines as defined in SAE J1116.

1.1 Purpose—To provide general guidelines and design parameters for lighting assemblies used on construction and industrial machinery.

2. References

2.1 Applicable Documents—The following publications form a part of this specification to the extent specified herein. Unless otherwise specified, the latest issue of SAE publications shall apply.

2.1.1 SAE PUBLICATIONS—Available from SAE, 400 Commonwealth Drive, Warrendale, PA 15096-0001.

SAE J180—Electrical Charging Systems for Construction and Industrial Machinery

SAE J1116—Categories of Off-Road Self Propelled Work Machines

2.1.2 ASTM PUBLICATION—Available from ASTM, 1916 Race Street, Philadelphia, PA 19103-1187.

ASTM B 117-90—Standard Test Method of Salt Spray (Fog) Testing

3. Definitions

3.1 Composite Lighting Assembly—A lighting device comprised of lens, reflector and holding mechanism, housing, and a replaceable light source.

3.2 Design Beam Pattern—The beam distribution which establishes 90% of the light output. It is defined typically by angular degrees horizontal by angular degrees vertical.

3.3 Design Voltage—That voltage assigned by the burner manufacturer to establish the specifications for current, light output, and life.

3.4 Test Fixture—A fixture which simulates the mounting interface of the lighting unit to a machine. It may be used for the icing and pressure water test.

3.5 Design Life—The rated quiescent life of a burner or light source in hours, at design voltage. The B_{10} Stand Life.

3.6 Application Voltage—The voltage, generated and distributed by the machine electrical system, that is applied to the lamp terminals.

4. Light Source Requirements

4.1 Life—Acceptable life is often determined by the application requirements. These are primarily shock, vibration, voltage transients, and steady-state voltage. The design life of the light source shall be mutually agreed upon between lamp manufacturer and machine manufacturer.

4.2 Steady-State Voltage—The control of steady-state voltage can be very important in the application of a light assembly (especially tungsten lamps).

For tungsten lamps, the re-rating rules are:
a. Rerated Light Power = $(V/V_D)^{3.5}$ x light power at V_D
b. Rerated Life = $(V_D/V)^{12}$ x life at V_D
c. Rerated Current = $(V/V_D)^{0.55}$ x current at V_D

where:
V = Application voltage
V_D = Design voltage

In order to maximize the life and effectiveness of a lamp, the application voltage should be identical to the design voltage. The application voltage is the result of the following:
a. Alternator output voltage which is dictated by the requirements to recharge the battery.
b. Voltage drops resulting from the various control devices such as switches, circuit breakers, etc., in the lamp circuit.
c. Voltage drop in the electrical cables and ground return of the lamp circuit.

The application voltage is typically adjusted by selecting the lamp circuit cable to provide the appropriate resistance and voltage drop.

Quiescent life tests shall be performed at the nominal design voltage level within 0.1 V. The voltage shall be measured at the light assembly electrical interface.

4.3 Voltage Transients—As shown in Table 1, voltage transients take on many forms depending on their source. Transients can cause immediate failure or significantly shorten the life of the lamp. The system design shall take into account these transients to eliminate or reduce their effect on the life of the light assemblies.

TABLE 1—TRANSIENT VOLTAGES	
Cause	Effect
Voltage Regulator Failure	50% over Voltage
Jump Starts	100% over Voltage
Alternator Load Dump (Disconnect Battery)	12V System: $(14+100\ e^{-t/.2})$ V 24V System: $(28+200\ e^{-t/.2})$ V (t=time in seconds)
Inductive Load Transients	$\pm 200\ e^{-t/.2}$ V (t=time in seconds)
Mutual Coupling in Harness	$\pm 200\ e^{-t/.001}$ V (t=time in seconds)
Accessory Noise	1.5 vpk (50 Hz to 10 kHz)
Radio Frequency Interference	R F Energy
Machine Welding	100% over Voltage

5. Operating Ambient Temperature—The light assembly shall operate throughout the temperature range of −40 to 85 °C. No permanent deformation or cracking is acceptable throughout this range over the design life of the assembly.

6. Maximum Operating Temperature—If contact with the lens or housing is likely due to the lamp mounting location, consideration shall be given to the surface temperatures and the protection that may be required.

7. Shock and Vibration—Shock and vibration are common in off-road equipment and the following situations are typical: Operating over rough terrain, running into immovable objects, and using the mounted tools as hammers. The shock levels induced and the resulting structural vibrations have a negative effect upon light filament life. Light mounting methods and locations should be selected to reduce shock and vibration effects. Both level and frequency are important to the overall life of the light. Lower voltage filaments are more rugged and are better able to withstand shock and vibration.

The test criteria to evaluate the ability of the light assembly to withstand shock and vibration shall be determined and agreed upon by the lamp manufacturer and the machine manufacturer. The test criteria shall define the frequency range, acceleration, length of test in each axis, sweep rate, and the power cycle in order to establish a quantitative value of lamp life for the application.

8. Dust—The light assembly shall be sealed to dust and the following dust test shall be used. An initial light power test to measure peak candlepower shall be performed. An enclosure, with a minimal inside dimension of 1 m shall contain 15 kg of AC fine dust (as referenced in SAE J180). The light assemblies shall be mounted not closer than 150 mm from any wall in the normal operating orientation toward the bottom of the enclosure. Every 15 min the dust shall be agitated by a fan blower for enough time to completely and uniformly diffuse the dust throughout the enclosure. The dust is then allowed to settle.

This test is to continue for 500 h. After the dust test, each assembly exterior is to be cleaned and the peak candlepower determined. The light assembly shall be operable within 90% of its initial value to pass this test.

9. Moisture Sealing

9.1 Pressure Washer—The light assembly, as installed, shall not accept water internally from a high-pressure washer when operated at 140 bar with a solid cone angle and orifice of 2 mm. The nozzle shall pass not closer than 300 mm from the front surface of the light during washing while the light is mounted into its test fixture in its proper orientation.

9.2 Rain and Shine—The light assembly, as installed, shall be subjected to 100 cycles of rain and shine operation. Each cycle shall consist of 1 h of simulated precipitation of 5.0 mm/h of water from one or more solid cone nozzles followed by 1 h where the test sample lamp is energized at rated voltage. After the 100 cycle test, the samples shall be examined. Moisture ingression or corrosion that results in degradation in performance shall constitute a failure.

10. Fluid Compatibility—The light assembly shall remain functional and shall not degrade when it comes into contact with chemicals commonly used in off-road machinery. The assembly will be brushed with engine oil, hydraulic and transmission oils, #1 diesel fuel, brake fluid, ethylene glycol, and phosphatizing agents at room temperature. The samples shall be completely brushed eight times with each fluid with a 1 h interval between each brushing. The samples will be allowed to stand 16 h minimum in this condition. At the completion of this period, rinse, air dry, and then test the light assemblies with criteria being 90% of its initial peak light output and no discoloration or degradation.

11. Icing—The light assembly shall show no damage when allowed to ice over. The test procedure for each 24 h cycle is shown in Figure 1. The light assembly may be mounted into its test fixture for this test. The light assembly and test fixture shall be turned upward to aid in distributing the water over the exterior surface. The light assemblies shall be subjected to ten of these 24 h cycles. Any assemblies found with cracks, open seams, or other damage shall because for failure of this test.

Hour	0	1	2	3	4	5	6	7	8	9	10	11	12	13	14	15	16	17	18	19	20	21	22	23	24
Time Period		A		B									C									D	E	F	

Time Period	Procedure
A	For 3 s every 15 min the surface of the light assembly shall be sprayed with a fine mist of water cooled to 0 to 3 °C while the light assembly is cooled from room temperature to −5 °C.
B	Spray mist shall continue with the light assembly temperature maintained at −5 °C.
C	Test fixtures shall be cooled from −5 to −40 °C over a 16 h period without any further spraying.
D	Light assembly shall be energized for 1 h and then removed from the cold chamber.
E	Light assembly shall be energized for 1 h while at room temperature.
F	Light assembly shall be rinsed, dried, and reviewed for any damage along the surfaces and seams of the light assembly.

FIGURE 1—ICING TEST PROCEDURE

12. Illumination Performance—The light output or performance is a function of the intended design and application. The illumination effects in any given application are very subjective and need to be quantified by measurable features. Measurable parameters of this performance are beam pattern intensities, measured in candela, and beam distribution as displayed in an iso-candela curve or contour plot.

General desirable qualities of all beam pattern distributions are smooth, even lighting gradients throughout the entire beam pattern. This will eliminate hot spots, voids, and stria which can cause false cuing or poor acuity to the operator of a machine using this light pattern.

To allow for the optimum flexibility in providing lighting pattern that perform specific illumination objectives, an agreement between the supplier and customer should be reached as to the desired characteristics of the lighting pattern and method of measurment. Two methods of depicting lamp output are shown in Figure 2 (vertical plane) and Figure 3 (horizontal or ground plane).

13. Corrosion Environment (As Required)—Corrosion environments exist throughout the world where salt air and salt water splash, and immersion of the light assembly may occur. Where operation in a salt-free environment is intended, this test may not be applicable. It is recommended that grounds be isolated from the structure because positive voltages tend to accelerate the corrosion process. Consideration shall be given to environmental protection for the electrical connections.

To determine the ability of the light to withstand corrosive environments, a 5% salt spray (fog) test is required (Reference ASTM B 117). The corrosion test shall extend to 96 h with the lights powered to the design voltage.12 h on and 12 h off. The chamber ambient temperature during the between 6.5 and 7.2. Interconnecting harnesses, connectors, and grounding must be representative of the design.

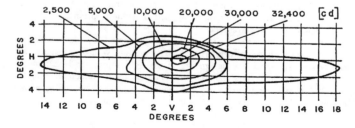

FIGURE 2—ISO-CANDELA CURVE

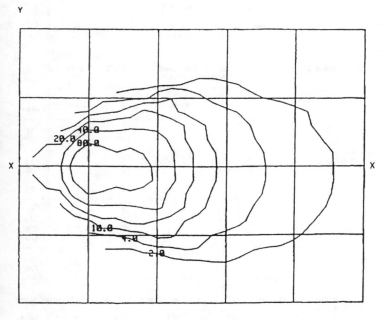

FIGURE 3—ISO-LUX CURVE

After the completion of the test, the light assemblies shall be examined for function, material, deterioration, seal integrity and oxidation of the metals. Electrical connections shall not degrade relative to their condition at the start of the test.

14. Water Submersion (As Required)—Some applications may have a water submersion requirement. In building or maintaining docks or dikes, some submersion of lights may occur. In those applications, a submersible light is required

The light assembly shall be energized for 1 h at its design voltage, and then submerged in water. After 1 min, the power shall be removed and the light shall be allowed to cool another hour.

The light assembly shall be removed from the water and the outer surfaces dried. If there is no sign of water on the inner surfaces of the light, the light assembly is acceptable to submersion.

15. Serviceability/Adjustability—Lamps, as installed, shall provide serviceability and adjustability as required for the application. Consideration must be given to bulb/burner replacement as well as ease of adjustment when installed.

Report of the Lighting Committee and Motorcycle Committee, approved October 1969, completely revised by the Motorcycle Committee March 1983. Rationale statement available.

1. Scope—This Engineering Design Specification provides design parameters and general requirements for motorcycle turn signal lamps. It does not apply to mopeds.

2. Definition—Motorcycle turn signal lamps are the signalling elements of a turn signal system which indicate a change in direction by giving flashing lights on the side toward which the turn will be made.

3. General Requirements—The effective projected illuminated area measured on a plane at right angles to the axis of a lamp shall not be less than 22 cm² (3½ in²).

   3.1 The following sections from SAE J575 are a part of this standard:
   3.1.1 Section 2—Samples for Test
   3.1.2 Section 2.2—Bulbs
   3.1.3 Section 3—Laboratory Facilities
   3.1.4 Section 4.1—Vibration Test
   3.1.5 Section 4.2—Moisture Test
   3.1.6 Section 4.3—Dust Test
   3.1.7 Section 4.4—Corrosion Test
   3.1.8 Section 4.6—Photometry
   3.1.8.1 See Table 1 for Class A and D motorcycles and Table 2 for Class B and C motorcycles.
   3.1.8.2 All intensity measurements shall be made with the filament of the signal lamp at least 3 m (10 ft) from the photometer screen. The H-V axis shall be taken as parallel to the longitudinal axis of the vehicle.
   3.1.9 Section 4.8—Warpage Test on Devices with Plastic Components

4. Color Test—The color of the light emitted from turn signal lamps shall be red or yellow to the rear and yellow to the front of the vehicle. See SAE J578.

5. Plastic Materials—Any plastic materials used in optical parts shall comply with requirements set forth in SAE J576.

6. Installation Requirements—The following requirements apply to the device as used on the vehicle and are not a part of the laboratory requirements and test procedures.

   6.1 The filament center of each signal lamp on the front shall be symmetrically spaced a minimum of 200 mm (8 in) from the centerline

TABLE 1—MINIMUM INTENSITY REQUIREMENTS (cd)—CLASS A AND D MOTORCYCLES

Test Points (deg)		Front Signal	Rear Signal	
		Yellow	Red	Yellow
10 U and D	10 L and R	25	6	15
	V	60	15	40
5 U and D	20 L and R	25	6	15
	10 L and R	75	20	50
	5 L and R	125	30	80
	V	175	40	110
H	20 L and R	35	10	25
	10 L and R	100	25	65
	5 L and R	200	50	120
	V	200	50	130
Maximum Rear Lamp Only		—	300	750

TABLE 2—MINIMUM INTENSITY REQUIREMENTS (cd)—CLASS B AND C MOTORCYCLES

Test Points (deg)		Red	Yellow
10 U and D	10 L and R	5	15
	V	13	30
5 U and D	20 L and R	5	15
	10 L and R	15	40
	5 L and R	25	60
	V	35	90
H	20 L and R	8	20
	10 L and R	20	45
	5 L and R	40	120
	V	40	120
Maximum Rear Lamp Only		300	750

NOTES:
   1. Specifications in Tables 1 and 2 are based on laboratories using accurate, rated bulbs during testing.
   2. Lamps designed for use in both 6V and 12V systems shall be tested with 12V bulbs. Lamps designed to operate on the vehicle through a resistor or equivalent shall be photometered with the listed design voltage of the design source applied across the combination of resistance and filament.

of the vehicle and 100 mm (4 in) from the inside diameter of the retaining ring of the headlamp unit providing the lower beam. On the rear, the symmetrical spacing shall be a minimum of 110 mm (4½ in) from the centerline of the vehicle to the filament axis of the signal lamp.

   6.1.1 Visibility of the front turn signal to the front and the rear turn signal to the rear shall not be obstructed by any part of the vehicle throughout the test angles for the lamps, if such obstruction causes the lamp to fail to meet minimum photometric visibility requirements.

   6.1.2 The signals from each lamp shall be visible through a horizontal angle of 45 deg outboard. To be considered visible, the lamp must project a minimum unobstructed illuminated area of 12.5 cm² (2 in²), measured at all angles throughout the 45 deg requirement.

   6.2 Turn Signal Pilot Indicator—There shall be either a light or sound signal to give the operator a clear and unmistakable indication that the turn signal system is functioning correctly. The illuminated indicator shall consist of one or more lights flashing at the same frequency as the signal lamps, and shall be plainly visible to operators of all heights when seated in normal position in the operator's seat, while driving in bright sunlight.

If a sound signal is used, it shall be audible to the operator when the motorcycle is operating at 55 km/h (35 mph) or less. The signal shall cycle on and off at the same frequency as the signal lamps. Failure of one or more turn signal lamps to operate shall be indicated by a continuous tone or by failure of the signal to sound.

APPENDIX

A1. As a matter of information, attention is called to SAE J567 for requirements and gages to be used in socket design.
A2. For flashing rate and "on" time, see SAE J590.
A3. All motorcycle class designations are those given in SAE J213.

Report of Motorcycle Committee approved November 1970 and last revised March 1972.

1. Scope—This SAE Recommended Practice provides uniform definitions for various types of motorcycles, their components, and basic characteristics.

2. Definitions

2.1 Motorcycle—A motorcycle is any motor vehicle, other than a tractor, designed to operate on no more than three wheels in contact with the ground weighing less than 1500 lb (680 kg) curb weight. Motorcycles are further defined by class as follows:

2.1.1 CLASS A MOTORCYCLE—Any two-wheeled motorcycle with a propelling engine having a piston displacement 170 cc and larger.

2.1.2 CLASS B MOTORCYCLE (commonly referred to as a motor-driven cycle) —Any motorcycle with a propelling engine having a piston displacement 50 cc and larger, but less than 170 cc.

2.1.3 CLASS C MOTORCYCLE—Any motorcycle with a propelling engine having a piston displacement of less than 50 cc, and not meeting the definition for Class E.

2.1.4 CLASS D MOTORCYCLE—Any three-wheeled motorcycle with a propelling engine having a piston displacement of 170 cc and larger.

2.1.5 CLASS E MOTORCYCLE (commonly referrred to as a mini-bike)—Any motorcycle having one or more of the following characteristics:

(a) Less than 10 in. (254 mm) nominal wheel rim size.

(b) Less than a 40 in. (1016 mm) wheelbase.

(c) Less than 25 in. (635 mm) at seat height measured at the lowest point on the top of seat cushion without rider.

2.2 Side Car—An attached third wheel to either side of a motorcycle, generally for the purpose of transporting persons or property. The attachment of a side car does not change the classification of a motorcycle.

2.3 Curb Weight—The total weight of a vehicle, including a full load of fuel, oil, and water, but without any passengers or cargo.

2.4 Longitudinal Plane of Symmetry

2.4.1 TWO-WHEELED MOTORCYCLE—A vertical plane which passes through the centerline of the front and rear wheels.

2.4.2 THREE-WHEELED MOTORCYCLE—A vertical plane which passes through the centerline of the single wheel and through the midpoint of the two wheels sharing the same axis of rotation.

2.5 Rake Angle (Caster Angle)—The acute angle in the longitudinal plane of symmetry between the steering head or kingpin axis and the vertical.

2.6 Trail—The horizontal distance between a vertical line through the front wheel centerline and the projection of the steering head measured at the tire to ground contact surface.

MOTORCYCLE AND MOTOR DRIVEN CYCLE ELECTRICAL SYSTEM MAINTENANCE OF DESIGN VOLTAGE —SAE J392 FEB92   SAE Recommended Practice

Report of the Motorcycle Committee and Lighting Committee, approved December 1969, completely revised by the Motorcycle Committee May 1984. Rationale statement available. Reaffirmed by the SAE Motorcycle Electrical Systems Subcommittee of the SAE Motorcycle Committee February 1992.

Foreword—This reaffirmed document has been changed only to reflect the new SAE Technical Standards Board format.

1. Scope—This SAE Recommended Practice pertains to both battery-equipped and batteryless motorcycle electrical systems.

1.1 Purpose—This document provides minimum illumination voltage values for motorcycle and motor driven cycle electrical systems and accompanying test procedures.

NOTE: Wherever the word "motorcycle" appears in the report, it is understood to include "motor driven cycle."

2. References—There are no referenced publications specified herein.

3. Test Apparatus

3.1 Voltmeter—0 to 20 V maximum full-scale deflection, accuracy ±1/2% (two voltmeters required).

3.2 Ammeter—Capable of carrying full system load current. Accuracy ±3% FS.

3.3 Means for Measuring Engine rpm—Accuracy ±3%.

4. Test Procedure

4.1 Install fully charged original equipment or equal battery on the motorcycle (if motorcycle is battery equipped).

4.1.1 Battery temperature to be 26.7 °C ± 5.6 °C (80 °F ± 10 °F).

4.2 Connect one voltmeter between the headlamp low beam terminal and the ground; connect the other voltmeter between the taillamp terminal and the ground.

4.3 Connect the ammeter in series with the battery.

NOTE: Disregard 4.3 for batteryless machines.

4.4 Start engine and turn on headlamp(s).

4.4.1 Switch headlamp to the low beam position.

4.4.2 External fan cooling may be applied to the motorcycle engine.

4.5 Run the engine at an rpm equivalent to 48.3 km/h (30 mph) in top gear for 10 min.

4.5.1 Record the lowest and highest headlamp voltage and taillamp voltage observed during the 10 min period.

4.6 Run the engine at an rpm equivalent to 88.5 km/h (55 mph) in top gear for 10 min.

4.6.1 Record the lowest and highest headlamp voltage and taillamp voltage observed during the 10 min period.

4.7 Increase speed to manufacturer's suggested maximum rpm.

4.7.1 Record the highest and lowest headlamp and taillamp voltages observed during a 5 s period.

4.8 Run the engine at manufacturer's rated idle speed for 10 min.

4.8.1 Record the lowest and highest taillamp voltage observed during the 10 min period.

4.8.2 Record the lowest and highest headlamp voltage observed during the 10 min period.

4.9 Slowly increase the engine speed until generating equipment cancels the system load, indicated by "0" reading on the ammeter.

NOTE: Disregard 4.9 for batteryless motorcycles.

4.9.1 Record the engine rpm at ammeter zero point.

5. Test Limits

5.1 Voltages recorded in 4.5.1, 4.6.1, 4.7.1, and 4.8.1 shall be between 90 and 120% of the rated headlamp design voltage.

5.2 Voltages observed in 4.8.2 shall be between 60 and 120% of the rated headlamp design voltage.

5.3 Engine rpm observed in 4.9.1 shall be less than the motorcycle equivalent speed at 48.3 km/h (30 mph) in top gear operation.

(R) MOTORCYCLE HEADLAMPS
—SAE J584 OCT93

SAE Standard

Report of the Lighting Committee approved January 1949. Completely revised by the Motorcycle Committee December 1983. Rationale statement available. Completely revised by the Motorcycle Electrical Systems Subcommittee of the SAE Motorcycle Committee October 1993.

1. Scope—This SAE Standard provides design parameter and general requirements for motorcycle headlamps.

2. References

2.1 Applicable Documents—The following publications form a part of this specification to the extent specified herein. The latest issue of SAE publications shall apply.

2.1.1 SAE PUBLICATIONS—Available from SAE, 400 Commonwealth Drive, Warrendale, PA 15096-0001.

SAE J107—Operator Controls and Displays on Motorcycles

SAE J213—Definitions—Motorcycles

SAE J565—Semiautomatic Headlamp Beam Switching Device

SAE J575—Tests for Motor Vehicle Lighting Devices and Components

SAE J576—Plastic Materials for Use in Optical Parts Such as Lenses and
    Reflectors of Motor Vehicle Lighting Devices

SAE J578—Color Specification

SAE J579 DEC84—Sealed Beam Headlamp Units for Motor Vehicles

SAE J1383—Performance Requirements for Motor Vehicle Headlamps

2.2 Definition

2.2.1 A MOTORCYCLE HEADLAMP is a major lighting device used to provide general illumination ahead of the vehicle. For definition and classes of motorcycles, see SAE J213.

3. Laboratory Requirements

3.1 The following sections from SAE J575 are a part of this document:

3.1.1 SECTION 2—SAMPLES FOR TEST

3.1.2 SECTION 2.2—BULBS

3.1.3 SECTION 3—LABORATORY FACILITIES

3.1.4 SECTION 4.1—VIBRATION TEST

3.1.5 SECTION 4.2—MOISTURE TEST

3.1.6 SECTION 4.3—DUST TEST

3.1.7 SECTION 4.4—CORROSION TEST

3.1.8 SECTION 4.6—PHOTOMETRY

3.1.9 SECTION 4.8—WARPAGE TEST ON DEVICES WITH PLASTIC COMPONENTS

3.2 Plastic Materials—Any plastic material used in optical parts shall comply with the requirements set forth in SAE J576.

3.3 Color Test—Color of the light from a motorcycle headlamp shall be white, as defined in SAE J578.

3.4 Aiming Adjustment Tests

3.4.1 A minimum aiming adjustment of 4 degrees in each direction from the vertical and horizontal planes shall be provided.

3.4.2 Headlamps with independent vertical and horizontal aiming adjusting mechanisms:

3.4.2.1 The headlamp unit mounting shall be provided with independent vertical and horizontal aiming adjustments. The adjustment mechanisms shall be designed so that neither the vertical nor horizontal aim will deviate more than 100 mm (4 in) from the horizontal or vertical planes, respectively, at a distance of 7.6 m (25 ft) through an angle of ±4 degrees.

3.4.2.2 When adjusting screws are employed, they shall be equipped with self-locking devices which operate satisfactorily for a minimum of 10 adjustments on each screw, over a length of screw thread of ±3 mm (±1/8 in).

3.4.3 Headlamps with ball and socket or equivalent adjustment means need not conform with 3.4.2.

3.5 Inward Force Test—The mechanism, including the aiming adjusters, shall be designed to prevent the unit from receding permanently by more than 2.5 mm (0.1 in) into the lamp body or housing when an inward force of 222 N (50 lbf) is exerted at the geometric center of the outer surface of the lens.

3.6 Clarity of Hot Spot Definition—The geometric center of the high intensity zone of the upper beam of the multiple beam headlamps shall be deemed sufficiently defined for the purpose of service aiming if it can be set by three experienced observers on a vertical screen at 7.6 m (25 ft) within a maximum vertical deviation of ±0.3 degrees and within a maximum horizontal deviation of ±0.4 degrees. The aim for each observer shall be taken as the average of at least three observations.

3.7 Beam Aim During Photometric Test

3.7.1 The upper beam of a multiple beam headlamp shall be aimed photoelectrically so that the center of the zone of highest intensity falls 0.4

degrees vertically below the lamp axis and is centered laterally. The center of the zone of highest intensity shall be established by the intersection of a horizontal plane passing through the point of maximum intensity, and the vertical plane established by balancing the photometric values at 3 degrees left and 3 degrees right.

3.7.2 The beam of a single beam Class C (moped) lamp shall be aimed photoelectrically so that the center of the zone at highest intensity falls 1.5 degrees vertically below the lamp axis and is centered laterally. The center of the zone of highest intensity shall be established by the intersection of a horizontal plane passing through the point of maximum intensity, and the vertical plane established by balancing the photometric values at 3 degrees left and 3 degrees right.

3.8 Photometric Design Requirements

3.8.1 TEST PROCEDURES—Photometric tests shall be made with photometer at a distance of at least 18.3 m (60 ft) from the unit. The bulb or unit shall be operated at 6.4 V for a 6 V system and 12.8 V for a 12 V system during the test.

3.8.2 DESIGN INTENSITY REQUIREMENTS—The beam or beams from the unit shall be designed to conform to the intensity specifications in Tables 1, 2, or 3. A tolerance of ±0.25 degree in location may be allowed for any test point.

TABLE 1—CLASS A AND D MOTORCYCLE

Test Points (Degrees)	Min cd	Max cd
Upper Beam		
2U-V	1000	
1U-3L and 3R	2000	
H-V	12 500	
1/2D-V	20 000	
1/2D-3L and 3R	10 000	
1/2D-6L and 6R	3300	
1/2D-9L and 9R	1500	
1/2D-12L and 12R	800	
1D-V	17 500	
2D-V	5000	
3D-V	2500	
3D-9L and 9R	1500	
3D-12L and 12R	300	
4D-V	1500	7500
Anywhere		75 000
Lower Beam		
1-1/2U-1R to R		1400
1U-1-1/2L to L		700
1/2U-1-1/2L to L		1000
1/2U-1R to 3R		2700
1-1/2D-9L and 9R	700	
2D-V	7000	
2D-3L and 3R	4000	
2D-6L and 6R	1500	
2D-12L and 12R	700	
3D-6L and 6R	800	
4D-V	2000	
4D-4R		12 500

4. Optional Systems—One half of any headlighting system meeting the requirements of SAE J579 DEC84 or J1383, not including aim, may be used, where applicable, on Class A, B, C, and D motorcycles.

NOTE—Although automotive headlamp units may be optionally used it should be noted that they conventionally supply a lesser amount of low beam light on the left side.

5. Installation Requirements—The following requirements apply to the devices as used on the vehicle and are not part of laboratory test requirements and procedures.

5.1 Beam Switching—The switching of motorcycle headlamps between the upper and lower beams should be by means of a switch designed and located so that it may be operated conventionally by a simple movement of the operator's hand or foot. The switch shall have no dead point between upper and lower beam switch position.

TABLE 2—CLASS B, C, AND E MOTORCYCLE

Test Points (Degrees)	Class B Min cd	Class B Max cd	Class C and E Min cd	Class C and E Max cd
Upper Beam			1000	
1U-3L and 3R	2000		5000	
H-V	10 000		7500	
1/2D-V	20 000		3000	
1/2D-3L and 3R	5000		800	
1/2D-6L and 6R	2000		5000	
1D-V	15 000		3000	
2D-V	5000		1000	
3D-V	2500		500	
3D-6L and 6R	800			
4D-V		7500		7500
Anywhere		75 000		75 000
Lower Beam				
1-1/2U-1R to R		1400		1400
1U-1-1/2L to L		700		700
1/2U-1-1/2L to L		1000		1000
1/2U-1R to 3R		2700		2700
2D-V	5000		4000	
2D-3L and 3R	3000		3000	
2D-6L and 6R	1500		1500	
3D-6L and 6R	800		800	
4D-V	2000		2000	
4D-4R		12 500		12 500

5.2 Means shall be provided for indicating to the driver that the upper beam is on. The upper beam indicator shall be plainly visible to the operator under normal night time driving conditions. See SAE J107 for recommended high beam indicator.

5.3 Semi-automatic headlamp beam switching devices are permitted. See SAE J565.

TABLE 3—CLASS C AND E MOTORCYCLE

Test Points (Degrees)	Min cd	Max cd
Single Beam		
1-1/2U-1R to 3R		1400
1U-1-1/2L to L		700
1/2U-1-1/2L to L		1000
1/2U-1R to 3R		2700
2D-V	4000	
2D-3L and 3R	3000	
2D-6L and 6R	1500	
4D-V	1000	
4D-4R		12 500

MOTORCYCLE STOP LAMP SWITCH— SAE J1167 JUN89

SAE Recommended Practice

Report of the Motorcycle Committee, approved December 1977, completely revised June 1984, and reaffirmed June 1989.

1. Scope—This SAE Recommended Practice establishes test procedures and performance requirements for stop lamp switches intended for use in an AC or a DC circuit on motorcycles. In service use may impose specific conditions on the switch which can affect its functional life. Those conditions should be replicated, as necessary, during the testing described in this document to ensure the adequate functioning of the device.

2. Definition

2.1 A motorcycle stop lamp switch is a device used to energize the stop lamp circuit on a motorcycle with operator actuation of the brake control.

2.2 Motorcycle Classes—For motorcycle class definitions, see SAE J213.

2.3 For the tests described in this recommended practice, the switch shall be operated at 6.4 DC V for a 6 V circuit and 12.8 DC V for a 12 V circuit. These voltages shall be measured at the terminals.[1]

2.4 As used in this document, one cycle shall be defined as the energizing and de-energizing of the stop lamp circuit with the switch mechanism working throughout its designed travel and/or pressure.

3. Temperature Test

3.1 To ensure basic function, the switch shall be operated for 10 cycles at design electrical load at each of the following temperatures:

24°C ± 5.5	(75°F ± 10)
74°C + 0, −2.8	(165°F + 0, −5)
−32°C + 2.8, −0	(−25°F + 5, −0)

This is to be done after a 1 h exposure at each temperature. The switch shall be electrically and mechanically operable during each of these cycles.

[1] If wiring is an integral part of the switch, the voltage drop measurement shall be made including 76 mm (3 in) of wire on each side of the switch.

3.2 The voltage drop at the terminals[1] shall be measured before and at the end of this test. The voltage drop shall not, at either time, exceed the following values, using the average of three consecutive readings at design load:

6 V Circuit	0.30 V
12 V Circuit	0.40 V

3.3 This same switch shall be used for the endurance test described below.

4. Endurance Test (see 3.3)

4.1 The switch shall be set up to operate its design electrical load.

4.2 The switch shall be operated for the number of cycles and at the temperature described in paragraph 4.4.

4.3 The voltage drop at the terminals[1] shall be measured before and at the end of this test. The voltage drop shall not, at either time, exceed the following values, using the average of three consecutive readings at design load:

6 V Circuit	0.30 V
12 V Circuit	0.40 V

4.4 The switch shall be capable of satisfactory operation during the following number of operations at 24°C ± 5.5 (75°F ± 10):

Class A and D motorcycles—100 000 operations
Class B and C motorcycles—50 000 operations

5. Other tests—The switch shall be subjected to the following tests in SAE J575 and shall meet the requirements therein. A separate switch from that used in Sections 3 and 4 may be used in each of the following tests:

Section 4.2—Moisture Test
Section 4.4—Corrosion Test

Report of the Motorcycle Committee, approved June 1980 and completely revised June 1989.

1. Scope—This engineering design specification provides parameters and general requirements for auxiliary front lamps to be used on motorcycles. It may be supplemented by a service performance requirement.

2. Definition—An auxiliary lamp as covered by this specification is a unit, including sealed beam, intended to supplement either the upper or the lower beam from motorcycle headlamps.

3. Laboratory Requirements

3.1 The following sections of SAE J575 are a part of this recommended practice:

Section 2   —Samples for Tests
Section 2.2—Bulbs
Section 3   —Laboratory Facilities
Section 4.1—Vibration Test
Section 4.2—Moisture Test
Section 4.3—Dust Test
Section 4.4—Corrosion Test
Section 4.6—Photometry Test
Section 4.8—Warpage Test on Devices with Plastic Components

3.2 Sealed beam units need to comply only with Sections 2, 3, and 4.6 of SAE J575.

3.3 Color Test—The color of the light from a motorcycle auxiliary front lamp shall be white. (See SAE J578.)

3.4 Plastic Materials—Any plastic materials used in exterior optical parts shall comply with the requirements set forth in SAE J576.

3.5 Photometric Tests—These shall be made with the photometer at a distance of at least 60 ft (18.3 m) from the lamp.

3.5.1 AT-FOCUS TESTS—The light source shall be located in the designed position as specified by the manufacturer.

The beam from the lamp shall be aimed with the left edge of the high intensity zone at a vertical line straight ahead of the lamp center and with the top edge of the high intensity zone at the level of the lamp center at a distance of 25 ft (7.6 m) from the lens.

The beam from the lamp shall meet the photometric specifications listed in Table 1 when it is aimed as specified.

3.5.2 OUT-OF-FOCUS TESTS ON UNSEALED UNITS— Similar tests shall be made for each of four out-of-focus filament positions, except that the completed distribution may be omitted. Where conventional bulbs with two-pin bayonet bases are used, intensity tests shall be made with the light source 0.060 in (1.5 mm) above, below, ahead, and behind the designed position. If prefocused bulbs are used, the limiting positions at which tests are made shall be 0.020 in (0.5 mm) above, below, ahead, and behind the designed position.

The beam from the lamp may be reaimed as specified in paragraph 3.5.1 for each of the out-of-focus positions of light source.

3.5.3 The lamp shall be designed to comply with the photometric requirements shown in Table 1 for the design filament position and the required out-of-focus filament position. An aiming tolerance of ±0.25 deg shall be allowed at each test point.

4. Installation and Usage Requirements—The following items apply to the device as used on the motorcycle and are not a part of the laboratory test requirements and procedures.

For greatest visibility, with reasonable limitation of glare to approaching drivers, the beam from the lamp shall be aimed in accordance with paragraph 3.5.1. The unit should be turned off when traveling in congested areas in cities. It may be wired so that it can be turned on or off with either beam of the regular headlamps.

APPENDIX A

A.1 As a matter of information, attention is called to SAE J567 for requirements and gages to be used in socket design for unsealed units.

TABLE 1—TEST POSITIONS AND LUMINOUS INTENSITY REQUIREMENTS

Position, deg[a]	Max Intensity (cd)
1U-1L to left and above	400
1/2U-1L to left	500
1/2D-1L to left	1000
1-1/2D-1L to left	3000
2U-1R to right and above	1000
1U-1R to right	3000
H-1R to right	7000
1-1/2D-2R to 4R	10 000 min

[a]An aiming tolerance of ±1/4 deg should be allowed on individual points.

REPLACEABLE MOTORCYCLE HEADLAMP BULBS—SAE J1577 JUN91

SAE Recommended Practice

Report of the SAE Motorcycle Electrical Systems Subcommittee of the SAE Motorcycle Committee approved June 1991. Rationale statement available.

1. Scope—This SAE Recommended Practice provides performance parameters and dimensional specifications for available light sources (replaceable bulbs) which are appropriate for motorcycle headlamps.

2. References

2.1 Applicable Documents—The following publications form a part of this specification to the extent specified herein.

2.1.1 SAE PUBLICATIONS—Available from SAE, 400 Commonwealth Drive, Warrendale, PA 15096-0001.

SAE J584 DEC83—Motorcycle Headlamps

SAE J1383 APR85—Performance Requirements for Motor Vehicle Headlamps

2.1.2 IEC PUBLICATIONS (SEE TABLE 1)—Available from International Electrotechnical Commission, 3, rue de Verambe, P.O. Box 131, 1211 Geneva 20, Switzerland.

2.2 Definitions

2.2.1 REPLACEABLE MOTORCYCLE HEADLAMP BULB (HEREINAFTER REFERRED TO AS "BULB" OR "BULBS")—A radiant energy source with related envelope and mounting base which is removable from the motorcycle headlamp for the purpose of replacement.

2.2.2 SEASONING—Process of energizing the filament of a bulb at design voltage for a period of time equal to 1% of design life or 10 h, whichever is shorter.

3. Bulb Type and Specifications

3.1 Table 2 lists each bulb type with its specifications. Bulbs may be added to Table 2 in the future after review.

3.2 All the bulbs shall satisfy the following vibration test requirements.

3.2.1 Bulb shall be seasoned and mounted in a relevant headlamp and photometered to the applicable test points in accordance with article 3.8 of SAE J584 DEC83 before the vibration test.

3.2.2 Bulbs shall be mounted on the vibration test machine in their designed operating position.

3.2.3 Conditions of vibration test are shown in Table 3.

3.2.4 During the vibration test, the upper beam filament and the lower beam filament shall be energized alternately at 1 h intervals at design voltage.

3.2.5 Filament(s) shall not fail throughout the test period.

3.2.6 After the vibration test, the bulb shall be photometered to the applicable test points in accordance with article 3.8 of SAE J584 DEC83. The values shall not vary by more than ±10% from the values measured before the test.

TABLE 1—IEC PUBLICATIONS

Type	Bulb	Base	Socket (Holder)
H4	Figures 1 and 2	Figure 3	Figure 4
Reference	Data sheet: 809-IEC-2120-1 (1985) of Doc. IEC Publication 809, 1st edition Title: Road Vehicle Lamp Data Sheet Category: H4 Cap: P43t-38	Data sheet: 7004-39-3 (1980) of Doc. IEC Publication 61-1J Title: Prefocus Cap for Automobile Lamps P43t-38 Assembly of Ring and Cap on Finished Lamps	Data sheet: 7005-39-2 (1983) of Doc. IEC Publication 61-2, 3rd edition Title: Lampholder for Automobile Lamps P43t-38
HS1	Figures 5 and 6	Figure 7	Figure 8
Reference	Data sheet: 809-IEC-2130-1 (1988) of Doc. IEC Publication 809, Amendment 2 Title: Road Vehicle Lamp Data Sheet Category: HS1 Cap: PX43t	Data sheet: 7004-34-1 (1987) of Doc. IEC Publication 61-1L Title: Prefocus Cap PX43t Assembly of Ring and Cap on Finished Lamps	Data sheet: 7005-34-1 (1987) of Doc. IEC Publication 61-2H Title: Lampholder PX43t

TABLE 2—TYPICAL REPLACEABLE MOTORCYCLE HEADLAMP BULBS

Bulb Type	Number of Filaments	Rated Watts	Rated Volts	Design Voltage (D.V.)	Luminous Flux (Lumens Approx.) at D.V.	Max. Wattage at D.V.	Rated Average Laboratory Life at D.V.[3]	Filament Type	Dimensions
H4	2 (U.B./L.B.)	60/55	12/12	13.2	1650/[1,2] 1000[1,2]	75/68	450	Axial/ Axial	See Figures 1 to 4
HS1	2 (U.B./L.B.)	35/35	12/12	13.2	825/[1,2] 525[1,2]	36.75/ 36.75	[4]	Axial/ Axial	See Figures 5 to 8

U.B. = upper beam
L.B. = lower beam

[1] With black cap.
[2] Tolerances are ±15% for both U.B./L.B.
[3] The filaments are operated alternately according to the following cycle and starting with the lower beam filament: lower beam filament 15 h on 45 min off, then the upper beam filament 7.5 h on 45 min off; repeat the cycle.
The end of bulb life is determined by failure of either filament. The off periods are not considered as part of the bulb life.
[4] Not determined at this time.

TABLE 3—CONDITIONS OF VIBRATION TEST

Wave Form	Sinusoidal
Frequency	50-500-50 Hz at a linear sweep period of two minutes
Acceleration and Direction	98 m/s² at bulb retaining portion. Vertical
Test Cycle	180 cycles

Dimensions in mm

The drawings are not mandatory; their sole purpose is to show which dimensions must be verified.

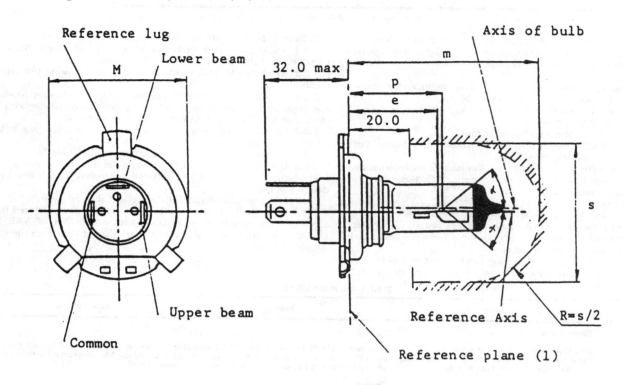

Reference	Dimension	Tolerance
e	28.5	+0.45/−0.25
p	28.95	—
m (2)	max. 60.0	—
s (3)	45.0	—
α (4)	max. 40	—

(1) The reference plane is the plane formed by the seating points of the three lugs of the base.
(2) Dimension m denotes maximum length of the bulb.
(3) It must be possible to insert the bulb into a cylinder of diameter s concentric with the reference axis and limited at one end by a plane parallel to and 20 mm distant from the reference plane and at the other end by a hemisphere of radius s/2.
(4) The obscuration must extend at least as far as the cylindrical part of the capsule. It must also overlap the internal shield when the latter is viewed in a direction perpendicular to the reference axis. The effect sought by obscuration may also be achieved by other means.

FIGURE 1—TYPE H4 REPLACEABLE MOTORCYCLE HEADLAMP BULB—DIMENSIONAL SPECIFICATIONS

Dimensions in mm

The drawings are not mandatory with respect to the design of the shield.

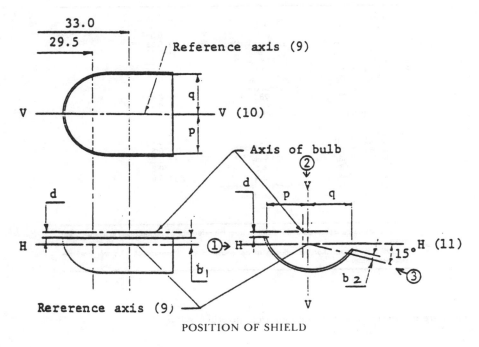

POSITION OF SHIELD

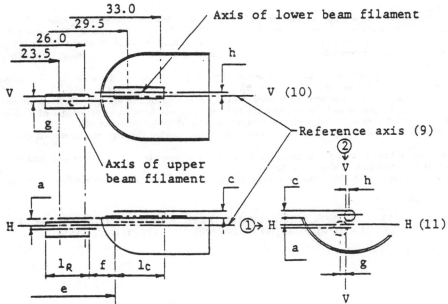

POSITION OF FILAMENTS

271

Reference			Dimension		Tolerance (in mm)
a/26	*	(4)	0.8		± 0.35
a/23.5	*	(4)	0.8		± 0.6
b₁/29.5	*	(3)	0		± 0.35
b₁/33	*	(3)	b₁/29.5 mv	**	± 0.35
b₂/29.5	*	(3)	0		± 0.35
b₂/33	*	(3)	b₂/29.5 mv	**	± 0.35
c/29.5	*	(3)	0.6		± 0.35
c/33	*	(3)	c/29.5 mv	**	± 0.35
d			min 0.1		—
e		(7)	28.5		+ 0.45 − 0.25
f	(5)(6)(8)		1.7		+ 0.5 − 0.3
g/26	*	(4)	0		± 0.5
g/23.5	*	(4)	0		± 0.7
h/29.5	*	(3)	0		± 0.5
h/33	*	(3)	h/29.5 mv	**	± 0.35
lᵣ	(5)(8)		4.5		± 0.8
lc	(5)(6)		5.5		± 0.8
p/33	*	(2)	Depends on the shape of the shield		—
q/33	*	(2)	$\frac{p + q}{2}$		± 0.6

* Dimension to be measured at the distance from the reference plane indicated in mm after the stroke.

** "./29.5 mv means that the value is to be measured at a distance of 29.5 mm from the reference plane.

(1) The dimensions noted are measured as seen in the indicated directions.
   ① for dimensions a, b₁, c, d, e, f, lᵣ, and lc;
   ② for dimensions g, h, p, and q;
   ③ for dimension b₂.
(2) Dimensions p and q are measured in a plane parallel to and 33 mm away from the reference plane.
(3) Dimensions b₁, b₂, c, and h are measured in planes parallel to and 29.5 mm and 33 mm away from the reference plane.
(4) Dimensions a and g are measured in planes parallel to and 26 mm and 23.5 mm away from the reference plane.
(5) The end turns of the filament are defined as being the first luminous turn and the last luminous turn that are at substantially the correct helix angle.
(6) For the lower-beam filament the points to be measured are the intersections, seen in direction①, of the lateral edge of the shield with the outside of the end turns defined under footnote (5).
(7) Dimension e denotes the distance from the reference plane to the beginning of the lower-beam filament as defined above.
(8) For the upper-beam filament the points to be measured are the intersections, seen in direction①, of a plane, parallel to plane HH and situated at a distance of 0.8 mm below it, with the end turns defined under footnote (5).
(9) The reference axis is the line perpendicular to the reference plane and passing through the center of the circle of diameter M (see Figure 1).
(10) Plane VV is the plane perpendicular to the reference plane and passing through the reference axis and through the intersection of the circle of diameter M with the axis of the reference lug.
(11) Plane HH is the plane perpendicular to both the reference plane and plane VV and passing through the reference axis.

FIGURE 2—TYPE H4 REPLACEABLE MOTORCYCLE HEADLAMP BULB—SHIELD AND FILAMENT POSITION DIMENSIONAL SPECIFICATIONS

Dimensions in mm

The drawing is intended only to indicate the dimensions essential for interchangeability.

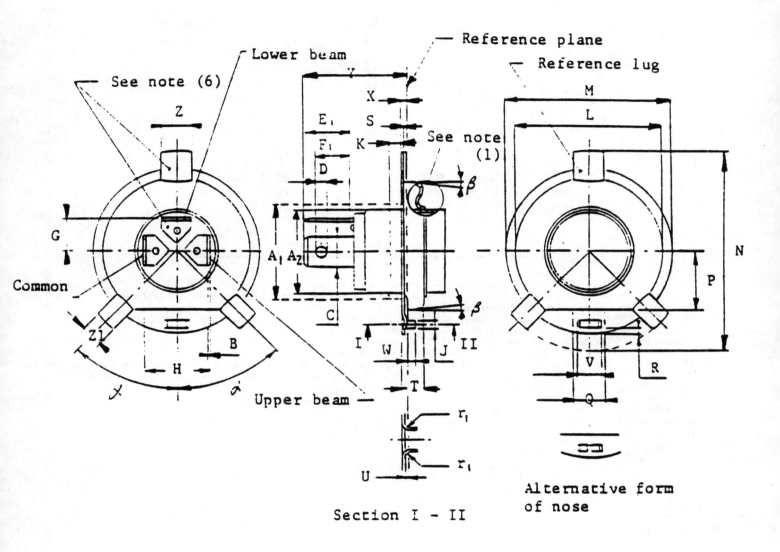

Section I - II

Alternative form
of nose

273

Dimension		Min.	Max.
A_1	(8)	25.0	—
A_2		21.94	22.0
B		0.7	0.8
C		7.7	8.1
D		3.0	3.3
E_1		11.8	13.6
F_1		8.8	10.3
G		8.5	9.0
H		17.0	17.9
J		1.9	2.1
K	(10)	2.0	—
L	(2)(4)	37.8	38.0
M	(3)	42.8	43.0
N		51.6	52.0
P	(2)(7)	15.3	15.5
Q	(2)(7)	8.5	—
R		1.3	1.7
S		0.5	—
T		5.0	6.0
U			(9)
V	(2)(5)	6.3	6.5
W		1.8	2.2
X		1.1	1.3
Y		—	32.0
Z		7.9	8.0
Z_1		5.8	6.2
r			(9)
α		44	46
β		—	5

(1) The form of this annular part of the ring is optional and may be flat or recessed. However, the form shall be such that it will not cause any abnormal glare from the lower-beam filament when the bulb is in its normal operating position in the vehicle.

(2) This dimension is measured at the reference plane.

(3) Dimension M is the diameter on which the bulb is centered when checking the dimensional characteristics of the bulb.

(4) The maximum allowable eccentricity of cylinder L with respect to the circle of diameter M is 0.05 mm.

(5) The maximum allowable displacement of the center of the nose from the line running through the centers of the reference lug and the circle of diameter M is 0.05 mm. The sides of the nose shall not bend outward.

(6) The relative positions of the contact tabs and the reference lug shall not deviate from the position shown by more than ±20 degrees.

(7) Dimension Q denotes the minimum width over which both the minimum and maximum limits of dimension P shall be observed. Outside dimension Q, the maximum limit for dimension P shall not be exceeded.

(8) The means of securing the ring in the headlamp shall not encroach on this cylindrical zone.

(9) The radius r shall be equal to or smaller than dimension U.

(10) Beyond distance K, in the direction of the contact tabs, both the minimum and the maximum limits of dimension A_2 shall be measured.

FIGURE 3—TYPE H4 REPLACEABLE MOTORCYCLE HEADLAMP BULB—ASSEMBLED
BASE P43t-38 ON FINISHED BULB—DIMENSIONAL SPECIFICATIONS

Dimensions in mm

The drawings are intended only to indicate the dimensions essential for interchangeability.

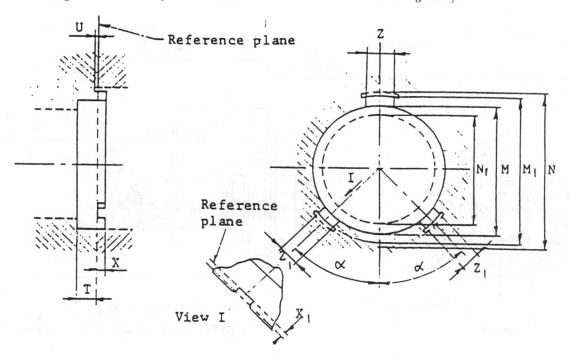

Dimension	Min.	Max.
M	43.02 (1)	43.2
M_1	—	49.0
N	52.2	—
N_1	35.0	—
T	5.5	—
U	0.4	—
X	1.8	—
X_1	1.4	—
Z	8.05	8.15
Z_1	8.0	8.5
α	44	46

The holder shall be so designed that the means of retention of the bulb can be applied only when the bulb is in the correct position.

The means of retention shall make contact only with the prefocus ring of the base and the total force exerted, when the bulb is in position, shall be not less than 10 N and be not greater than 60 N.
  (1) This value shall be complied with between the rim of the bulbholder and the reference plane (dimension X).
      However, it may be reduced to 38.5 mm within the dimensions Z and Z_1 which correspond with the support points for the lugs of the cap.
  (2) Dimension X_1 denotes the minimum distance over which dimensions Z and Z_1 shall apply.
      Outside dimension X_1 the slots may be chamfered or rounded.

FIGURE 4—TYPE H4 REPLACEABLE MOTORCYCLE HEADLAMP BULB—
BULBHOLDER P43t—DIMENSIONAL SPECIFICATIONS

Dimensions in mm

The drawings are not mandatory; their sole purpose is to show which dimensions must be verified.

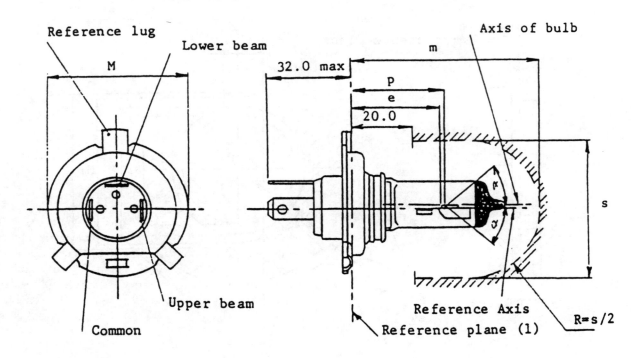

Reference	Dimension	Tolerance
e	28.5	+0.45/−0.25
p	28.95	—
m (2)	max. 60.0	—
s (3)	45.0	—
α (4)	max. 40	—

(1) The reference plane is the plane formed by the seating points of the three lugs of the base.
(2) Dimension m denotes maximum length of the bulb.
(3) It must be possible to insert the bulb into a cylinder of diameter s concentric with the reference axis and limited at one end by a plane parallel to and 20 mm distant from the reference plane and at the other end by a hemisphere of radius s/2.
(4) The obscuration must extend at least as far as the cylindrical part of the capsule. It must also overlap the internal shield when the latter is viewed in a direction perpendicular to the reference axis. The effect sought by obscuration may also be achieved by other means.

FIGURE 5—TYPE HS1 REPLACEABLE MOTORCYCLE HEADLAMP
BULB—DIMENSIONAL SPECIFICATIONS

276

Dimensions in mm

The drawings are not mandatory with respect to the design of the shield.

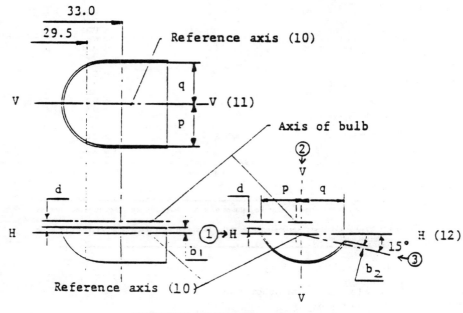

POSITION OF SHIELD

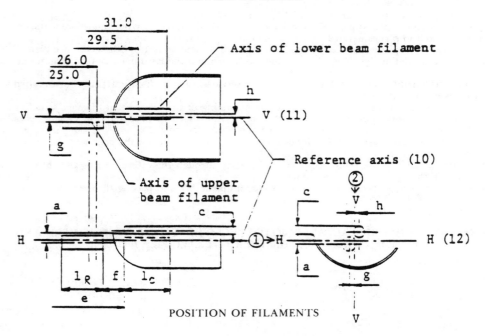

POSITION OF FILAMENTS

277

Reference			Dimension		Tolerance (in mm)
a/26	*	(4)	0.8		± 0.35
a/25	*	(4)	0.8		± 0.55
b_1/29.5	*	(3)	0		± 0.35
b_1/33	*	(3)	b_1/29.5 mv	**	± 0.35
b_2/29.5	*	(3)	0		± 0.35
b_2/33	*	(3)	b_2/29.5 mv	**	± 0.35
c/29.5	*	(5)	0.6		± 0.35
c/31	*	(5)	c/29.5 mv	**	± 0.3
d			min 0.1/max 1.5		—
e		(8)	28.5		+ 0.45 − 0.25
f		(6)(7)(9)	1.7		+ 0.5 − 0.3
g/26	*	(4)	0		± 0.5
g/25	*	(4)	0		± 0.7
h/29.5	*	(5)	0		± 0.5
h/31	*	(5)	h/29.5 mv	**	± 0.3
l_R		(6)(9)	4.0		± 0.8
lc		(6)(7)	4.5		± 0.8
p/33	*	(2)	Depends on the shape of the shield		—
q/33	*	(2)	$\frac{p+q}{2}$		± 0.6

* Dimension to be measured at the distance from the reference plane indicated in mm after the stroke.

** ".../29.5 mv means that the value is to be measured at a distance of 29.5 mm from the reference plane.

(1) The dimensions noted are measured as seen in the indicated directions.
  ① for dimensions a, b_1, c, d, e, f, l_R, and lc;
  ② for dimensions g, h, p, and q;
  ③ for dimension b_2.
(2) Dimensions p and q are measured in a plane parallel to and 33 mm away from the reference plane.
(3) Dimensions b_1 and b_2 are measured in planes parallel to and 29.5 mm and 33 mm away from the reference plane.
(4) Dimensions a and g are measured in planes parallel to and 25 mm and 26 mm away from the reference plane.
(5) Dimensions c and h are measured in planes parallel to and 29.5 mm and 31 mm away from the reference plane.
(6) The end turns of the filament are defined as being the first luminous turn and the last luminous turn that are at substantially the correct helix angle.
(7) For the lower-beam filament the points to be measured are the intersections, seen in direction ①, of the lateral edge of the shield with the outside of the end turns defined under footnote (5).
(8) Dimension e denotes the distance from the reference plane to the beginning of the lower-beam filament as defined above.
(9) For the upper-beam filament the points to be measured are the intersections, seen in direction ① of a plane, parallel to plane HH and situated at a distance of 0.8 mm below it, with the end turns defined under footnote (5).
(10) The reference axis is the line perpendicular to the reference plane and passing through the center of the circle of diameter M (see Figure 5).
(11) Plane VV is the plane perpendicular to the reference plane and passing through the reference axis and through the intersection of the circle of diameter M with the axis of the reference lug.
(12) Plane HH is the plane perpendicular to both the reference plane and plane VV and passing through the reference axis.

FIGURE 6—TYPE HS1 REPLACEABLE MOTORCYCLE HEADLAMP BULB—SHIELD AND FILAMENT POSITION DIMENSIONAL SPECIFICATIONS

Dimensions in mm

The drawing is intended only to indicate the dimensions essential for interchangeability.

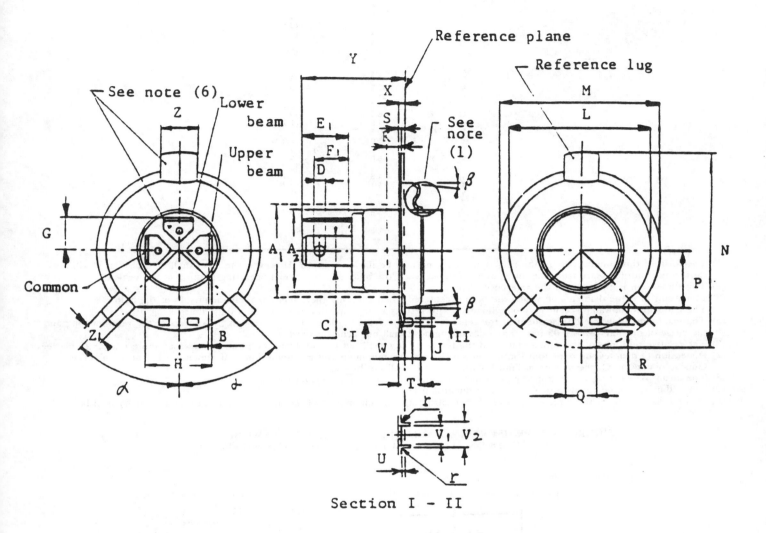

Section I - II

Dimension		Min.	Max.
A_1	(8)	25.0	—
A_2		21.94	22.0
B		0.7	0.8
C		7.7	8.1
D		3.0	3.3
E_1		11.8	13.6
F_1		8.8	10.3
G		8.5	9.0
H		17.0	17.9
J		1.9	2.1
K	(10)	2.0	—
L	(2)(4)	37.5	38.0
M	(3)	42.8	43.0
N		51.6	52.0
P	(2)(7)	15.3	15.5
Q	(2)(7)	8.5	—
R		1.8	2.2
S		0.5	—
T		5.0	6.0
U			(9)
V_1	(2)(5)	8.0	
V_2	(2)(5)	—	10.0
W		1.8	2.2
X		1.1	1.3
Y		—	32.0
Z		9.9	10.0
Z_1		5.8	6.2
r			(9)
α		44	46
β		—	5

(1) The form of this annular part of the ring is optional and may be flat or recessed. However, the form shall be such that it will not cause any abnormal glare from the lower-beam filament when the bulb is in its normal operating position in the vehicle.
(2) This dimension is measured at the reference plane.
(3) Dimension M is the diameter on which the bulb is centered when checking the dimensional characteristics of the bulb.
(4) The maximum allowable eccentricity of cylinder L with respect to the circle of diameter M is 0.05 mm.
(5) The maximum allowable displacement of the center of the nose from the line running through the centers of the reference lug and the circle of diameter M is 0.05 mm. The sides of the nose shall not bend outward.
(6) The relative positions of the contact tabs and the reference lug shall not deviate from the position shown by more than ±20 degrees.
(7) Dimension Q denotes the minimum width over which both the minimum and maximum limits of dimension P shall be observed. Outside dimension Q, the maximum limit for dimension P shall not be exceeded.
(8) The means of securing the ring in the headlamp shall not encroach on this cylindrical zone.
(9) The radius r shall be equal to or smaller than dimension U.
(10) Beyond distance K, in the direction of the contact tabs, both the minimum and the maximum limits of dimension A_2 shall be measured.

FIGURE 7—TYPE HS1 REPLACEABLE MOTORCYCLE HEADLAMP BULB—ASSEMBLED BASE PX43t-38 ON FINISHED BULB—DIMENSIONAL SPECIFICATIONS

Dimensions in mm

The drawings are intended only to indicate the dimensions essential for interchangeability.

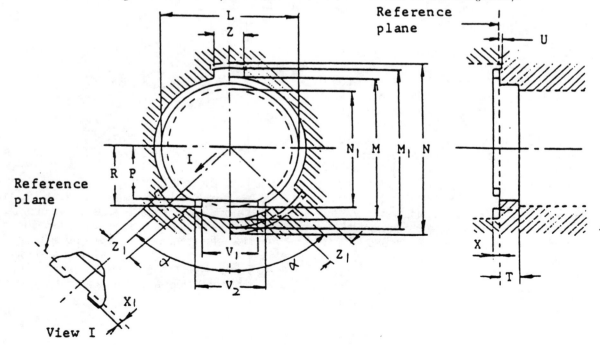

Dimension	Min.	Max.
M	43.02 (1)	43.2
M₁	—	49.0
N	52.2	—
N₁	35.0	—
L	38.2	38.5
P	15.7	16.7
R	20.0	—
T	5.5	—
U	0.4	—
V₁	7.5	7.8
V₂	10.2	—
X	1.8	—
X₁ (2)	1.4	—
Z	10.05	10.15
Z₁	8.0	8.5
α	44	46

The holder shall be so designed that the means of retention of the bulb can be applied only when the bulb is in the correct position.
The means of retention shall make contact only with the prefocus ring of the base and the total force exerted, when the bulb is in position, shall be not less than 10 N and be not greater than 60 N.

(1) This value shall be complied with between the rim of the bulbholder and the reference plane (dimension X).
   However, it may be reduced to 38.5 mm within the dimensions Z and Z₁ which correspond with the support points for the lugs of the cap.
(2) Dimension X₁ denotes the minimum distance over which dimensions Z and Z₁ shall apply.
   Outside dimension X₁ the slots may be chamfered or rounded.

FIGURE 8—TYPE HS1 REPLACEABLE MOTORCYCLE HEADLAMP BULB—
BULBHOLDER PX43t—DIMENSIONAL SPECIFICATIONS

TESTS FOR SNOWMOBILE SWITCHING DEVICES AND COMPONENTS—SAE J68 DEC91 — SAE Recommended Practice

Report of the Snowmobile Committee, approved October 1979, reaffirmed without change October 1984. Revised by the SAE Snowmobile Committee December 1991. Rationale statement available.

1. Scope—This SAE Recommended Practice covers standardized basic tests, test methods, and requirements applicable to electromechanical switching devices which may be used on snowmobiles as defined in SAE J33.

(R) *2. References*

2.1 Applicable Documents—The following publications form a part of this specification to the extent specified herein. The latest issue of SAE publications shall apply.

2.1.1 SAE PUBLICATIONS—Available from SAE, 400 Commonwealth Drive, Warrendale, PA 15096-0001.

SAE J33—Definitions for Snowmobiles
SAE J45—Brake System Test Procedure—Snowmobiles
SAE J575—Tests for Motor Vehicle Lighting Devices and Components
SAE J1222—Speed Control Assurance for Snowmobiles

2.2 Definitions

2.2.1 A headlamp beam switch is a driver-controlled device used to select the high or low beam headlamp circuit.

2.2.2 A headlamp switch is a driver-controlled device used to activate headlights, taillights, and certain marking lights.

2.2.3 A stop lamp switch is a device used to energize the stop lamp circuit with the operator actuation of the brake.

2.2.4 An accessory switch is a driver-controlled device used to activate accessories (i.e., hand warmers, etc.).

2.2.5 An ignition system switch is a device(s) used to interrupt engine ignition such as: emergency shutoff switch, key switch, or speed control assurance device.

2.2.6 A starter motor switch is a driver-controlled device used to activate the starter motor.

3. Reference Standards

3.1 The following sections from SAE J575 are a part of this document.

3.1.1 PARAGRAPH 2.1—Samples for Tests
3.1.2 PARAGRAPH 2.2—Lamp Bulbs
3.1.3 PARAGRAPH 2.3—Test Fixture
3.1.4 SECTION 3—Laboratory Facilities
3.1.5 PARAGRAPH 4.1—Vibration Tests
3.1.6 PARAGRAPH 4.4—Corrosion Test

NOTE—To expedite testing, separate switching device samples may be used for the vibration and corrosion test.

4. High Temperature Test

4.1 Determine effect of high temperature on the basic function of the switching device.

4.1.1 The switching device shall be exposed to a temperature of 49 °C ± 3 °C (120 °F ± 5 °F) for a minimum of 2 h; however, if the switching device is exposed to a higher temperature in service, then the device shall be tested at this higher temperature. (Refer to 4.1.1.1.)

4.1.1.1 To determine the maximum temperature to which the switching device is exposed, the snowmobile shall be operated for a minimum of 30 min under load, immediately followed by the fade and recovery test of paragraph 6.5 of SAE J45 at a temperature of at least 10 °C (50 °F) and use this temperature to conduct 4.1.1. If a minimum ambient of 10 °C (50 °F) cannot be obtained, subtract the available ambient temperature from 10 °C (50 °F) and add this difference to the maximum temperature to which the switching device is exposed.

4.1.2 After conditioning per 4.1.1, the switching device, while still at 49 °C ± 3 °C (120 °F ± 5 °F) or the higher service temperature, shall be manually cycled for 10 cycles per sequence requirements of Table 1. The switching device shall be electrically and mechanically operable during and after each cycle.

4.1.3 The same switching device shall be used for the Low Temperature and Humidity Test, Section 5.

5. Low Temperature and Humidity Test

5.1 Determine effect of low temperature and high relative humidity on the basic function of the switching device.

5.1.1 The switching device shall be exposed to a temperature of −40 °C ± 3 °C (−40 °F ± 5 °F) for a minimum of 2 h and then within no more than 2 min be exposed to a minimum relative humidity of 60% at a temperature of 21 °C ± 6 °C (70 °F ± 10 °F) for 30 min ± 10 min, after which the switching device shall be exposed again to a temperature of −40 °C ± 3 °C (−40 °F ± 5 °F) for 2 h ± 30 min.

(R) TABLE 1—ENDURANCE TEST AND REQUIREMENTS

Device	Sequence	Cycle	Design Performance Requirements
Headlamp beam switch	Hi-beam-Lo-beam-Hi-beam	10 000	The switch shall be designed so that the headlight circuits are never maintained open
Headlamp switch	Off-on-off	5000	
Brake light switch	Off-on-off	50 000	
Accessory switch	Off-on-off	5000	
Ignition system switch			
Emergency shutoff switch	On-off-on (Single throw switch)	10 000	
	or		
	On-off-on-off-on (Dual throw switch)		
Key switch	On-off-on	5000	May include headlamp and start switch
Speed control assurance device			
Passive (Device used only during speed control malfunction)	On-off-on	10 000	Refer to J1222
Active (Device actuated during every operation of speed controller)	Off-on-off	300 000	
Starter motor switch	Off-on-off	5000	Shall include solenoid if used

5.1.2 After conditioning per 5.1.1, the switching device, while still at −40 °C ± 3 °C (−40 °F ± 5 °F), shall be manually cycled for 10 cycles per sequence requirements of Table 1. The switching device shall be electrically and mechanically operable during and after each cycle.

5.1.3 The same switching device shall be used for the Endurance Test, Section 6.

6. Endurance Test and Requirements

6.1 Determine effect of cycling on the basic function of the switching device.

6.1.1 The switch shall be operated at no less than the rated electrical load of the circuit it is switching (i.e., headlamp, stop lamp, ignition system, etc.). The test shall be run with DC except systems designed to operate on AC only, which may be tested with AC.

6.1.1.1 The power supply shall not generate any adverse transients not present in the snowmobile and shall comply with the following specifications:

a. Output Current—Capable of supplying output and inrush current as required in 6.1.1.

b. Regulator—DC supplies

Dynamic—The output voltage shall not deviate more than 1.0 V from zero to maximum load (including inrush current). DC supplies should recover 63% of maximum excursion within 5 ms.

Static—The output voltage shall not deviate more than 2% with changes in static load (not including inrush current) and means shall be provided to compensate for static line voltage variations.

Ripple Voltage—(DC supplies only) Maximum 300 MV peak to peak.

(R) 6.1.1.2 Speed control assurance devices actuated during every operation of the speed control shall be mechanically sequenced 300 000 cycles, per Table 1. However, those same switching devices interrupting their electrical load only during speed control malfunction shall have the electrical load applied only during the last 10 000 of the total 300 000 cycles.

6.1.2 The switch shall be subjected to an endurance test as specified in Table 1, at a temperature of 21 °C ± 6 °C (70 °F ± 10 °F) and at a rate not exceeding 30 cycles/min.

a. Travel time—0.1 to 0.5 s maximum. (Time from one position to the next position.)

b. Dwell time—0.4 s minimum (in each position).

The switch shall be electrically and mechanically operable during and after this test.

6.1.3 The voltage drop from the input to output terminals of the switching device shall be measured before and after the completion of the endurance test. This voltage drop shall not exceed 2% of the applied voltage at the rated electrical load of the circuit as in 6.1.1. If the wiring is an integral part of the switching device, the voltage drop measurement is to be made including 76 mm (3 in) of wire on each side of the switch terminals.

MAINTENANCE OF DESIGN VOLTAGE
—SNOWMOBILE ELECTRICAL SYSTEMS
—SAE J277 MAY95

SAE Recommended Practice

Report of the Snowmobile and All-Terrain Vehicle Committee approved December 1971. Revised by the SAE Snowmobile Committee June 1990, and reaffirmed May 1995. Rationale statement available.

Foreword—This SAE Recommended Practice is intended as a guide toward standard practice, but may be subject to frequent change to keep pace with experience and technical advances. Hence, its use where flexibility of revision is impractical is not recommended.

This reaffirmed document has been changed only to reflect the new SAE Technical Standards Board format and also a few editorial changes for clarification.

1. Scope—This SAE Recommended Practice provides test methods and requirements for maintenance of design voltage in snowmobile electrical systems. It pertains to both battery-equipped and batteryless systems.

2. References—There are no referenced publications specified herein.

3. Samples for Test—Samples submitted for laboratory test shall be representative of the systems as regularly manufactured and marketed. Each sample shall include not only the electrical system, but also accessory equipment necessary to operate it in the normal manner.

4. Test Apparatus

4.1 Voltmeter—Alternating current (AC) or direct current (DC), as required, capable of ±2% accuracy of the measured reading. For AC measurements, either a true RMS voltmeter is required or the AC and DC components of the AC waveform must be measured separately and added algebraically as follows in Equation 1:

$$V_{True\ Rms} = V_{DC}{}^2 + V_{AC}{}^2 \qquad (Eq.1)$$

For AC measurements, the voltmeter must have a minimum crest factor of 3.

4.2 Ammeter—DC, capable of ±2% accuracy of the measured reading.

4.3 Tachometer—Means of measuring engine rpm within ±3%.

5. Test Procedure

5.1 Preliminary Instruction

5.1.1 If snowmobile is battery equipped, install a fully charged original equipment battery.

5.1.2 If snowmobile is battery equipped, install the ammeter in series with the battery such that it indicates negative current for discharge and positive current for charge conditions. Do not install the ammeter in series with the electric starter motor.

5.1.3 VOLTMETER INSTALLATION

5.1.3.1 Install the voltmeter(s) between the lamp terminals and the system ground. For the purpose of this document, the terminal voltages are designated as follows:

 a. V_1—Headlamp low beam terminal to ground
 b. V_2—Headlamp high beam terminal to ground
 c. V_3—Tail lamp terminal to ground
 d. V_4—Stop lamp terminal to ground

5.1.3.2 Take the required voltage readings simultaneously. If this is not possible, record the average of three consecutive readings that are within 1 V of each other.

5.1.4 ENGINE RPM

5.1.4.1 Do not use a tachometer operating from the alternator signal unless: it is standard equipment in the system being tested, or it affects the system's output voltage less than 0.5%.

5.1.5 SYSTEM OPERATION—Verify proper operation of all lamps, switches, and associated equipment both before and after the test is completed.

5.1.6 DATA SHEET—Prepare data sheet to record the voltage measurements indicated in Table 1 and the rpm recorded in 5.2.2.2.

5.2 Data Recording

5.2.1 Record the voltage measurements for the various switch positions and rpms as indicated in Table 1.

5.2.1.1 Idle rpm equals manufacturer's recommended idle rpm.

5.2.1.2 Clutch engagement rpm equals the rpm of initial clutch engagement (for systems not using a centrifugal clutch, run the engine at an rpm equivalent to 40% of top speed in top gear).

5.2.1.3 Rated rpm equals the engine rpm at maximum bhp, as installed in the snowmobile.

5.2.2 RPM FOR "0" AMMETER READING—For battery-equipped systems only.

5.2.2.1 Switch headlamp to upper beam.

5.2.2.2 Record the engine rpm at which the ammeter reads "0".

5.2.3 SYSTEMS WITH TWO OR MORE HEADLAMPS

5.2.3.1 Simulate a field lamp failure.

5.2.3.2 Repeat 5.2.1.

TABLE 1—SWITCH POSITION FOR VOLTAGE MEASUREMENT

Engine RPM	Switch Positions Headlamp Low V_1	Switch Positions Headlamp High V_2	Switch Positions Tail Lamp V_3	Switch Positions Stop Lamp V_4
1. Idle	O	X	X	O
2. Idle	X	O	X	O
3. Clutch Engagement	X	O	X	O
4. Clutch Engagement	O	X	X	O
5. Rated	O	X	X	O
6. Rated	O	X	X	X
7. Rated	X	O	X	O
8. Rated	X	O	X	X
9. Rated	O	O	O	X

NOTE:
X = Switch in "ON" position and measure voltage
O = Switch in "OFF" position, no voltage measurement

6. Test Limits

6.1 Except as provided in 6.1.1, record all measurements in 5.2.1 and 5.2.3.2 between 80 and 120% of the rated lamp design voltage.

6.1.1 At idle rpm, the lamp voltages (V_1, V_2, and V_3) are to be between 40 and 120% of the rated lamp design voltage.

6.2 Do not use or record the rpm of 5.2.2.2 if it is greater than the manufacturer's clutch engagement rpm.

7. Test Conditions—Condition the snowmobile before testing. Snowmobile conditioning consists of either running the snowmobile at the manufacturer's recommended idle rpm for 5 min, or soaking the snowmobile for 2 h at a temperature of no less than 10 °C.

Report of the Snowmobile and All-Terrain Vehicle Committee approved December 1971, reaffirmed without change October 1984. Reaffirmed by the SAE Snowmobile Committee May 1995.

Foreword—This SAE Recommended Practice is intended as a guide toward standard practice, but may be subject to frequent change to keep pace with experience and technical advances. Hence, its use where flexibility of revision is impractical is not recommended.

This reaffirmed document has been changed only to reflect the new SAE Technical Standards Board format.

1. Scope—This SAE Recommended Practice provides test methods and requirements for the stop lamp on snowmobiles.

2. References

2.1 Applicable Documents—The following publications form a part of this specification to the extent specified herein. The latest issue of SAE publications shall apply.

2.1.1 SAE PUBLICATIONS—Available from SAE, 400 Commonwealth Drive, Warrendale, PA 15096-0001.

SAE J567—Lamp Bulb Retention System

SAE J575—Test Methods and Equipment for Lighting Devices and Components, for use on Vehicles Less than 2032 mm in Overall Width

SAE J576—Plastic Materials for Use in Optical Parts Such as Lenses and Reflectors of Motor Vehicle Lighting Devices

SAE J578—Color Specifications

3. Definitions

3.1 Stop Lamp—Lamp giving a steady light to the rear of a vehicle to indicate the intent of the operator of a vehicle to stop or diminish speed.

3.2 Multiple-Compartment Lamp—A device which gives its indication by two or more separately lighted areas which are joined by one or more common parts such as a housing or lens.

3.3 Multiple Lamp Arrangement—An array of two or more separated lamps on each side of the snowmobile which operate together to give a signal.

4. Laboratory Requirements

4.1 A multiple compartment lamp or multiple lamps may be used.

4.2 The following sections from SAE J575 are a part of this document.

4.2.1 PARAGRAPH 2.2.1—Samples for Test

4.2.2 PARAGRAPH 2.2.2—Lamp Bulbs

4.2.3 PARAGRAPH 2.2.3—Laboratory Facilities

4.2.4 PARAGRAPH 3.1—Vibration Test

4.2.5 PARAGRAPH 3.2—Moisture Test

4.2.6 PARAGRAPH 3.3—Dust Exposure Test

4.2.7 PARAGRAPH 3.4—Corrosion Test

4.2.8 PARAGRAPH 3.5—Photometry

4.2.9 PARAGRAPH 3.6—Warpage Test on Devices with Plastic Components, except that the lamp is to be operated 5 min on and 5 min off until the total time equals 1 h. If the tail lamp and/or side marker lamps are incorporated in the same device, they shall be operated continuously during the test. (The test is to be conducted in a circulating air type oven.)

4.3 Plastic Materials—Any plastic materials used in optical parts shall comply with the requirements set forth in SAE J576.

4.4 Color Test—The color of the light from a tail lamp shall be red. (See SAE J578.)

4.5 If the stop lamp is optically combined with the tail lamp and a two-filament bulb is used, the bulb shall have an indexing base and the socket shall be designed so that bulbs with nonindexing bases cannot be used. As a matter of information, attention is called to typical sockets shown in SAE J567.

TABLE 1—MINIMUM DESIGN CANDELA REQUIREMENTS

Test Points, degrees	Test Points, degrees	Lighted Sections 1	Lighted Sections 2	Lighted Sections 3
10U	10L	5	6	8
and	V	13	15	18
10D	10R	5	6	8
	20L	5	6	8
	10L	15	18	20
5U	5L	25	30	35
and	V	35	41	48
5D	5R	25	30	35
	10R	15	18	20
	20R	5	6	8
	20L	8	9	10
	10L	20	24	28
	5L	40	48	55
H	V	40	48	55
	5R	40	48	55
	10R	20	24	28
	20R	8	9	10

NOTES

1. Specifications are based on laboratories using accurate, rated bulbs during testing.
2. Lamps designed to operate on the vehicle through a resistor or equivalent shall be photometered with the listed design voltage of the design source applied across the combination of resistance and filament.
3. A multiple device signaling unit gives its indication by two or more separately lighted sections which may be separate lamps or areas that are joined by common parts. The photometric values are to apply when all sections which provide the same signal are considered as a unit.
4. When a tail lamp is combined with the stop lamp, the stop lamp shall not be less than three times the candela of the tail lamp at any test point on or above horizontal; except that at H-V, H-5L, H-5R, and 5U-V, the stop lamp shall not be less than five times the candela of the tail lamp.

4.6 Photometric Requirements

4.6.1 All beam candela measurements shall be made with the incandescent filament of the signal lamp at least 3.05 m (10 ft) from the photometer screen. The H-V axis shall be taken as parallel to the longitudinal axis of the vehicle. When compartments or lamps are photometered together, the H-V axis shall intersect the midpoint between the optical center (filament).

4.6.2 Beam candela measurements of multiple compartment lamp(s) or multiple lamp arrangements shall be made by either of the following methods:

a. All compartments or lamps may be photometered together, provided that a line from the optical center (filament) of each compartment or lamp to the center of the photometer sensing device does not make an angle of more than 0.6 degree with the photometer (H-V) axis.

b. Each compartment or lamp may be photometered separately by aligning its axis with the photometer and adding the value at each test point.

4.6.3 Table 1 lists design candela requirements for a stop lamp.

5. Installation Requirements—The following requirements apply to the device as used on the snowmobile and are not part of the laboratory test requirements and procedures.

Visibility of the stop lamp shall not be obstructed by any part of the snowmobile throughout the photometric test angles for the lamp, unless the lamp is designed to comply with all photometric and visibility requirements with these obstructions considered. Signal from lamps on both sides of the snowmobile shall be visible through a horizontal angle from 45 degrees to the left to 45 degrees to the right. Where more than one lamp or optical area is lighted on each side of the snowmobile, only one such area on each side need comply. To be considered visible, the lamp must provide an unobstructed projected illuminated area of outer lens surface, excluding reflex, at least 129 mm² (2 in²) in extent, measured at 45 degrees to the longitudinal axis of the vehicle.

SNOWMOBILE TAIL LAMP (REAR POSITION LAMP)
—SAE J279 MAY95   SAE Recommended Practice

Report of the Snowmobile and All-Terrain Vehicle Committee approved March 1972, editorial change May 1972. Reaffirmed without change by the SAE Snowmobile Committee October 1984, and reaffirmed May 1995.

Foreword—This SAE Recommended Practice is intended as a guide toward standard practice, but may be subject to frequent change to keep pace with experience and technical advances. Hence, its use where flexibility of revision is impractical is not recommended.

This reaffirmed document has been changed only to reflect the new SAE Technical Standards Board format.

1. Scope—This SAE Recommended Practice provides test methods and requirements for tail lamps for snowmobiles.

2. References

2.1 Applicable Documents—The following publications form a part of this specification to the extent specified herein. The latest issue of SAE publications shall apply.

2.1.1 SAE PUBLICATIONS—Available from SAE, 400 Commonwealth Drive, Warrendale, PA 15096-0001.

SAE J567—Lamp Bulb Retention System

SAE J575—Test Methods and Equipment for Lighting Devices and Components, for use on Vehicles Less than 2032 mm in Overall Width

SAE J576—Plastic Materials for Use in Optical Parts Such as Lenses and Reflectors of Motor Vehicle Lighting Devices

SAE J578—Color Specifications

3. Definitions

3.1 Tail Lamp—Lamp used to designate the rear of a snowmobile by a steady-burning, low-intensity light.

3.2 Multiple-Compartment Lamp—A device which gives its indication by two or more separately lighted areas which are joined by one or more common parts such as a housing or lens.

3.3 Multiple Lamp Arrangement—An array of two or more separated lamps on each side of the snowmobile which operate together to give a signal.

4. Laboratory Requirements

4.1 A multiple compartment lamp or multiple lamps may be used.

4.2 The following sections from SAE J575 are a part of this document.

4.2.1 PARAGRAPH 2.2.1—Samples for Test

4.2.2 PARAGRAPH 2.2.2—Lamp Bulbs

4.2.3 PARAGRAPH 2.2.3—Laboratory Facilities

4.2.4 PARAGRAPH 3.1—Vibration Test

4.2.5 PARAGRAPH 3.2—Moisture Test

4.2.6 PARAGRAPH 3.3—Dust Exposure Test

4.2.7 PARAGRAPH 3.4—Corrosion Test

4.2.8 PARAGRAPH 3.5—Photometry

4.2.9 PARAGRAPH 3.6—Warpage Test on Devices with Plastic Components

4.3 Plastic Materials—Any plastic materials used in optical parts shall comply with the requirements set forth in SAE J576.

4.4 Color Test—The color of the light from a tail lamp shall be red. (See SAE J578.)

4.5 If the tail lamp is optically combined with another lamp such as a stop lamp or turn signal and a two-filament bulb is used, the bulb shall have an indexing base and the socket shall be designed so that bulbs with nonindexing bases cannot be used. As a matter of information, attention is called to typical sockets shown in SAE J567.

4.6 Photometric Requirements

4.6.1 All beam candela measurements shall be made with the incandescent filament of the signal lamp at least 3 m (10 ft) from the photometric screen. The H-V axis shall be taken as parallel to the longitudinal axis of the vehicle. When compartments or lamps are photometered together, the H-V axis shall intersect the midpoint between the optical centers (filament).

4.6.2 Beam candela measurements of multiple compartment lamp or multiple lamp arrangements shall be made by either of the following methods:

a. All compartments or lamps may be photometered together, provided that a line from the optical axis (filament centers) of each compartment or lamp to the center of the photometer sensing device does not make an angle of more than 0.6 degree with the photometer (H-V) axis.

b. Each compartment or lamp may be photometered separately by aligning its axis with the photometer and adding the value at each test point.

4.6.3 Table 1 lists design candela requirements for a tail lamp.

TABLE 1—MINIMUM DESIGN CANDELA REQUIREMENTS

Test Points, degrees	Test Points, degrees	Lighted Sections 1	Lighted Sections 2	Lighted Sections 3
10U	10L	0.2	0.3	0.4
and	V	0.3	0.5	0.8
10D	10R	0.2	0.3	0.4
	20L	0.2	0.3	0.4
	10L	0.4	0.7	1.0
5U	5L	0.7	1.0	1.5
and	V	0.9	1.5	2.3
5D	5R	0.7	1.0	1.5
	10R	0.4	0.7	1.0
	20R	0.2	0.3	0.4
	20L	0.2	0.4	0.5
	10L	0.4	0.7	1.0
	5L	1.0	1.8	2.5
H	V	1.0	1.8	2.5
	5R	1.0	1.8	2.5
	10R	0.4	0.7	1.0
	20R	0.2	0.4	0.5

NOTES:
1. Specifications are based on laboratories using accurate, rated bulbs during testing.
2. Lamps designed to operate on the vehicle through a resistor or equivalent shall be photometered with the listed design voltage of the design source applied across the combination of resistance and filament.
3. A multiple device tail lamp gives its indication by two or more separately lighted sections which may be separate lamps, or areas that are joined by common parts. The photometric values are to apply when all sections which provide the tail signal are considered as a unit.

5. Installation Requirements—The following requirements apply to the device as used on the vehicle and are not part of the laboratory test requirements and procedures.

Visibility of the tail lamp shall not be obstructed by any part of the vehicle throughout the photometric test angles for the lamp, unless the lamp is designed to comply with all photometric and visibility requirements with these obstructions considered. Signals from lamps on both sides of the vehicle shall be visible through a horizontal angle from 45 degrees to the left to 45 degrees to the right. Where more than one lamp or optical area is lighted on each side of the snowmobile, only one such area on each side need comply. To be considered visible, the lamp must provide an unobstructed projected illuminated area of outer lens surface, excluding reflex, at least 129 mm^2 (2 in^2) in extent, measured at 45 degrees to the longitudinal axis of the vehicle.

As a minimum, the taillight shall be lighted when the headlight is energized.

Report of the Snowmobile and All-Terrain Vehicle Committee, approved January 1972, editorial change June 1973, revised by the Snowmobile Committee June 1984.

NOTE: This SAE Recommended Practice is intended as a guide toward standard practice, but may be subject to frequent change to keep pace with experience and technical advances. Hence, its use where flexibility of revision is impractical is not recommended.

1. Scope—This recommended practice provides test methods and requirements for snowmobile headlamps.

2. Definition—Snowmobile headlamps are one or more lamps mounted on the front of a snowmobile used as the major lighting device to provide general illumination ahead of the snowmobile. The photometric requirements stated in Tables 1 and 2 represent the total headlamp illumination requirement for a snowmobile.

2.1 If multiple headlamps are used to meet this recommended practice, the combination of lamps, as mounted on the snowmobile, shall meet the requirements when treated as one lamp.

2.2 The headlamp shall not be obstructed by any part of the snowmobile throughout the photometric test angles for the lamp, unless the lamp is designed to comply with all photometric requirements with these obstructions considered.

3. References—The following sections from SAE J575 are a part of this recommended practice:

Section B—Samples for test
Section C—Lamp Bulbs
Section D—Laboratory Facilities
Section E—Vibration Test
Section F—Moisture Test
Section G—Dust Test
Section H—Corrosion Test
Section I—Color Test—The light should be white to amber.
Section J—Photometry
Section L—Warpage Test Devices with Plastic Lenses

3.1 Sealed Beam headlamps do not need to comply with sections F or G of SAE J575.

4. Aiming Adjustment Tests

4.1 A minimum aiming adjustment of ±4 deg shall be provided in φ the vertical plane from a basic aiming position of ½ D-V (±0.5 deg) with the machine on a hard surface, the suspension adjusted to the manufacturers recommended setting and the machine loaded to simulate an 80 kg operator at the designated seating position.

4.2 The mechanism, including the aiming adjustment, shall be so designed as to prevent the unit from receding into the lamp body or housing when an inward force of 50 lb (22.7 N) is exerted at the geometric center of the outer surface of the lens.

4.3 When adjusting screws are employed, they shall be equipped with self-locking devices which will operate satisfactorily for a minimum of 10 adjustments on each screw, over a length of screw thread of ±⅛ in (3.175 mm).

4.4 Headlamp Mounting—The headlamp should be mounted on the snowmobile as high as practicable above the surface of the ground and below the snowmobile operator's line of sight.

In order to facilitate setting and maintaining the proper adjustment of the headlamp on snowmobiles in use, the following requirements for headlamp design and mounting shall be adopted and followed in general practice and be equally applicable to new designs of headlamps and headlamp mountings. Headlamps and headlamp mountings shall be designed and constructed so that:

4.4.1 The axis of the light beam may be adjusted conveniently by one person using ordinary tools, up and down from the designed setting, in the amount determined by practical operating conditions.

4.4.2 When the headlamp is secured, the aim will not be disturbed under ordinary conditions of operation.

4.5 Visual Service Aiming—The geometric center of the high intensity zone of the upper beam of the multiple beam headlamps shall be deemed sufficiently defined for the purpose of service aiming if it can be set by three experienced observers on a vertical screen at 25 ft

(7.6 m) within a maximum vertical deviation of ±0.2 deg [1 in (25.4 mm)] and within a maximum horizontal deviation of ±0.4 deg [2 in (50.8 mm)]. The aim for each observer shall be taken as the average of at least three observations.

4.6 Beam Aim During Photometric Test—The upper beam of a multiple beam headlamp shall be aimed photoelectrically so that the center of the zone of highest intensity falls 0.4 deg vertically below the lamp axis and is centered laterally. The center of the zone of highest intensity shall be established by the intersection of a horizontal plane passing through the point of maximum intensity, and the vertical plane established by balancing the photometric values at 6 deg left and 6 deg right.

4.7 Photometric Tests—Shall be made with the photometer at a distance of 60 ft (18.3 m) from the lamp. The headlamp shall be operated at its rated voltage during the test and in accordance with paragraph 2.2.

4.8 At Focus Tests—The light source shall be located in the design position with respect to the reflector as specified by the manufacturer.

4.8.1 When aimed as described in paragraph 4.6, the high beam of the headlamp shall meet the candela requirements in Table 1.

4.8.2 When aimed as described in paragraph 4.6, the low beam of the headlamp shall meet the candela requirements in Table 2.

TABLE 1—UPPER BEAM

Position, deg	Candela, cd
3U–V	1200 min
1/2D–V	12 000 min
1-1/2D–6L to 6R	6000 min
1-1/2D–9L to 9R	3000 min
1-1/2D–15L to 15R	1000 min
4-1/2D–V	1200 min

NOTE: A tolerance of ± 1/4 deg should be allowed at any test point.

TABLE 2—LOWER BEAM

Position, deg	Candela, cd
1/2U–Anywhere	2000 max
1-1/2D–V	5000 min
3D–V	9000 min
1-1/2D–6L to 6R	3000 min
3D–6L to 6R	6000 min
1-1/2D–9L to 9R	2000 min
3D–9L to 9R	3000 min
3D–15L to 15R	1000 min
4-1/2D–V	1500 min

NOTE: A tolerance of ± 1/4 deg should be allowed at any test point.

SNOWMOBILE AND SNOWMOBILE CUTTER LAMPS, REFLECTIVE DEVICES, AND ASSOCIATED EQUIPMENT—SAE J292 MAY95

SAE Recommended Practice

Report of the Snowmobile and All-Terrain Vehicle Committee approved March 1973. Reaffirmed without change by the SAE Snowmobile Committee October 1984, and reaffirmed May 1995.

Foreword—This SAE Recommended Practice is intended as a guide toward standard practice, but may be subject to frequent change to keep pace with experience and technical advances. Hence, its use where flexibility of revision is impractical, is not recommended.

This reaffirmed document has been changed only to reflect the new SAE Technical Standards Board Format.

1. Scope—This SAE Recommended Practice describes requirements for lamps, reflective devices, and associated equipment for signaling to enable safe operation in darkness and other conditions of reduced visibility.

2. References

2.1 Applicable Documents—The following publications form a part of this specification to the extent specified herein. The latest issue of SAE publications shall apply.

2.1.1 SAE PUBLICATIONS—Available from SAE, 400 Commonwealth Drive, Warrendale, PA 15096-0001.

SAE J68—Tests for Snowmobile Switching Devices and Components

SAEJ277—Maintenance of Design Voltage—Snowmobile Electrical Systems

SAE J278—Snowmobile Stop Lamp

SAE J279—Snowmobile Tail Lamp (Rear Position Lamp)

SAE J280—Snowmobile Headlamps

SAE J564—Headlamp Beam Switching

SAE J592—Clearance, Side Marker, and Identification Lamps

SAE J594—Reflex Reflectors

3. Application—This document applies to snowmobiles and snowmobile cutters.[1]

4. Requirements

4.1 Vehicles shall be equipped with lamps, reflective devices, and associated equipment, in the numbers of units and designed to conform to the references cited in Table 1.

Reflex reflectors as used for rear and side markers shall conform to one of the following.

4.1.1 Unit-type reflex reflectors in accordance with SAE J594.

4.1.2 Area-type reflex reflectors of any shape, which conform to color limitations, may be used which provide a minimum reflective intensity of 1.5 cd per incident foot-candle (lux) at all incidence angles of 0 to 20 degrees at 0.2 degree divergence when measured within a 230 cm² (36 in²) area not exceeding 600 mm (24 in) in length.

Front reflectors may be of any color or color combination; however, only the color red shall be used for rear and rear side reflectors.

In addition, the reflective sheeting used in manufacturing area-type reflex reflectors shall conform to Federal Specifications L-S-300A, Sheeting and Tape, Reflective: Nonexposed Lens, Adhesive Backing, and Canadian Specification Board 62GP11P for the following characteristics:

Adhesive—Class 1-2-3-4-5, 4.3.4, Adhesive Backing.

Photometric Measurement—4.4.7, Reflective Intensity, and 3.5.6.1, Rainfall.

Durability—4.4.9, Resistance to Accelerated Weathering—Exposure 1000 h and retain 50% of the previously specified reflective intensity; 4.4.10, Resistance to Heat, Cold, and Humidity.

4.1.3 Lighted side markers conforming to SAE J592 may be used in addition to reflex reflectors.

4.1.4 No additional lamp, reflective device, or associated equipment shall be installed if it impairs the effectiveness of the required equipment.

TABLE 1—EQUIPMENT (MINIMUM) SNOWMOBILE AND SNOWMOBILE CUTTER

Item	Number and Color Required on Snowmobile	Number and Color Required on Snowmobile Cutter	In Accordance With
Headlamp	1 white or amber	—	SAE J280
Tail lamp	1 red	—	SAE J279
Stop lamp	1 red	—	SAE J278
Reflex reflectors	3 red[1,2] and 2 amber[1,2] or colors as indicated in 4.1.2	3 red[1,2] and 2 amber[1,2] or colors as indicated in 4.1.2	SAE J594 or Federal Specification L-S-300A and CGSB62GP11P
Side marker Lamps (optional)	2 red, 2 amber[3]	—	SAE J592

[1]See 4.1.1.
[2]See 4.1.2.
[3]See 4.1.3.

4.2 Location of Lamps and Reflectors—Lamps, reflective devices, and associated equipment required by 3.1 shall be installed in accordance with Table 2.

4.3 Lamp Combinations and Equipment Combinations—Two or more lamps, reflective devices, and items of associated equipment may be combined if the requirements for each lamp, reflective device, and item of associated equipment are met.

---

[1] As presently defined by law in Canada.

4.4 Special Wiring Requirements

4.4.1 A means for switching between lower and upper headlamp beams shall be provided that is designed to conform to SAE J564, except that in 3.2.2, Temperature Test, the temperature range shall be between –40 and +52 °F (–40 and +125 °F); in 3.2.3, Endurance Requirements, the cycle requirements shall be reduced by a factor of 10; and in 3.2.3.2, Upper Beam Indicator, the indicator is not required and if used, the signal color need not be red.

4.4.2 As a minimum, the tail lamp shall be illuminated when the headlamp is illuminated.

4.4.3 The stop lamp shall be illuminated upon application of the service brake or by some other means that automatically results in the steady illumination of the stop lamp to indicate the intent of the operator of the snowmobile to stop or diminish speed.

A means for illuminating the stop lamp shall be provided, which is designed to conform to SAE J68.

4.5 Lighting Display—When energized, each lamp specified in Table 1 shall, in normal operation, be steady burning.

4.6 Maintenance of Design Voltage—The snowmobile electrical system shall be designed to conform to SAE J277.

TABLE 2—LOCATION OF EQUIPMENT SNOWMOBILE AND SNOWMOBILE CUTTER

Item	Location on Snowmobile	Location on Snowmobile Cutter	Height Above Trail Surface Measured from Center of Item on Vehicle at Curb Weight
Headlamp	On or within 150 mm (6 in) of front centerline, except that, if two lamps are used, they shall be symmetrically disposed about the front centerline	—	Not less than (380 mm) 15 in
Tail lamp	On rear centerline, except that, if two lamps are used, they shall be symmetrically disposed about the rear centerline	—	Not less than 200 mm (8 in) nor more than 760 mm (30 in)
Stop lamp	On rear centerline, except that, if two lamps are used, they shall be symmetrically disposed about the rear centerline	—	Not less than 200 mm (8 in) nor more than 760 mm (30 in)
Reflex reflectors	1 red on rear centerline, except that, if two reflectors are used on the rear, they shall be symmetrically disposed about the rear centerline[1,2]	1 red on rear centerline, except that, if two reflectors are used on the rear, they shall be symmetrically disposed about the rear centerline[1,2]	Not less than 200 mm (8 in) nor more than 760 mm (30 in)
	2 red, 1 on each side, as far to rear as practicable[1,2]	2 red, 1 on each side, as far to rear as practicable[1,2]	—
	2 amber or other color, 1 on each side, as far forward as practicable[1,2]	2 amber or other color, 1 on each side, as far forward as practicable[1,2]	—
Side marker lamps (optional)	On each side: 1 amber lamp as far forward as practicable and 1 red lamp as far to rear as practicable	—	Not less than 200 mm (8 in) nor more than 760 mm (30 in)

[1]See 4.1.1.
[2]See 4.1.2.

(R) SEVEN CONDUCTOR ELECTRICAL CONNECTOR FOR TRUCK-TRAILER JUMPER CABLE—SAE J560 JUN93   SAE Standard

Report of Electrical Equipment Committee approved January 1951 and revised September 1974. Completely revised by the SAE Truck and Bus Electrical and Electronics Committee June 1993. Rationale statement available.

Foreword—The seven conductor electrical connector is used exclusively in the United States and Canada as the electrical interface between highway tractors and trailers. The exclusive use of this connector makes it possible to pull any trailer with any tractor without the use of adapters.

This connector is comparable to only one unit currently being considered as an ISO Standard. In addition to the seven conductor unit, ISO is considering twelve, thirteen, and fifteen conductor units. All of these may be included in any ISO Standard which will require a number of adapters to achieve universal compatibility of tractors and trailers.

1. Scope—This SAE Standard provides the minimum design requirements for the jumper cable plug and receptacle for the truck-trailer jumper cable system. It includes the test procedures, design, and performance requirements.

2. References

2.1 Applicable Documents—The following publications form a part of this specification to the extent specified herein. The latest issue of SAE publications shall apply.

2.1.1 SAE PUBLICATION—Available from SAE, 400 Commonwealth Drive, Warrendale, PA 15096-0001.

SAE J1067—Seven Conductor Jacketed Cable for Truck-Trailer Connections

2.1.2 ASTM PUBLICATION—Available from ASTM, 1916 Race Street, Philadelphia, PA 19103-1187.

ASTM B 117-73—Standard Method of Salt Spray (Fog) Testing

2.2 Definitions

2.2.1 RECEPTACLE—The receptacle consists of the connector socket, its housing, and a cover which latches the cable plug in place. The socket contains the male contacts. See Figures 1 and 2.

2.2.2 CABLE PLUG—The cable plug is part of the jumper cable assembly. The cable plug contains the female contacts. See Figure 3.

2.2.3 COUPLING CYCLE—Coupling and uncoupling the plug and receptacle is one coupling cycle.

3. Identification Code Designation—Devices conforming to this document shall be identified with the manufacturer's identification, model or part number, and shall be identified with SAE J560 and the revision (month and year) of the document to which the device conforms. For example:

XYZ Corp.
9999
SAE J560
Jun, 93

4. Tests

4.1 Test Equipment and Instrumentation

4.1.1 POWER SUPPLY—The power supply shall be capable of supplying the continuous current required to perform all tests.

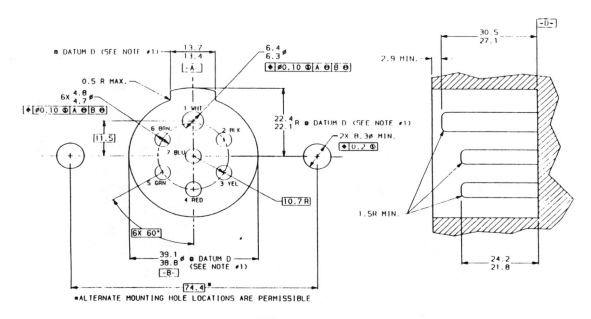

NOTES: 1. ALLOWABLE DRAFT ½ DEGREE PER SIDE.
2. REFER TO PARAGRAPH 7.7 FOR CIRCUIT IDENTIFICATION REQUIREMENTS.

FIGURE 1—RECEPTACLE SOCKET

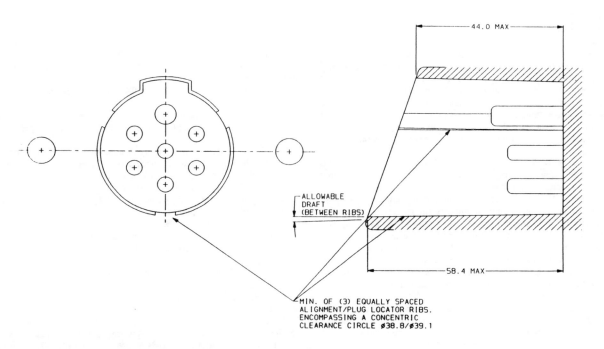

ALL DATUMS, NOTES, AND DIMENSIONS ON FIGURE 1 APPLY TO THIS FIGURE

FIGURE 2—ALTERNATE CONSTRUCTION RECEPTACLE SOCKET

4.1.2 VOLTMETER—A d-c voltmeter with an input resistance greater than 1000 Ω/V and with a resolution of 0.1 V shall be used. To achieve this resolution, the full-scale deflection shall be appropriate to the voltage rating of the system being tested.

A digital meter having at least a 3-1/2-digit readout with an accuracy of ±1% plus one digit is recommended for millivolt readings.

4.1.3 AMMETER—A d-c ammeter shall be used for current measurements. The meter range resolution shall be 0.1 A.

4.1.4 MILLIAMMETER—A d-c ammeter shall be used for current measurements. The meter range resolution shall be 1.0 mA.

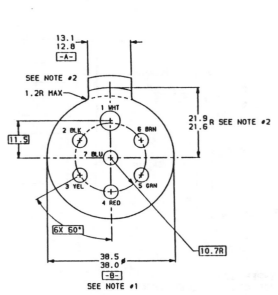
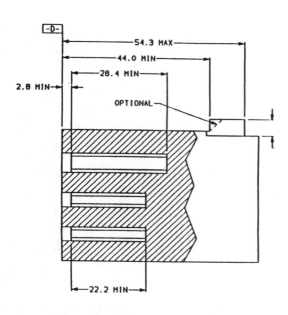

NOTES:
1. DIMENSION MUST BE MAINTAINED FOR 50.4 FROM DATUM "D"
2. DIMENSION MUST BE MAINTAINED FOR 44.0 FROM DATUM "D"

FIGURE 3—CABLE PLUG

4.2 Test Procedures

4.2.1 VOLTAGE DROP

4.2.1.1 Connectors Without Circuit Breakers—Connect a length of SAE J1067 type cable to the plug and receptacle terminals, then couple the mating parts. Connect to a power supply and apply a minimum of 35 A to each circuit which has a 4.75 mm (0.188 in) diameter terminal and a minimum of 70 A to each circuit which has a 6.35 mm (0.25 in) diameter terminal. After temperature stabilization, measure the voltage drop across each circuit of the assembly at a convenient point on the wire at least 25 mm (1 in) from the terminal. The test is to be conducted in a draft-free room maintained at an ambient temperature of 25 °C ± 5 °C.

4.2.1.2 Connectors With Circuit Breakers—Connect a length of SAE J1067 type cable to the plug and receptacle terminals, then couple the mating parts. Connect to a power supply and apply a minimum of 35 A to each circuit which has a 4.75 mm (0.188 in) diameter terminal and a minimum of 70 A to each circuit which has a 6.35 mm (0.25 in) diameter terminal. After temperature stabilization, measure the voltage drop across each circuit of the assembly at a convenient point on the wire at least 25 mm (1 in) from the terminal. Devices with circuit breakers may be certified using the noncircuit breaker version provided the construction is otherwise identical. If this is not possible, devices with circuit breakers may be tested by installing low-resistance shunts across the circuit breakers of the devices tested. The test is to be conducted in a draft-free room maintained at an ambient temperature of 25 °C ± 5 °C.

4.2.2 SHORT AND GROUNDED CIRCUIT—The test for shorts between circuits and ground is to be made with 70 V DC ± 5 V DC. Connect a milliammeter between the circuits to determine a circuit-to-circuit short and between each circuit and ground to determine a circuit-to-ground condition.

4.2.3 COUPLING FORCE—Measure the force to connect and disconnect the plug and receptacle.

4.2.4 STRAIGHT PULL—An assembled cable plug and jumper cable shall be securely mounted in a suitable fixture and a pull of 667 N (150 lb) exerted on the cable along the axis of the cable plug.

4.2.5 SALT SPRAY

4.2.5.1 With the plug inserted into the receptacle and with the assembly mounted in normal truck-trailer position, subject the normally exposed portion of the assembly to a 48 h salt spray test per ASTM B 117.

4.2.5.2 With the receptacle mounted in a normal position with the cover closed and with the open end of the plug pointed down, subject the uncoupled units to a 48 h salt spray test per ASTM B 117.

4.2.6 EXTREME TEMPERATURE—Use the same connector assembly for each extreme temperature condition test.

4.2.6.1 Connect a length of SAE J1067 type cable to the plug and receptacle.

4.2.6.2 Subject each assembly to a minimum ambient temperature of +82.2 °C. After the assembly has stabilized at +82.2 °C, perform a coupling cycle.

4.2.6.3 Subject each assembly to a maximum ambient temperature of -40 °C. After the assembly has stabilized at -40 °C, perform a coupling cycle.

4.2.7 DURABILITY—Connect a length of SAE J1067 type cable to the plug and receptacle and conduct the following test:
  a. Conduct the voltage drop test per 4.2.1.1.
  b. Perform 2500 coupling cycles.
  c. Conduct salt spray test per 4.2.4.1.
  d. Conduct voltage drop, short circuit, and grounded circuit tests per 4.2.1.
  e. Conduct salt spray test per 4.2.4.2.
  f. Repeat d.
  g. Perform 2500 additional coupling cycles.
  h. Repeat d.

5. *Performance Requirements*

5.1 Electrical

5.1.1 VOLTAGE DROP—After temperature stabilization, the voltage drop for each circuit shall not exceed 3 mV/A when tested in accordance with 4.2.1.

5.1.2 SHORT CIRCUIT AND GROUNDED CIRCUIT—The current flowing between any two circuits or between each circuit and ground shall not exceed 50 mA when tested in accordance with 4.2.2.1.

5.2 Coupling Force—The unlatched coupling force shall not exceed 223 N (50 lb) and the latched uncoupling force shall not be less than 110 N (25 lb) in accordance with 4.2.3.

5.3 Straight Pull—An assembled cable plug and trailer jumper cable shall not be damaged when tested in accordance with 4.2.4.

5.4 Extreme Temperature—Insulating materials shall not fracture and shall not deform when tested in accordance with 4.2.6.

290

5.5 Durability—Shall conform to the requirements of 5.1 during and after the test when tested in accordance with 4.2.7.

6. Design Requirements

6.1 Interchangeability—The cable plug shall be designed to conform to the performance requirements of this document with any receptacle which conforms to this document and vice versa.

6.2 Latchability—The cable plug shall be designed to mate and latch to any receptacle designed to conform to this document and vice versa. The latch mechanism shall be constructed to latch and release without interference.

6.3 Indexing—The cable plug shall be designed to provide indexing to any receptacle designed to this document and vice versa. Indexing is required to insure proper electrical mating.

6.4 Wiring Circuits—The function and color code of each circuit is shown in Table 1. The location of each circuit is shown in Figures 1 and 3. The wire color code refers to the color of the insulation on the conductors as specified in SAE J1067. The receptacle and cable plug shall be constructed so that the "WHT" terminal shall accommodate at least a No. 8 AWG wire and all other terminals at least a No. 10 AWG wire.

6.5 Receptacle—Figure 1 shows receptacle dimensions and design requirements. Figure 2 shows alternate construction features. A cover with a weather-tight seal shall be provided to protect the male contacts when uncoupled. The male contacts shall not be split. Formed contacts are acceptable provided the seams are closed.

6.6 Cable Plug—Figure 3 shows cable plug dimensions and design requirements. The terminals in the plug shall be free floating for ease of alignment with the receptacle during coupling. Cable plug assemblies shall incorporate a strain relief to relieve the tension on the electrical connection between the plug contacts and the jumper cable conductors.

6.7 Circuit identification by color or numeric is mandatory on the wire connection side of the cable plug and receptacle. It is recommended that circuit identification be on both the front and back sides of each.

6.8 Either the plug or receptacle or both shall be provided with a latching means which has to be disengaged to uncouple.

7. Guidelines

7.1 Electrical current-carrying parts should be copper or copper alloy. Protective coating or metallic plating is recommended to provide improved corrosion resistance.

7.2 A device should be provided to protect the plug in the uncoupled state. The device should be designed to prevent contaminated or corrosive liquid from entering the plug from either end.

7.3 For ease of alignment, receptacle contacts may be free floating.

TABLE 1—WIRING CIRCUITS

Conductor Identification Terminal Number	Conductor Identification Wire Color	Lamp and Signal Circuits
1	Wht (white)	Ground return to towing vehicle
2	Blk (Black)	Clearance, side marker, and identification lamps
3	Yel (Yellow)	Left turn signal and hazard lamps
4	Red (Red)	Stop lamps and antilock devices
5	Grn (Green)	Right turn signal and hazard lamps
6	Brn (Brown)	Tail and license plate lamps
7	Blu (Blue)	Auxiliary

FIVE CONDUCTOR ELECTRICAL CONNECTORS FOR AUTOMOTIVE TYPE TRAILERS—SAE J895 APR86

SAE Recommended Practice

Report of Electrical Equipment Committee approved June 1964 and reaffirmed by the Electrical and Electronic Systems Technical Committee, April 1986. This report is currently under revision by the Electrical Distribution Systems Subcommittee.

1. Scope—This SAE Recommended Practice covers the wiring and connector standards for nonpassenger carrying trailers, SAE Classes 1–3[1], with circuit loads not to exceed 7.5 amp per circuit. It provides the lighting circuits of these trailers with a universal connecting device, standard circuit coding and protection for the wiring from hazards and shorts.

2. Receptacle—The receptacle shall be of the design as shown in Fig. 1 and shall be attached to the towing vehicle as follows:
   (a) White—Ground to frame
   (b) Brown—Spliced to tail and license light circuit
   (c) Yellow—Spliced to left turn and stop circuit
   (d) Green—Spliced to right turn and stop circuit
   (e) Blue—Auxiliary

The receptacle leads shall be attached to the vehicle wiring harness in a workmanlike manner, mechanically and electrically secure. Further, a well insulated strain relief shall be provided between the receptacle and the towing vehicle wiring harness connections so that there will be no strain on the vehicle harness in the event of an abnormal pull on the receptacle. The receptacle shall be placed in a location where it will not be exposed to road hazards either when connected or loose. The receptacle leads must be properly routed and protected against damage from cutting and pinching where they leave the vehicle body. No receptacle leads shall be smaller than 16 gage (single) or smaller than 18 gage

(in multiconductor cables) heavy duty SAE insulated automotive primary wire.

3. Plug—The plug shall be as shown in Fig. 2, and wiring, shall be attached to the trailer so that the wires have the maximum protection against road splash, stones, abrasion, grease, oil, and fuel. The wiring shall be secured to the trailer frame at intervals not greater than 18 in so that the wiring does not shift or sag. The circuits used shall be color coded as follows:
   (a) White—Ground
   (b) Brown—The tail and license light
   (c) Yellow—Left turn and stop light
   (d) Green—Right turn and stop light
   (e) Blue—Auxiliary

No plug leads shall be smaller than 16 gage (single) or smaller than 18 gage (in multiconductor cables) heavy duty SAE insulated automotive primary wire. Extra insulation should be provided between the strain relief at the trailer hitch and the wiring assembly so that an abnormal pull on the plug will not damage the wiring.

APPENDIX

A.1 Material Requirements—The receptacle and plug shall be made of an insulating material such that they can be processed to provide the spacing and splash protection indicated in Figs. 1 and 2. The material used shall have a hardness of Shore "A" 50 minimum and shall be compatible with the insulation used on the wire leads and/or jacket over the

[1] See SAE J684.

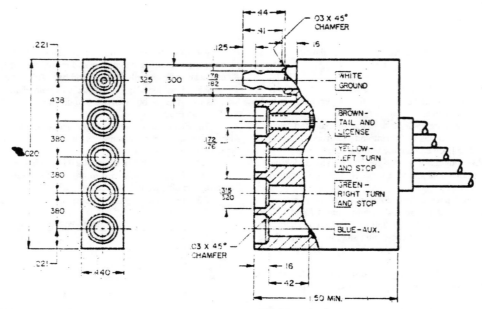

FIG. 1—RECEPTACLE

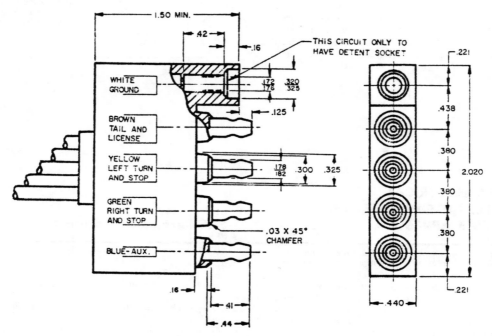

FIG. 2—PLUG

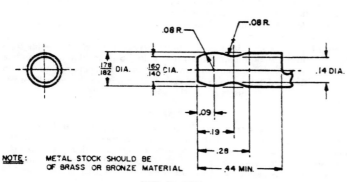

NOTE: METAL STOCK SHOULD BE
OF BRASS OR BRONZE MATERIAL

FIG. 3—PIN

NOTE THIS SOCKET TO BE USED ONLY ON THE
GROUND CIRCUIT OF THE MOLDED PLUG.
SOCKETS SIMILAR TO THIS, EXCEPT WITH
THE DETENT OMITTED, ARE TO BE USED
IN THE MOLDED RECEPTACLE.

METAL STOCK SHOULD BE OF 3/4 HARD
TEMPER BRASS OR BRONZE MATERIAL.

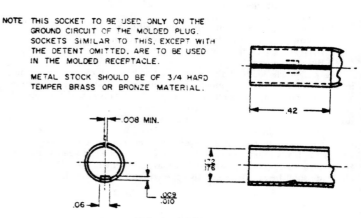

FIG. 4—SOCKET

292

leads. Where thermoplastic materials are used the hardness shall not exceed Shore "A" 70. The jacket on the leads shall be as deemed necessary to adequately protect the wiring. The metal pins and sockets shall be of the size and type shown in Figs. 3 and 4 made of either brass or bronze and suitably coated to protect against corrosion. The coating shall be smooth so as not to bind when the parts are engaged.

A.2 Assembly Requirements—The plug and receptacle assembly shall disengage with a minimum force of 3 lb per circuit and a maximum of 7 lb per circuit, except the ground circuit which can be 12 lb max. The mechanical force requirement of disengagement does not preclude the requirement for good electrical connections between the male and female connectors of the circuits.

SEVEN CONDUCTOR JACKETED CABLE FOR TRUCK TRAILER CONNECTIONS—SAE J1067

SAE Standard

Report of Electrical Equipment Committee approved October 1973.

1. Scope—This standard covers the minimum construction requirements and the configuration of the conductors in the cable to connect electrically a tractor to a trailer and/or trailer to trailer. This cable is used with the connector described in SAE J560.

2. Construction

2.1 Conductor

2.1.1 The conductors shall be made with tinned annealed copper wire according to ASTM B-33. Steel strands may be added to increase flexibility life.

2.1.2 The conductor stranding and lay shall be as shown in Table 1.

2.2 Insulation

2.2.1 The insulation on the No. 8 wire shall be a layer of .001 in. (.0254 mm) white polyethylene terephthalate film helically wrapped around the conductor with $\frac{1}{3}$-$\frac{1}{2}$ lap.

2.2.2 The insulation on the No. 10 wire and No. 12 wires shall be as specified in Table 2. The colors of the insulating compounds shall be as shown in Fig. 1. The nominal wall thickness of the insulation shall be 0.032 in. (.813 mm).

2.3 Cabling—The conductors shall be cabled together with a maximum lay of 6 in. (152.4 mm). The configuration of the conductors shall be as shown in Fig. 1. A suitable filler may be applied in twisting so as to fill the interstices between the conductors to produce a circular cross section. Use of a suitable separator over the conductors is required.

2.4 Jacket—A 0.062 in. (1.57 mm) minimum thickness jacket shall be applied over the conductors and separator. The jacket compound shall meet the specifications in Table 3. The color of the jacket shall be red.

2.5 Cable Diameter and Finish—The finished outside diameter of the cable shall be 0.690 ± 0.020 in. (17.53 ± 0.508 mm). The finish of the cable shall be smooth and free from defects. Adjacent layers must not stick together when wound around a spool at any temperature below 120°F (49°C).

3. Tests

3.1 The cable shall be free from open circuits or twisted conductor splices.

3.2 Cold Test—A suitable length of cable shall be subjected to −20°F (−29°C) for a period of 4 h. While still at this temperature, it shall be bent 360 deg around a 3 in. (76.2 mm) diameter mandrel. The jacket shall not crack.

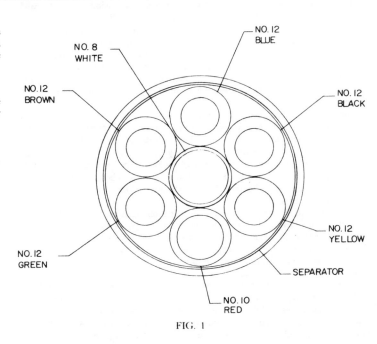

FIG. 1

TABLE 2—INSULATION COMPOUND[a]

Recovery, in.	5 in. (127.0 mm) str, 1/2 (12.7 mm)
Elongation, %	250
Tensile strength, psi (MPa)	600 (4.12)
Oxygen-bomb aged (96 h at 70°C, 300 psi) elongation	70% of orig. min
Oxygen-bomb aged (96 h at 70°C, 300 psi) tensile	70% of orig. min

[a]Underwriters' Laboratories requirements for Class 3 Rubber—UL 62.

TABLE 3—JACKET COMPOUND[a]

Recovery, in.	6 in. (152.4 mm) str, 3/8 (9.53 mm)
Elongation, %	300
Tensile strength, psi (MPa)	1500 (10.35)
Oxygen-bomb aged (96 h at 70°C, 300 psi (2.06 MPa)) elongation	70% of orig. min[b]
Oxygen-bomb aged (96 h at 70°C, 300 psi (2.06 MPa)) tensile	70% of orig. min[b]
Air-oven aged (168 h at 70°C) tensile and elongation	70% of orig. min
Oil immersed (18 h at 121°C) tensile and elongation	60% of orig. min

[a]Underwriters' Laboratories requirements for Class 15 Neoprene—UL 62.
[b]65% of result with unaged specimens if sum of tensile and elongation percentages is at least 140.

TABLE 1—CONDUCTORS

SAE Wire[a] Size	No. of Wires	Nominal Size of Strand AWG	Nominal Size of Strand in.	Lay in.	Conductor Area Cir Mils	Max Dia of Stranded Conductor, in.
12	65	30	.010 (.254 mm)	1.5 (38.1 mm)	6487	.100 (2.54 mm)
10	105	30	.010 (.254 mm)	1.5 (38.1 mm)	10479	.125 (3.18 mm)
8	168 or	30	.010 (.254 mm)	2.0 (50.8 mm)	16414	.175 (4.45 mm)
	427	34	.0063 (.160 mm)	2.0 (50.8 mm)		

[a]SAE wire size numbers indicate that the circular mil area of the stranded conductor approximates the circular mil area of American Wire Gage for equivalent gage size.

LIMITS AND METHODS OF MEASUREMENT OF RADIO DISTURBANCE CHARACTERISTICS OF COMPONENTS AND MODULES FOR THE PROTECTION OF RECEIVERS USED ON BOARD VEHICLES—SAE J1113/41 JUL95

SAE Standard

Report of the SAE EMR Standards Committee approved July 1995. Rationale statement available.

1. Scope—This SAE Standard contains limits[1] and procedures for the measurement of radio disturbances in the frequency range of 150 kHz to 1000 MHz. The standard applies to any electronic/electrical component intended for use in vehicles and large devices. Refer to International Telecommunications Union (ITU) Publications for details of frequency allocations. The limits are intended to provide protection for receivers installed in a vehicle from disturbances produced by components/modules in the same vehicle.[2]

The receiver types to be protected are: sound and television receivers[3], land mobile radio, radio telephone, amateur and citizens' radio. For the purpose of this document, a vehicle is a machine which is self-propelled. Vehicles include (but are not limited to) passenger cars, trucks, agricultural tractors, and snowmobiles.

The limits in this document are recommended and subject to modification as agreed between the vehicle manufacturer and the component supplier. This document shall also be applied by manufacturers and suppliers of components and equipment which are to be added and connected to the vehicle harness or to an on-board power connector after delivery of the vehicle.

This document does not include protection of electronic control systems from radio frequency (RF) emissions, or from transient or pulse type voltage fluctuations. These subjects are included in other parts of SAE J1113.

Since the mounting location, vehicle body construction and harness design can affect the coupling of radio disturbances to the on-board radio, this document defines multiple limit levels. The level class to be used (as a function of frequency band) shall be agreed upon between the vehicle manufacturer and the component supplier.

The World Administrative Radiocommunications Conference (WARC) lower frequency limit in Region 1 was reduced to 148.5 kHz in 1979. For vehicular purposes, tests at 150 kHz are considered adequate. For the purposes of this document, test frequency ranges have been generalized to cover radio services in various parts of the world. Protection of radio reception at adjacent frequencies can be expected in most cases.

It is assumed that protection of services operating on frequencies below 30 MHz will most likely be provided if the limits for services above 30 MHz are observed.

2. References—The following standards contain provisions which, through reference in this text, constitute provisions of this document. At the time of publication, the editions indicated were valid. All standards are subject to revision, and parties to agreements based on this document are encouraged to investigate the possibility of applying the most recent editions of the standards indicated as follows. Members of IEC and ISO maintain registers of currently valid International Standards.

2.1 SAE Publications—Available from SAE, 400 Commonwealth Drive, Warrendale, PA 15096-0001.

SAE J1113/1—Electromagnetic Compatibility Measurement Procedures and Limits for Vehicle Components

SAE J1752/3—Electromagnetic Compatibility Measurement Procedures for Integrated Circuits—Integrated Circuit Radiated Emissions Measurement Procedure 150 kHz to 1000 MHz TEM Cell

SAE ARP958—Electromagnetic Interference Measurement Antennas; Standard Calibration Methods

2.2 ANSI Publication—Available from ANSI, 11 West 42nd Street, New York, NY 10036-8002.

ANSI C63.5-1988—Electromagnetic Compatibility—Radiated Emission Measurements in Electromagnetic Interference (EMI) Control—Calibration of Antennas

2.3 CISPR Publications—Available from ANSI, 11 West 42nd Street, New York, NY 10036-8002.

CISPR 12: 1990—Limits and methods of measurement of radio interference characteristics of vehicles, motor boats, and spark-ignited engine driven devices

CISPR 16-1: 1993—Specification for radio disturbance measuring apparatus and methods—Part 1: Radio disturbance and immunity measuring apparatus

CISPR 20: 1990—Limits and methods of measurement of immunity characteristics of sound and television broadcast receivers and associated equipment

CISPR 25—Limits and methods of measurement of radio disturbance characteristics for the protection of receivers used on-board vehicles

3. Definitions—See SAE J1113/1 for definitions

For this document, Equipment under test (EUT) and Device under test (DUT) are used interchangeably.

4. Requirements for Component/Module Emissions Measurement

4.1 General Test Requirements and Test Plan

4.1.1 TEST PLAN—A test plan shall be established for each item to be tested. The test plan shall specify the frequency range to be tested, the emissions limits, the disturbance classification (broadband, long or short duration—or narrowband), antenna types and locations, test report requirements, supply voltage, and other relevant parameters.

4.1.2 DETERMINATION OF CONFORMANCE WITH LIMITS—If the type of disturbance is unknown, tests shall be made to determine whether measured emissions are narrowband and/or broadband to apply limits properly as specified in the test plan.

Figure 1 outlines the procedure to be followed in determining conformance with limits.

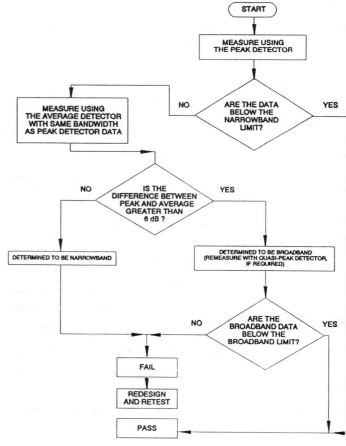

FIGURE 1—METHOD OF DETERMINATION OF CONFORMANCE OF RADIATED/CONDUCTED DISTURBANCE

---

[1] Only a complete vehicle test can be used to determine the component compatibility with respect to a vehicle's limit.
[2] Adjacent vehicles can be expected to be protected in most situations.
[3] Adequate television protection will result from compliance with the levels at the mobile service frequencies.

4.1.3 CATEGORIES OF DISTURBANCE SOURCES (AS APPLIED IN THE TEST PLAN)—Electromagnetic disturbance sources can be divided into three types:

a. Continuous/long duration broadband and automatically actuated short duration equipment
b. Manually actuated short duration broadband
c. Narrowband

NOTE—For examples see 4.1.4 and 4.1.5 and Table 1.

4.1.4 EXAMPLES OF BROADBAND DISTURBANCE SOURCES

NOTE—The examples in Table 1 are intended as a guide to assist in determining which limits to use in the test plan.

TABLE 1—EXAMPLES OF BROADBAND DISTURBANCE SOURCES BY DURATION

Continuous	Long Duration[1]	Short Duration[1]
Ignition system	Wiper motor	Power antenna
Active ride control	Heater blower motor	Washer pump motor
Fuel injection	Rear wiper motor	Door mirror motor
Instrument regulator	Air conditioning compressor	Central door lock
Alternator	Engine cooling	Power seat

[1] As defined in the test plan.

4.1.5 NARROWBAND DISTURBANCE SOURCES—Sources employing microprocessors, digital logic, oscillators or clock generators, etc., can cause narrowband emissions.

4.1.6 OPERATING CONDITIONS—When performing component/module tests, the equipment under test (EUT) shall be exercised using typical loads and conditions which simulate installation and operation in the vehicle.

4.1.7 TEST REPORT—The report shall contain the information agreed upon by the customer and the supplier.

4.2 Measuring Equipment Requirements—All equipment shall be calibrated on a regular basis to assure continued conformance of equipment to required characteristics. The measuring equipment noise floor shall be at least 6 dB less than the limit specified in the test plan.

4.3 Shielded Enclosure—The ambient electromagnetic noise levels shall be at least 6 dB below the limits specified in the test plan for each test to be performed. The shielding effectiveness of the shielded enclosure shall be sufficient to assure that the required ambient electromagnetic noise level requirement is met.

NOTE—Although there will be reflected energy from the interior surfaces of the shielded enclosure, this is of minimal concern for the measurement of conducted disturbances because of the direct coupling of the measuring instrument to the leads of the EUT. The shielded enclosure may be as simple as a suitably grounded bench top screened cage.

4.4 Absorber-Lined Shielded Enclosure (ALSE)—For radiated emission measurements, however, the reflected energy can cause errors of as much as 20 dB. Therefore, it is necessary to apply RF absorber material to the walls and ceiling of a shielded enclosure that is to be used for radiated emissions measurements. No absorber material is required for the floor. The following ALSE requirements shall also be met for performing radiated RF emissions measurements:

4.4.1 SIZE—For radiated emission tests, the shielded enclosure shall be of sufficient size to ensure that neither the EUT nor the test antenna shall be closer than (a) 2 m from the walls or ceiling, and (b) 1 m to the nearest surface of the absorber material used.

4.4.2 REFLECTION CHARACTERISTICS—The reflection characteristics of the ALSE shall be such that the maximum error caused by reflected energy from the walls and ceiling is less than 6 dB in the frequency range of 70 to 1000 MHz.

4.4.3 OBJECTS IN ALSE—In particular, for radiated emissions measurements the ALSE shall be cleared of all items not pertinent to the tests. This is required in order to reduce any effect they may have on the measurement. Included are unnecessary equipment, cable racks, storage cabinets, desks, chairs, etc. Personnel not actively involved in the test shall be excluded from the ALSE.

4.5 Receiver—Scanning receivers which meet the requirements of CISPR 16-1 are satisfactory for measurements. Manual or automatic frequency scanning may be used. Special consideration shall be given to overload, linearity, selectivity, and the normal response to pulses.

NOTE—Spectrum analyzers and scanning receivers are particularly useful for disturbance measurements. Special consideration shall be given to overload, linearity, selectivity, and the normal response to pulses. The peak detection mode of spectrum analyzers and scanning receivers provides a display indication which is never less than the quasi-peak indication for the same bandwidth. It may be

convenient to measure emissions using peak detection because of the faster scan possible than with quasi-peak detection.

When quasi-peak limits are being used, any peak measurements above the limit shall be measured using the quasi-peak detector.

4.5.1 MINIMUM SCAN TIME—The scan rate of a spectrum analyzer or scanning receiver shall be adjusted for the CISPR frequency band and detection mode used. The minimum sweep time/frequency, (i.e., most rapid scan rate) is listed in Table 2:

TABLE 2—MINIMUM SCAN TIME

Band[1]		Peak Detection	Quasi-peak Detection
A	9-150 kHz	Does not apply	Does not apply
B	0.15-30 MHz	100 ms/MHz	200 s/MHz
C,D	30-1000 MHz	1 ms/MHz or 100 ms/MHz[2]	20 s/MHz

[1] Band definition from CISPR 16-1.
[2] When 9 kHz bandwidth is used, the 100 ms/MHz value shall be used.

NOTE—Certain signals (e.g., low repetition rate or intermittent signals) may require slower scan rates or multiple scans to insure that the maximum amplitude has been measured. For the measurement of pure broadband emission, scanning steps greater than the measurement bandwidth are permitted; thus accelerating the measurement of the emission spectrum.

4.5.2 MEASURING INSTRUMENT BANDWIDTH—The bandwidth of the measuring instrument shall be chosen such that the noise floor is at least 6 dB lower than the limit curve. The bandwidths in Table 3 are recommended.

NOTE—When the bandwidth of the measuring instrument exceeds the bandwidth of a narrowband signal, the measured signal amplitude will not be affected. The indicated value of impulsive broadband noise will be lower when the measuring instrument bandwidth is reduced.

TABLE 3—MEASURING INSTRUMENT BANDWIDTH (6 DB)

Frequency Band MHz		Broadband Peak and Quasi-Peak	Narrowband Peak and Average
0.15 - 30		9 kHz	9 kHz
30 - 1000	FM Broadcast	120 kHz	120 kHz
30 - 1000	Mobile Service	120 kHz	9 kHz

If a spectrum analyzer is used for peak measurements, the video bandwidth shall be at least three times the resolution bandwidth.

For the narrowband/broadband discrimination according to Figure 1, both bandwidths (with peak and average detectors) shall be identical.

4.6 Power Supply—The EUT power supply shall have adequate regulation to maintain the supply voltage within the limits specified: 13.5 V ± 0.5 V for 12 V systems, 27 V ± 1.0 V for 24 V systems, unless otherwise specified in the test plan.

The power supply shall also be adequately filtered such that the RF noise produced by the power supply is at least 6 dB lower than the limits specified in the test plan.

4.7 Battery—When specified in the test plan, a vehicle battery shall be connected in parallel with the power supply.

4.8 Ground Plane—The ground plane shall be made of 0.5 mm thick (minimum) copper, brass or galvanized steel of the size specified in Figures 5 through 10 for the measurement of conducted or radiated emissions.

The ground plane shall be bonded to the shielded enclosure such that the DC resistance shall not exceed 2.5 mΩ. In addition, the bond straps shall be placed at a distance no greater than 0.9 m apart.

4.9 Test Equipment Unique to Conducted Emissions Measurements

4.9.1 ARTIFICIAL MAINS NETWORK (AN)

4.9.1.1 AN Impedance Characteristics—The AN shall have a nominal 5 μH inductance and shall meet the impedance characteristics of CISPR 16-1. A suggested schematic is shown in Appendix E. The measuring port of all AN's shall be terminated with a 50 Ω load (either a measuring instrument or a resistor). For the purpose of this document, the AN may be used to 108 MHz.

4.9.1.2 AN Connection—For the emissions tests of Sections 7 and 9, a standard AN according to 4.9.1.1 shall be used. For the TEM cell emissions test of Section 9, an AN with a coaxial connector will facilitate connection to the TEM cell EUT power connector.

4.9.2 CURRENT PROBE—The current probe shall be selected considering the following: the size of the harness to be measured, the frequency range required by the test plan, and the sensitivity of the probe necessary to measure signals at the limit level.

NOTE—Typically, a current probe is a transducer which converts current to voltage. As such, its calibration factor is often called a transfer impedance curve and is given in Ω or dB(Ω). (See Appendix B.)

4.10 Equipment Unique to Component/Module Radiated Measurements

4.10.1 ANTENNA SYSTEMS—The limits shown in Tables 8 and 9 are listed in decibels relative to 1 µV/m, and thus theoretically any antenna can be used, provided that it has adequate sensitivity, the antenna correction factor is applied, and the antenna provides a 50 Ω match to the measuring receiver. For the purposes of this standard, the limits shown in Tables 8 and 9 are based upon the following antennas:

   a. 0.15 to 30 MHz—1 m vertical monopole (where this is not 50 Ω, a suitable antenna matching unit shall be used).

   b. 30 to 200 MHz—A biconical antenna used in vertical and horizontal polarization.

   c. 200 to 1000 MHz—A log-periodic antenna used in vertical and horizontal polarization.

Commercially available antennas with known antenna correction factors may be used. The cable loss factor can be determined in accordance with CISPR 12, Appendix A.

NOTE—A method for determining antenna factor is described in SAE ARP958.

4.10.2 ANTENNA MATCHING UNIT—Correct impedance matching between the antenna and the measuring receiver of 50 Ω must be maintained at all frequencies. There shall be a maximum SWR of 2:1. Appropriate correction shall be made for any attenuation/gain of the antenna system from the antenna to the receiver.

NOTE 1—Care should be taken to ensure input voltages do not exceed the pulse input rating of the unit or overloading may occur. This is particularly important when active matching units are used.

NOTE 2—Biconical antennas usually have a SWR of up to 10:1 in the frequency range of 30 to 80 MHz. Therefore an additional measurement error may occur when the receiver input impedance differs from 50 Ω. The use of an attenuator (3 dB minimum) at the receiver input (if possible) will keep this additional error low.

4.11 Equipment Unique to the TEM Cell Method

4.11.1 TEM CELL SIZE—An example of a TEM cell is shown in Figure 2. Information relating to the size and construction of a TEM cell for component measurement is given in Appendix D.

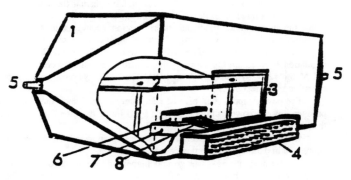

1. Outer shield
2. Septum (inner conductor)
3. Access door
4. Connector panel
5. Coaxial connectors
6. EUT
7. Dielectric equipment support
8. Artificial harness

FIGURE 2—TEM CELL (EXAMPLE)

4.11.2 TEM CELL TEST SETUP (EUT WITH LEADFRAME)

4.11.2.1 TEM Cell—For the purpose of these tests, the septum of the TEM cell functions in a similar way to a receiving antenna.

4.11.2.2 Supply and Signal Leads—The TEM cell shall have a connector panel connected as close as possible to a plug connector (see Figure 3).

All supply and signal leads from the EUT are directly connected to the artificial harness (e.g., a leadframe). The plugs at the connector panel, which are not required must be sealed so that they are RF-tight.

The connection of the positive power lead shall be through the AN (see 4.9.1.2), direct at the connector panel.

It is not permitted to ground the EUT to the TEM cell floor. The grounding shall be done at the connector panel.

4.11.3 TEM CELL TEST SETUP (EUT WITHOUT LEADFRAME)

4.11.3.1 The test setup is similar to the method shown above, except that the leads to the EUT are positioned and shielded to minimize electromagnetic radiation from the leads. This is accomplished by positioning the leads flat

across the bottom of the TEM cell and bringing them vertically to the EUT. The use of a sealed battery and shielded wiring in the TEM cell will further reduce the electromagnetic radiation from power and signal leads. To minimize the radiation from the wiring further, shielding foil tape can be applied over the leads.

4.12 Special Test for Integrated Circuits—Methods are under development in Europe and in North America for directly measuring the emissions from integrated circuits using a TEM cell or other equipment. The intent is to minimize extraneous effects of leads and test circuitry mask changes. See SAE J1752/3.

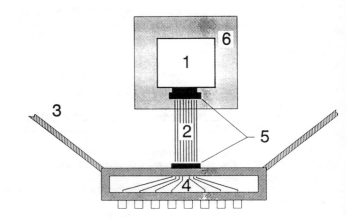

1. EUT
2. Artificial Harness (e.g., printed leadframe)
3. TEM cell wall
4. Connector panel
5. Connector
6. Dielectric equipment support (e, £ 1.4)

FIGURE 3—EXAMPLE OF ARRANGEMENT OF LEADS IN THE TEM CELL AND TO THE CONNECTOR PANEL

5. Conducted Emissions—Component/Module

5.1 General—Emissions on power leads are to be measured using an artificial mains network (voltage measurement). Emissions on control/signal leads are to be measured using a current probe.

NOTE—Conducted emissions will contribute to the radiated emission measurements because of radiation from the wiring in the test setup. Therefore, it is advisable to establish conformance with the conducted emissions requirement before performing the radiated emissions test.

5.2 Test Procedure

5.2.1 VOLTAGE MEASUREMENTS—Voltage measurements on all power leads shall be made relative to the case of the EUT (when the case provides the ground return path) or the ground lead as close to the EUT as practical.

For EUT with return line remotely grounded, the voltage measurements shall be made on each lead (supply and return) relative to the ground plane.

The test harness shall be spaced 50 mm above the ground plane.

5.2.2 CURRENT PROBE MEASUREMENTS—Current probe measurements shall be made on the control/signal leads as a single cable or in subgroups as is compatible with the physical size of the current probe. The test harness length shall be nominally 1.5 m long (or as specified in the test plan), spaced 50 mm above the ground plane. The test harness leads shall be nominally parallel and adjacent unless otherwise defined in the test plan.

Position the current probe 50 mm from the EUT connector and measure the emissions. To assure that the maximum level is measured at frequencies above 30 MHz, position the current probe in the following additional positions:

   a. 0.5 m from the EUT connector

   b. 1 m from the EUT connector

   c. 50 mm from the AN terminal

In most cases, the position of maximum emission will be as close to the EUT connector as possible. Where the EUT is equipped with a metal shell connector the probe shall be clamped to the cable immediately adjacent to the connector shell, but not around the connector shell itself. The EUT and all parts of the test setup shall be a minimum of 100 mm from the edge of the ground plane.

5.2.3 EQUIPMENT ARRANGEMENT—For voltage measurements, the arrangement of the EUT and measuring equipment shall be as shown in Figures 4, 5, and 6 depending on the intended EUT installation in the vehicle:

a. EUT—Remotely Grounded (Power Return Line Longer Than 200 mm)—Use Figure 4.
b. EUT—Locally Grounded (Power Return Line 200 mm or Shorter)—Use Figure 5.
c. Alternators and Generators—Use Figure 6.

Remote versus local grounding, the use of an insulating spacer, and the electrical connection of the EUT case to the ground plane shall simulate the actual vehicle configuration and be specified in the test plan.

For current measurements, the measuring equipment shall be as shown in Figure 7.

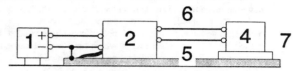

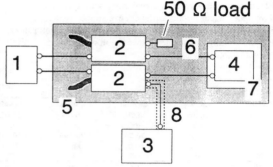

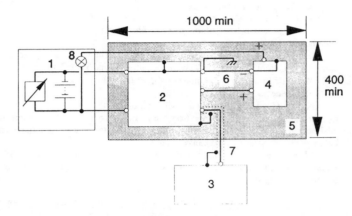

1. Power supply
2. Artificial mains network (two units)/ control box / loads
3. Measuring instrument
4. EUT
5. Ground plane
6. Test harness (Power leads 200 mm maximum length)
7. Insulating spacer (50 mm thick), when required in test plan
8. Double shielded or solid shielded coaxial cable (50 W)

FIGURE 4—CONDUCTED EMISSIONS - EUT WITH POWER RETURN LINE REMOTELY GROUNDED

Dimensions in millimeters

1. Load (battery and resistor)
2. Artificial mains network
3. Measuring equipment
4. EUT
5. Ground plane
6. Test Harness (Power leads 200 mm maximum length)
7. Double shielded or solid shielded coaxial cable (50 W)
8. Indicator lamp / control resistor (where applicable)

FIGURE 6—CONDUCTED EMISSIONS—TEST LAYOUT FOR ALTERNATORS AND GENERATORS

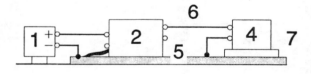

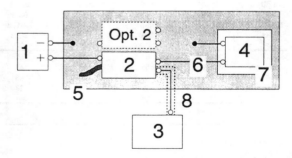

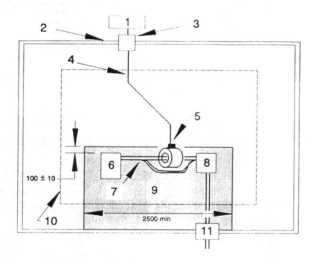

1. Power supply
2. Artificial mains network (one unit, second optional)/ control box/loads
3. Measuring instrument
4. EUT
5. Ground plane
6. Test harness (power leads 200 mm maximum length)
7. Insulating spacer (50 mm thick), when required in test plan
8. Double shielded or solid shielded coaxial cable (50 W)

FIGURE 5—CONDUCTED EMISSIONS—EUT WITH POWER RETURN LINE LOCALLY GROUNDED

Dimensions in millimeters

1. Measuring instrument (allowed in shielded enclosure if ambient requirement is met)
2. Shielded enclosure
3. Bulkhead connector
4. Double shielded or solid shielded coaxial cable (50 W)
5. Current probe for signal/control line test
6. EUT
7. Test harness (1500 mm ± 75 mm) long or as specified up to 2000 mm length (50 mm ± 5 mm) above ground plane.
8. Artificial network
9. Test bench - 2500 mm long by 900 mm high
10. Typical RF absorber (optional)
11. Filter to power supply

FIGURE 7—CONDUCTED EMISSIONS—EXAMPLE OF TEST LAYOUT FOR CURRENT PROBE MEASUREMENTS

5.2.4 TEST PROCEDURE FOR GENERATORS/ALTERNATORS—Generators/alternators shall be loaded with a battery and parallel resistor combination, and connected to the artificial mains network in the manner shown in Figure 6. The load current, operating speed, harness length, and other conditions shall be defined in the test plan.

6. Limits for Component Conducted Disturbances

6.1 Limits for Power Leads—For acceptable radio reception in a vehicle, the conducted noise shall not exceed the values shown in Tables 4 and 5, broadband and narrowband limits, respectively. Refer to Footnote 1) Scope for statement on limits.

6.2 Limits for Control/Signal Lines—The limits for RF currents on control/signal lines are given in Table 6 (broadband) and Table 7 (narrowband).

7. Radiated Emissions—Component/Module

7.1 General

NOTE—Conducted emissions will contribute to the radiated emissions measurements because of radiation from the wiring in the test setup. Therefore, it is advisable to establish conformance with the conducted emissions requirements before performing the radiated emissions test.

Measurements of radiated field strength shall be made in a ALSE to eliminate the high levels of extraneous disturbance from electrical equipment and broadcasting stations.

The reflection characteristics of the shielded enclosure shall be checked by performing comparative measurements in an open field test site and in the ALSE. The difference of results shall comply with 4.4.2. For further details see Appendix A. For restrictions on size see 4.4.1.

NOTE—Disturbance to the vehicle on-board receiver can be caused by direct radiation from one or more leads in the vehicle wiring harness. This coupling mode to the vehicle receiver affects both the type of testing and the means of reducing the disturbance at the source.

Vehicle components which are not effectively grounded to the vehicle by short ground leads, or which have several harness leads carrying the disturbance voltage, will require a radiated emissions test. This has been shown to give better correlation with the complete vehicle test for components installed in this way.

Examples of component installations for which this test is applicable include, but are not limited to:

a. Electronic control systems containing microprocessors
b. Two speed wiper motors with negative supply switching
c. Suspension control systems with strut-mounted actuator motors
d. Engine cooling and heater blower motors mounted in plastic or other insulated housings

TABLE 4—LIMITS FOR BROADBAND CONDUCTED DISTURBANCES ON POWER INPUT TERMINALS (PEAK OR QUASI-PEAK DETECTOR)

Class	Levels in dB (μV) 0.15-0.3 MHz P	Levels in dB (μV) 0.15-0.3 MHz QP	Levels in dB (μV) 0.53-2.0 MHz P	Levels in dB (μV) 0.53-2.0 MHz QP	Levels in dB (μV) 5.9-6.2 MHz P	Levels in dB (μV) 5.9-6.2 MHz QP	Levels in dB (μV) 30-54 MHz P	Levels in dB (μV) 30-54 MHz QP	Levels in dB (μV) 70-108 MHz P	Levels in dB (μV) 70-108 MHz QP
1	113	100	95	82	77	64	77	64	61	48
2	103	90	87	74	71	58	71	58	55	42
3	93	80	79	66	65	52	65	52	49	36
4	83	70	71	58	59	46	59	46	43	30
5	73	60	63	50	53	40	53	40	37	24

For short duration disturbances, add 6 dB to the levels shown in the table.
NOTE—All values listed in this table are valid for the bandwidths specified in Table 3.

TABLE 5—LIMITS FOR NARROWBAND CONDUCTED DISTURBANCES ON POWER INPUT TERMINALS (PEAK DETECTOR)

Class	Levels in dB (μV) 0.15-0.13 MHz	Levels in dB (μV) 0.53-2.0 MHz	Levels in dB (μV) 5.9-6.2 MHz	Levels in dB (μV) 30-54 MHz	Levels in dB (μV) 70-108 MHz
1	90	66	57	52	42
2	80	58	51	46	36
3	70	50	45	40	30
4	60	42	39	34	24
5	50	34	33	28	18

For 87 - 108 MHz add 6 dB to the level shown in the table.

TABLE 6—LIMITS FOR BROADBAND CONDUCTED DISTURBANCES ON CONTROL/SIGNAL LINES (PEAK OR QUASI-PEAK DETECTOR)

Class	Levels in dB (μA) 0.15-0.3 MHz P	Levels in dB (μA) 0.15-0.3 MHz QP	Levels in dB (μA) 0.53-2.0 MHz P	Levels in dB (μA) 0.53-2.0 MHz QP	Levels in dB (μA) 5.9-6.2 MHz P	Levels in dB (μA) 5.9-6.2 MHz QP	Levels in dB (μA) 30-54 MHz P	Levels in dB (μA) 30-54 MHz QP	Levels in dB (μA) 70-108 MHz P	Levels in dB (μA) 70-108 MHz QP
1	100	87	92	79	74	61	74	61	68	55
2	90	77	84	71	68	55	68	55	62	49
3	80	67	76	63	62	49	62	49	56	43
4	70	57	68	55	56	43	56	43	50	37
5	60	47	60	47	50	37	50	37	44	31

For short duration disturbances, add 6 dB to the levels shown in the table.
NOTE—All values listed in this table are valid for the bandwidths specified in Table 3.

TABLE 7—LIMITS FOR NARROWBAND CONDUCTED CURRENT DISTURBANCES ON CONTROL/SIGNAL LINES (PEAK DETECTOR)

Class	Levels in dB (μA) 0.15-0.13 MHz	Levels in dB (μA) 0.53-2.0 MHz	Levels in dB (μA) 5.9-6.2 MHz	Levels in dB (μA) 30-54 MHz	Levels in dB (μA) 70-108 MHz
1	80	66	57	52	52
2	70	58	51	46	46
3	60	50	45	40	40
4	50	42	39	34	34
5	40	34	33	28	28

For 87 - 108 MHz add 6 dB to the level shown in the table.

7.2 Test Procedure—The general arrangement of the disturbance source, and connecting harnesses, etc., represents a standardized test condition. Any deviations from the standard test harness length, etc., shall be agreed upon prior to testing, and recorded in the test report. The harness (power and control/signal lines) shall be supported 50 mm above the ground plane by nonconductive, low dielectric constant material, and arranged in a straight line (see Figures 8 and 9).

The EUT shall be made to operate under typical loading and other conditions as in the vehicle such that the maximum emission state occurs. These operating conditions must be clearly defined in the test plan to ensure supplier and customer are performing identical tests. Depending on the intended EUT installation in the vehicle:

   a. EUT With Power Return Line Remotely Grounded—Two artificial networks are required—one for the positive supply line and one for the power return line.

   b. EUT With Power Return Line Locally Grounded—One artificial network is required for the positive supply line.

The EUT shall be wired as in the vehicle (see Figures 5 and 6). The measuring port of the artificial mains network shall be terminated with a 50 Ω load.

The face of the disturbance source causing the greatest RF emission shall be closest to the antenna. Where this face changes with frequency, measurements shall be made in three orthogonal planes, and the highest level at each frequency shall be noted in the test report.

NOTE—If the EUT is small in comparison to the wavelength, orientation in three planes may be omitted.

At frequencies above 30 MHz the antenna shall be oriented in horizontal and vertical polarization to receive maximum indication of the RF noise level at the measuring receiver. See Figures 11 and 12 for further test requirements. The distance between the wiring harness and the antenna shall 1000 mm ± 10 mm. This distance is measured from the center of the wiring harness to:

   a. The vertical monopole element or

   b. The midpoint of the biconical antenna or

   c. The nearest part of the log periodic antenna

The EUT shall be mounted 100 mm ± 10 mm from the edge of the test bench as shown in Figure 9.

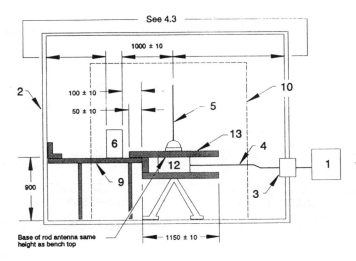

Dimensions in millimeters

1. Measuring receiver
2. ALSE
3. Bulkhead connector
4. Double shielded or solid shielded coaxial cable (50 W)
5. Antenna (see 4.10.1)
6. EUT
9. Test bench - 2500 mm long by 900 mm high
10. Typical absorber material
12. Antenna matching unit
13. Counterpoise - 600 mm by 600 mm typical with full width bond to ground plane

NOTES
1 The preferred location for antenna matching unit is below the counterpoise. As an alternative, the matching unit may be above the counterpoise, but the base of the antenna rod shall be at the height of the bench ground plane.
2 Numbers 7, 8, and 11 not used to maintain numbering scheme in Figure 8.

FIGURE 9—RADIATED EMISSIONS—EXAMPLE FOR TEST LAYOUT
(SIDE VIEW WITH MONOPOLE ANTENNA)

8. Limits for Component Radiated Disturbances—Some disturbance sources are continuous emitters and require a more stringent limit than a disturbance source which is only on periodically or for a short time. The limits in Tables 8 and 9 have been adjusted to take account of this fact. Levels in Tables 8 and 9 were established by the application of engineering judgment to empirical values obtained from multinational testing during 1990. Measurements need only be performed with one detection type. Refer to Footnote 1 Scope for statement on limits.

9. Radiated Emissions—Component/Module; TEM Cell Method

9.1 General—Measurements of radiated field strength shall be made in a shielded enclosure to eliminate the high levels of extraneous disturbance from electrical equipment and broadcast stations. The TEM cell works as a shielded enclosure. For further details, see Appendix D.

The TEM cell method of emission measurements is more suited to narrowband measurements than broadband.

NOTE—The upper frequency limit of this test method is a direct function of the TEM cell dimensions, the component/module dimensions (arrangement included), and the RF filter characteristic. Measurements shall not be made in the region of the TEM cell resonances.

A TEM cell is recommended for testing automotive electronic systems in the frequency range of 150 kHz to 200 MHz. The TEM cells boxed in Table D.1, Appendix D, are typical of those used in automotive work.

In order to achieve reproducible test results the EUT and the test harness shall be placed in the TEM cell in the same position for each repeated measurement.

9.2 Test Procedure—The general arrangement of the EUT, the harness, the filter system at the TEM cell's wall, etc., represents a standardized test condition. Any deviations from the standard test configuration shall be agreed upon prior to testing and recorded in the test report.

The EUT shall be supported b/6 (see Figure 10) above the TEM cell floor by nonconductive material ($\varepsilon_r \leq 1.4$) in the allowed working region. The length of the artificial harness (e.g., a leadframe) shall be 450 mm and positioned as shown in Figure 3.

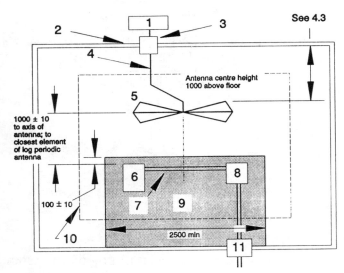

Dimensions in millimeters

1. Measuring receiver
2. ALSE
3. Bulkhead connector
4. Double shielded or solid shielded coaxial cable (50 W)
5. Antenna (see 4.10.1)
6. EUT
7. Test harness (1500 mm ± 75 mm) long (or as specified up to 2000 mm long) (50 mm ± 5 mm) above ground plane.
8. Artificial network(s)
9. Test bench - 2500 mm long by 900 mm high
10. Typical RF absorber
11. Filter to power supply

FIGURE 8—RADIATED EMISSIONS—EXAMPLE OF TEST LAYOUT
(GENERAL PLAN VIEW)

TABLE 8—LIMITS FOR COMPONENT BROADBAND RADIATED DISTURBANCE (PEAK OR QUASI-PEAK DETECTOR)

Class	Levels in dB (µV/m) 0.15-0.3 MHz P	Levels in dB (µV/m) 0.15-0.3 MHz QP	Levels in dB (µV/m) 0.53-2.0 MHz P	Levels in dB (µV/m) 0.53-2.0 MHz QP	Levels in dB (µV/m) 5.9-6.2 MHz P	Levels in dB (µV/m) 5.9-6.2 MHz QP	Levels in dB (µV/m) 30-54 MHz P	Levels in dB (µV/m) 30-54 MHz QP	Levels in dB (µV/m) 70-108 144-172 420-512 820-960 MHz P	Levels in dB (µV/m) 70-108 144-172 420-512 820-960 MHz QP
1	96	83	83	70	60	47	60	47	49	36
2	86	73	75	62	54	41	54	41	43	30
3	76	63	67	54	48	35	48	35	37	24
4	66	53	59	46	42	29	42	29	31	18
5	56	43	51	38	36	23	36	23	25	12

For short duration disturbances, add 6 dB to the levels shown in the table.
NOTE—All values listed in this table are valid for the bandwidths specified in Table 3.

TABLE 9—LIMITS FOR NARROWBAND COMPONENT RADIATED DISTURBANCE (PEAK DETECTOR)

Class	Levels in dB (µV/m) 0.15-0.13 MHz	Levels in dB (µV/m) 0.53-2.0 MHz	Levels in dB (µV/m) 5.9-6.2 MHz	Levels in dB (µV/m) 30-54 MHz	Levels in dB (µV/m) 70-108 144-172 420-512 820-960 MHz
1	61	50	46	46	36
2	51	42	40	40	30
3	41	34	34	34	24
4	31	26	28	28	18
5	21	18	22	22	12

For 87 - 108 MHz add 6 dB to the level shown in the table.

The electrical loop between EUT and the connector panel shall not be influenced by the connector system at the EUT as far as possible. Variations of the loop can be balanced with transfer measurements. Care shall be taken, if the size of the EUT and the allowed working region is nearly the same. In such case, special definitions between the users are necessary.

The EUT shall be installed to operate under typical loading and other conditions as in the vehicle in such a way that the maximum emission state occurs. These operating conditions must be defined in the test plan to ensure supplier and customer are performing identical tests.

The positive supply line shall have an RF filter at the TEM cell input. The artificial network (AN) of 4.9.1.2 shall be used as the filter. The AN shall be connected directly to the TEM cell and shall be screened, so that the negative supply line is grounded at the connector panel.

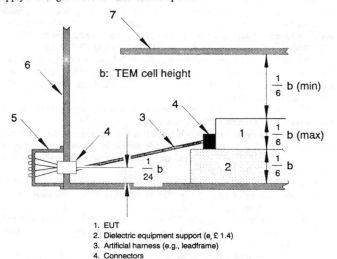

1. EUT
2. Dielectric equipment support (e, £ 1.4)
3. Artificial harness (e.g., leadframe)
4. Connectors
5. Connector panel (optional)
6. TEM cell wall
7. Septum

FIGURE 10—EXAMPLE OF THE ARRANGEMENT OF THE CONNECTORS, THE LEADFRAME AND THE DIELECTRIC SUPPORT

Figure 11 shows a typical example of a TEM cell method test layout.

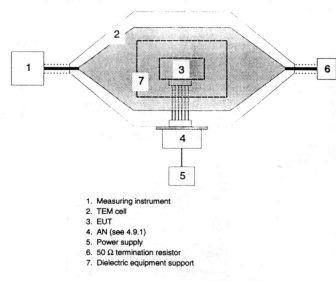

1. Measuring instrument
2. TEM cell
3. EUT
4. AN (see 4.9.1)
5. Power supply
6. 50 Ω termination resistor
7. Dielectric equipment support

FIGURE 11—EXAMPLE OF THE TEM CELL METHOD TEST LAYOUT

10. Limits for Component Radiated Disturbances; TEM Cell Method (Both the Leadframe and EUT and the EUT Only Methods)—Some disturbance sources are continuous emitters and require a more stringent limit than a disturbance source which operates only periodically and/or for a short time.

The limits of the radiated electromagnetic energy may be different for each disturbance source and arrangement (coupling between antenna and electronic device in the vehicle). The class from Table 10 for each applicable band in Table 11 shall be selected by the vehicle manufacturer and the component supplier, and documented in the test plan. For continuous emitters, it is recommended to use class 5 in bands E and F. The class 6 and 7 limits are used for special protection cases.

11. Limits for Integrated Circuit Radiated Disturbances—TEM Cell Method—See SAE J1752/3.

TABLE 10—DISTURBANCE LIMITS	
Class	Levels-dB (μV)
0	user defined
1	60
2	50
3	40
4	30
5	20
6	10
7	0

NOTES

1 The limits in Table 10 are for narrowband measurements (peak- and quasi-peak detector) and continuous emitters.

2 For broadband measurements with quasi-peak detector add 10 dB and with peak detector add 23 dB to the levels in Table 10.

3 For short duration broadband measurements with quasi-peak detector add 16 dB to the levels in Table 10, for similar peak detector measurements add 29 dB.

4 Levels in Table 10 were established by application of engineering judgment to empirical values obtained from national testing.

TABLE 11—FREQUENCY BANDS	
Band	Frequency-MHz
A	0.15 - 0.3
B	0.53 - 2.0
C	5.90 - 6.2
D	30.0 - 54.0
E	70.0 - 108.0
F	144.0 - 172.0
G	user defined
H	user defined

APPENDIX A
CALIBRATION PROCEDURE FOR COMPONENT SHIELDED ENCLOSURE
(INFORMATIVE)

A.1 Shielded Enclosure Reflection Test and Calibration Procedure—The following test procedure is recommended for calibration of any shielded enclosure of dimensions not less than 7.0 m x 6.5 m x 4.0 m (L x W x H) for radiated emissions measurements.

A.2 Standard Noise Source—A standard noise source with defined output characteristics shall be used for calibration purposes. A calibration curve shall be obtained with the standard noise source for field strength at 1 m distance in an open field test site, using the same test setup, i.e., antennas, calibration harness, artificial mains network, etc.

A.3 Standard Noise Source Characteristics—The standard noise source shall have a stable output amplitude spectrum throughout the frequency range of interest.

A.4 Calibration Procedure—Arrange the standard noise source in place of the EUT in the test setup shown in Figures 8 and 9. The noise source shall be attached to the artificial mains network by the standard 1500 mm harness lead supported 50 mm above the ground plane.

Measurements shall be made at the same frequencies and with the same antennas as will be used for the subsequent testing of the EUT. A plot of field strength versus frequency shall be produced.

The difference between the open test site curve and that taken in the ALSE shall be used to check whether the reflection characteristics of the ALSE comply with 4.4.2, but they cannot be used as a calibration factor.

To ensure uniformity of testing, steps shall be taken to reduce any reflections in the shielded enclosure which may cause variations in measured levels.

NOTE—Radio frequency absorbent material, properly applied, will reduce reflections at the higher frequencies.

APPENDIX B
CURRENT PROBE REQUIREMENTS
(INFORMATIVE)

B.1 General Information—An RF current probe is a clamp-on type RF current transformer used as a transducer with a calibrated EMI meter (receiver), oscilloscope, or other voltage sensitive instrument to determine the intensity of radio frequency current present in an electrical conductor or cable.

Direct connection to a conductor is not required. The probe is clamped around the test conductor which then becomes a one-turn primary with the probe as a multi-turn secondary.

The design of the core of the probe must be such that it will not saturate under the most severe current which will be contained within the bundle it is measuring. Core saturation will produce erroneous readings as long as the core remains in the saturated condition.

B.2 Electrical Characteristics
a. Circuit—Current transformer
b. Transfer Impedance—See B.3
c. Frequency Range—0.15 MHz to 108 MHz
d. Saturation Current—Saturation must not occur at 1.25 times the maximum expected current
e. Maximum Primary Voltage—Subject to cable insulation.
f. Rated Output Load Impedance—$50 + j0 \ \Omega$
g. Output Connector—Coaxial
h. Window Size—Adequate for the cable to be tested

B.3 Transfer Impedance—The RF current in microamperes (Ip) in a conductor under test is determined from the electromagnetic disturbance meter reading of the current probe output in microvolts (Es) divided by the current probe transfer impedance (Zt), or,

$$Ip = Es \ / \ Zt \qquad \text{(Eq.B1)}$$

The transfer impedance in ohms of the current probe throughout the frequency range is determined by passing a known RF current Ip through the primary test conductor and noting the voltage Es developed across a 50 Ω load. Then,

$$Zt = Es \ / \ Ip \qquad \text{(Eq.B2)}$$

B.4 Transfer Factor—For practical reasons, the term "transfer admittance" is frequently used instead of transfer impedance. The logarithm of transfer admittance is:

$$y_t \ [dB(S)] = 20 \log Y_t = 20 \log (1/Z_t) \qquad \text{(Eq.B3)}$$

Current in dB(μA) is obtained from the voltage level in dB(mV) from Equation B4:

$$I \ [dB(\mu A)] = V \ [dB(\mu V)] + y_t \ [dB(S)] \qquad \text{(Eq.B4)}$$

APPENDIX C
NOTES ON THE SUPPRESSION OF DISTURBANCE
(INFORMATIVE)

C.1 Introduction—Success in providing radio disturbance suppression for a vehicle requires a systematic investigation to identify sources of disturbance which can be heard in the loudspeaker. This disturbance may reach the receiver and loudspeaker in various ways:
a. Disturbances coupled to the antenna
b. Disturbances coupled to the antenna cable
c. Penetration into the receiver enclosure via the power supply cables
d. Direct radiation into the receiver (immunity of an automobile radio to radiated disturbance)
e. Disturbances coupled to all other cables connected to the automobile receiver

Before the start of the investigation, the receiver housing, the antenna base and each end of the shield of the antenna cable must be correctly grounded.

C.2 Disturbances Coupled to the Antenna—Most types of disturbances reach the receiver via the antenna. Suppressors can be fitted to the sources of disturbances to reduce these effects.

C.3 Coupling to the Antenna Cable—To minimize coupling, the antenna cable should not be routed parallel to the wiring harness or other electrical cables, and should be placed as remotely as possible from them.

C.4 Clock Oscillators—Radiation/conduction from on-board electronic modules may affect other components on the vehicle. Significant harmonics of the clock oscillator must not coincide with duplex transceiver spacings, nor with receiver channel frequencies. The fundamental frequency of oscillators used in automotive modules/components shall not be an integer fraction of the duplex frequency of any mobile transceiver system in operation in the country in which the vehicle will be used.

C.5 Other Sources of Information—Corrective measures for penetration by receiver wiring and by direct radiation are covered in other publications. Similarly, tests to evaluate the immunity of a receiver to conducted and direct radiated disturbances are also covered in other publications (e.g., CISPR 20).

APPENDIX D
TEM CELL DIMENSIONS
(INFORMATIVE)

D.1 The dimensions for designing a rectangular TEM cell are shown in Figures D1, D2, and D3.

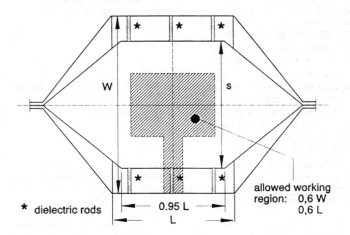

FIGURE D1—TEM CELL; HORIZONTAL SECTION VIEW AT SEPTUM

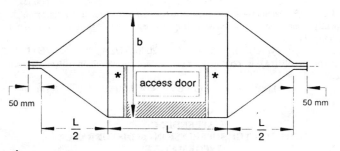

FIGURE D2—TEM CELL; VERTICAL SECTION VIEW AT SEPTUM

Figure D3 shows the dimensions for constructing TEM cells with specific upper frequency limits.

Upper frequency MHz	Cell form factor W : b	Cell form factor L : W	TEM cell height b mm	Septum width S mm
100	1.00	1.00	1200	1000
200	1.69	0.66	560	700
200	1.00	1.00	600	500
300	1.67	1.00	300	360
500	1.50	1.00	200	230

NOTE—The TEM cells in the box are typical for automotive component testing. For integrated circuit testing, even smaller TEM cells may be applicable for testing up to and above 1 GHz.

FIGURE D3—DIMENSIONS FOR TEM CELLS

APPENDIX E
ARTIFICIAL NETWORK SCHEMATIC
(INFORMATIVE)

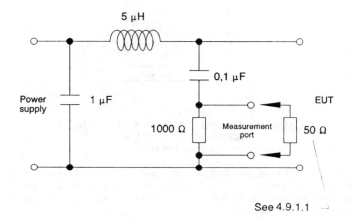

See 4.9.1.1

FIGURE E1—EXAMPLE 5 µH AN SCHEMATIC

302

R) LOW-TENSION PRIMARY CABLE
—SAE J1128 JAN95

SAE Standard

Report of the Electrical Equipment Committee approved November 1975. Completely revised by the Electrical and Electronic Systems Technical Committee June 1988. Completely revised by the SAE Cable Task Force January 1995. Rationale statement available.

1. Scope—This SAE Standard covers low-tension primary cable intended for use at a nominal system voltage of 50 V rms or less in surface vehicle electrical systems. The tests are intended to qualify cables for normal applications with limited exposure to fluids and physical abuse.

2. References

2.1 Applicable Documents—The following publications form a part of this specification to the extent specified herein. The latest issue of SAE publications shall apply.

2.1.1 SAE PUBLICATION—Available from SAE, 400 Commonwealth Drive, Warrendale, PA 15096-0001.

Color Tolerance Reference Set

2.1.2 ASTM PUBLICATIONS—Available from ASTM, 1916 Race Street, Philadelphia, PA 19103-1187.

ASTM B 1—Standard Specification for Hard-Drawn Copper Wire

ASTM B 3—Standard Specification for Soft or Annealed Copper Wire

ASTM B 33—Standard Specification for Tinned Soft or Annealed Copper Wire

ASTM B 49—Standard Specification for Copper Redraw Rod for Electrical Purposes

ASTM B 174—Standard Specification for Bunch-Stranded Copper Conductors for Electrical Conductors

ASTM B 189—Standard Specification for Lead-Coated and Lead-Alloy-Coated Soft or Annealed Copper Wire

ASTM B 193—Standard Test Method for Resistivity of Electrical Conductor Materials

ASTM B 263—Method for Determination of Cross-Sectional Area of Standard Conductors

ASTM D 412—Standard Test Methods for Vulcanized Rubber and Thermoplastic Rubbers and Thermoplastic Elastomers—Tension

ASTM D 471—Standard Test Method for Rubber Property—Effect of Liquids

ASTM D 573—Standard Test Method for Rubber—Deterioration in an Air Oven

ASTM E 145—Standard Specification for Gravity-Convection and Forced-Ventilation Ovens

2.1.3 MILITARY PUBLICATION—Available from Commander, Naval Air Systems Command Headquarters, Attn: Code 52021, Washington, D.C. 20360.

MIL-T-5438—TESTER; ABRASION, ELECTRICAL CABLE (Obsolete)

2.2 Related Specifications—The following publications are provided for information purposes only and are not a required part of this specification.

2.2.1 SAE PUBLICATIONS—Available from SAE, 400 Commonwealth Drive, Warrendale, PA 15096-0001.

SAE J156—Fusible Links

SAE J1127—Low Tension Battery Cable

SAE J1292—Automobile, Truck, Truck-Tractor, Trailer, and Motor Coach Wiring

SAE J1654—High Voltage Primary Cable

SAE J1673—High Voltage Automotive Wiring

2.2.2 ISO PUBLICATION—Available from ANSI, 11 West 42nd Street, New York, NY 10036-8002.

ISO 6722—Road Vehicles - Unscreened low-tension cables

3. Cable Types—See Figure 1

Type TWP Thin Wall, Thermoplastic Insulated

Type GPT General Purpose, Thermoplastic Insulated

Type HDT Heavy-Duty, Thermoplastic Insulated

Type STS Standard-Duty, Thermoset Elastomer (Synthetic Rubber) Insulated

Type HTS Heavy-Duty, Thermoset Elastomer (Synthetic Rubber) Insulated

Type TXL Thin Wall, Cross (X) Linked Polyolefin Insulated

Type GXL General Purpose, Cross (X) Linked Polyolefin Insulated

Type SXL Special Purpose, Cross (X) Linked Polyolefin Insulated

Type TWE Thin Wall, Thermoplastic Elastomer Insulated

Type GTE General Purpose, Thermoplastic Elastomer Insulated

Type HTE Heavy-Duty, Thermoplastic Elastomer Insulated

Insulation	SAE Cable Types			
	Thin Wall	General Purpose	Special Purpose	Heavy Wall
Thermoplastic	TWP	GPT		HDT
Thermoset Elastomer			STS	HTS
Crosslinked Polyolefin	TXL	GXL	SXL	
Thermoplastic Elastomer	TWE	GTE		HTE

**FIGURE 1—DEFINITION OF SAE CABLE TYPES
REFERENCE SECTION 3**

4. General Specifications—The finished cable shall meet the requirements for all tests specified in Figure 2 for each cable type.

4.1 Conductors—The finished, uninsulated conductor shall meet the elongation requirements specified in ASTM B 174. When tin, lead, or lead alloy coated wires are used, they shall withstand the applicable continuity of coating tests specified in 5.1 and Figure 2. The cross-sectional area of stranded conductors shall not be less than the values specified in Figure 3. The cross-sectional area may be verified by measuring actual strand sizes or by using the weight method in ASTM B 263 with a calculated factor to account for the twist loss.

NOTE—Hard copper wire per ASTM B 1 may be used for wire sizes smaller than SAE wire size 0.50 mm^2 (No. 20) when agreed between the supplier and purchaser.

Tests[1]	SAE Cable Types	
	TWP GPT HDT TWE GTE HTE	STS HTS TXL GXL SXL
Conductor Area	X	X
Strand Coating	X	X
Surface Condition	X	X
Maximum OD	X	X
Minimum Wall	X	X
Mechanical Properties	X	X
Dielectric	X	X
Cold Bend	X	X
Flame	X	X
Fluid Compatibility	X	X
Ozone Resistance[2]	X	X
Pinch	X	X
Abrasion	X	X
Crosslinking		X
Strip Force	X	X

[1] The frequency of testing will be established by agreement between the user and supplier.

[2] At least one wire size shall be tested; however, for comparative purposes 0.8 mm^2 (No. 18) is preferred.

**FIGURE 2—REQUIRED TESTS
REFERENCE SECTIONS 4 AND 5**

4.2 Insulation—The insulation shall be homogeneous and shall be placed concentrically within commercial tolerances about the conductor. The insulation shall adhere closely to, but strip readily from, the conductors leaving them in suitable condition for terminating. A separator shall be used between uncoated conductors and insulations with a sulfur cure. Separators are optional for other constructions.

4.2.1 OUTSIDE DIAMETER—The outside diameter shall be measured at five separate cross sections spaced approximately 50 mm (2 in) apart with an optical device accurate to at least 0.01 mm (0.001 in). Other devices may be used; however, in case of dispute, the referee shall be the optical device. A minimum of two readings shall be taken at each cross section. The sample should be rotated approximately 90 degrees between readings. The mean of the diameter readings shall determine the finished cable diameter and shall be in accordance with Figure 4 for the various cable types.

4.2.2 MINIMUM WALL THICKNESS—The minimum wall thickness shall be measured at five separate cross sections spaced approximately 400 mm (16 in) apart using the equipment described in 4.2.1. All individual minimum wall measurements must be in accordance with Figure 4.

Metric		English	
SAE Wire Size mm^2	Minimum Conductor Area mm^2	SAE Wire Size No.	Minimum Conductor Area cir mils
0.22	0.205	24	405
0.35	0.324	22	681
0.5	0.508	20	1,072
0.8	0.760	18	1,537
1	1.13	16	2,336
2	1.85	14	3,702
3	2.91	12	5,833
5	4.65	10	9,343
8	7.23	8	14,810

NOTES

1. English units are not direct conversions from metric.

2. The metric wire size is the approximate nominal area of the conductor.

3. The SAE wire size number indicates that the cross sectional area of the conductor approximates the area of the American Wire Gauge for the equivalent size.

4. When agreed between the supplier and the purchaser, splices may be used for the conductor as a whole provided that they meet the following conditions:

   a. The break strength shall not be reduced by more than 20%.
   b. The resistance shall not be increased.
   c. The diameter of the splice must not exceed the diameter of the uninsulated conductor.

**FIGURE 3—CONDUCTORS
REFERENCE 4.1**

5. Tests—Unless otherwise specified, all tests shall be conducted at room temperature, i.e., 23 °C ± 5 °C. Also, all samples shall be conditioned for a minimum of 4 h at room temperature.

5.1 Strand Coating—The continuity of coating test shall be conducted on individual strands prior to stranding and shall be conducted per ASTM B 33 or B 189. This test is not required for uncoated strands.

5.2 Surface Condition—The surface condition of the strands shall be determined by either of the methods shown below. This test is not required for coated strands.

5.2.1 METHOD #1—25 mm (1 in) of insulation shall be removed from a 300 mm (12 in) sample of finished cable. Approximately 12 mm (0.5 in) of the stripped end shall be immersed into a component lead tinning flux such as Kester 2164 flux for 3 to 5 s. The stripped end shall then be immersed in solder (30 to 40% Sn, remainder Pb) at 400 to 425 °C for 3 to 5 s. Other fluxes and solders may be used; however, in case of a dispute, the referee shall be the Kester #2164 and solder shown in this specification. A visual inspection shall reveal no area in the immersed section which is not covered by solder.

5.2.2 METHOD #2—ASTM B 49—The maximum oxide thickness shall be 200 Å.

5.3 Mechanical Properties—An accelerated aging test shall be conducted in accordance with ASTM D 412, D 573, E 145 Type II except using specimens of insulation removed from finished cable. The sample shall be stretched at a rate of 50 mm/min (2 in/min). 500 mm/min may be used as the strain rate; however, in case of a dispute, the referee method will be a 50 mm/min strain rate. The original and conditioned samples must both be elongated at the same strain rate. The original properties shall conform to the values shown in Figure 5. Samples of insulation shall be aged 168 h in a circulating air oven. The test temperature shall be as shown in Figure 5. After aging, the tensile strength shall not be less than 80% of the original test value and the elongation shall not be less than 50% of the original test value.

	TWP TWE TXL			GPT GTE GXL			STS SXL			HDT HTE HTS		
SAE Wire Size mm²	**Wall Thickness** Nom mm	Min mm	Max OD mm	**Wall Thickness** Nom mm	Min mm	Max OD mm	**Wall Thickness** Nom mm	Min mm	Max OD mm	**Wall Thickness** Nom mm	Min mm	Max OD mm
.22	.40	.28	1.50									
.35	.40	.28	1.70									
.5	.40	.28	1.90	.58	.41	2.40	.74	.52	2.80	.91	.64	3.10
.8	.40	.28	2.20	.58	.41	2.50	.76	.53	3.00	.94	.66	3.40
1	.40	.28	2.40	.58	.41	2.90	.81	.57	3.40	1.02	.71	3.70
2	.40	.28	2.70	.58	.41	3.20	.89	.62	3.90	1.04	.73	4.20
3	.45	.32	3.30	.66	.46	3.80	.94	.66	4.60	1.17	.82	5.10
5	.50	.35	4.00	.79	.55	4.70	1.04	.73	5.30	1.17	.82	5.70
8	.55	.39	4.90	.94	.66	6.00	1.09	.76	6.20	1.40	.98	7.00

FIGURE 4—METRIC DIMENSIONS FOR CABLE
REFERENCE 4.2

	TWP TWE TXL			GPT GTE GXL			STS SXL			HDT HTE HTS		
SAE Wire Size No.	**Wall Thickness** Nom in	Min in	Max OD in	**Wall Thickness** Nom in	Min in	Max OD in	**Wall Thickness** Nom in	Min in	Max OD in	**Wall Thickness** Nom in	Min in	Max OD in
24	.016	.011	.062									
22	.016	.011	.069									
20	.016	.011	.076	.023	.016	.095	.029	.020	.110	.036	.025	.125
18	.016	.011	.084	.023	.016	.100	.030	.021	.120	.037	.026	.135
16	.016	.011	.095	.023	.016	.115	.032	.022	.135	.040	.028	.150
14	.016	.011	.109	.023	.016	.125	.035	.025	.155	.041	.029	.165
12	.018	.013	.132	.026	.018	.150	.037	.026	.180	.046	.032	.200
10	.020	.014	.161	.031	.022	.185	.041	.029	.210	.046	.032	.255
8	.022	.015	.196	.037	.026	.235	.043	.030	.245	.055	.039	.280

NOTE—English units are not direct conversions from metric.

FIGURE 4 (CONTINUED)—ENGLISH DIMENSIONS FOR CABLE
REFERENCE 4.2

SAE Cable Type	Minimum Tensile Strength MPa	psi	Minimum Elongation %	Test Temperature °C ± 2 C°
TWP GPT HDT	11	1600	125	110
STS HTS	7	1000	150	110
TXL GXL SXL	10	1500	150	155
TWE GTE HTE	11	1600	200	150

NOTES

1. The above accelerated aging temperatures are appropriate for insulating materials currently specified in this standard. Different test conditions may be necessary for other materials.

2. English units are not direct conversions from metric.

FIGURE 5—MECHANICAL PROPERTIES
REFERENCE 5.3

TWE, GTE, or HTE samples may be conditioned at the test temperature for 24 h prior to taking the original measurements. The samples will then be conditioned for an additional 168 h (192 h total). The tensile strength after 192 h of conditioning shall not be less than 80% of the measured value after 24 h. The elongation after 192 h of conditioning shall not be less than 50% of the measured value after 24 h.

5.4 Dielectric Test—25 mm (1 in) of insulation shall be removed from each end of a 600 mm (24 in) sample of finished cable and the two ends twisted together. The loop thus formed shall be immersed in water containing 5% salt by weight at room temperature so that not more than 150 mm (6 in) of each end of the sample protrudes above the solution. After being immersed for 5 h and while still immersed, the sample shall withstand the application of 1000 V rms at 50 to 60 Hz between the conductor and the solution for one minute without failure of the insulation.

5.5 Cold Bend Test—25 mm (1 in) of insulation shall be removed from each end of a 600 mm (24 in) sample of finished cable. The sample shall be placed in a cold chamber at -40 °C ± 2 °C for a period of 3 h. While the sample is still at this low temperature, it shall be wrapped around a mandrel for a minimum of 180 degrees at a uniform rate of one turn in 10 s. The mass and mandrel size shall be as specified in Figure 6. Either a revolving or stationary mandrel may be used. When a revolving mandrel is used, fasten one end of the sample to the mandrel and the specified mass to the other end. No mass is required when using a stationary mandrel. A visual inspection shall reveal no cracks or splits. The sample is to be returned to room temperature and then subjected to the dielectric test specified in 5.4.

Metric					English				
	SAE Cable Type					SAE Cable Type			
	TWP GPT HDT STS HTS		TXL GXL SXL TWE GTE HTE			TWP GPT HDT STS HTS		TXL GXL SXL TWE GTE HTE	
SAE Wire Size mm²	Man. Dia. mm	Mass kg	Man. Dia. mm	Mass kg	SAE Wire Size No.	Man. Dia. in	Mass lb	Man. Dia. in	Mass lb
.22	25	.45	25	.68	24	1.0	1.0	1.0	1.5
.35	25	.45	25	.68	22	1.0	1.0	1.0	1.5
.5	75	.45	25	.68	20	3.0	1.0	1.0	1.5
.8	75	.45	25	.68	18	3.0	1.0	1.0	1.5
1	75	.45	25	.68	16	3.0	1.0	1.0	1.5
2	150	.45	75	1.4	14	6.0	1.0	3.0	3.0
3	150	1.4	75	2.3	12	6.0	3.0	3.0	5.0
5	150	1.4	75	2.3	10	6.0	3.0	3.0	5.0
8	150	1.4	150	2.3	8	6.0	3.0	6.0	5.0

NOTE—English dimensions are not direct conversions from metric.

FIGURE 6—COLD BEND AND FLUID COMPATIBILITY TEST CONDITIONS
REFERENCE 5.5 AND 5.7

5.6 Flame Test—A 600 mm (24 in) sample of finished cable shall be suspended taut at approximately 45 degrees to a horizontal plane within a partial enclosure which allows a flow of sufficient air for complete combustion but is free from drafts. A Bunsen burner shall be used having a 13 mm (1/2 in) inlet, a nominal core of 10 mm (3/8 in), and a length of approximately 100 mm (4 in) above the primary inlets. The burner shall be adjusted to produce a 100 mm (4 in) gas flame with an inner cone 1/2 of its height. The temperature of the inner cone shall be a minimum of 900 °C. The burner shall be positioned beneath the sample and perpendicular to the axis of the sample. The top of the inner cone of the flame shall be applied to the center of the cable. The time of application of the flame shall be 15 s. After removal of the Bunsen burner flame, the sample shall not continue to burn for more than 70 s.

5.7 Fluid Compatibility Test—25 mm (1 in) of insulation shall be removed from each end of a 600 mm (24 in) samples of finished cable. A separate sample shall be used for each fluid. The original outside diameter shall be measured using the procedure described in 4.2.1. The area of the sample to be subjected to the bend test shall be immersed in the fluid shown in Figure 7 for a period of 20 h. After removal from the fluid, remove excess fluid from the sample and then condition the sample for 4 h at room temperature. After conditioning, the outside diameter of the cable shall again be measured using the procedure in 4.2.1. The mean of the diameter readings taken after conditioning shall be compared to the mean of the original diameter readings. The maximum diameter change shall be in accordance with Figure 7. The conditioned sample shall be wrapped around a mandrel as specified in Figure 6 for a minimum of 180 degrees at a uniform rate of one turn in 10 s. Either a revolving or

stationary mandrel may be used. When a revolving mandrel is used, fasten one end of the sample to the mandrel and the specified mass to the other end. No mass is required when using a stationary mandrel. A visual inspection shall reveal no cracks or splits. The sample shall then be subjected to the dielectric test specified in 5.4.

5.8 Ozone Resistance— At least one wire size shall be tested; however, for comparative purposes 0.8 mm² (No. 18) is preferred. A 300 mm (12 in) sample of finished cable shall be wound a minimum of 180 degrees around the mandrel specified in Figure 8 at a uniform rate of one turn in 10 s and secured. The assembly shall then be conditioned for 192 h at 65 °C ± 3 °C in an atmosphere containing 100 pphm ± 5 pphm of ozone. A visual inspection shall reveal no cracks or splits.

5.9 Pinch Test—25 mm (1 in) of insulation shall be removed from one end of a 900 mm (36 in) sample of finished cable. The sample shall then be placed taut without stretching across a 3 mm (1/8 in) diameter steel rod as shown in Figure 9. The counter balance shall be adjusted so that no force will be exerted on the sample until a mass is applied to the end of the lever with a mechanical advantage of 10. The sample shall then be subjected to an increasing force applied through the steel anvil by increasing the applied mass at a rate of 2.3 kg/min (5 lb/min). At the moment the insulation is pinched through, the 3 mm (1/8 in) diameter rod will contact the conductor and the test shall stop. The applied mass shall then be recorded. After each reading the sample shall be moved approximately 50 mm (2 in) and rotated clockwise 90 degrees. Four readings shall be obtained for each sample. The mean of the four readings shall determine the pinch resistance of the cable under test. The minimum values for each cable type and size are shown in Figure 10.

Test Fluid			Test Temp °C	Max OD Change %
Name	Standard	Referee Fluid		
Engine Oil		ASTM D 471, IRM-902	50 ± 3	15
Gasoline		ASTM D 471, Ref. Fuel C	Room Temp.	15
Methanol	85% Methanol + 15% Ref. Fuel C	ASTM D 471, Ref. Fuel K	Room Temp.	15
Power Steering		ASTM D 471, IRM-903	50 ± 3	30
Auto Trans	SAE J311	Citgo # 33123	50 ± 3	25
Engine Coolant	50% Distilled Water 50% Ethylene Glycol	ASTM D 471, Service Fluid 104	50 ± 3	15
Battery Acid		H₂SO₄, Specific Gravity = 1.260 ± 0.005	Room Temp.	5

FIGURE 7—FLUID COMPATIBILITY
REFERENCE 5.7

Metric					English				
	SAE Cable Type					SAE Cable Type			
	TWP TXL TWE	GPT GXL GTE	STS SXL	HDT HTS HTE		TWP TXL TWE	GPT GXL GTE	STS SXL	HDT HTS HTE
SAE Wire Size mm²	Man. Dia. mm	Man. Dia. mm	Man. Dia. mm	Man. Dia. mm	SAE Wire Size No.	Man. Dia. in	Man. Dia. in	Man. Dia. in	Man. Dia. in
.22	6				24	.25			
.35	6				22	.25			
.5	6	6	6	13	20	.25	.25	.25	.50
.8	6	6	13	13	18	.25	.25	.50	.50
1	6	13	13	13	16	.25	.50	.50	.50
2	6	13	13	13	14	.25	.50	.50	.50
3	13	13	13	19	12	.50	.50	.50	.75
5	13	13	19	19	10	.50	.50	.75	.75
8	13	19	19	19	8	.50	.75	.75	.75

NOTE—English dimensions are not direct conversions from metric.

FIGURE 8—OZONE TEST CONDITIONS
REFERENCE 5.8

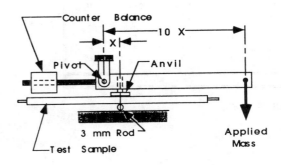

FIGURE 9—PINCH RESISTANCE

5.10 Abrasion Resistance—Reference MIL-T-5438 (Obsolete)—25 mm (1 in) of insulation shall be removed from one end of a 900 mm (36 in) sample of finished cable. The sample shall then be placed taut, without stretching in a horizontal position (see Figure 11). The mass specified in Figure 12 and a suitable bracket shall be used to maintain the cable position over an unused area of the abrasion tape. The total weight of the bracket, mass support rod, and supporting arm shall be 0.63 N ± 0.05 N (0.14 lb ± 0.01 lb). 150J garnet sandpaper with 10 mm (0.38 in) conductive strips perpendicular to the edge of the sandpaper spaced a maximum of every 75 mm (3.0 in) shall be used to abrade the insulation. The sandpaper shall be pulled under the cable at a rate of 1500 mm/min ± 75 mm/min (60 in/min ± 3.0 in/min) until a conductive strip contacts the metallic core. A reading shall be taken of the length of sandpaper used to abrade through the insulation. The sandpaper shall approach and exit the sample from below at an angle of 29 degrees ± 2 degrees to the axis of the cable and shall be supported by a rod 6.9 mm (0.27 in) in diameter. After each

reading, the sample shall be moved approximately 50 mm (2 in) and rotated clockwise 90 degrees. Four readings shall be obtained for each sample. The mean shall define the abrasion resistance of the cable under test. Minimum values for individual cables are shown in Figure 13.

5.11 Crosslinking—25 mm (1 in) of insulation shall be removed from each end of a 600 mm (24 in) sample of finished cable. The sample shall be bent a minimum of 135 degrees around a 6 mm (1/4 in) mandrel. The cable and mandrel shall be placed against a hot plate approximately 150 mm by 150 mm (6 in by 6 in) which has been preheated to 250 °C ± 25 °C. A force of 5 to 7 N (1 to 1.5 lb) shall be applied for 5 to 6 s without rubbing or scraping the cable on the plate. After exposure, the cable core shall not be visible through the insulation. If the visual inspection is not conclusive, the sample is to be returned to room temperature and then subjected to a dielectric test similar to that specified in 5.4. However, the immersion time and application of the voltage shall be 1 min.

5.12 Strip Force—Remove all but 50 mm (2 in) of insulation from a sample of finished cable at least 75 mm (3 in) in length. Care must be taken not to disturb the 50 mm (2 in) section when removing the residual insulation. No burrs are permitted on the ends of the metallic conductor. Insert the stripped end through a plate with an appropriate diameter hole. The core shall be pulled through the plate at a rate of 500 mm/min (20 in/min). The maximum force shall be recorded. A minimum of four readings shall be obtained. The mean of all readings shall determine the strip force of the cable under test. The strip force shall be established by agreement between the supplier and customer.

5.13 Alternative—A 25 mm (1 in) sample of undisturbed insulation may be used.

6. Reference Information

6.1 Color Code

6.1.1 RECOMMENDED COLORS—The color of the cables should match as closely as possible the central colors specified in Appendix A (see Figure A1). The color limits may not apply to Types STS and HTS.

6.1.2 STRIPES—When additional color coding is required, various colored stripes may be applied longitudinally, spirally, or by other manner agreed upon by the supplier and user. The color standards do not apply to stripes.

Metric											
SAE Wire Size mm²	SAE Cable Type										
	TWP kg	GPT kg	HDT kg	STS kg	HTS kg	TXL kg	GXL kg	SXL kg	TWE kg	GTE kg	HTE kg
.22	1.2					2.3			1.5		
.35	1.2					2.7			1.5		
.5	1.5	2.3	4.1	3.6	4.5	2.7	5.0	8.2	2.0	3.6	5.9
.8	1.5	2.7	4.5	3.6	4.5	3.2	6.4	9.1	2.0	4.1	6.8
1	2.0	2.7	5.9	3.6	4.5	3.6	6.8	10	2.5	4.1	7.3
2	2.0	3.6	6.8	3.6	4.5	4.1	7.3	11	2.5	4.5	8.6
3	2.5	3.6	8.2	3.6	4.5	4.5	8.6	12	3.0	5.3	10
5	2.5	4.5	11	3.6	4.5	5.5	10	15	3.0	6.4	11
8	3.0	5.0	15	3.6	4.5	5.9	13	16	3.5	7.7	13

English											
SAE Wire Size No.	SAE Cable Type										
	TWP lb	GPT lb	HDT lb	STS lb	HTS lb	TXL lb	GXL lb	SXL lb	TWE lb	GTE lb	HTE lb
24	2.6					5.0			3.3		
22	2.6					6.0			3.3		
20	3.3	5.0	9.0	8.0	10	6.0	11	18	4.4	8.0	13
18	3.3	6.0	10	8.0	10	7.0	14	20	4.4	9.0	15
16	4.4	6.0	13	8.0	10	8.0	15	22	5.5	9.0	16
14	4.4	8.0	15	8.0	10	9.0	16	25	5.5	10	19
12	5.5	8.0	18	8.0	10	10	19	27	6.6	12	22
10	5.5	10	24	8.0	10	12	22	33	6.6	14	23
8	6.6	11	32	8.0	10	13	28	36	7.7	17	28

NOTE—English units are not direct conversions from metric.

FIGURE 10—MINIMUM PINCH RESISTANCE
REFERENCE 5.9

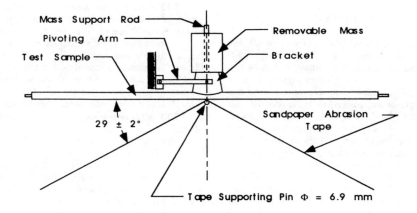

FIGURE 11—SANDPAPER ABRASION

	Metric									
	SAE Cable Types									
SAE Wire Size mm²	**TWP TXL TWE**		**GPT GXL GTE**		**HDT HTE**		**STS SXL**		**HTS**	
	Rec. Br	Mass kg	Rec. Br	Mass kg	Rec. Br	Mass kg	Rec. Br	Mass kg	Rec. Br	Mass kg
.22	A	.22								
.35	A	.22								
.5	A	.22	A	.45	B	1.4	A	.45	B	.45
.8	A	.22	A	.45	B	1.4	A	.45	B	.45
1	A	.22	A	.45	B	1.4	B	.45	B	.45
2	B	.22	B	.45	B	1.9	B	.45	B	1.4
3	B	.45	B	1.4	B	1.9	B	1.4	B	1.4
5	B	.45	B	1.4	B	1.9	B	1.4	B	1.4
8	B	.45	B	1.4	C	1.9	B	1.4	C	1.4

	English									
	SAE Cable Types									
SAE Wire Size No.	**TWP TXL TWE**		**GPT GXL GTE**		**HDT HTE**		**STS SXL**		**HTS**	
	Rec. Br	Mass lb	Rec. Br	Mass lb	Rec. Br	Mass lb	Rec. Br	Mass lb	Rec. Br	Mass lb
24	A	.5								
22	A	.5								
20	A	.5	A	1.0	B	3.0	A	1.0	B	1.0
18	A	.5	A	1.0	B	3.0	A	1.0	B	1.0
16	A	.5	A	1.0	B	3.0	B	1.0	B	1.0
14	B	.5	B	1.0	B	4.25	B	1.0	B	3.0
12	B	1.0	B	3.0	B	4.25	B	3.0	B	3.0
10	B	1.0	B	3.0	B	4.25	B	3.0	B	3.0
8	B	1.0	B	3.0	C	4.25	B	3.0	C	3.0

NOTES

1. English units are not direct conversions from metric.

2. See Figure 13 for minimum abrasion resistance.

FIGURE 12—ABRASION TEST CONDITIONS
REFERENCE 5.11

Metric											
SAE Wire Size mm²	SAE Cable Type										
	TWP mm	GPT mm	HDT mm	STS mm	HTS mm	TXL mm	GXL mm	SXL mm	TWE mm	GTE mm	HTE mm
.22	TBD					TBD			TBD		
.35	250					250			250		
.5	300	400	350	460	760	300	400	550	300	400	350
.8	350	410	400	530	890	350	410	700	350	410	400
1	400	420	450	560	1020	400	420	850	400	420	450
2	450	430	400	760	460	450	430	1000	450	430	400
3	250	280	500	290	560	250	280	500	250	280	500
5	350	400	600	510	760	350	400	600	350	400	600
8	500	500	900	920	890	500	500	900	500	500	900

English											
SAE Wire Size No.	SAE Cable Type										
	TWP in	GPT in	HDT in	STS in	HTS in	TXL in	GXL in	SXL in	TWE in	GTE in	HTE in
24	TBD					TBD			TBD		
22	10					10			10		
20	12	16	14	18	30	12	16	22	12	16	14
18	14	16	16	21	35	14	16	28	14	16	16
16	16	17	18	22	40	16	17	33	16	17	18
14	18	17	16	30	18	18	17	39	18	17	16
12	10	11	20	11	22	10	11	20	10	11	20
10	14	16	24	20	30	14	16	24	14	16	24
8	20	20	35	36	35	20	20	35	20	20	35

NOTE—English units are not direct conversions from metric.

FIGURE 13—MINIMUM ABRASION RESISTANCE
REFERENCE 5.10

APPENDIX A
RECOMMENDED COLORS

Color	Light	Central	Dark
Red	2.5R 4.2/11.2	3.3R 3.8/11.0	4.4R 3.4/10.4
Orange	8.75R 6.0/11.5	8.75R 5.75/12.5	8.75R 5.5/13.5
Brown	10R 3.5/1.0	0.8YR 3.0/1.0	4.6YR 2.5/1.0
Tan	5YR 6.25/4.0	5YR 5.9/4.3	5YR 5.5/4.6
Yellow	8.4Y 8.5/8.3	8.2Y 8.5/9.8	8Y 8.5/11.2
Lt Green	0.5G 6.25/6.3	0.5G 5.6/7.0	0.5G 5.1/7.5
Dk Green	2.2BG 4.75/9.4	1.3BG 4.25/9.4	0.5BG 3.75/9.4
Lt Blue	9B 5.4/5.0	9B 5.0/5.0	9B 4.7/5.0
Dk Blue	4.6PB 3.8/10.2	5.2PB 3.3/9.8	5.6PB 2.75/9.4
Purple	4.4P 3.9/6.7	3.9P 3.4/6.7	3.4P 2.8/6.7
Pink	7RP 6.1/11.5	7.2RP 5.6/12.1	7.7RP 5.2/12.5
Gray	N6.3/(10GY,0.2)	N5.7/(10GY,0.2)	N5.2/(10GY,0.2)
White	Not Applicable	5Y 9/1	5Y 8.5/1
Black	N3	N 2.25	Not Applicable

NOTES

1. Comparison must be made by a person with normal color sensitivity, under cool white fluorescent lighting. The surface being inspected and the tolerance set must be in the same plane. Cable samples must be placed flat, overlapping the color standard.

2. FMII, measured under CIE illuminant C, 2 degree observer.

FIGURE A1—RECOMMENDED COLORS

APPENDIX B
SOURCES FOR SAE FLUIDS

Fluid	Supplier	Packaging
Engine Oil ASTM D 471 IRM 902 Oil	R. E. Carol, Inc. P. O. Box 5806 Trenton, NJ 08638-0806 Contact: Chuck Pascoe Phone: (609)-695-6311 Fax: (609)-695-0102	5 Gal Can
	Penreco 4426 East Washington Blvd. Los Angeles, CA 90023 Phone: (213)-268-4271 Fax: (213)-268-7972	5 Gal Can
Methanol, M-85 ASTM D 471 Ref. Fuel K	Howell Hydrocarbon P.O. Box 429 Channelview, TX 77530 Contact: Norma Phone: (713)-457-2768	55 Gal Drum
Power Steering ASTM S 471 IRM 903 Oil	R. E. Carol, Inc. P. O. Box 5806 Trenton, NJ 08638-0806 Contact: Chuck Pascoe Phone: (609)-695-6311 Fax: (609)-695-0102	5 Gal Can
	Penreco 4426 East Washington Blvd. Los Angeles, CA 90023 Phone: (213)-268-4271 Fax: (213)-268-7972	5 Gal Can
Automatic Trans Fluid SAE J311 Citgo Part No. 33123	Citgo Petroleum 555 East Butterfield Rd. Lombard IL, 60148 Contact: Steve Sewell Phone: (800)-331-4068	55 Gal Drum
Engine Coolant ASTM D 471 Service Fluid 104	Interstate Chemical Co. 2797 Freedland Rd. Hermitage, PA 16148 Contact: Cindy Graham Phone: (412)-981-3771	1 Gal 5 Gal Pail 55 Gal Drum

FIGURE B1—SOURCES FOR SAE FLUIDS

(R) FOUR-, FIVE-, AND EIGHT-CONDUCTOR RECTANGULAR ELECTRICAL CONNECTORS FOR AUTOMOTIVE TYPE TRAILERS—SAE J1239 OCT95   SAE Recommended Practice

Report of the Electrical Equipment Committee approved June 1978. Completely revised by the SAE Electrical Distribution Systems Standards Committee October 1995.

1. Scope—This SAE Recommended Practice covers the wiring and rectangularly shaped connector standards for all types of trailers whose gross weight does not exceed 4540 kg (10 000 lb). These trailers are grouped in SAE J684, with running light circuit loads not to exceed 7.5 A per circuit. This document provides circuits for lighting, electric brakes, trailer battery charging, and an auxiliary circuit color coding and protection for the wiring from hazards or short circuits. Color coding is compatible with SAE J560 and ISO 1724-1980(E).

2. References

2.1 Applicable Documents—The following publications form a part of this specification to the extent specified herein. Unless otherwise indicated, the latest issue of SAE publications shall apply.

2.1.1 SAE PUBLICATIONS—Available from SAE, 400 Commonwealth Drive, Warrendale, PA 15096-0001.

SAE J560 JUN93—Seven Conductor Electrical Connector for Truck-Trailer Jumper Cable

SAE J684 MAR94—Trailer Couplings, Hitches and Safety Chains—Automotive Type

SAE J928 JUL89—Electrical Terminals—Pin and Receptacle Type

SAE J1128 JAN95—Low-Tension Primary Cable

SAE J2223/1 FEB94—Connection for On-Board Road Vehicle Electrical Wiring Harnesses—Part 1: Single-Pole Connectors—Flat Blade Terminals—Dimensional Characteristics and Specific Requirements

SAE J2223/2 FEB94—Connections for On-Board Road Vehicle Electrical Wiring Harnesses—Part 2: Tests and General Performances Requirements

SAE J2223/3 FEB94—Connections for On-Board Road Vehicle Electrical Wiring Harnesses—Part 3: Multipole Connectors—Flat Blade Terminals—Dimensional Characteristics and Specific Requirements

2.1.2 ASTM PUBLICATION—Available from ASTM, 100 Barr Harbor Drive, West Conshohocken, PA 19428-2959.

ASTM G 90-94—Standard Practice for Performing Accelerated Outdoor Weathering of Nonmetallic Materials Using Concentrated Natural Sunlight

2.1.3 ISO PUBLICATION—Available from ANSI, 11 West 42nd Street, New York, NY 10036-8002.

ISO 1724-1980(E)—Road vehicles—Electrical connections between towing vehicles and towed vehicles with 6-or 12-V electrical equipment—Type 12 N (normal)

3. Receptacles

3.1 Four-Way Receptacle—The receptacle shall be of the configuration and design dimensions shown in Figure 1 for four circuits and as shown in Figure 3 for eight circuits.

3.1.1 The four-circuit receptacle (Figure 1) shall be color coded and attached to the towing vehicle as follows:

a. White—Ground to frame SAE wire size 1 mm² (SAE wire size no. 16 gauge) minimum

b. Brown—Spliced to tail and license lamp circuit

c. Yellow—Spliced to left turn and stop circuit

d. Green—Spliced to right turn and stop circuit

3.1.2 FIVE-WAY RECEPTACLE—Figure 2 shall be color coded and shall be attached to the towing vehicle as follows:

a. White—Ground to frame

b. Brown—Spliced to tail and license light circuit

c. Yellow—Spliced to left turn and stop circuit

d. Green—Spliced to right turn and stop circuit

e. Blue—Auxiliary

3.1.3 EIGHT-WAY RECEPTACLE—Figure 3 shall be color coded and shall be attached to the towing vehicle as follows:

3.1.3.1 Left Bank of Receptacles:

a. Red—Independent stop

b. Blue—Brake circuit spliced to controller of brake

c. Optional—Auxiliary (see Figure 3, Note 1)

d. Orange—Battery charge circuit-connect to battery positive terminal through separate fuse or circuit breaker

3.1.3.2 Right Bank of Receptacles:

a. White—Direct to battery negative SAE wire size 3 mm² (SAE wire size no. 12 gauge) minimum

b. Brown—Spliced to tail and license lamp circuit

c. Yellow—Spliced to left turn and stop lamp circuit

d. Green—Spliced to right turn and stop lamp circuit

3.1.4 The receptacle leads shall be attached to the vehicle wiring harness in a workmanlike manner, mechanically and electrically secure. Further, a well-insulated strain relief shall be provided between the receptacle and the towing vehicle wiring harness connections so that there will be no strain on the vehicle harness in the event of an abnormal pull on the receptacle. The receptacle shall be placed in a location where it will not be exposed to road hazards either when connected or loose. The receptacle leads must be properly routed and protected against damage from cutting and pinching where they leave the vehicle body. Extra insulation should be provided between the strain relief at the trailer hitch and the wiring assembly so that an abnormal pull on the plug will not damage the wiring.

3.1.5 No receptacle leads designated for lighting shall be smaller than SAE wire size 1 mm² (SAE wire size no. 16 gauge) minimum if a single conductor, or smaller than SAE wire size 0.8 mm² (SAE wire size no. 12 gauge) if a multiconductor cable.

3.1.6 No receptacle leads for brake circuits shall be smaller than SAE wire size 2 mm² (SAE wire size no. 14 gauge) and no circuits shall be smaller than SAE wire size 3 mm² for (SAE wire size no. 12 gauge) trailer battery charge circuit or battery return circuit.

3.1.7 The gauge of conductors for the auxiliary circuits shall be sized to provide at least the maximum ampacity for the load it will service with a voltage drop not exceeding 3%. The receptacle shall be placed in a location where it will not be exposed to road hazards when disconnected from trailer.

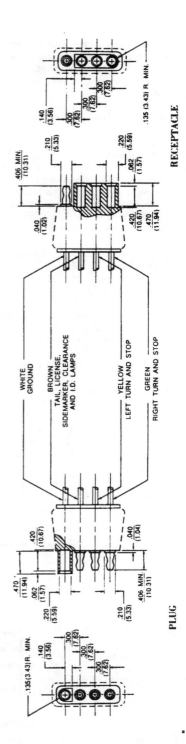

FIGURE 1—FOUR-WAY RECEPTACLE

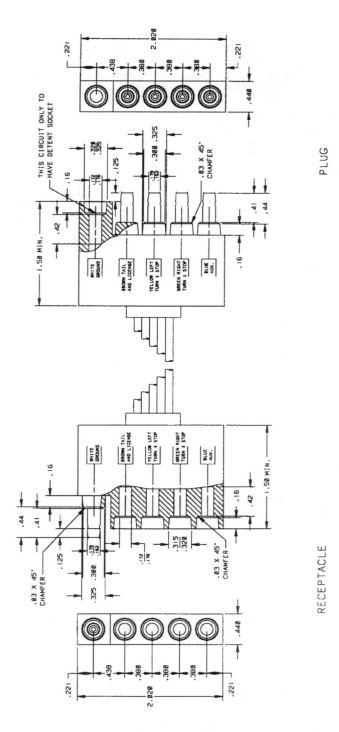

FIGURE 2—FIVE-WAY RECEPTACLE

4. Plug—The plug shall be of the configuration and design dimensions shown in Figure 1 for four circuits, Figure 2 for five circuits, and Figure 3 for eight circuits.

4.1 Four-Way Plug—The four circuit plug (Figure 1) shall be color coded and attached to the trailer harness as follows:

    a. White—Ground to frame SAE wire size 1 mm² (SAE wire size 16 gauge)

    b. Brown—Spliced to tail and license lamp circuit

    c. Yellow—Spliced to left turn and stop circuit

    d. Green—Spliced to right turn and stop lamp circuit

4.2 Five-Way Plug—The plug shall be as shown in Figure 2, and wiring shall be attached to the trailer so that the wires have the maximum protection

against road splash, stones, abrasion, grease, oil, and fuel. The wiring shall be secured to the trailer frame at intervals not greater than 457 mm (18 in), so that the wiring does not shift or sag. The circuits used shall be color coded as follows:

    a. White—Ground

    b. Brown—Tail and license lamp

    c. Yellow—Left turn and stop lamp

    d. Green—Right turn and stop lamp

    e. Blue—Auxiliary

4.3 Eight-Way Plug—Figure 3 shall be color coded and attached to the trailer harness as follows:

    4.3.1 RIGHT BANK PLUG

313

a. Red—Independent stop

b. Blue—Brake circuit spliced to controller of brake circuit

c. Optional—Auxiliary (see Figure 3, Note 1)

d. Orange—Battery Charge Circuit—Connect to trailer battery positive terminal through separate fuse or circuit breaker

4.3.2 LEFT BANK PLUG

a. White—Ground to frame and trailer battery negative terminal

b. Brown—Spliced to tail and license lamp circuit

c. Yellow—Spliced to left turn and stop lamp circuit

d. Green—Spliced to right turn and stop lamp circuit

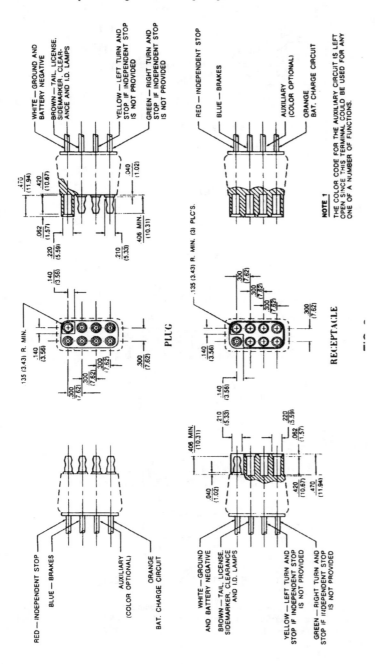

FIGURE 3—EIGHT-WAY RECEPTACLE

5. *Wiring*—All wire and insulation shall conform to the requirements of SAE J1128 Reference Low Tension Primary Cable data on stranded conductors for 12-V circuits with 3% voltage drop. (See Appendix A, Figures A1 and A2.)

5.1 Exposed trailer wiring shall be run in conduits or secured at intervals not greater than 457 mm (18 in) to stop lateral movement and prevent rubbing or chafing.

5.2 So far as practicable, wiring should be located to afford protection from road splash, stones, or abrasion. Wiring exposed to such conditions shall be further protected by the use of or combination of additional tape covering, plastic sleeving, nonmetallic, or other suitable shielding or covering.

6. *Material Requirements*

6.1 The receptacle and plug shall be made of an insulating material such that they can be processed to provide the spacing and splash protection indicated in Figures 1, 2, and 3.

6.2 If the receptacles and plugs are fabricated of either compression molded or extruded plastic, the plastic material shall be stabilized for protection against exposure to ultraviolet light. Reference to ASTM standard practice for conducting a general test on plastic material using a radiometer to measure radiant energy incidents upon a unit surface over a unit of time per area and accelerating outdoor exposures with a fresnel reflector concentrator are explained in ASTM G 90-94. The practice does not specify materials to be tested. Sample preparation and evaluation of results are covered by existing specifications for specific materials.

6.2.1 The hardness of a molded receptacle or plug shall generally fall within the limits of Shore A 50 as minimum and Shore A 70 as a maximum. Shore A 85 has also been known to perform well if properly reinforced and stabilized.

6.3 The metal pins and sockets shall be of the size and type shown in Figures 4 and 5.

6.3.1 Pins and receptacles shall be fabricated from brass or bronze and suitably coated to protect against corrosion. Finished surfaces of plugs and interior walls of sockets shall be smooth so as not to bind when the parts are engaged.

6.3.2 Pins and receptacles shall conform to TYPE 1—PIN TERMINALS, nominal diameter 0.180 (5) specified as SAE J928. Detailed pin and receptacle dimensions are illustrated in Figures 4 and 5.

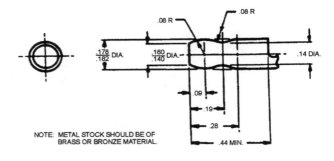

FIGURE 4—PIN

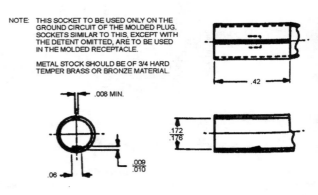

FIGURE 5—SOCKET

7. *Assembly Requirements*

7.1 The plug and receptacle of a four-way connector assembly shall disengage with a minimum force of 22.24 N (5 lb) per assembly and a maximum force of 88.96 N (20 lb) per assembly.

7.2 The plug and receptacle of a five-way connector assembly shall disengage with a minimum force of 13.34 N (3 lb) per circuit and a maximum of 31.14 N (7 lb) per circuit except the ground circuit which can be 53.38 N (12 lb) maximum.

7.3 The plug and receptacle of an eight-way connector assembly shall disengage with a minimum of 35.58 N (8 lb) per assembly and a maximum force of 133.44 N (30 lb) per assembly.

7.4 The mechanical force requirements of disengagement do not preclude the requirements for good electrical connections between the male and female connectors of the circuits.

8. Alternate Connector Selection—This specification provides fundamental performance characteristics pertaining to mold-on connectors, which have been established for Class I trailer applications. There is no intention to limit the application to the example four-, five-, and eight-way pin/sleeve connectors, provided that mating pair connectors have equal or superior performance characteristics. Also, additional performance standards for connectors can be referenced in SAE J2223.

SAE Wire Size	20	18	16	14	12	10
Stranding	7 x 28	16 x 30	19 x 29	19 x 27	19 x 25	19 x 23
Metric Wire Size	0.5	0.8	1.0	2.0	3.0	5.0
Min Cond Area Cir Mil	1072	1537	2336	3702	5833	9343
Min Cond Area mm²	0.508	0.760	1.12	1.85	2.91	4.65

[1] NOTE—This abstracted table is not intended to limit conductor constructions; but samples the stranding range shown.

FIGURE A1—STRANDED CONDUCTORS FOR 12-V CIRCUITS (PRIMARY CABLE DATA ABSTRACTED FROM J1128)[1] 3% VOLTAGE DROP

SAE Wire Size	0.6 mm	(20)	0.8 mm	(18)	1 mm	(16)	2 mm	(14)	3 mm	(12)	5 mm	(10)
Circuit Current in AMPS	m	ft	m	ft	m	ft	m	ft	m	ft	m	ft
1	12	39.4	16	52.5	24	78.7						
2	6	19.7	8	26.2	12	39.4	19.5	64	30.5	100.0		
3	4	13.2	5.5	19.7	8	26.2	13	42.7	20.5	67.2		
4	3	9.8	4	13.1	6	19.7	10	32.8	15	49.2	24	78.8
5	2.5	8.2	3.5	11.5	5	16.4	8	26.2	12	39.4	19.5	63.9
6	3	9.8	3	9.8	4	13.1	6.5	21.3	10	32.8	16	52.5
7	2	6.6	2.5	8.2	3.5	11.4	5.5	18.1	9	29.5	14	45.9
8			2	6.6	3	9.8	5	16.4	8	26.2	12	39.4
9			2	6.6	3	9.8	4.5	14.8	7	23.0	11	36.1
10			2	6.6	2.5	8.2	4	13.1	6	19.7	10	32.8
15					2	6.6	3	9.8	4	13.1	6.5	21.3
20							2	6.6	3	9.8	5	16.4
20									2	6.6	3.5	11.5

FIGURE A2—MAXIMUM LENGTH OF CONDUCTOR IN FEET FROM POWER SOURCE TO LOAD

AUTOMOBILE, TRUCK, TRUCK-TRACTOR, TRAILER, AND MOTOR COACH WIRING— SAE J1292 OCT81

SAE Recommended Practice

Report of the Electrical Equipment Committee, approved June 1980, editorial change October 1981.

[This SAE Recommended Practice combines, revises, and replaces two previous recommended practices: SAE J555a and SAE J556.]

1. Scope—This SAE Recommended Practice covers the application of primary wiring distribution system harnesses to automotive, truck, and similar type vehicles. This is written principally for new vehicles but is also applicable to rewiring and service. It covers the areas of performance, operating integrity, efficiency, economy, uniformity, facility of manufacturing, and service. This practice applies to wiring systems of less than 50 V.

2. General Section
2.1 Definition—The systems of installation known as two wire or single wire are to be designated respectively as *insulated–return* and *ground–return* systems. Installations in which the frame and/or body of the vehicle are used as part of the return circuit are considered as *ground–return* systems.

2.2 Insulated Cable—All insulated cable shall conform to SAE Standards J1127 and J1128.

2.2.1 CONDUCTORS

2.2.1.1 All conductors are to be constructed in accordance with SAE J1127 and J1128 except when good engineering practice dictates special strand constructions.

2.2.1.2 Conductor materials and stranding other than copper can be used if all applicable requirements for physical, electrical, and environmental conditions are met as dictated by the end application.

2.2.2 CONDUCTOR INSULATION—Physical and dimensional values of conductor insulation are to be in conformance with the requirements of SAE J1127 or J1128 except when good engineering practice dictates special conductor insulations.

2.3 Insulated Cable Application

2.3.1 Select cable insulation in accordance with the vehicle's working environment. Consideration is given to physical and environmental factors such as flexing, heat, cold, bend, oil and fuel contact, dielectric, abrasion, short circuit, and pinch resistance among others.

NOTE—Most vehicle working environments permit the use of a thermoplastic insulated, SAE type GPT, general purpose cable. A cable of this type is generally used in static (non-flexing) applications when nominal abrasion, heat, cold, oil, dielectric, short circuit, and pinch resistance properties are desired.

2.3.2 Where vehicle working environments for cable require additional physical and environmental characteristics, upgraded insulations such as SAE types HDT, GPB, HDB, STS, HTS, and SXL shall be used as the severity of the applications dictate.

2.3.3 Specific continuous duty temperature limitations for each SAE cable type shall be observed. The total of the ambient temperature plus cable temperature rise, due to current flow, should not exceed the continuous duty guideline temperatures as shown in Table 1, unless extensive testing and/or evaluation has indicated that higher temperatures can be tolerated.

In addition, the maximum continuous duty temperature rating for any wire insulation shall be determined by an accelerated aging test conducted in accordance with ASTM D 573, with the samples of insulation being removed from the finished wire and aged 168 h. The test temperature shall be 30°C above the intended rated temperature. Tensile strength after aging shall be not less than 80% of the original tensile strength. The elongation after aging shall be at least 50% of the original elongation.

NOTE—Heavier conductors may be required to protect the carrying of current in wire bundles when all conductors are carrying maximum current. Temperature rise tests of the conductor bundle shall be run to determine the proper conductor size and insulation.

Resistance wire low tension cable may be used to limit the voltage applied to electrical devices. Since the nature of the wire is to limit the voltage applied to electrical devices, the distance of the device from the power source and the current demand of the device will determine the materials used. Because every application is different, no materials, conducting or insulating, can be specifically described as standard; thus the conductor and insulating materials must be carefully chosen for each application by the design engineer. It is desirable to identify resistance wire by printing the words *resistance wire* on the conductor.

Extreme care shall be used by the design engineer in choosing resistance wire as a conducting material to satisfy the current demand of the device and not create a temperature rise in the conductor that would deteriorate the insulating material even though the device is left on continuously.

Circuits using resistance wire shall be carefully placed in the vehicle so that their temperature rise will not create a hazard to, or malfunction of, any part of the vehicle. A general design guide would be that the conductor be required to dissipate no more than 5 W per insulated conductor foot.

2.3.4 FUSIBLE LINKS—A special section of low tension cable designed to open circuit when subjected to an extreme current overload shall conform to SAE J156.

2.3.5 It is desirable to color code each conductor in an electrical circuit to facilitate manufacture and service of a wire assembly. It is further desirable for all motor vehicle manufacturers to assign and use similar color code identifications for commonly used electrical circuits to promote ease of circuit analysis in service among the various manufacturers.

2.3.5.1 When feasible each circuit shall conform to a recommended color code by category of equipment as shown in Table 2. Otherwise, the color code may be a solid color (basic) and/or a basic color with secondary color stripes, dots, or hashes.

TABLE 2—CIRCUIT COLOR CODE—BASIC CIRCUITS (AUTOMOTIVE ONLY)

Function	Color
Left rear stop and turn	Yellow
Right rear stop and turn	Dark green
Auxiliary	Blue
Tail, side marker, license	Brown
Ground	White

NOTE: The above code is identical to the color code adopted for automotive type trailers—SAE J895.

2.3.5.2 Secondary color markings to be applied as to be visible throughout the entire length of the wire, or at each end of a lead.

2.3.5.3 Color combinations for special circuits not shown on Table 2 are to be selected by the user. As special circuit functions become standard with manufacturers, they shall be added to the recommended Color Code by category and shown in Table 2.

NOTE—It is desirable for the wire of any one circuit to be of uniform color code throughout the circuit regardless of the number of connections. A circuit is assumed to be continous until it can be interrupted by a relay or switch contacts, or when it reaches a load (such as bulbs, motors, etc.). Fusible links may differ in color from the circuits they are protecting as it could be advantageous to identify fusible link wire gauge size by insulation color.

2.3.5.4 Each circuit in the same wire assembly shall be distinguished from one another in some manner such as color code, or some substantial difference in insulation diameter (that is, two or more gauge sizes).

2.4 Conductor Termination

2.4.1 All stranded conductor stripped ends are to be fitted with terminals (exception—splices). Solid, precisely shaped conductors whose ends are the termination shall not have this fitting.

2.4.2 All terminal attachments to conductors shall conform with the physical and electrical performance requirements of SAE J163.

2.4.3 As a general practice, all terminations have integral and functional insulation grips, except where other secondary applications preclude their use. Special applications without insulation grips may be employed where other means of relieving strain are provided.

2.4.4 A terminal shall be attached to a conductor by a simple mechanical *crimp-type* process that will conform to the intent of paragraph 2.4.2. For maximum reliability and surety of connection, the *crimp* may also be soldered, swaged, brazed, or welded in a workmanlike manner. Care shall be taken to minimize wicking of solder in a stranded wire to avoid impairment of the strain relief or cable flexing.

2.4.5 CIRCUIT GROUNDING—Ground terminal lugs shall be solder dipped, cadmium, tin, or zinc plated. Ground terminals shall be accessible for service. A serrated paint cutting terminal may be utilized to make proper contact on painted surfaces. Ground terminal devices shall be cadmium, tin, or zinc plated. In special cases, plating may not be required for lugs and/or attaching devices.

Ground return connections shall be made to the vehicle structure, frame, or engine. In cases where the engine or body is mounted on rubber or other insulation, proper ground shall be provided.

2.4.6 Terminations used shall comply with the requirements of SAE J561, ring and spade types; SAE J858, blade type; and SAE J928, pin and receptacle type. Secondary applications will dictate the use of special terminations for special use or application.

NOTE—Terminations may be plated with a conductive and corrosion resistant material such as tin or silver to upgrade the current carrying capacity and to improve their resistance to corrosion.

2.5 Conductor Splicing

2.5.1 Conductors shall be mechanically crimped, soldered, swaged, brazed, or welded with other conductors to form a wire splice. All wire splices shall conform with the electrical specifications for splices per SAE J163.

2.5.2 Splices shall be mechanically secure to withstand all fabrication installation and vehicle environment abuse. The splice must be insulated.

2.6 Terminal and Connector Function

2.6.1 Single terminations shall be used only where there is no possibility of misconnections in assembly or service except when special applications may require otherwise.

2.6.2 Multiple terminal connect-disconnect connector bodies shall be used at all points where two or more conductors are terminated and where there is a possibility of misconnection in fabrication, assembly, or service; secondary applications may require a deviation from this practice.

2.6.3 All connections shall be designed to maintain surety of connections while subjected to vibration, shock, and the extreme temperatures

TABLE 1

SAE Cable (Ref. SAE J1128)	Temperature*
Type GPT, HDT, GPD, HDB	194°F (90°C)
Type STS, HTS	221°F (105°C)
Type SXL	275°F (135°C)

* Recommended maximum continuous duty temperature (ambient plus rise).

that are normal environmental conditions for motor vehicles. Surety may be accomplished by employing the use of integral-molded lock devices, terminal to terminal interferences (detents), secondary locking clips, or attaching devices.

2.6.4 All multiple connect-disconnect connector bodies shall be polarized to prevent incorrect assembly unless circuitry permits use of a nonpolarized connector.

2.6.5 Connections shall be located in clean, dry areas when possible. Connections shall be designed to maintain circuit integrity regardless of environmental conditions (such as high humidity, road splash, rain, drainge, earth particles, fuels, lubricants, high and low temperatures, and solvent).

2.7 Conductor Grouping

2.7.1 Conductors are to be grouped together into multiple conductor assemblies whenever possible.

2.7.2 The number of wiring assemblies and electrical connections per vehicle shall be kept to a minimum with overlay or option wiring used only when justified by the economics of fabrication, vehicle installation, and service.

2.8 Wire Assembly Construction

2.8.1 Conductors are to be grouped, where practical, in cable or harness form.

NOTE—Suitable material such as braided cotton, braided paper and cotton, braided vinyl/nylon, flexible plastic conduit, friction or thermoplastic tape, extruded rubber and thermoplastic jackets, or woven loom may be used to form the assembly.

2.8.2 Wiring harness covering shall be adequate to protect the harness in the vehicle routing environment and shall furnish protection during all phases of vehicle assembly and operation.

NOTE—A general guideline to be used in the selection of coverings is specified in Table 3.

2.9 Wire Assembly Installation and Protection

2.9.1 Wiring and related devices shall be installed in a workmanlike manner, mechanically and electrically secure. Devices, lamps, and so forth requiring periodic service shall be serviceable and accessible by providing wire length sufficient to reasonably accomplish this.

2.9.2 In general, wire routing shall be such that maximum protection is provided by the vehicle sheet metal and structural components. Smooth protective channels especially designed for wiring and built into the vehicle body structure should be used when practicable. Avoid areas of excessive heat, vibration, and abrasion.

NOTE—Extra protection (such as braid, loom, conduit, etc.) should be provided when these areas cannot be avoided (Ref. Table 3).

2.9.3 All parts of the electrical system shall be adequately protected against corrosion.

2.9.4 If significant vibration levels exist, the edges of all metal members through which cables and harnesses pass shall be deburred, flanged, rolled, or bushed with suitable grommets. Suitable tubing or conduit over cables may be substituted for grommets if properly secured. Clips for retaining cables and harnesses shall be securely attached to body or frame member and cable or harness. Clips also assist in locating and routing at assembly.

2.9.5 Wiring shall be located to afford protection from road splash, stones, abrasion, grease, oil, and fuel. Wiring exposed to such conditions shall be further protected by either, or a combination of, the use of heavy wall thermoplastic insulated cable, (see SAE Standard J1128, Low Tension Primary Cable) additional tape application, plastic sleeving or conduit, nonmetallic loom, or metallic or other suitable shielding or covering.

2.9.6 Where cables must flex between moving parts, the last supporting clip shall be securely mounted and secure the cable in a permanent manner.

2.9.7 Wiring fasteners shall be non-conductive unless the wiring or

fastener involved is provided with extra heavy outer covering such as nonmetallic conduit, tape, or dip.

NOTE—Overlay or option wiring should be routed in the same fasteners with standard wiring where practical, or should be fastened to the standard wiring with plastic straps or other mechanical means.

2.9.8 Electrical apparatus with integral wiring shall be supplied with grommets or other suitable mechanical fasteners for strain relief.

2.10 Wiring Overload Protective Devices

2.10.1 The current to all low-tension circuits, except starting motor and ignition circuits, shall pass through short circuit protective devices connected to the battery feed side of switches. Headlight systems shall be independently protected. Circuit protection shall be accomplished by utilizing fuses, circuit breakers, or fusible links which conform to SAE Standards.

2.10.2 The protective device shall be selected to prevent wire damage when subjected to extreme current overload.

2.10.2.1 *Fuses*—Fuse sizes shall be selected using guidelines presented in SAE J554, Electric Fuses.

2.10.2.2 *Circuit Breakers*—Fail-safe automatic reset circuit breakers shall be employed when it is necessary to quickly re-establish circuit continuity when that portion of the wiring has been subjected to an overload condition. Non-cycling type circuit breakers will not reset until the overload is removed, (unless they are the non-cycling manual-reset type). Circuit breakers shall conform to SAE J553 and SAE J258.

2.10.2.3 Fusible links shall be employed when heavy feed circuits exceed the continuous working limits of the fuses or circuit breakers. The link of wire, acting like a fuse, shall conform to the guidelines presented in SAE J156, Fusible Links.

3. Truck, Truck-Tractor Section

3.1 The following SAE Recommended Practice relates to wiring for exterior lamps, exclusive of head lamps, of commercial vehicles 80 in (203 cm) or more in width. Except as noted, the wiring system shall conform to the guidelines of Section 2.

3.1.1 LAMP—A lamp is a complete lighting unit. All lamps shall meet the requirements of SAE Standard J575, Lighting Equipment for Motor Vehicles. Lamps with pigtails not in excess of 12 in (30 cm) long shall have a minimum of 16-gauge wire; pigtails in excess of 12 in (30 cm) long shall have wire gauge conforming to the wiring requirements of the vehicle.

3.1.2 WIRE SIZE—To minimize voltage drops, the feed wire size for all circuits shall be a minimum of 12-gauge; branches or taps not in excess of 50 ft (15.2 m) in length shall be 14-gauge. The ground wire for insulated-return systems shall be equal to the respective feed wire. The main ground wire shall be a minimum of 10-gauge.

NOTE—In many cases 4 or 6 gauge may be required.

3.1.3 DESIGN VOLTAGE OF LAMPS—Reference SAE Standard J573, Lamp Bulb and Sealed Units for design voltage values applicable to various bulbs.

3.1.4 Truck-tractors shall conform to Section 2 and the following:

3.1.4.1 *Circuit Identification*—It is desirable to follow the SAE Recommended Practice J1067, Seven Conductor Jacketed Cable for Truck and Trailer Connections, for coding of truck-tractor jumper cable throughout the circuit. Where impractical, the coding is to be followed to a junction block or harness terminating point where visual inspection will identify the circuit coding change. The coding may also be numbers and/or letters printed on the wire insulation. Whatever coding system is chosen, the system shall facilitate in harness manufacturing and in service.

3.1.4.2 *Circuit Termination*—Wiring for trailer circuits shall terminate in:

(a) A connector socket conforming to SAE Recommended Practice J560, Seven-Conductor Electrical Connector for Truck-Trailer Jumper Cable, or

(b) A jumper cable with cable plug conforming to SAE J560.

4. Trailer Section

4.1 Trailers shall conform to Section 2 and the following:

4.1.1 WIRING—All wiring shall be installed in:

(a) Suitable conduit and boxes,

(b) Structure of the trailer, and

(c) Housings and/or raceways which provide equal protection.

Wiring shall be protected from stones, excess dirt, ice, moisture, chafing, and so forth, that will result in harmful effects.

All wiring for legally required lights shall be serviceable in a manner permitting removal and reinstallation from outside the trailer.

4.1.2 GROUNDING—The trailer shall be grounded to the tractor through the jumper cable.

NOTE—Contact of the trailer king pin or apron plate with the lower coupler or *grounding through the lower coupler* is not to be considered as providing a tractor-to-trailer ground.

TABLE 3

Type	Wire Harness Covering	General Application
1	Vinyl Plastic Tape—0.007 in (0.18 mm)	Primarily used for grouping cables into wire harnesses. Wiring not subject to damage from scuffing or scrubbing on rough metal edges.
2	Friction Tape, Cotton and Kraft Paper Braid	Generally optional; improved scuff and scrub resistance.
3	Vinyl/Nylon Braid	Improved abrasion resistance.
4	Non-Metallic Loom (Woven Asphalt, Impregnated Loom, Extruded Vinyl Plastic, or Elastomeric Tubing)	Improved scuff and abrasion resistance.
5	Rigid and Flexible Conduit	For maximum abrasion resistance and/or positive positioning for clearance to moving or heated vehicle components.

4.1.3 MARKING—The voltage of the lighting system shall be permanently or semi-permanently marked in a legible manner on a mounting surface, in proximity to the electrical connector receptacle. Preferably, the marking shall be in amber reflective letters.

4.1.4 TRAILER CONNECTOR SOCKET—The trailer connector socket for receiving the jumper cable plug shall conform to SAE J560.

4.1.5 CIRCUIT PROTECTION—Circuit protection independent of truck-tractor system shall be provided. Trailer circuit protective devices shall conform to SAE Standard J554, Electric Fuses or SAE Recommended Practice J553, Circuit Breakers and shall be located near the trailer wiring connector socket and be readily accessible for service.

5. Motor Coach Section

5.1 Motor coaches shall conform to Section 2 and the following:

5.1.1 WIRING—Where practical, wiring is to be located within the structure of the coach where it will not be subjected to damage by road splash, stones, grease, oil, fuel, or abrasion.

Wiring so located that it will be subjected to more than normal wear or hard usage shall be equipped with a means of disconnecting from the main harness and be easily removable for replacement or repair.

Wiring connections to lights mounted on the coach body shall be accessible from outside, with the light removed or through an access door in an interior trim panel.

6. Storage Battery Cables

6.1 Definition—Battery cables provide the link between the battery(s) and the balance of the starting/charging circuit. Items that dictate the design are:

6.1.1 ROUTING—Routing shall be established with the following guidelines:

6.1.1.1 Areas of excessive heat, abrasion, and vibration are to be avoided. Extra protection (such as loom, conduit, tubing, heat shield, etc.) shall be provided when these areas cannot be avoided.

6.1.1.2 Grommets or ferrules and nipples shall be provided when routed through holes in the frame or sheet metal.

6.1.1.3 Support at intervals of approximately 24 in (61 cm). Insulated or nonconductive supports shall be used.

6.1.1.4 Provide strain relief for the battery and starter motor terminals as close to terminals as practical.

6.1.1.5 Tailor such that the cables are not too loose nor too tight, considering engine rocking due to torque changes.

6.1.2 VOLTAGE DROP—Voltage drop for starting motor circuits as recommended in SAE J541, determines the maximum drop allowed for the total cranking circuits from the battery to the starter motor and the return to the battery.

6.1.3 CABLE SIZE—Cable size is determined by knowing the system parameters and subtracting their fixed resistances (such as connections, starter solenoid, ground path other than the battery cable, etc.) from the total specified in paragraph 6.1.2. This remaining resistance is the maximum allowed for the battery cables.

6.1.4 CABLE CONSTRUCTION—Cable construction is determined from the environment in which the battery cables must survive.

6.1.4.1 *Core Stranding*—Core stranding of conventional cable can be either bunched, concentric stranded, or rope lay. Bunched or concentric will suffice in most applications, except those requiring higher flex life. For larger cable sizes, rope stranding is needed for routing purposes as well. Battery strap is available for extreme flex requirements and restricted space or routing problems. Reference SAE J1127.

6.1.4.2 *Insulation*—Insulation provides electrical as well as environmental protection for the core. Polyvinyl chloride (PVC) can be used in most applications; cross-linked polyethylene, hypalon, neoprene, etc., may be needed for added protection against short circuit, high temperature, abrasion, etc. Reference SAE J1127 and Table 1.

6.1.4.3 *Terminals*—Terminals provide the connection to the battery, starter solenoid, junction blocks, switches, and grounding locations. A multitude of different types and styles are available for the variety of cable sizes. Also available are sleeves and covers which provide additional circuit and corrosion protection. Reference SAE J561 and SAE J163.

HIGH VOLTAGE PRIMARY CABLE—SAE J1654 JUN94   SAE Standard

Report of the Cable Task Force of the SAE Electrical Distribution Systems Standards Committee approved June 1994. Rationale statement available.

1. Scope—This SAE Standard covers cable intended for use at a nominal system voltage higher than those in SAE J1127, SAE J1128, or SAE J1560 but less than or equal to 600 V rms. It is intended for use in surface vehicle electrical systems.

2. References

2.1 Applicable Documents—The following publications form a part of this specification to the extent specified herein. The latest issue of SAE publications shall apply.

2.1.1 SAE PUBLICATIONS—Available from SAE, 400 Commonwealth Drive, Warrendale, PA 15096-0001.

SAE J1127—Battery Cable

SAE J1128—Low Tension Primary Cable

SAE J1560—Low Tension Thin Wall Primary Cable

SAE J1673—High Voltage Primary Automotive Wiring Assemblies

3. General Requirements—The cable shall meet all of the requirements of SAE J1127, SAE J1128, or SAE J1560 for the applicable cable type.

4. Additional Requirements

4.1 Dielectric Test—The test shall be conducted according to the applicable section of SAE J1127, SAE J1128, or SAE J1560 except the voltage shall be as defined in Table 1. This test shall be used for virgin cable and after all other tests which require a "Dielectric Test," such as cold bend, fluid exposure, etc.

4.2 Spark Test—100% of the in process cable shall be subjected to a spark test at the voltage specified in Table 1. Every point on the cable shall

withstand a minimum of 18 positive and negative crests of the supply voltage (the equivalent of nine full cycles of the supply voltage) without failure of the insulation.

TABLE 1—TEST VOLTAGE
(REFERENCE TO 4.1 AND 4.2)

SAE Wire Size Range Metric (mm²)	SAE Wire Size Range English No.	Test Voltage (Volts AC rms) Dielectric Reference 4.1	Test Voltage (Volts AC rms) Spark Test Reference 4.2
0.2 to 0.5	24 to 20	2500	5 000
0.6 to 5	19 to 10	2500	6 000
5.1 to 32	9 to 2	2500	10 000
32.1 to 120	1 to 0000	2500	12 500

NOTE—Round the wire size to the nearest 0.1 mm²

4.3 Insulation Resistance—25 mm (1 in) of insulation shall be removed from each end of a 5 m (16 ft) sample of finished cable. Twist the ends together. Immerse the sample to within 1 m (3 ft) from the end of the insulation in tap water at 21 °C ± 6 °C (70 °F ± 10 °F) for a minimum of 6 h. Measure the resistance between the core and water using a bridge that is accurate to within ±10% of the measured value and having an open circuit potential of 125 V or more. The sample shall have a minimum resistance of 30 MΩ.

4.4 Battery Electrolyte Compatibility—TBD

4.5 Battery Coolant Compatibility—TBD

Report of the Off-Road Machinery Technical Committee —SC5, approved August 1990. Rationale statement available. Reaffirmed by the Electrical Components and Systems Subcommittee of the SAE Common Tests Technical Committee January 1996.

Foreword—This reaffirmed document has been changed only to reflect the new SAE Technical Standards Board format.

1. Scope—This SAE Standard outlines general procedures for the grounding of electrical components in both 12- and 24-V systems for off-road machines, as defined in SAE J1116.

1.1 General—The voltage drops specified throughout this document are for a 12-V system. For 24-V systems, the allowable voltage drops may be doubled. These voltage drops are nominal at room temperature (25 °C ± 5 °C), and may not be sufficient to guarantee proper operation of voltage sensitive devices, such as gauges, alternators, and electronic devices. Manufacturer's recommendations for the grounding of components must be followed whenever provided.

2. Reference

2.1 Applicable Document—The following publication forms a part of this specification to the extent specified herein. Unless otherwise specified, the latest issue of SAE publications shall apply.

2.1.1 SAE PUBLICATION—Available from SAE, 400 Commonwealth Drive, Warrendale, PA 15096-0001.

SAE J1116—Categories of Off-Road Self-Propelled Work Machines

3. Definitions

3.1 Common Ground—The machine member to which all wire grounds are connected. Typically, this is either the frame or the engine block.

3.2 Low Current Ground—A ground path in which the current in any one segment is limited to 3 A.

3.3 Medium Current Ground—A ground path in which the current in any one segment is limited to 30 A.

3.4 High Current Ground—A ground path in which the allowable current in any segment may exceed 30 A.

3.5 Primary Ground Path—The intended lowest resistance electrical path which interconnects the cranking motor and the battery.

3.6 Secondary Ground—A connection node which is the terminating point for one or more medium current grounds and which is, in turn, connected to common ground.

4. Low Current Grounds—Used primarily for instrumentation systems.

4.1 The voltage differential between any point along the low current ground path and the common ground shall not exceed 150 mV.

4.2 Low current ground connections shall be made directly from an electrical part(s) to the common ground via a dedicated wire(s) in the harness. Although no secondary grounds should be included in a low current ground path, it is permissible to loop ground conductors between several components if the user adheres to the voltage drop provision of 4.1.

5. Medium Current Grounds—Includes, but is not restricted to, grounds for lights, blower motors, solenoids, warning flashers, etc.

5.1 Medium current grounds may be made either directly to the common ground or to a secondary grounding point.

5.2 The voltage differential between any point along the medium current ground path and common ground shall not exceed 500 mV.

6. High Current Grounds—May include, but is not restricted to, alternator grounds, cranking motor grounds, and cab to frame grounds.

6.1 High current grounds shall be made directly to the common ground. Connecting a high current ground to the common ground via a secondary ground is not recommended.

6.2 A wire sized to carry the full alternator output current shall connect directly from the alternator negative output terminal to the engine block or cranking motor ground terminal, if provided.

6.3 The maximum voltage differential between any point along a high current ground path and the negative battery terminal shall not exceed 500 mV under any combination of loads and conditions.

6.4 To ensure acceptable battery charging characteristics, the total voltage difference between the battery terminal voltage and the alternator output voltage shall not exceed 500 mV at maximum alternator output current. The voltage drop in the ground circuit between the alternator and the battery shall not exceed 250 mV under the same conditions. Consult alternator and battery suppliers for specific application information.

7. Primary Grounds—Includes cranking motor, common ground, battery cable, disconnect switch, and any other component in the ground path between the cranking motor and the battery.

7.1 Primary ground paths shall not pass through any bolted metal surfaces or structures. Exceptions can be made for cranking motors and other similar devices which, by design, complete the ground path through mounting hardware.

7.2 The maximum voltage differential between any two points on the primary ground path shall not exceed 100 mV under any conditions except during engine cranking.

8. Secondary Grounds—Any sheet metal part, cast part, buss bar, rollover protection structure, etc., which is a continuous metal part not broken by any bolted joints, can be used as a grounding point for one or more electrical devices. It is, in turn, connected to the common ground using either wire or cable. It is preferred, however, that all grounds have a wire or cable connection to the common ground.

8.1 The voltage difference from any point on the secondary ground and the common ground shall not exceed 300 mV under conditions of maximum load.

8.2 Each secondary ground shall have a wire or cable connected directly to common ground.

8.3 For noncritical functions, several grounds may be made to a single connection node, which is then connected to a secondary ground through a single conductor. An example is a dash panel which is connected to the cab structure (secondary ground), which is in turn connected to the common ground. Instrument lights and cigar lighter grounds may then be connected to the dash ground.

8.3.1 The connection node shall be provided with a dedicated wire or cable connection to the secondary ground. Bolted joints, hinges, latches, etc., are not acceptable. The maximum current in this conductor shall be limited to 30 A or less.

8.3.2 The maximum voltage differential between any device grounded in this manner and common ground shall not exceed 1.25 V.

9. Ground Connections—Ground connections made to metal surfaces shall maintain contact integrity with the normal effects of aging, temperature cycling, moisture, splash, spray washing, fatigue, and other environmental conditions.

9.1 Metal surfaces shall be free of primer, paint, rust, and corrosion. The surface shall have a bright, polished appearance immediately before the ground terminal is connected.

9.2 The terminal cross section shall be equal to or greater than the wire cross section. The mating surfaces shall be sufficiently flat to ensure that the total contact area is equal to or greater than the sum of the cross-sectional areas of all wires connected to a common grounding point.

9.2.1 A steel flat washer (with an OD approximately equal to the ring terminal diameter) shall be placed between the bolt head and the terminal.

9.2.2 For punched holes, care shall be taken to ensure that the edge distortion on the breakout side does not inhibit contact between mating surfaces.

9.2.3 Star washers have not been proven to be effective as a means of ensuring long-term connection integrity with the effects of aging and environmental extremes. The use of star washers is not recommended.

9.3 Stacking of up to three ring terminals of the same size in medium current, low current, and signal ground applications is acceptable.

9.3.1 It is good practice to place the terminal carrying the highest current closest to the grounding surface.

9.3.2 It is desirable that all ring terminals in a stack have the same OD. However, if ring terminals of dissimilar ODs are used, the largest terminal shall be placed closest to the grounding surface.

9.4 Grounding studs and joints shall be dedicated, and shall not also be used as structural joints. Mixing softer terminal material with stress-bearing joints can lead to loss of electrical and structural integrity.

9.5 All grounding locations shall be accessible for maintenance.

9.6 A wire loop with its low point at a level below the termination itself may be provided to prevent water from following the wire back to the termination.

9.7 Painting the completed connection or coating the connection with an electrical grease designed to improve electrical contact integrity may be used as added protection against corrosion.

9.8 For high current grounds, cable or ground strap terminals shall bolt directly to a welded boss or a prepared flat surface on a cast part.

ELECTRICAL/ELECTRONIC SYSTEMS DIAGNOSTIC TERMS, DEFINITIONS, ABBREVIATIONS, AND ACRONYMS—SAE J1930 SEP95

SAE Recommended Practice

Report of the SAE Vehicle E/E Systems Diagnostics Standards Committee approved June 1988, and completely revised September 1991 and June 1993. Revised by the J1930 Task Force of the SAE Vehicle E/E Systems Diagnostics Standards Committee September 1995.

Foreword—As the number of sophisticated electrical and electronic (E/E) systems on motor vehicles has increased, the number of terms, abbreviations, and acronyms which describe various components of these systems has increased enormously. To bring some order to the proliferation of such terms, abbreviations, and acronyms, the Vehicle E/E Diagnostic Systems Committee has prepared this document.

The nomenclature used to convey automotive service information is being standardized in order to more accurately convey information to technicians faced with the diagnosis and repair of increasingly complex vehicles.

To be properly descriptive, each type of automotive nomenclature requires a consistent methodology. This document is concerned with a methodology for naming objects and systems and with the set of words from which names are built.

The methodology allows objects and systems to be completely described without ambiguity. It also is able to generate names which distinguish among similar objects or systems without confusion but with brevity. Using terms which are well-defined within the context of the automotive service industry, the methodology allows already existing imprecise names to be suitably changed and future names to be assigned in a predictable way which will reliably convey meaning to the technician.

The structure of this SAE document is open ended by design. As the need arises, additional entries can be added. Because of this flexibility, particular attention should be paid to the month and year publishing code contained in the full "J" number designation.

TABLE OF CONTENTS

1. Scope—This SAE Recommended Practice is applicable to all light-duty gasoline and diesel passenger vehicles and trucks, and to heavy-duty gasoline vehicles. Specific applications of this document include diagnostic, service and repair manuals, bulletins and updates, training manuals, repair databases, under-hood emission labels, and emission certification applications.

This document focuses on diagnostic terms applicable to electrical/electronic systems, and therefore also contains related mechanical terms, definitions, abbreviations, and acronyms.

Even though the use and appropriate updating of this document is strongly encouraged, nothing in this document should be construed as prohibiting the introduction of a term, abbreviation, or acronym not covered by this document.

Certain terms have already been in common use and are readily understood by manufacturers and technicians, but do not follow the methodology of this document. To preserve this understanding, these terms were included and have been identified with the footnote (2), "historically acceptable common usage," so they will not erroneously serve as a precedent in the construction of new names. These terms fall into three categories:

a. Acronyms that do not logically fit the term.
b. Acronyms existing at the component level, i.e., their terms contain the base word or noun that describes the generic item that is being further defined.
c. Acronyms for terms that appear to contain the base word, but are frequently used as a modifier to another base word. (This use may possibly be thought of as following the methodology since the acronym is normally used as a modifier.)

2. References—There are no referenced publications specified herein.

3. How to Use This Document—To find the recommended term corresponding to an existing term, abbreviation or acronym, see Table 1, Cross Reference and Look Up. See Table 2, Recommended Terms, and Table 3, Glossary of Terms, for definitions of the recommended terms. Use Section 3.0, Methodology to construct a new name. Appropriate acceptable usage's of Recommended Terms and Acronyms are contained in Table 1.

4. Methodology—This naming methodology of describing objects and systems uses modifiers attached to base words. Appropriate modifiers are added to a base word until an object or system is uniquely specified within its context.

4.1 Naming Objects—When building names, select the most descriptive base word from the Glossary of Terms (Table 3). Add modifiers as necessary or as desirable within the context, in the order of most significance to least significance. The most significant word will be the base word, which denotes the basic function of the object. The most significant modifier will be adjacent to the base word, the second most significant will be next to that modifier, and so on until the least significant modifier is added. For the sake of future clarity, an additional modifier can be added to a name at any time, even if there is no present conflict with another object name. Figure 1 illustrates how modifiers can be added to build the name, "Instrumentation Engine Coolant Temperature Sensor."

When naming an object, it is tempting to choose the first modifiers according to the initial purpose for which the object was designed, but this will not always result in the name which is most helpful in the long run to a service technician. The information a technician needs is most often supplied by a term which describes a functional attribute, not purpose.

MODIFIERS				BASE WORD	
What is its purpose?	Where is it?	Which Temp?	What does it sense?	What is it?	
				Sensor	Most generic
			Temperature	Sensor	
		Coolant	Temperature	Sensor	
	Engine	Coolant	Temperature	Sensor	Most specific
Instrumentation	Engine	Coolant	Temperature	Sensor	
Least <---------------------------- SIGNIFICANCE ----------------------------> Most					

FIGURE 1—MODIFIER USAGE EXAMPLE

To ensure accuracy, always check the Glossary definitions of base words and modifiers before including them in a name. The Glossary is intended for diagnostic purposes, but provides only electrical/electronic terms for base words. Base words which describe nonÄelectrical objects (e.g., bolt, screw, bumper) should be used as in the past. Often, names for these objects are created by attaching the appropriate electrical/electronic object name to the mechanical base word. When using a common multiple word modifier, see Tables 1 and 2 to be sure that the modifier is acceptable or if it should be replaced with a more precise term.

4.1.1 BASE WORDS—The base word is the most generic term in a name. Simply stated, it answers the question, "What is this object?" In answering this question, the base word does not include information about the location or function of an object within a particular system. Specific information like this is provided by modifiers that are added to the base word. The following are examples of base words: diode, engine, module, motor, pump, relay, sensor, solenoid, switch, valve. The base word is always a noun and the last term in a name.

4.1.2 MODIFIERS—Modifiers provide functional/applicational meaning, system differentiation, and locational/ directional information. Modifiers usually express non-electrical ideas to describe base words which, in turn, convey electrical/electronic meaning. The range of modifiers is not limited and is used as necessary to uniquely describe an object in light of present knowledge, past experience, and potential future conflicts.

Although modifiers are used as adjectives, they are not necessarily terms which would normally be classified as adjectives. While neither "Air" or "Flow" are adjectives, the meaning of "Air Flow Valve" is clear to technicians; it is the name of a valve which regulates the flow of air. Both modifiers are nouns functioning as adjectives because of their position.

System modifiers can be added to object names to describe an object's purpose. When using a system name as a modifier in an object name, the word "System" is not included. For example, the device that directs the exhaust gases in the Exhaust Gas Recirculation (EGR) System is named "Exhaust Gas Recirculation (EGR) Valve."

4.1.3 TECHNOLOGICAL TERMS—Technologically specific terms tend to lengthen names without adding a corresponding level of useful service information about the function of an object. Add an appropriate technological modifier to a name only when it describes the primary difference between two objects. For example, the "thick film" technology used to construct the internal circuit of an Air Flow Sensor should not be identified in the object's name. However, if necessary for clarity, it would be appropriate to differentiate the relation to a specific external provision by adding "Hot Wire" to "Air Flow Sensor."

A technological term should be the first modifier conversationally (farthest from the base word, the position of least significance), unless a directional modifier is also present.

4.2 Naming Systems—When constructing a name for a system, consider it to be a combination of a "concept" and the word "System." Develop the concept name according to the rules for object naming and add the word "System." Keep in mind that a concept's most basic attribute is its purpose and that this attribute is described by the term closest to the word "System." For example, "recirculation" is the basic attribute of the Exhaust Gas Recirculation (EGR) concept. The group of components that embody the concept are together named the "EGR System."

4.3 Shortened Names—Techniques of shortening, including acronyms and abbreviations, are often necessary when space is limited and when names become awkwardly long. It is preferable to create a name first and its shortened form later, rather than the other way around.

Abbreviations and acronyms may be constructed not only of the letters of the alphabet, but of numbers, space characters, punctuation marks (such as "/" and "-"), subscripts and any other ASCII characters. Treat the individual acronyms, modifier abbreviations, and base word abbreviations as words, separating them by space characters.

4.3.1 ACRONYMS—Specific definitions of acronyms vary, but for the purpose of this document, an acronym is a memorable combination of the first letters of the words of a name. While abbreviations are useful in text where space is limited, acronyms are particularly convenient for shortening verbal communication in addition to written materials. For this reason, acronyms are often pronounceable, which also makes them easy to remember. They are especially useful if a name is long and bulky both on paper and in conversation.

Use acronyms as modifiers or base words within names, such as "EGR System" and "Primary ECM." Do not use them as entire names, like "EGRS". Acronyms and other modifiers may be combined in any meaningful order to modify a base word. The following are examples of acceptable uses of acronyms:

EGR System EGRT Sensor Low Speed FC Switch High Speed FC Switch

Because there are a limited number of useful letter combinations for acronyms, new acronyms should be created for only the most commonly used terms. Also, avoid creating new acronyms by adding letters to those that already exist. For example, when using the acronym "FC" (Fan Control), do not add "H" or "L" to indicate "High Speed" or "Low Speed." Instead, use additional modifiers.

Usually, the first letters of each word of a name are used to build an acronym, but if a particular word is of little significance, it may be omitted ("United States of America" becomes "USA"). Also, more than the first letter of each word may be used ("Radio Detecting And Ranging" becomes "RADAR"). An acronym like "USA" which contains three letters or fewer may have its letters spoken separately, but a longer acronym such as "RADAR" must be pronounceable or its purpose will be defeated.

All of the letters of an acronym should be capitalized. Acronyms should not contain periods. Until an acronym is widely well-known, it should be accompanied by the spelled-out form when necessary for accurate reader comprehension in any given context.

In the very rare cases of strong historical meaning across all manufacturers, the rules for naming and acronym usage may be broken. For example, "AIR" is the approved acronym for "Secondary Air Injection," instead of "SAI." In fact, because there is no approved name "Primary Air Injection," the term "Secondary Air Injection" would be considered inappropriate. Despite this, historical precedent renders "AIR" and "Secondary Air Injection" the most easily understood terms. "AIR" originally meant "Air Injection Reactor." However, vehicles no longer necessarily use a separate air injector reactor, but instead might have additional air injected to the catalytic converter. Because of the similarity to the previous system, technicians have expressed a strong desire to retain "AIR" rather than "SAI."

Before using a new acronym, be sure to check Tables 1 and 2 for any conflicts with acronyms already in use.

4.3.2 ABBREVIATIONS—Use abbreviations to shorten base words and directional modifiers in written materials. Unlike an acronym, an abbreviation should have only its first letter capitalized and should end with a period. Wire colors are an exception to the rules of capitalization and punctuation. As in the past, they should continue to be completely capitalized in text and not followed by a period (for example, "a BLK wire"). Currently identified abbreviations for base words and modifiers are found in Table 1.

4.4 Indexing of Names—Service information index designers consider the importance of each term in a name, and select the most appropriate word(s) to index. They most frequently index base words; following each by its modifier(s) to enhance users retrieval. This document allows the designer flexibility to choose the indexed word(s); while it describes, in detail, the methodology for the conversational word order in text and illustrations. For example, the designer can conform to the methodology of this document and provide the user with the effective retrieval of the conversational name "Left Front Wheel Speed Sensor" by indexing it as "Sensor, Left Front Wheel Speed."

(R) **4.5 Alphanumeric Descriptors**—Sections 4.1 through 4.3 describe the appropriate methodology to completely described object and system without ambiguity. This section includes naming objects (with base words, modifiers, and technological terms), naming systems and building shortened names.

An "alphanumeric descriptor" can be used in information delivered to the end-user of a scan tool having an 8-character display limitation. An alphanumeric descriptor is not recommended for general use, but can be built from a Recommended Term by replacing position modifier words with numeric digits, and omitting certain self-evident letters.

Alphanumeric position modifiers in an alphanumeric descriptor should be positioned to follow the base word, rather than the conversational practice of preceding the base word.

Figure 2 illustrates how several Recommended Terms and Acronyms can be further shortened into alphanumeric descriptors.

The following guidelines should be followed when using or developing alphanumeric descriptors:

   a. First consult Table 2, Recommended Terms in the Acronyms column.

   b. If the term is not included, build a suitable term using 4.1 Naming Object or 4.2 Naming System. Then shorten the term using 4.3 Shortened Names.

   c. If the resultant term is too long for a scan tool with an 8-character display limitation, build an Alphanumeric Descriptor for electronic delivery according to the pattern shown in Figure 2:

   d. Delete or replace characters as required.

   e. Omit spaces depending on the display limitation.
     (example: FUEL PRES becomes FUELPRES)

   f. Consult Table 4 for a matching Alphanumeric Descriptor.

   g. If Table 4 does not contain a matching Alphanumeric Descriptor, request an addition, using the Request for Revision form in Appendix A.

5. Cross Reference and Look Up—See Table 1. The left column lists existing terms, acronyms and abbreviations. The center column provides the corresponding acceptable usage's constructed of recommended terms combined with other modifiers and/or base words. The acceptable acronized usage is shown in the right column.

For information about using acronyms and abbreviations, see 4.3.1 (Acronyms) and 4.3.2 (Abbreviations). For additional information about Recommended Terms, see Tables 2 and 3.

Recommended Term	Acceptable Acronized Usage	Alphanumeric Descriptor
Diagnostic Trouble Code Freeze Frame	DTC Freeze Frame	DTC FRZF
Engine Coolant Temperature	ECT	None Required
Flexible Fuel	FF	None Required
Freeze Frame	Freeze Frame	FRZF
Fuel Pressure	Fuel Pressure	FUEL PRES
Fuel System 1 Status	Fuel System 1 Status	FUEL SYS1
Long Term Fuel Trim Bank 2	Long Term FT Bank 2	LONG FT2
Oxygen Sensor Location Bank 1 Position 1	O2S Bank 1 Position 1	O2SLOC11

FIGURE 2—ALPHANUMERIC DESCRIPTORS EXAMPLE

TABLE 1—CROSS REFERENCE AND LOOK UP

Existing Usage	Acceptable Usage	Acceptable Acronized Usage
A/C (Air Conditioning)	Air Conditioning	A/C
A/C Cycling Switch	Air Conditioning Cycling Switch	A/C Cycling Switch
A/T (Automatic Transaxle)	Automatic Transaxle[1]	A/T[1]
A/T (Automatic Transmission)	Automatic Transmission[1]	A/T[1]
AAT (Ambient Air Temperature)	**Ambient Air Temperature**	**AAT**
AC (Air Conditioning)	Air Conditioning	A/C
ACC (Air Conditioning Clutch)	Air Conditioning Clutch	A/C Clutch
Accelerator	Accelerator Pedal	AP
Accelerator Pedal Position	**Accelerator Pedal Position[1]**	**APP[1]**
ACCS (Air Conditioning Cyclic Switch)	Air Conditioning Cycling Switch	A/C Cycling Switch
ACH (Air Cleaner Housing)	Air Cleaner Housing[1]	ACL Housing1
ACL (Air Cleaner)	Air Cleaner[1]	ACL[1]
ACL (Air Cleaner) Element	Air Cleaner Element[1]	ACL Element[1]
ACL (Air Cleaner) Housing	Air Cleaner Housing[1]	ACL Housing[1]
ACL (Air Cleaner) Housing Cover	Air Cleaner Housing Cover[1]	ACL Housing Cover[1]
ACS (Air Conditioning System)	Air Conditioning System	A/C System
ACT (Air Charge Temperature)	Intake Air Temperature[1]	IAT[1]
Adaptive Fuel Strategy	Fuel Trim[1]	FT[1]
AFC (Air Flow Control)	Mass Air Flow	MAF
AFC (Air Flow Control(	Volume Air Flow	VAF
AFS (Air Flow Sensor)	Mass Air Flow Sensor	MAF Sensor
AFS (Air Flow Sensor)	Volume Air Flow Sensor	VAF Sensor
After Cooler	Charge Air Cooler[1]	CAC[1]
AI (Air Injection)	Secondary Air Injection[1]	AIR[1]
AIP (Air Injection Pump)	Secondary Air Injection Pump[1]	AIR Pump[1]
AIR (Air Injection Reactor)	Pulsed Secondary Air Injection[1]	PAIR[1]
AIR (Air Injection Reactor)	Secondary Air Injection[1]	AIR[1]
AIRB (Secondary Air Injection Bypass)	Secondary Air Injection Bypass[1]	AIR Bypass[1]
AIRD (Secondary Air Injection Diverter)	Secondary Air Injection Diverter[1]	AIR Diverter[1]
Air Cleaner	Air Cleaner[1]	ACL[1]
Air Cleaner Element	Air Cleaner Element[1]	ACL Element[1]
Air Cleaner Housing	Air Cleaner Housing[1]	ACL Housing[1]
Air Cleaner Housing Cover	Air Cleaner Housing Cover[1]	ACL Housing Cover[1]
Air Conditioning	Air Conditioning	A/C
Air Conditioning Sensor	Air Conditioning Sensor	A/C Sensor
Air Control Valve	Secondary Air Injection Control Valve[1]	AIR Control Valve[1]
Air Flow Meter	Mass Air Flow Sensor[1]	MAF Sensor[1]
Air Flow Meter	Volume Air Flow Sensor[1]	VAF Sensor[1]
Air Intake System	Intake Air System[1]	IA System[1]
Air Flow Sensor	Mass Air Flow Sensor[1]	MAF Sensor[1]
Air Management 1	Secondary Air Injection Bypass[1]	AIR Bypass[1]
Air Management 2	Secondary Air Injection Diverter[1]	AIR Diverter[1]
Air Temperature Sensor	Intake Air Temperature Sensor[1]	IAT Sensor[1]
Air Valve	Idle Air Control Valve[1]	IAC Valve[1]
AIV (Air Injection Valve)	Pulsed Secondary Air Injection[1]	PAIR[1]
ALCL (Assembly Line Communication Link)	Data Link Connector[1]	DLC[1]
Alcohol Concentration Sensor	Flexible Fuel Sensor[1]	FF Sensor[1]
ALDL (Assembly Line Diagnostic Link)	Data Link Connector[1]	DLC[1]
ALT (Alternator)	Generator	GEN
Alternator	Generator	GEN
Ambient Air Temperature	**Ambient Air Temperature**	**AAT**
AM1 (Air Management 1)	Secondary Air Injection Bypass[1]	AIR Bypass[1]
AM2 (Air Management 2)	Secondary Air Injection Diverter[1]	AIR Diverter[1]

TABLE 1—CROSS REFERENCE AND LOOK UP (CONTINUED)

Existing Usage	Acceptable Usage	Acceptable Acronized Usage
APP (Accelerator Pedal Position)	Accelerator Pedal Position[1]	APP[1]
APS (Absolute Pressure Sensor)	Barometric Pressure Sensor[1]	BARO Sensor[1]
ATS (Air Temperature Sensor)	Intake Air Temperature Sensor[1]	IAT Sensor[1]
Automatic Transaxle	Automatic Transaxle[1]	A/T[1]
Automatic Transmission	Automatic Transmission[1]	A/T[1]
B+ (Battery Positive Voltage)	Battery Positive Voltage	B+
Backpressure Transducer	Exhaust Gas Recirculation Backpressure Transducer[1]	EGR Backpressure Transducer[1]
BARO (Barometric Pressure)	Barometric Pressure[1]	BARO[1]
Barometric Pressure Sensor	Barometric Pressure Sensor[1]	BARO Sensor[1]
Battery Positive Voltage	Battery Positive Voltage	B+
BLM (Block Learn Memory)	Long Term Fuel Trim[1]	Long Term FT[1]
BLM (Block Learn Multiplier)	Long Term Fuel Trim[1]	Long Term FT[1]
BLM (Block Learn Matrix)	Long Term Fuel Trim[1]	Long Term FT[1]
Block Learn Integrator	Long Term Fuel Trim[1]	Long Term FT[1]
Block Learn Matrix	Long Term Fuel Trim[1]	Long Term FT[1]
Block Learn Memory	Long Term Fuel Trim[1]	Long Term FT[1]
Block Learn Multiplier	Long Term Fuel Trim[1]	Long Term FT
BP (Barometric Pressure) Sensor	Barometric Pressure Sensor[1]	BARO Sensor[1]
BPP (Brake Pedal Position)	Brake Pedal Position[1]	BPP[1]
Brake Pressure	Brake Pressure	Brake Pressure
Brake Pedal Position	Brake Pedal Position[1]	BPP[1]
C3I (Computer Controlled Coil Ignition)	Electronic Ignition[1]	EI[1]
CAC (Charge Air Cooler)	Charge Air Cooler[1]	CAC[1]
Calculated Load Value	Calculated Load Value	LOAD
Camshaft Position	Camshaft Position[1]	CMP[1]
Camshaft Position Actuator	Camshaft Position Actuator[1]	CMP Actuator[1]
Camshaft Position Controller	Camshaft Position Actuator[1]	CMP Actuator[1]
Camshaft Position Sensor	Camshaft Position Sensor[1]	CMP Sensor[1]
Camshaft Sensor	Camshaft Position Sensor[1]	CMP Sensor[1]
Camshaft Timing Actuator	Camshaft Position Actuator[1]	CMP Actuator[1]
Canister	Canister[1]	Canister[1]
Canister	Evaporative Emission Canister[1]	EVAP Canister[1]
Canister Purge	Evaporative Emission Canister Purge[1]	EVAP Canister Purge[1]
Canister Purge Vacuum Switching Valve	Evaporative Emission Canister Purge Valve[1]	EVAP Canister Purge Valve[1]
Canister Purge Valve	Evaporative Emission Canister Purge Valve[1]	EVAP Canister Purge Valve[1]
Canister Purge VSV (Vacuum Switching Valve)	Evaporative Emission Canister Purge Valve[1]	EVAP Canister Purge Valve[1]
CANP (Canister Purge)	Evaporative Emission Canister Purge[1]	EVAP Canister Purge[1]
CARB (Carburetor)	Carburetor[1]	CARB[1]
Carburetor	Carburetor[1]	CARB[1]
Catalytic Converter Heater	Catalytic Converter Heater	Catalytic Converter Heater
CCC (Converter Clutch Control)	Torque Converter Clutch[1]	TCC[1]
CCO (Converter Clutch Override)	Torque Converter Clutch[1]	TCC[1]
CCS (Coast Clutch Solenoid)	Coast Clutch Solenoid	CCS
CCS (Coast Clutch Solenoid) Valve	Coast Clutch Solenoid Valve	CCS Valve
CCRM (Constant Control Relay Module)	Constant Control RM	Constant Control RM
CDI (Capacitive Discharge Ignition)	Distributor Ignition[1]	DI[1]
CDROM (Compact Disc Read Only Memory)	Compact Disc Read Only Memory[1]	CDROM[1]
CES (Clutch Engage Switch)	Clutch Pedal Position Switch	CPP Switch[1]
Central Multiport Fuel Injection	Central Multiport Fuel Injection[1]	Central MFI[1]
Central Sequential Multiport Fuel Injection	Central Sequential Multiport Fuel Injection	Central SFI
CFI (Continuous Fuel Injection)	Continuous Fuel Injection[1]	CFI[1]
CFI (Central Fuel Injection)	Throttle Body Fuel Injection[1]	TBI[1]
CFV	Critical Flow Venturi	CFV
Charcoal Canister	Evaporative Emission Canister	EVAP Canister[1]
Charge Air Cooler	Charge Air Cooler	CAC[1]
Check Engine	Service Reminder Indicator[1]	SRI[1]
Check Engine	Malfunction Indicator Lamp[1]	MIL[1]
CID (Cylinder Identification) Sensor	Camshaft Position Sensor	CMP Sensor[1]
CIS (Continuous Injection System)	Continuous Fuel Injection[1]	CFI[1]
CIS-E (Continuous Injection System Electronic)	Continuous Fuel Injection[1]	CFI[1]
CKP (Crankshaft Position)	Crankshaft Position[1]	CKP[1]
CKP (Crankshaft Position) Sensor	Crankshaft Position Sensor[1]	CKP Sensor[1]
CL (Closed Loop)	Closed Loop[1]	CL[1]
Closed Bowl Distributor	Distributor Ignition[1]	DI[1]
Closed Throttle Position	Closed Throttle Position[1]	CTP[1]
Closed Throttle Switch	Closed Throttle Position Switch[1]	CTP Switch[1]
CLS (Closed Loop System)	Closed Loop[1]	CL[1]
CLV	Calculated Load Value	LOAD
Clutch Engage Switch	Clutch Pedal Position Switch[1]	CPP Switch[1]
Clutch Pedal Position Switch	Clutch Pedal Position Switch[1]	CPP Switch[1]
Clutch Start Switch	Clutch Pedal Position Switch[1]	CPP Switch[1]
Clutch Switch	Clutch Pedal Position Switch[1]	CPP Switch[1]
CMFI (Central Multiport Fuel Injection)	Central Multiport Fuel Injection[1]	Central MFI[1]
CMP (Camshaft Position)	Camshaft Position[1]	CMP[1]
CMP (Camshaft Position) Sensor	Camshaft Position Sensor[1]	CMP Sensor[1]
COC (Continuous Oxidation Catalyst)	Oxidation Catalytic Converter[1]	OC[1]
Coast Clutch Solenoid	Coast Clutch Solenoid	CCS
Coast Clutch Solenoid Valve	Coast Clutch Solenoid Valve	CCS Valve
Condenser	Distributor Ignition Capacitor[1]	DI Capacitor[1]
Constant Control Relay Module	Relay Module	RM
Constant Volume Sampler	Constant Volume Sampler	CVS

323

TABLE 1—CROSS REFERENCE AND LOOK UP (CONTINUED)

Existing Usage	Acceptable Usage	Acceptable Acronized Usage
Continuous Fuel Injection	Continuous Fuel Injection[1]	CFI[1]
Continuous Fuel Injection System	Continuous Fuel Injection System[1]	CFI System[1]
Continuous Injection System-E	Electronic Continuous Fuel Injection System[1]	Electronic CFI System[1]
Continuous Trap Oxidizer	Continuous Trap Oxidizer[1]	CTOX[1]
Coolant Temperature Sensor	Engine Coolant Temperature Sensor[1]	ECT Sensor[1]
CP (Crankshaft Position)	Crankshaft Position[1]	CKP[1]
CPP (Clutch Pedal Position)	Clutch Pedal Position[1]	CPP[1]
CPP (Clutch Pedal Position) Switch	Clutch Pedal Position Switch	CPP Switch[1]
CPS (Camshaft Position Sensor)	Camshaft Position Sensor[1]	CMP Sensor[1]
CPS (Crankshaft Position Sensor)	Crankshaft Position Sensor[1]	CKP Sensor[1]
Crank Angle Sensor	Crankshaft Position Sensor[1]	CKP Sensor[1]
Crankshaft Position	Crankshaft Position[1]	CKP[1]
Crankshaft Position Sensor	Crankshaft Position Sensor[1]	CKP Sensor[1]
Crankshaft Speed	Engine Speed[1]	RPM[1]
Crankshaft Speed Sensor	Engine Speed Sensor[1]	RPM Sensor[1]
Critical Flow Venturi	**Critical Flow Venturi**	**CFV**
CTO (Continuous Trap Oxidizer)	Continuous Trap Oxidizer[1]	CTOX[1]
CTOX (Continuous Trap Oxidizer)	Continuous Trap Oxidizer[1]	CTOX[1]
CTP (Closed Throttle Position)	Closed Throttle Position[1]	CTP[1]
CTS (Coolant Temperature Sensor)	Engine Coolant Temperature Sensor[1]	ECT Sensor[1]
CTS (Coolant Temperature Switch)	Engine Coolant Temperature Switch[1]	ECT Switch[1]
CVS	**Constant Volume Sampler**	**CVS**
Cylinder ID (Identification) Sensor	Camshaft Position Sensor[1]	CMP Sensor[1]
D-Jetronic	Multiport Fuel Injection[1]	MFI[1]
Data Link Connector	Data Link Connector[1]	DLC[1]
Detonation Sensor	Knock Sensor[1]	KS[1]
DFI (Direct Fuel Injection)	Direct Fuel Injection[1]	DFI[1]
DFI (Digital Fuel Injection)	Multiport Fuel Injection[1]	MFI[1]
DI (Direct Injection)	Direct Fuel Injection[1]	DFI[1]
DI (Distributor Ignition)	Distributor Ignition[1]	DI[1]
DI (Distributor Ignition) Capacitor	Distributor Ignition Capacitor[1]	DI Capacitor[1]
Diagnostic Test Mode	Diagnostic Test Mode[1]	DTM[1]
Diagnostic Trouble Code	Diagnostic Trouble Code[1]	DTC[1]
DID (Direct Injection - Diesel)	Direct Fuel Injection[1]	DFI[1]
Differential Pressure Feedback EGR (Exhaust Gas Recirculation) System	Differential Pressure Feedback Exhaust Gas Recirculation System[1]	Differential Pressure Feedback EGR System[1]
Digital EGR (Exhaust Gas Recirculation)	Exhaust Gas Recirculation[1]	EGR[1]
Direct Fuel Injection	Direct Fuel Injection[1]	DFI[1]
Direct Ignition System	Electronic Ignition System[1]	EI System[1]
DIS (Distributorless Ignition System)	Electronic Ignition System[1]	EI System[1]
DIS (Distributorless Ignition System) Module	Ignition Control Module[1]	ICM[1]
Distance Sensor	Vehicle Speed Sensor[1]	VSS[1]
Distributor Ignition	Distributor Ignition[1]	DI[1]
Distributorless Ignition	Electronic Ignition[1]	EI[1]
DLC (Data Link Connector)	Data Link Connector[1]	DLC[1]
DLI (Distributorless Ignition)	Electronic Ignition[1]	EI[1]
Driver	**Driver**	**Driver**
DS (Detonation Sensor)	Knock Sensor[1]	KS[1]
DTC (Diagnostic Trouble Code)	Diagnostic Trouble Code[1]	DTC[1]
DTM (Diagnostic Test Mode)	Diagnostic Test Mode[1]	DTM[1]
Dual Bed	Three Way + Oxidation Catalytic Converter[1]	TWC+OC[1]
Duty Solenoid for Purge Valve	Evaporative Emission Canister Purge Valve	EVAP Canister Purge Valve[1]
Dynamic Pressure Control	**Dynamic Pressure Control**	**Dynamic PC**
Dynamic Pressure Control Solenoid	**Dynamic Pressure Control Solenoid[1]**	**Dynamic PC Solenoid[1]**
Dynamic Pressure Control Solenoid Valve	**Dynamic Pressure Control Solenoid Valve[1]**	**Dynamic PC Solenoid Valve[1]**
E2PROM (Electrically Erasable Programmable Read Only Memory)	Electrically Erasable Programmable Read Only Memory[1]	EEPROM[1]
Early Fuel Evaporation	Early Fuel Evaporation[1]	EFE[1]
EATX (Electronic Automatic Transmission/Transaxle)	Automatic Transmission[1]	A/T[1]
EC (Engine Control)	Engine Control[1]	EC[1]
ECA (Electronic Control Assembly)	Powertrain Control Module[1]	PCM[1]
ECL (Engine Coolant Level)	Engine Coolant Level	ECL
ECM (Engine Control Module)	Engine Control Module[1]	ECM[1]
ECT (Engine Coolant Temperature)	Engine Coolant Temperature[1]	ECT[1]
ECT (Engine Coolant Temperature) Sender	Engine Coolant Temperature Sensor[1]	ECT Sensor[1]
ECT (Engine Coolant Temperature) Sensor	Engine Coolant Temperature Sensor[1]	ECT Sensor[1]
ECT (Engine Coolant Temperature) Switch	Engine Coolant Temperature Switch[1]	ECT Switch[1]
ECU4 (Electronic Control Unit 4)	Powertrain Control Module[1]	PCM[1]
EDF (Electro-Drive Fan) Control	Fan Control	FC
EDIS (Electronic Distributor Ignition System)	Distributor Ignition System[1]	DI System[1]
EDIS (Electronic Distributorless Ignition System)	Electronic Ignition System[1]	EI System[1]
EDIS (Electronic Distributor Ignition System) Module	Distributor Ignition Control Module[1]	Distributor ICM[1]
EEC (Electronic Engine Control)	Engine Control[1]	EC[1]
EEC (Electronic Engine Control) Processor	Powertrain Control Module[1]	PCM[1]
EECS (Evaporative Emission Control System)	Evaporative Emission System[1]	EVAP System[1]
EEPROM (Electrically Erasable Programmable Read Only Memory)	Electrically Erasable Programmable Read Only Memory[1]	EEPROM[1]
EFE (Early Fuel Evaporation)	Early Fuel Evaporation[1]	EFE[1]
EFI (Electronic Fuel Injection)	Multiport Fuel Injection[1]	MFI[1]
EFI (Electronic Fuel Injection)	Throttle Body Fuel Injection[1]	TBI[1]
EGO (Exhaust Gas Oxygen) Sensor	Oxygen Sensor[1]	O2S[1]

TABLE 1—CROSS REFERENCE AND LOOK UP (CONTINUED)

Existing Usage	Acceptable Usage	Acceptable Acronized Usage
EGOS (Exhaust Gas Oxygen Sensor)	Oxygen Sensor[1]	O2S[1]
EGR (Exhaust Gas Recirculation)	Exhaust Gas Recirculation[1]	EGR[1]
EGR (Exhaust Gas Recirculation) Diagnostic Valve	Exhaust Gas Recirculation Diagnostic Valve[1]	EGR Diagnostic Valve[1]
EGR (Exhaust Gas Recirculation) System	Exhaust Gas Recirculation System[1]	EGR System[1]
EGR (Exhaust Gas Recirculation) Thermal Vacuum Valve	Exhaust Gas Recirculation Thermal Vacuum Valve[1]	EGR TVV[1]
EGR (Exhaust Gas Recirculation) Valve	Exhaust Gas Recirculation Valve[1]	EGR Valve[1]
EGR TVV (Exhaust Gas Recirculation Thermal Vacuum Valve)	Exhaust Gas Recirculation Thermal Vacuum Valve[1]	EGR TVV[1]
EGRT (Exhaust Gas Recirculation Temperature)	Exhaust Gas Recirculation Temperature	EGRT[1]
EGRT (Exhaust Gas Recirculation Temperature) Sensor	Exhaust Gas Recirculation Temperature Sensor[1]	EGRT Sensor[1]
EGRV (Exhaust Gas Recirculation Valve)	Exhaust Gas Recirculation Valve[1]	EGR Valve[1]
EGRVC (Exhaust Gas Recirculation Valve Control)	Exhaust Gas Recirculation Valve Control[1]	EGR Valve Control[1]
EGS (Exhaust Gas Sensor)	Oxygen Sensor[1]	O2S[1]
EI (Electronic Ignition) (With Distributor)	Distributor Ignition[1]	DI[1]
EI (Electronic Ignition) (Without Distributor)	Electronic Ignition[1]	EI[1]
Electrically Erasable Programmable Read Only Memory	Electrically Erasable Programmable Read Only Memory[1]	EEPROM[1]
Electronic Engine Control	Electronic Engine Control[1]	Electronic EC[1]
Electronic Ignition	Electronic Ignition[1]	EI[1]
Electronic Spark Advance	Ignition Control[1]	IC[1]
Electronic Spark Timing	Ignition Control[1]	IC[1]
EM (Engine Modification)	Engine Modification[1]	EM[1]
EMR (Engine Maintenance Reminder)	Service Reminder Indicator[1]	SRI[1]
Engine Control	Engine Control[1]	EC[1]
Engine Coolant Fan Control	Fan Control	FC
Engine Coolant Level	Engine Coolant Level	ECL
Engine Coolant Level Indicator	Engine Coolant Level Indicator	ECL Indicator
Engine Coolant Temperature	Engine Coolant Temperature[1]	ECT[1]
Engine Coolant Temperature Sender	Engine Coolant Temperature Sensor[1]	ECT Sensor[1]
Engine Coolant Temperature Sensor	Engine Coolant Temperature Sensor[1]	ECT Sensor[1]
Engine Coolant Temperature Switch	Engine Coolant Temperature Switch[1]	ECT Switch[1]
Engine Modification	Engine Modification[1]	EM[1]
Engine Oil Pressure Sender	**Engine Oil Pressure** Sensor	EOP Sensor
Engine Oil Pressure Sensor	**Engine Oil Pressure** Sensor	EOP Sensor
Engine Oil Pressure Switch	**Engine Oil Pressure** Switch	EOP Switch
Engine Oil Temperature	**Engine Oil Temperature**	EOT
Engine Speed	Engine Speed[1]	RPM[1]
EOS (Exhaust Oxygen Sensor)	Oxygen Sensor[1]	O2S[1]
EOT (Engine Oil Temperature)	**Engine Oil Temperature**	EOT
EP (Exhaust Pressure)	**Exhaust Pressure**	EP
EPROM (Erasable Programmable Read Only Memory)	Erasable Programmable Read Only Memory[1]	EPROM[1]
Erasable Programmable Read Only Memory	Erasable Programmable Read Only Memory[1]	EPROM[1]
ESA (Electronic Spark Advance)	Ignition Control[1]	IC[1]
ESAC (Electronic Spark Advance Control)	Distributor Ignition[1]	DI[1]
EST (Electronic Spark Timing)	Ignition Control[1]	IC[1]
EVAP (Evaporate Emission) CANP (Canister Purge)	**Evaporative Emission Canister Purge[1]**	**EVAP Canister Purge[1]**
EVAP (Evaporative Emission)	Evaporative Emission[1]	EVAP[1]
EVAP (Evaporative Emission) Canister	Evaporative Emission Canister[1]	EVAP Canister[1]
EVAP (Evaporative Emission) Purge Valve	Evaporative Emission Canister Purge Valve[1]	EVAP Canister Purge Valve[1]
Evaporative Emission	Evaporative Emission[1]	EVAP[1]
Evaporative Emission Canister	Evaporative Emission Canister[1]	EVAP Canister[1]
EVP (Exhaust Gas Recirculation Valve Position) Sensor	Exhaust Gas Recirculation Valve Position Sensor[1]	EGR Valve Position Sensor[1]
EVR (Exhaust Gas Recirculation Vacuum Regulator) Solenoid	Exhaust Gas Recirculation Vacuum Regulator Solenoid[1]	EGR Vacuum Regulator Solenoid[1]
EVRV (Exhaust Gas Recirculation Vacuum Regulator Valve)	Exhaust Gas Recirculation Vacuum Regulator Valve[1]	EGR Vacuum Regulator Valve[1]
Exhaust Gas Recirculation	Exhaust Gas Recirculation[1]	EGR[1]
Exhaust Gas Recirculation Temperature	Exhaust Gas Recirculation Temperature[1]	EGRT[1]
Exhaust Gas Recirculation Temperature Sensor	Exhaust Gas Recirculation Temperature Sensor[1]	EGRT Sensor[1]
Exhaust Gas Recirculation Vacuum Solenoid Valve Regulator	**Exhaust Gas Recirculation Vacuum Regulator Solenoid Valve[1]**	**EGR Vacuum Regulator Solenoid Valve[1]**
Exhaust Gas Recirculation Vacuum Regulator Valve	**Exhaust Gas Recirculation Vacuum Regulator Valve[1]**	**EGR Vacuum Regulator Valve[1]**
Exhaust Gas Recirculation Valve	Exhaust Gas Recirculation Valve[1]	EGR Valve[1]
Exhaust Pressure	**Exhaust Pressure**	EP
4GR (Fourth Gear)	Fourth Gear	4GR
4WD (Four Wheel Drive)	**Full Time Four Wheel Drive**	F4WD
4WD (Four Wheel Drive)	**Selectable Four Wheel Drive**	S4WD
F4WD	**Full Time Four Wheel Drive**	F4WD
Fan Control	Fan Control	FC
Fan Control Module	Fan Control Module	FC Module
Fan Control Relay	Fan Control Relay	FC Relay
Fan Motor Control Relay	Fan Control Relay	FC Relay
Fast Idle Thermo Valve	Idle Air Control Thermal Valve[1]	IAC Thermal Valve[1]
FBC (Feed Back Carburetor)	Carburetor[1]	CARB[1]
FBC (Feed Back Control)	Mixture Control[1]	MC[1]
FC (Fan Control)	Fan Control	FC
FC (Fan Control) Relay	Fan Control Relay	FC Relay

TABLE 1—CROSS REFERENCE AND LOOK UP (CONTINUED)

Existing Usage	Acceptable Usage	Acceptable Acronized Usage
FEEPROM (Flash Electrically Erasable Programmable Read Only Memory)	Flash Electrically Erasable Programmable Read Only Memory[1]	FEEPROM[1]
FEPROM (Flash Erasable Programmable Read Only Memory)	Flash Erasable Programmable Read Only Memory[1]	FEPROM[1]
FF (Flexible Fuel)	Flexible Fuel[1]	FF[1]
FI (Fuel Injection)	Central Multiport Fuel Injection[1]	Central MFI[1]
FI (Fuel Injection)	Continuous Fuel Injection[1]	CFI[1]
FI (Fuel Injection)	Direct Fuel Injection[1]	DFI[1]
FI (Fuel Injection)	Indirect Fuel Injection[1]	IFI[1]
FI (Fuel Injection)	Multiport Fuel Injection[1]	MFI[1]
FI (Fuel Injection)	Sequential Multiport Fuel Injection[1]	SFI[1]
FI (Fuel Injection)	Throttle Body Fuel Injection[1]	TBI[1]
Flame Ionization Detector	**Flame Ionization Detector**	**FID**
Flash EEPROM (Electrically Erasable Programmable Read Only Memory)	Flash Electrically Erasable Programmable Read Only Memory[1]	FEEPROM[1]
Flash EPROM (Erasable Programmable Read Only Memory)	Flash Erasable Programmable Read Only Memory[1]	FEPROM[1]
Flexible Fuel	Flexible Fuel[1]	FF[1]
Flexible Fuel Sensor	Flexible Fuel Sensor[1]	FF Sensor
Fourth Gear	Fourth Gear	4GR
FP (Fuel Pump)	Fuel Pump	FP
FP (Fuel Pump) Module	Fuel Pump Module	FP Module
Freeze Frame	**Freeze Frame**	**See Table 4**
Front Wheel Drive	**Front Wheel Drive**	**FWD**
FRZF (Freeze Frame)	**Freeze Frame**	**See Table 4**
FT (Fuel Trim)	Fuel Trim[1]	FT[1]
Fuel Charging Station	Throttle Body[1]	TB[1]
Fuel Concentration Sensor	Flexible Fuel Sensor[1]	FF Sensor[1]
Fuel Injection	Central Multiport Fuel Injection[1]	Central MFI[1]
Fuel Injection	Continuous Fuel Injection[1]	CFI[1]
Fuel Injection	Direct Fuel Injection[1]	DFI[1]
Fuel Injection	Indirect Fuel Injection[1]	IFI[1]
Fuel Injection	Multiport Fuel Injection[1]	MFI[1]
Fuel Injection	Sequential Multiport Fuel Injection[1]	SFI[1]
Fuel Injection	Throttle Body Fuel Injection[1]	TBI[1]
Fuel Level Sensor	Fuel Level Sensor	Fuel Level Sensor
Fuel Module	Fuel Pump Module	FP Module
Fuel Pressure	Fuel Pressure[1]	Fuel Pressure[1]
Fuel Pressure	**Fuel Pressure**	**See Table 4**
Fuel Pressure Regulator	Fuel Pressure Regulator[1]	Fuel Pressure Regulator[1]
Fuel Pump	Fuel Pump	FP
Fuel Pump Relay	Fuel Pump Relay	FP Relay
Fuel Quality Sensor	Flexible Fuel Sensor[1]	FF Sensor[1]
Fuel Regulator	Fuel Pressure Regulator[1]	Fuel Pressure Regulator[1]
Fuel Sender	Fuel Pump Module	FP Module
Fuel Sensor	Fuel Level Sensor	Fuel Level Sensor
Fuel System Status	**Fuel System Status**	**See Table 4**
FUEL SYS	**Fuel System Status**	**See Table 4**
Fuel Tank Unit	Fuel Pump Module	FP Module
Fuel Trim	Fuel Trim[1]	FT[1]
Full Time Four Wheel Drive	**Full Time Four Wheel Drive**	**F4WD**
Full Throttle	Wide Open Throttle[1]	WOT[1]
FWD	**Front Wheel Drive**	**FWD**
GCM (Governor Control Module)	Governor Control Module	GCM
GEM (Governor Electronic Module)	Governor Control Module	GCM
GEN (Generator)	Generator	GEN
Generator	Generator	GEN
Glow Plug	**Glow Plug[1]**	**Glow Plug[1]**
GND (Ground)	Ground	GND
Governor	Governor	Governor
Governor Control Module	Governor Control Module	GCM
Governor Electronic Module	Governor Control Module	GCM
Gram Per Mile	**Gram Per Mile**	**GPM**
GRD (Ground)	Ground	GND
Ground	Ground	GND
Heated Oxygen Sensor	Heated Oxygen Sensor[1]	HO2S[1]
HEDF (High Electro-Drive Fan) Control	Fan Control	FC
HEGO (Heated Exhaust Gas Oxygen) Sensor	Heated Oxygen Sensor[1]	HO2S[1]
HEI (High Energy Ignition)	Distributor Ignition[1]	DI[1]
High Speed FC (Fan Control) Switch	High Speed Fan Control Switch	High Speed FC Switch
HO2S (Heated Oxygen Sensor)	Heated Oxygen Sensor[1]	HO2S[1]
HOS (Heated Oxygen Sensor)	Heated Oxygen Sensor[1]	HO2S[1]
Hot Wire Anemometer	Mass Air Flow Sensor[1]	MAF Sensor[1]
IA (Intake Air)	Intake Air	IA
IA (Intake Air) Duct	Intake Air Duct	IA Duct
IAC (Idle Air Control)	Idle Air Control[1]	IAC[1]
IAC (Idle Air Control) Thermal Valve	Idle Air Control Thermal Valve[1]	IAC Thermal Valve[1]
IAC (Idle Air Control) Valve	Idle Air Control Valve[1]	IAC Valve[1]
IACV (Idle Air Control Valve)	Idle Air Control Valve[1]	IAC Valve[1]
IAT (Intake Air Temperature)	Intake Air Temperature[1]	IAT[1]
IAT (Intake Air Temperature) Sensor	Intake Air Temperature Sensor[1]	IAT Sensor[1]
IATS (Intake Air Temperature Sensor)	Intake Air Temperature Sensor[1]	IAT Sensor[1]
IC (Ignition Control)	Ignition Control[1]	IC[1]

TABLE 1—CROSS REFERENCE AND LOOK UP (CONTINUED)

Existing Usage	Acceptable Usage	Acceptable Acronized Usage
ICM (Ignition Control Module)	Ignition Control Module[1]	ICM[1]
ICP (Injection Control Pressure)	**Injection Control Pressure[1]**	**ICP[1]**
IDFI (Indirect Fuel Injection)	Indirect Fuel Injection[1]	IFI[1]
IDI (Integrated Direct Ignition)	Electronic Ignition[1]	EI[1]
IDI (Indirect Diesel Injection)	Indirect Fuel Injection[1]	IFI[1]
Idle Air Bypass Control	Idle Air Control[1]	IAC[1]
Idle Air Control	Idle Air Control[1]	IAC[1]
Idle Air Control Valve	Idle Air Control Valve[1]	IAC Valve[1]
Idle Speed Control	Idle Air Control[1]	IAC[1]
Idle Speed Control	Idle Speed Control[1]	ISC[1]
Idle Speed Control Actuator	Idle Speed Control Actuator[1]	ISC Actuator[1]
IFI (Indirect Fuel Injection)	Indirect Fuel Injection[1]	IFI[1]
IFS (Inertia Fuel Shutoff)	Inertia Fuel Shutoff	IFS
Ignition Control	Ignition Control[1]	IC[1]
Ignition Control Module	Ignition Control Module[1]	ICM[1]
I/M (Inspection and Maintenance)	**Inspection and Maintenance**	**I/M**
IMRC (Intake Manifold Runner Control)	**Intake Manifold Runner Control**	**IMRC**
In Tank Module	Fuel Pump Module	FP Module
Indirect Fuel Injection	Indirect Fuel Injection[1]	IFI[1]
Inertia Fuel Shutoff	Inertia Fuel Shutoff	IFS
Inertia Fuel - Shutoff Switch	Inertia Fuel Shutoff Switch	IFS Switch
Inertia Switch	Inertia Fuel Shutoff Switch	IFS Switch
Injection Control Pressure	**Injection Control Pressure[1]**	**ICP[1]**
Input Shaft Speed	**Input Shaft Speed**	**ISS**
INT (Integrator)	Short Term Fuel Trim[1]	Short Term FT[1]
Inspection and Maintenance	**Inspection and Maintenance**	**I/M**
Intake Air	Intake Air	IA
Intake Air Duct	Intake Air Duct	IA Duct
Intake Air Temperature	Intake Air Temperature[1]	IAT[1]
Intake Air Temperature Sensor	Intake Air Temperature Sensor[1]	IAT Sensor[1]
Intake Manifold Absolute Pressure Sensor	Manifold Absolute Pressure Sensor[1]	MAP Sensor[1]
Intake Manifold Runner Control	**Intake Manifold Runner Control**	**IMRC**
Integrated Relay Module	Relay Module	RM
Integrator	Short Term Fuel Trim[1]	Short Term FT[1]
Inter Cooler	Charge Air Cooler[1]	CAC[1]
ISC (Idle Speed Control)	Idle Air Control[1]	IAC[1]
ISC (Idle Speed Control)	Idle Speed Control[1]	ISC[1]
ISC (Idle Speed Control) Actuator	Idle Speed Control Actuator[1]	ISC Actuator[1]
ISC BPA (Idle Speed Control By Pass Air)	Idle Air Control[1]	IAC
ISC (Idle Speed Control) Solenoid Vacuum Valve	Idle Speed Control Solenoid Vacuum Valve[1]	ISC Solenoid Vacuum Valve[1]
ISS (Input Shaft Speed)	**Input Shaft Speed**	**ISS**
K-Jetronic	Continuous Fuel Injection[1]	CFI[1]
KAM (Keep Alive Memory)	Non Volatile Random Access Memory[1]	NVRAM[1]
KAM (Keep Alive Memory)	Keep Alive Random Access Memory[1]	Keep Alive RAM[1]
KE-Jetronic	Continuous Fuel Injection[1]	CFI[1]
KE-Motronic	Continuous Fuel Injection[1]	CFI[1]
Knock Sensor	Knock Sensor[1]	KS[1]
KS (Knock Sensor)	Knock Sensor[1]	KS[1]
L-Jetronic	Multiport Fuel Injection[1]	MFI[1]
Lambda	Oxygen Sensor[1]	O2S[1]
LH-Jetronic	Multiport Fuel Injection[1]	MFI[1]
Light Off Catalyst	Warm Up Three Way Catalytic Converter[1]	WU-TWC[1]
Light Off Catalyst	Warm Up Oxidation Catalytic Converter[1]	WU-OC[1]
Line Pressure Control Solenoid Valve	**Line Pressure Control Solenoid Valve**	**Line PC Solenoid Valve**
LOAD (Calculated Load Value)	**Calculated Load Value**	**LOAD**
Lock Up Relay	Torque converter Clutch Relay[1]	TCC Relay[1]
Long Term FT (Fuel Trim)	Long Term Fuel Trim[1]	Long Term FT[1]
Long Term Fuel Trim	**Long Term FT**	**Long Term FT**
LONG FT	**Long Term Fuel Trim**	**See Table 4**
Low Speed FC (Fan Control) Switch	Low Speed Fan Control Switch	Low Speed FC Switch
LUS (Lock Up Solenoid) Valve	Torque Converter Clutch Solenoid Valve[1]	TCC Solenoid Valve[1]
M/C (Mixture Control)	Mixture Control[1]	MC[1]
MAF (Mass Air Flow)	Mass Air Flow[1]	MAF[1]
MAF (Mass Air Flow) Sensor	Mass Air Flow Sensor[1]	MAF Sensor[1]
Malfunction Indicator Lamp	Malfunction Indicator Lamp[1]	MIL[1]
Manifold Absolute Pressure	Manifold Absolute Pressure[1]	MAP[1]
Manifold Absolute Pressure Sensor	Manifold Absolute Pressure Sensor	MAP Sensor[1]
Manifold Differential Pressure	Manifold Differential Pressure[1]	MDP[1]
Manifold Surface Temperature	Manifold Surface Temperature[1]	MST[1]
Manifold Vacuum Zone	Manifold Vacuum Zone[1]	MVZ[1]
Manual Lever Position Sensor	Transmission Range Sensor[1]	TR Sensor[1]
MAP (Manifold Absolute Pressure)	Manifold Absolute Pressure[1]	MAP[1]
MAP (Manifold Absolute Pressure) Sensor	Manifold Absolute Pressure Sensor[1]	MAP Sensor[1]
MAPS (Manifold Absolute Pressure Sensor)	Manifold Absolute Pressure Sensor[1]	MAP Sensor[1]
Mass Air Flow	Mass Air Flow[1]	MAF[1]
Mass Air Flow Sensor	Mass Air Flow Sensor[1]	MAF Sensor[1]
MAT (Manifold Air Temperature)	Intake Air Temperature[1]	IAT[1]
MATS (Manifold Air Temperature Sensor)	Intake Air Temperature Sensor[1]	IAT Sensor[1]
MC (Mixture Control)	Mixture Control[1]	MC[1]
MCS (Mixture Control Solenoid)	Mixture Control Solenoid[1]	MC Solenoid[1]
MCU (Microprocessor Control Unit)	Powertrain Control Module[1]	PCM[1]
MDP (Manifold Differential Pressure)	Manifold Differential Pressure[1]	MDP[1]

TABLE 1—CROSS REFERENCE AND LOOK UP (CONTINUED)

Existing Usage	Acceptable Usage	Acceptable Acronized Usage
MFI (Multiport Fuel Injection)	Multiport Fuel Injection[1]	MFI[1]
MIL (Malfunction Indicator Lamp)	Malfunction Indicator Lamp[1]	MIL[1]
Mixture Control	Mixture Control[1]	MC[1]
MLPS (Manual Lever Position Sensor)	**Transmission Range Sensor[1]**	TR Sensor[1]
Modes	Diagnostic Test Mode[1]	DTM[1]
Mono-Jetronic	**Throttle Body Injection[1]**	TBI[1]
Mono-Motronic	**Throttle Body Injection[1]**	TBI[1]
Monotronic	Throttle Body Fuel Injection[1]	TBI[1]
Motronic-Pressure	**Multiport Fuel Injection[1]**	MFI[1]
Motronic	Multiport Fuel Injection[1]	MFI[1]
MPI (Multipoint Injection)	Multiport Fuel Injection[1]	MFI[1]
MPI (Multiport Injection)	Multiport Fuel Injection[1]	MFI[1]
MRPS (Manual Range Position Switch)	Transmission Range Switch	TR Switch
MST (Manifold Surface Temperature)	Manifold Surface Temperature[1]	MST[1]
Multiport Fuel Injection	Multiport Fuel Injection[1]	MFI[1]
MVZ (Manifold Vacuum Zone)	Manifold Vacuum Zone[1]	MVZ[1]
NDS (Neutral Drive Switch)	Park/Neutral Position Switch[1]	PNP Switch[1]
Neutral Safety Switch	Park/Neutral Position Switch[1]	PNP Switch[1]
NGS (Neutral Gear Switch)	Park/Neutral Position Switch[1]	PNP Switch[1]
Non Dispersive Infrared	**Non Dispersive Infrared**	NDIR
Non Volatile Random Access Memory	Non Volatile Random Access Memory[1]	NVRAM[1]
NPS (Neutral Position Switch)	Park/Neutral Position Switch[1]	PNP Switch[1]
NVM (Non Volatile Memory)	Non Volatile Random Access Memory[1]	NVRAM[1]
NVRAM (Non Volatile Random Access Memory)	Non Volatile Random Access Memory[1]	NVRAM[1]
O2 (Oxygen) Sensor	Oxygen Sensor[1]	O2S[1]
O2S (Oxygen Sensor)	Oxygen Sensor[1]	O2S[1]
Oxygen Sensor Location	**Oxygen Sensor Location**	See Table 4
OBD (On Board Diagnostic)	On Board Diagnostic[1]	OBD[1]
OBD Status	**OBD Status**	see Table 4
OBD STAT	**OBD Status**	see Table 4
OC (Oxidation Catalyst)	Oxidation Catalytic Converter[1]	OC[1]
Oil Pressure Sender	Engine Oil Pressure Sensor	EOP Sensor
Oil Pressure Sensor	Engine Oil Pressure Sensor	EOP Sensor
Oil Pressure Switch	Engine Oil Pressure Switch	EOP Switch
OL (Open Loop)	Open Loop[1]	OL[1]
On Board Diagnostic	On Board Diagnostic[1]	OBD[1]
Open Loop	Open Loop[1]	OL[1]
OS (Oxygen Sensor)	Oxygen Sensor[1]	O2S[1]
OSS (Output Shaft Speed) Sensor	**Output Shaft Speed Sensor[1]**	OSS Sensor[1]
Output Driver	**Driver**	**Driver**
Output Shaft Speed Sensor	**Output Shaft Speed Sensor[1]**	OSS Sensor[1]
Oxidation Catalytic Converter	Oxidation Catalytic Converter[1]	OC[1]
OXS (Oxygen Sensor) Indicator	Service Reminder Indicator[1]	SRI[1]
Oxygen Sensor	Oxygen Sensor[1]	O2S[1]
P/N (Park/Neutral)	Park/Neutral Position[1]	PNP[1]
P/S (Power Steering) Pressure Switch	Power Steering Pressure Switch	PSP Switch
P- (Pressure) Sensor	Manifold Absolute Pressure Sensor[1]	MAP Sensor[1]
PAIR (Pulsed Secondary Air Injection)	Pulsed Secondary Air Injection[1]	PAIR[1]
Parameter Identification	**Parameter Identification**	PID
Parameter Identification Supported	**Parameter Identification Supported**	See Table 4
Park/Neutral Position	Park/Neutral Position[1]	PNP[1]
PC (Pressure Control) Solenoid Valve	**Pressure Control Solenoid Valve[1]**	PC Solenoid Valve[1]
PCM (Powertrain Control Module)	Powertrain Control Module[1]	PCM[1]
PCV (Positive Crankcase Ventilation)	Positive Crankcase Ventilation[1]	PCV[1]
PCV (Positive Crankcase Ventilation) Valve	Positive Crankcase Ventilation Valve[1]	PCV Valve[1]
Percent Alcohol Sensor	Flexible Fuel Sensor[1]	FF Sensor[1]
Periodic Trap Oxidizer	Periodic Trap Oxidizer[1]	PTOX[1]
PFE (Pressure Feedback Exhaust Gas Recirculation Sensor	**Feedback Pressure Exhaust Gas Recirculation Sensor[1]**	**Feedback Pressure EGR Sensor[1]**
PFI (Port Fuel Injection)	Multiport Fuel Injection[1]	MFI[1]
PG (Pulse Generator)	Vehicle Speed Sensor[1]	VSS[1]
PGM-FI (Programmed Fuel Injection)	Multiport Fuel Injection[1]	MFI[1]
PID (Parameter Identification)	**Parameter Identification**	PID
PID SUP	**Parameter Identification Supported**	See Table 4
PIP (Position Indicator Pulse)	Crankshaft Position[1]	CKP[1]
PNP (Park/Neutral Position)	Park/Neutral Position[1]	PNP[1]
Positive Crankcase Ventilation	Positive Crankcase Ventilation[1]	PCV[1]
Positive Crankcase Ventilation Valve	Positive Crankcase Ventilation Valve[1]	PCV Valve[1]
Power Steering Pressure	Power Steering Pressure	PSP
Power Steering Pressure Switch	Power Steering Pressure Switch	PSP Switch
Powertrain Control Module	Powertrain Control Module[1]	PCM[1]
Pressure Control Solenoid Valve	**Pressure Control Solenoid Valve[1]**	PC Solenoid Valve[1]
Pressure Feedback EGR (Exhaust Gas Recirculation)	Feedback Pressure Exhaust Gas Recirculation[1]	Feedback Pressure EGR[1]
Pressure Sensor	Manifold Absolute Pressure Sensor[1]	MAP Sensor[1]
Pressure Feedback EGR (Exhaust Gas Recirculation) System	**Feedback Pressure Exhaust Gas Recirculation System[1]**	**Feedback Pressure EGR System[1]**
Pressure Transducer EGR (Exhaust Gas Recirculation) System	Pressure Transducer Exhaust Gas Recirculation System[1]	Pressure Transducer EGR System[1]
PRNDL (Park- Reverse- Neutral- Drive- Low)	Transmission Range	TR
Programmable Read Only Memory	Programmable Read Only Memory[1]	PROM[1]
PROM (Programmable Read Only Memory)	Programmable Read Only Memory[1]	PROM[1]
PSP (Power Steering Pressure)	Power Steering Pressure	PSP

TABLE 1—CROSS REFERENCE AND LOOK UP (CONTINUED)

Existing Usage	Acceptable Usage	Acceptable Acronized Usage
PSP (Power Steering Pressure) Switch	Power Steering Pressure Switch	PSP Switch
PSPS (Power Steering Pressure Switch)	Power Steering Pressure Switch	PSP Switch
PTOX (Periodic Trap Oxidizer)	Periodic Trap Oxidizer[1]	PTOX[1]
Pulsair	Pulsed Secondary Air Injection[1]	PAIR[1]
Pulsed Secondary Air Injection	Pulsed Secondary Air Injection[1]	PAIR[1]
Pulse Width Modulation	**Pulse Width Modulation**	**PWM**
PWM	**Pulse Width Modulation**	**PWM**
QDM (Quad Driver Module)	**Driver**	**Driver**
Quad Driver Module	**Driver**	**Driver**
Radiator Fan Control	Fan Control	FC
Radiator Fan Relay	Fan Control Relay	FC Relay
RAM (Random Access Memory)	Random Access Memory[1]	RAM[1]
Random Access Memory	Random Access Memory[1]	RAM[1]
Read Only Memory	Read Only Memory[1]	ROM[1]
Rear Wheel Drive	**Rear Wheel Drive**	**RWD**
Recirculated Exhaust Gas Temperature Sensor	Exhaust Gas Recirculation Temperature Sensor	EGRT Sensor[1]
Reed Valve	Pulsed Secondary Air Injection Valve[1]	PAIR Valve[1]
REGTS (Recirculated Exhaust Gas Temperature Sensor)	Exhaust Gas Recirculation Temperature Sensor[1]	EGRT Sensor[1]
Relay Module	Relay Module	RM
Remote Mount TFI (Thick Film Ignition)	Distributor Ignition[1]	DI[1]
Revolutions per Minute	Engine Speed[1]	RPM[1]
RM (Relay Module)	Relay Module	RM
ROM (Read Only Memory)	Read Only Memory[1]	ROM[1]
RPM (Revolutions per Minute)	Engine Speed[1]	RPM[1]
RWD	**Rear Wheel Drive**	**RWD**
S4WD	**Selectable Four Wheel Drive**	**S4WD**
SABV (Secondary Air Bypass Valve)	Secondary Air Injection Bypass Valve[1]	AIR Bypass Valve[1]
SACV (Secondary Air Check Valve)	Secondary Air Injection Control Valve[1]	AIR Control Valve[1]
SASV (Secondary Air Switching Valve)	Secondary Air Injection Switching Valve[1]	AIR Switching Valve[1]
SBEC (Single Board Engine Control)	Powertrain Control Module[1]	PCM[1]
SBS (Supercharger Bypass Solenoid)	Supercharger Bypass Solenoid[1]	SCB Solenoid[1]
SC (Supercharger)	Supercharger[1]	SC[1]
Scan Tool	Scan Tool[1]	ST[1]
SCB (Supercharger Bypass)	Supercharger Bypass[1]	SCB[1]
Secondary Air Bypass Valve	Secondary Air Injection Bypass Valve[1]	AIR Bypass Valve[1]
Secondary Air Check Valve	Secondary Air Injection Check Valve[1]	AIR Check Valve[1]
Secondary Air Injection	Secondary Air Injection[1]	AIR[1]
Secondary Air Injection Bypass	Secondary Air Injection Bypass[1]	AIR Bypass[1]
Secondary Air Injection Diverter	Secondary Air Injection Diverter[1]	AIR Diverter[1]
Secondary Air Switching Valve	Secondary Air Injection Switching Valve[1]	AIR Switching Valve[1]
Selectable Four Wheel Drive	**Selectable Four Wheel Drive**	**S4WD**
SEFI (Sequential Electronic Fuel Injection)	Sequential Multiport Fuel Injection[1]	SFI[1]
Self Test	On Board Diagnostic[1]	OBD[1]
Self Test Codes	Diagnostic Trouble Code[1]	DTC[1]
Self Test Connector	Data Link Connector[1]	DLC[1]
Sequential Multiport Fuel Injection	Sequential Multiport Fuel Injection[1]	SFI[1]
Service Engine Soon	Service Reminder Indicator[1]	SRI[1]
Service Engine Soon	Malfunction Indicator Lamp[1]	MIL[1]
Service Reminder Indicator	Service Reminder Indicator[1]	SRI[1]
SFI (Sequential Fuel Injection)	Sequential Multiport Fuel Injection[1]	SFI[1]
Shift Solenoid	**Shift Solenoid**[1]	**SS**[1]
Shift Solenoid Valve	**Shift Solenoid Valve**[1]	**SS Valve**[1]
Short Term FT (Fuel Trim)	Short Term Fuel Trim[1]	Short Term FT[1]
Short Term Fuel Trim	**Short Term Fuel Trim**[1]	**Short Term FT**[1]
SHRT FT	Short Term Fuel Trim[1]	See Table 4
SLP (Selection Lever Position)	Transmission Range	TR
SMEC (Single Module Engine Control)	Powertrain Control Module[1]	PCM[1]
Smoke Puff Limiter	Smoke Puff Limiter[1]	SPL[1]
SPARK ADV	**Spark Advance**	See Table 4
Spark Advance	**Spark Advance**	See Table 4
Spark Plug	**Spark Plug**[1]	**Spark Plug**[1]
SPI (Single Point Injection)	Throttle Body Fuel Injection[1]	TBI[1]
SPL (Smoke Puff Limiter)	Smoke Puff Limiter[1]	SPL[1]
SS (Shift Solenoid)	**Shift Solenoid**[1]	**SS**[1]
SRI (Service Reminder Indicator)	Service Reminder Indicator[1]	SRI[1]
SRT (System Readiness Test)	System Readiness Test[1]	SRT[1]
ST (Scan Tool)	Scan Tool[1]	ST[1]
Supercharger	Supercharger[1]	SC[1]
Supercharger Bypass	Supercharger Bypass[1]	SCB[1]
Sync Pickup	Camshaft Position[1]	CMP[1]
System Readiness Test	System Readiness Test[1]	SRT[1]
3-2TS (3-2 Timing Solenoid)	**3-2 Timing Solenoid**	**3-2TS**
3-2TS Valve (3-2 Timing Solenoid)Valve	**3-2 Timing Solenoid Valve**	**3-2TS Valve**
3-2 Timing Solenoid	**3-2 Timing Solenoid**	**3-2TS**
3-2 Timing Solenoid Valve	**3-2 Timing Solenoid Valve**	**3-2TS Valve**
3GR (Third Gear)	Third Gear	3GR
TAB (Thermactor Air Bypass)	Secondary Air Injection Bypass[1]	AIR Bypass[1]
TAC (Throttle Actuator Control)	**Throttle Actuator Control**	**TAC**
TAC (Throttle Actuator Control) Module	**Throttle Actuator Control Module**[1]	**TAC Module**[1]
TAD (Thermactor Air Diverter)	Secondary Air Injection Diverter[1]	AIR Diverter[1]
TB (Throttle Body)	Throttle Body[1]	TB[1]
TBI (Throttle Body Fuel Injection)	Throttle Body Fuel Injection[1]	TBI[1]

TABLE 1—CROSS REFERENCE AND LOOK UP (CONTINUED)

Existing Usage	Acceptable Usage	Acceptable Acronized Usage
TBT (Throttle Body Temperature)	Intake Air Temperature[1]	IAT[1]
TC (Turbocharger)	Turbocharger[1]	TC[1]
TC (Turbocharger) Wastegate	**Turbocharger Wastegate[1]**	**TC Wastegate[1]**
TC (Turbocharger) Wastegate Regulating Valve	**Turbocharger Wastegate Regulating Valve[1]**	**TC Wastegate Regulating Valve[1]**
TCC (Torque Converter Clutch)	Torque Converter Clutch[1]	TCC[1]
TCC (Torque Converter Clutch) Relay	Torque Converter Clutch Relay[1]	TCC Relay[1]
TCC (Torque Converter Clutch) Solenoid	**Torque Converter Clutch Solenoid[1]**	**TCC Solenoid[1]**
TCC (Torque Converter Clutch) Solenoid Valve	**Torque Converter Clutch Solenoid Valve[1]**	**TCC Solenoid Valve[1]**
TCM (Transmission Control Module)	Transmission Control Module	TCM
TCCP (Torque Converter Clutch Pressure)	**Torque Converter Clutch Pressure**	**TCCP**
TFI (Thick Film Ignition)	Distributor Ignition[1]	DI[1]
TFI (Thick Film Ignition) Module	Ignition Control Module[1]	ICM[1]
TFP (Transmission Fluid Pressure)	**Transmission Fluid Pressure**	**TFP**
TFT (Transmission Fluid Temperature) Sensor	**Transmission Fluid Temperature Sensor**	**TFT Sensor**
Thermac	Secondary Air Injection[1]	AIR[1]
Thermac Air Cleaner	Air Cleaner[1]	ACL[1]
Thermactor	Secondary Air Injection[1]	AIR[1]
Thermactor Air Bypass	Secondary Air Injection Bypass[1]	AIR Bypass[1]
Thermactor Air Diverter	Secondary Air Injection Diverter[1]	AIR Diverter[1]
Thermactor II	Pulsed Secondary Air Injection[1]	PAIR[1]
Thermal Vacuum Switch	Thermal Vacuum Valve[1]	TVV[1]
Thermal Vacuum Valve	Thermal Vacuum Valve[1]	TVV[1]
Third Gear	Third Gear	3GR
Three Way + Oxidation Catalytic Converter	Three Way + Oxidation Catalytic Converter[1]	TWC+OC[1]
Three Way Catalytic Converter	Three Way Catalytic Converter[1]	TWC[1]
Throttle Actuator Control	**Throttle Actuator Control**	**TAC**
Throttle Actuator Control Module	**Throttle Actuator Control Module**	**TAC Module**
Throttle Body	Throttle Body[1]	TB[1]
Throttle Body Fuel Injection	Throttle Body Fuel Injection[1]	TBI[1]
Throttle Opener	Idle Speed Control[1]	ISC[1]
Throttle Opener Vacuum Switching Valve	Idle Speed Control Solenoid Vacuum Valve[1]	ISC Solenoid Vacuum Valve[1]
Throttle Opener VSV (Vacuum Switching Valve)	Idle Speed Control Solenoid Vacuum Valve[1]	ISC Solenoid Vacuum Valve[1]
Throttle Position	Throttle Position[1]	TP
Throttle Position Sensor	Throttle Position Sensor[1]	TP Sensor[1]
Throttle Position Switch	Throttle Position Switch[1]	TP Switch[1]
Throttle Potentiometer	Throttle Position Sensor[1]	TP Sensor[1]
TOC (Trap Oxidizer - Continuous)	Continuous Trap Oxidizer[1]	CTOX[1]
TOP (Trap Oxidizer - Periodic)	Periodic Trap Oxidizer[1]	PTOX[1]
Torque Converter Clutch	Torque Converter Clutch[1]	TCC[1]
Torque Converter Clutch Pressure	**Torque Converter Clutch Pressure**	**TCCP**
Torque Converter Clutch Relay	Torque Converter Clutch Relay[1]	TCC Relay[1]
Torque Converter Clutch Solenoid	**Torque Converter Clutch Solenoid[1]**	**TCC Solenoid[1]**
Torque Converter Clutch Solenoid Valve	**Torque Converter Clutch Solenoid Valve[1]**	**TCC Solenoid Valve[1]**
TP (Throttle Position)	Throttle Position[1]	TP[1]
TP (Throttle Position) Sensor	Throttle Position Sensor[1]	TP Sensor[1]
TP (Throttle Position) Switch	Throttle Position Switch[1]	TP Switch[1]
TPI (Tuned Port Injection)	Multiport Fuel Injection[1]	MFI[1]
TPNP (Transmission Park Neutral Position)	**Park/Neutral Position[1]**	**PNP[1]**
TPS (Throttle Position Sensor)	Throttle Position Sensor[1]	TP Sensor[1]
TPS (Throttle Position Switch)	Throttle Position Switch[1]	TP Switch[1]
TR (Transmission Range)	Transmission Range	TR
Track Road Load Horsepower	**Track Road Load Horsepower**	**TRLHP**
Transmission Control Module	Transmission Control Module	TCM
Transmission Fluid Pressure	**Transmission Fluid Pressure**	**TFP**
Transmission Fluid Temperature Sensor	**Transmission Fluid Temperature Sensor**	**TFT Sensor**
Transmission Park Neutral Position	**Park/Neutral Position[1]**	**PNP[1]**
Transmission Position Switch	Transmission Range Switch	TR Switch
Transmission Range Selection	Transmission Range	TR
Transmission Range Sensor	**Transmission Range Sensor**	**TR Sensor**
TRS (Transmission Range Selection)	Transmission Range	TR
TRSS (Transmission Range Selection Switch)	Transmission Range Switch	TR Switch
TSS (Turbine Shaft Speed) Sensor	**Turbine Shaft Speed Sensor[1]**	**TSS Sensor[1]**
Tuned Port Injection	Multiport Fuel Injection[1]	MFI[1]
Turbine Shaft Speed Sensor	**Turbine Shaft Speed Sensor[1]**	**TSS Sensor[1]**
Turbo (Turbocharger)	Turbocharger[1]	TC[1]
Turbocharger	Turbocharger[1]	TC[1]
Turbocharger Wastegate	**Turbocharger Wastegate[1]**	**TC Wastegate[1]**
Turbocharger Wastegate Regulating Valve	**Turbocharger Wastegate Regulating Valve[1]**	**TC Wastegate Regulating Valve[1]**
TVS (Thermal Vacuum Switch)	Thermal Vacuum Valve[1]	TVV[1]
TVV (Thermal Vacuum Valve)	Thermal Vacuum Valve[1]	TVV[1]
TWC (Three Way Catalytic Converter)	Three Way Catalytic Converter[1]	TWC[1]
TWC + OC (Three Way + Oxidation Catalytic Converter)	Three Way + Oxidation Catalytic Converter[1]	TWC+OC[1]
VAC (Vacuum) Sensor	Manifold Differential Pressure Sensor[1]	MDP Sensor[1]
Vacuum Switches	Manifold Vacuum Zone Switch	MVZ Switch[1]
VAF (Volume Air Flow)	Volume Air Flow[1]	VAF[1]
Valve Position EGR (Exhaust Gas Recirculation) System	**Valve Position Exhaust Gas Recirculation System[1]**	**Valve Position EGR System[1]**
Vane Air Flow	Volume Air Flow[1]	VAF[1]
Variable Control Relay Module	**Variable Control Relay Module**	**VCRM**
Variable Fuel Sensor	Flexible Fuel Sensor	FF Sensor[1]
VAT (Vane Air Temperature)	Intake Air Temperature[1]	IAT[1]
VCC (Viscous Converter Clutch)	Torque Converter Clutch[1]	TCC[1]

TABLE 1—CROSS REFERENCE AND LOOK UP (CONTINUED)

Existing Usage	Acceptable Usage	Acceptable Acronized Usage
VCM	**Vehicle Control Module**	**VCM**
VCRM	**Variable Control Relay Module**	**VCRM**
Vehicle Control Module	**Vehicle Control Module**	**VCM**
Vehicle Identification Number	**Vehicle Identification Number**	**VIN**
Vehicle Speed Sensor	Vehicle Speed Sensor[1]	VSS[1]
VIN (Vehicle Identification Number)	**Vehicle Identification Number**	**VIN**
VIP (Vehicle In Process) Connector	Data Link Connector[1]	DLC[1]
Viscous Converter Clutch	Torque Converter Clutch[1]	TCC[1]
Voltage Regulator	Voltage Regulator	VR
Volume Air Flow	Volume Air Flow[1]	VAF[1]
VR (Voltage Regulator)	Voltage Regulator	VR
VSS (Vehicle Speed Sensor)	Vehicle Speed Sensor[1]	VSS[1]
VSV (Vacuum Solenoid Valve) (Canister)	Evaporative Emission Canister Purge Valve[1]	EVAP Canister Purge Valve[1]
VSV (Vacuum Solenoid Valve) (EVAP)	Evaporative Emission Canister Purge Valve[1]	EVAP Canister Purge Valve[1]
VSV (Vacuum Solenoid Valve) (Throttle)	Idle Speed Control Solenoid Vacuum Valve[1]	ISC Solenoid Vacuum Valve[1]
Warm Up Oxidation Catalytic Converter	Warm Up Oxidation Catalytic Converter[1]	WU-OC[1]
Warm Up Three Way Catalytic Converter	Warm Up Three Way Catalytic Converter[1]	WU-OC[1]
Wide Open Throttle	Wide Open Throttle[1]	WOT[1]
WOT (Wide Open Throttle)	Wide Open Throttle[1]	WOT[1]
WOTS (Wide Open Throttle Switch)	Wide Open Throttle Switch[1]	WOT Switch[1]
WU-OC (Warm Up Oxidation Catalytic Converter)	Warm Up Oxidation Catalytic Converter[1]	WU-OC[1]
WU-TWC (Warm Up Three Way Catalytic Converter)	Warm Up Three Way Catalytic Converter[1]	WU-TWC[1]

Recommended Terms and Recommended Acronyms See Table 2
[1] Emission-Related Term
Bold indicates new/revised entry

6. Recommended Terms—Table 2 is an alphabetical listing of modifiers to be used in combination with base words

TABLE 2—RECOMMENDED TERMS

Recommended Term	Acronym	Definition
3-2 Timing Solenoid	**3-2TS**	**A device that controls the "third to second" timing valve.**
Accelerator Pedal	AP[2]	See Glossary Entry "ACCELERATOR PEDAL."
Accelerator Pedal Position[1]	**APP**	**See Glossary Entry "ACCELERATOR PEDAL."**
Air Cleaner[1]	ACL	See Glossary Entry "CLEANER."
Air Conditioning	A/C	See Glossary Entry "AIR CONDITIONING."
Ambient Air Temperature	**AAT**	**Air Temperature Surrounding the vehicle.**
Automatic Transaxle	A/T	See Glossary Entry "TRANSAXLE."
Automatic Transmission	A/T	See Glossary Entry "TRANSMISSION."
Barometric Pressure[1]	BARO[2]	See Glossary Entry "PRESSURE."
Battery Positive Voltage	B+[2]	See Glossary Entry "BATTERY."
Brake Pedal Position[1]	**BPP**	**See Glossary Entry "BRAKE."**
Brake Pressure	---	**Positive Pressure in the brake system.**
Calculated Load Value	**LOAD**	**Percent of engine capacity being used.**
Camshaft Position[1]	CMP	See Glossary Entry "CAMSHAFT."
Canister[1]	---	See Glossary Entry "CANISTER."
Carburetor[1]	CARB[2]	See Glossary Entry "CARBURETOR."
Catalytic Converter Heater[1]	---	**A device to quickly heat a Catalytic Converter.**
Charge Air Cooler[1]	CAC[2]	A device which lowers the temperature of the pressurized intake air.
Closed Loop[1]	CL	See Glossary Entry "CLOSED LOOP."
Closed Throttle Position[1]	CTP	See Glossary Entry "THROTTLE."
Clutch Pedal Position[1]	CPP	See Glossary Entry "CLUTCH."
Coast Clutch Solenoid	**CCS**	**A device that controls the Coast Clutch Valve.**
Constant Volume Sampler	**CVS**	**An exhaust sampling system which flows a constant amount of ambient air diluted exhaust.**
Continuous Fuel Injection[1]	CFI	A fuel injection system with the injector flow controlled by fuel pressure.
Continuous Trap Oxidizer[1]	CTOX	A system for lowering diesel engine particulate emissions by collecting exhaust particulates and continuously burning them through oxidation.
Crankshaft Position[1]	CKP	See Glossary Entry "CRANKSHAFT."
Critical Flow Venturi	**CFV**	**An air flow regulating device which uses a sonic wave to limit air flow**
Data Link Connector[1]	DLC[2]	Connector providing access and/or control of the vehicle information, operating conditions, and diagnostic information.
Diagnostic Test Mode[1]	DTM	A level of diagnostic capability in an On-Board Diagnostic (OBD) system. This may include different functional states to observe signals, a base level to read diagnostic trouble codes, a monitor level which includes information on signal levels, bi-directional control with on/off board aids, and the ability to interface with remote diagnosis.
Diagnostic Trouble Code[1]	DTC	An alpha/numeric identifier for a fault condition identified by the On-Board Diagnostic System.
Direct Fuel Injection[1]	DFI	Fuel injection system that supplies fuel directly into the combustion chamber.
Distributor Ignition[1]	DI	A system in which the ignition coil secondary circuit is switched by a distributor in proper sequence to various spark plugs.
Driver	-----	**See Glossary Entry "Driver."**
Early Fuel Evaporation[1]	EFE	Enhancing air/fuel vaporization during engine warm up.
EGR Temperature[1]	EGRT	Sensing EGR function based on temperature change. Primarily in systems with mechanical flow control devices.
Electrically Erasable Programmable Read	EEPROM Only Memory[1]	An electronic device named electrically erasable programmable read only memory.
Electronic Ignition[1]	EI	A system in which the ignition coil secondary circuit is dedicated to specific spark plugs without the use of a distributor.

TABLE 2—RECOMMENDED TERMS (CONTINUED)

Recommended Term	Acronym	Definition
Engine Control[1]	EC	See Glossary Entries "ENGINE" and "CONTROL."
Engine Control Module[1]	ECM[2]	See Glossary Entries "ENGINE," "CONTROL" and "MODULE."
Engine Coolant Level	ECL	See Glossary Entries "ENGINE," "COOLANT" and "LEVEL."
Engine Coolant Temperature[1]	ECT	See Glossary Entries "ENGINE" and "COOLANT."
Engine Modification[1]	EM	A method of lowering engine emissions through changes in basic engine construction or in fuel and spark calibration.
Engine Oil Pressure	**EOP**	**Positive pressure in the engine's lubrication system.**
Engine Oil Temperature	**EOT**	**Temperature of engine lubricating oil.**
Engine Speed[1]	RPM[2]	See Glossary Entries "ENGINE" and "SPEED."
Erasable Programmable Read Only Memory[1]	EPROM	An electronic device named erasable programmable read only memory.
Evaporative Emission[1]	EVAP[2]	A system used to prevent fuel vapor from escaping into the atmosphere. Typically includes a charcoal canister to store fuel vapors.
Exhaust Gas Recirculation[1]	EGR	Reducing NOx emissions levels by adding exhaust gas to the incoming air/fuel mixture.
Exhaust Pressure	**EP**	**See glossary Entries "EXHAUST" and "PRESSURE."**
Fan Control	FC	See Glossary Entries "FAN" and "CONTROL."
Flame Ionization Detector	**FID**	**A device used to measure hydrocarbon concentrations.**
Flash Electrically Erasable Programmable Read Only Memory[1]	FEEPROM	An electronic device named flash electrically erasable programmable read only memory.
Flash Erasable Programmable Read Only Memory[1]	FEPROM	An electronic device named flash erasable programmable read only memory.
Flexible Fuel[1]	FF	A system capable of using a variety of fuels for vehicle operation.
Fourth Gear	4GR[2]	Identifies the gear in which the transmission is operating in at a particular moment (e.g., the Transmission Range (TR) switch may indicate that "drive" was selected, but the transmission is operating in 4th gear as indicated by 4GR switch).
Freeze Frame	**---[3]**	**A block of memory containing the vehicle operating conditions for a specific time.**
Front Wheel Drive	**FWD**	**A driveline configuration that transmits motive power only through the front axle.**
Fuel Level Sensor	---	See Glossary Entries "FUEL" and "SENSOR."
Fuel Pressure	---	See Glossary Entries "FUEL" and "PRESSURE."
Fuel Pump	FP[2]	See Glossary Entries "FUEL" and "PUMP."
Fuel System Status	**---[3]**	**Information describing operation of the fuel control. (i.e. Open Loop/Closed loop)**
Fuel Trim[1]	FT	A fuel correction term.
Full Time Four Wheel Drive	**F4WD**	**A driveline configuration that transmit motive power to both axles. The system does not allow the driver to select between one axle and two axle operation.**
Generator	GEN[2]	See Glossary Entry "GENERATOR."
Glow Plug	**---**	**See Glossary Entry "GLOW PLUG."**
Governor	---	See Glossary Entry "GOVERNOR."
Governor Control Module	GCM[2]	See Glossary Entries "GOVERNOR," "CONTROL" and "MODULE."
Gram Per Mile	**GPM**	**Grams of pollutant emitted per mile.**
Ground	GND	See Glossary Entry "GROUND."
Heated Oxygen Sensor[1]	HO2S[2]	An oxygen sensor (02S) that is electrically heated.
Idle Air Control[1]	IAC	Electrical or mechanical control of throttle bypass air.
Idle Speed Control[1]	ISC	Electronic control of minimum throttle position.
Ignition Control[1]	IC	See Glossary Entries "IGNITION" and "CONTROL."
Ignition Control Module[1]	ICM[2]	See Glossary Entries "IGNITION," "CONTROL" and "MODULE."
Indirect Fuel Injection[1]	IFI	An injection system that supplies fuel into a combustion pre-chamber (Diesel).
Inertia Fuel Shutoff	IFS	An inertia system that shuts off the fuel delivery system when activated by predetermined force limits.
Injection Control Pressure[1]	**ICP**	**Injection control pressure for hydraulically actuated injectors.**
Input Shaft Speed	**ISS**	**See Glossary Entries "Input Shaft' and "Speed".**
Inspection and Maintenance	**I/M[2]**	**An emission control program.**
Intake Air[1]	IA	See Glossary Entry "INTAKE AIR."
Intake Air Temperature[1]	IAT	See Glossary Entry "INTAKE AIR."
Intake Manifold Runner Control	**IMRC**	**Controls air flow through runners in the intake manifold.**
Knock Sensor[1]	KS[2]	See Glossary Entries "KNOCK" and "SENSOR."
Malfunction Indicator Lamp[1]	MIL[2]	A required on-board indicator to alert the driver of an emission related malfunction.
Manifold Absolute Pressure[1]	MAP	See Glossary Entries "MANIFOLD" and "PRESSURE."
Manifold Differential Pressure[1]	MDP	See Glossary Entries "MANIFOLD" and "PRESSURE."
Manifold Surface Temperature[1]	MST	See Glossary Entry "MANIFOLD."
Manifold Vacuum Zone[1]	MVZ	See Glossary Entries "MANIFOLD" and "VACUUM."
Mass Air Flow[1]	MAF	A system which provides information on the mass flow rate of the intake air to the engine.
Mixture Control[1]	MC	A device which regulates bleed air, fuel, or both, on carbureted vehicles.
Multiport Fuel Injection[1]	MFI	A fuel-delivery system in which each cylinder is individually fueled.
Non Dispersive Infra Red	**NDIR**	**An Emission measuring technique typically used for measuring carbon monoxide and carbon dioxide concentrations.**
Non Volatile Random Access Memory[1]	NVRAM	An electronic device named non-volatile random access memory.
On Board Diagnostic[1]	OBD	A system that monitors some or all computer input and control signals. Signal(s) outside of the predetermined limits imply a fault in the system or in a related system.
Open Loop[1]	OL	See Glossary Entry "OPEN LOOP."
Output Shaft Speed[1]	**OSS**	**See Glossary Entry "OUTPUT SHAFT " and "SPEED."**
Oxidation Catalytic Converter[1]	OC	A catalytic converter system that reduces levels of HC and CO.
Oxygen Sensor[1]	O2S[2]	A sensor which detects oxygen (O2) content in the exhaust gases.
Park/Neutral Position[1]	PNP	See Glossary Entry "PARK/NEUTRAL."
Parameter Identification	**PID**	**Identifies an address in memory which contains vehicle operating information.**

TABLE 2—RECOMMENDED TERMS (CONTINUED)

Recommended Term	Acronym	Definition
Periodic Trap Oxidizer[1]	PTOX	A system for lowering diesel engine particulate emissions by collecting exhaust particulates and periodically burning them through oxidation.
Positive Crankcase Ventilation[1]	PCV	Positive ventilation of crankcase emissions.
Power Steering Pressure	PSP	See Glossary Entry "POWER STEERING."
Powertrain Control Module[1]	PCM[2]	See Glossary Entries "POWERTRAIN," "CONTROL" and "MODULE."
Pressure Control[1]	**PC**	**See Glossary Entries "PRESSURE" and "CONTROL."**
Programmable Read Only Memory[1]	PROM	An electronic device named programmable (by the manufacturer) read only memory.
Pulsed Secondary Air Injection[1]	PAIR[2]	A pulse-driven system for providing secondary air without an air pump by using the engine exhaust system pressure fluctuations or pulses.
Pulse Width Modulation	**PWM**	**A rectangular wave with a variable on-off time.**
Random Access Memory[1]	RAM	An electronic device named random access memory.
Read Only Memory[1]	ROM	An electronic device named read only memory.
Rear Wheel Drive	**RWD**	**A driveline configuration that transmit motive power only through the rear axle.**
Relay Module	RM[2]	See Glossary Entries "RELAY" and "MODULE."
Scan Tool[1]	ST[2]	See Glossary Entry "SCAN TOOL."
Secondary Air Injection[1]	AIR[2]	A pump-driven system for providing secondary air.
Selectable Four Wheel Drive	**S4WD**	**A driveline configuration that allows the driver to select the option to transmit motive power either to both axles or only to one axle (front or rear).**
Sequential Multiport Fuel Injection[1]	SFI	A multiport fuel delivery system in which each injector is individually energized and timed relative to its cylinder intake event. Normally fuel is delivered to each cylinder once per two crankshaft revolutions in four cycle engines and once per crankshaft revolution in two cycle engines.
Service Reminder Indicator[1]	SRI[2]	An indicator used to identify a service requirement
Shift Solenoid	**SS**	**See Glossary Entry "SHIFT SOLENOID ".**
Smoke Puff Limiter[1]	SPL	A system to reduce diesel exhaust smoke during vehicle acceleration or gear changes.
Spark Advance	**---[3]**	**The relationship between the ignition timing and top dead center.**
Spark Plug [1]	**---**	**A device for producing an electrical spark inside the cylinder of an internal combustion engine to ignite the fuel mixture.**
Supercharger[1]	SC[2]	See Glossary Entry "SUPERCHARGER."
Supercharger Bypass[1]	SCB	See Glossary Entry "SUPERCHARGER."
System Readiness Test[1]	SRT	System readiness test as applicable to OBDII scan tool communications
Thermal Vacuum Valve[1]	TVV[2]	A valve that controls vacuum levels or routing based on temperature.
Third Gear	3GR[2]	Identifies the gear in which the transmission is operating in at a particular moment (e.g., the Transmission Range (TR) switch may indicate that "drive" was selected, but the transmission is operating in 3rd gear as indicated by 3GR switch).
Three Way + Oxidation Catalytic Converter[1]	TWC+OC	A catalytic converter system that has both Three Way Catalyst (TWC) and Oxidation Catalyst (OC). Usually secondary air is introduced between the two catalysts.
Three Way Catalytic Converter[1]	TWC	A catalytic converter system that reduces levels of HC, CO and Nox.
Throttle Actuator Control	**TAC**	**See Glossary Entries "THROTTLE", "ACTUATOR" and "CONTROL."**
Throttle Body[1]	TB[2]	See Glossary Entries "THROTTLE" and "BODY."
Throttle Body Fuel Injection[1]	TBI	An electronically controlled fuel injection system in which one or more fuel injectors are located in a throttle body.
Track Road Load Horsepower	**TRLHP**	**The power required for a vehicle to maintain a constant speed taking into account power losses due to such things as wind resistance, tire losses, bearing friction, etc.**
Throttle Position[1]	TP	See Glossary Entry "THROTTLE."
Torque Converter Clutch[1]	TCC[2]	See Glossary Entries "CONVERTER" and "CLUTCH."
Torque Converter Clutch Pressure	**TCCP**	**A positive pressure in a torque converter clutch hydraulic circuit.**
Transmission Control Module	TCM[2]	See Glossary Entries "TRANSMISSION," "CONTROL" and "MODULE."
Transmission Fluid Pressure	**TFP**	**Positive pressure in a transmission hydraulic system.**
Transmission Fluid Temperature	**TFT**	**Temperature of transmission fluid.**
Transmission Range	TR	See Glossary Entries "TRANSMISSION" and "RANGE."
Turbine Shaft Speed[1]	**TSS**	**See Glossary Entries "TURBINE SHAFT and "SPEED."**
Turbocharger[1]	TC[2]	See Glossary Entry "TURBOCHARGER."
Variable Control Relay Module	**VCRM**	**A module that variably controls engine cooling fan speed, operates the A/C compressor clutch, and controls some of the non A/C functions.**
Vehicle Control Module[1]	**VCM[2]**	**An electronic module that controls the powertrain plus chassis and/or body related functions.**
Vehicle Identification Number	**VIN**	**A unique number on the vehicle used for identification.**
Vehicle Speed Sensor[1]	VSS[2]	A sensor which provides vehicle speed information.
Voltage Regulator	VR[2]	See Glossary Entry "REGULATOR."
Volume Air Flow[1]	VAF	A system which provides information on the volume flow rate of the intake air to the engine.
Warm Up Oxidation Catalytic Converter[1]	WU-OC	A catalytic converter system designed to lower HC and CO emissions during engine warm up. Usually located in or near the exhaust manifold.
Warm Up Three Way Catalytic Converter[1]	WU-TWC	A catalytic converter system designed to lower HC, CO, & NOx emissions during engine warm up. Usually located in or near the exhaust manifold.
Wide Open Throttle[1]	WOT	See Glossary Entry "THROTTLE."

--- Use Recommended Term Only
[1] Emission-Related Term
[2] Historically acceptable common usage
[3] For Alphanumeric Descriptor see Table 4
Bold indicates new/revised entry

7. *Glossary of Terms*—Table 3 is an alphabetical listing of base words and single word modifiers, together with their definitions.

TABLE 3—GLOSSARY OF TERMS

Baseword/Single Word Modifier	Definition
Accelerator Pedal	A foot operated device, which, directly or indirectly, controls the flow of fuel and/or air to the engine, thereby, controlling engine speed.
Accumulator	A vessel in which fluid is stored, usually at greater than atmospheric pressure.
Actuator	A mechanism for moving or controlling something indirectly instead of by hand. Compare: Solenoid, relay, and valve.
Air Conditioning	A vehicular accessory system that modifies the passenger compartment air by cooling and drying the air.
Alternator	See Generator.
Battery	An electrical storage device designed to produce a DC voltage by means of an electrochemical reaction.
Blower	A device designed to supply a current of air at a moderate pressure. A blower usually consists of an impeller assembly, a motor and a suitable case. The blower case is usually designed as part of a ventilation system. Compare: Fan.
Brake	A device for retarding motion, usually by means of friction.
Body	(1) The assembly of sheet-metal components, windows, doors, seats, etc., that provide enclosures for passengers and/or cargo in a motor vehicle. It may or may not include the hood and fenders. (2) The primary, central or key part of a feature.
Bypass	**Providing a secondary path to relieve pressure in the primary passage.**
Camshaft	A shaft on which phased cams are mounted. The camshaft is used to regulate the opening and closing of the intake and exhaust valves.
Canister	An evaporative emission canister contains activated charcoal which absorbs fuel vapors and holds them until the vapors can be purged at an appropriate time.
Capacitor	An electrical device for accumulating and holding a charge of electricity.
Carburetor	A mechanism which automatically mixes fuel with air in the proper proportions to provide a desired power output from a spark ignition internal combustion engine.
Catalyst	A substance that can increase or decrease the rate of a chemical reaction between substances without being consumed in the process.
Chassis	The suspension, steering, and braking elements of a vehicle.
Circuit	A complete electrical path or channel, usually includes the source of electric energy. Circuit may also describe the electrical path between two or more components. May also be used with fluids, air or liquid.
Cleaner	A device used in the intake system of parts that require clean air. An air cleaner usually has a filter in it to trap particulates and only pass clean air through.
Closed Loop (Engine)	An operating condition or mode which enables modification of programmed instructions based on a feedback system.
Clutch	A mechanical device which uses mechanical, magnetic or friction type connections to facilitate engaging or disengaging of two shafts or rotating members.
Code	A system of symbols (as letters, numbers, or words) used to represent meaning of information.
Coil (Ignition)	A device consisting of windings of conductors around an iron core, designed to increase the voltage, and for use in a spark ignition system.
Control	A means or a device to direct and regulate a process or guide the operation of a machine, apparatus or system.
Converter (Catalytic)	An in-line, exhaust system device used to reduce the level of engine exhaust emissions.
Converter (Torque)	A device which by its design multiplies the torque in a fluid coupling between an engine and transmission/transaxle.
Coolant	A fluid used for heat transfer. Coolants usually contain additives such as rust inhibitors and antifreeze.
Cooler	A heat exchanger that reduces the temperature of the named medium.
Crankshaft	The part of an engine which converts the reciprocating motion of the pistons to rotary motion.
Data	General term for information, usually represented by numbers, letters, symbols.
Device	A piece of equipment or a mechanism designed for a specific purpose or function. DO NOT use "Device" in naming.
Diagnostics	The process of identifying the cause or nature of a condition, situation or problem. To determine corrective action in repair of automotive systems.
Differential	(1) A device with an arrangement of gears designed to permit the division of power to two shafts. (2) See Pressure.
Distributor	A mechanical device designed to switch a high voltage secondary circuit from an ignition coil to spark plugs in the proper firing sequence.
Drive	A device which provides a fixed increase or decrease ratio of relative rotation between its input and output shafts.
Driver	**A switched electronic device that controls output state.**
Electrical	A type of device or system using resistors, motors, generators, incandescent lamps, switches, capacitors, batteries, inductors or wires. Compare: Electronic.
Electronic	(1) A type of device or system using solid state devices or thermionic elements such as diodes, transistors, integrated circuits, vacuum fluorescent displays and liquid crystal displays. (2) The storage, retrieval and display of information through media such as magnetic tape, laser disc, electronic read only memory (ROM) and random access memory (RAM). Compare: Electrical.
Engine	A machine designed to convert thermal energy into mechanical energy to produce force or motion.
Exhaust	
Fan	A device designed to supply a current of air. A fan may also have a frame, motor, wiring harness and the like. Compare: Blower
Fuel	Any combustible substance burned to provide heat or power. Typical fuels include gasoline and diesel fuel. Other types of fuel include ethanol, methanol, natural gas, propane or in combination.

TABLE 3—GLOSSARY OF TERMS (CONTINUED)

Baseword/Single Word Modifier	Definition
Generator	A rotating machine designed to convert mechanical energy into electrical energy.
Glow Plug	**A combustion chamber heat generating device to aid starting diesel engines.**
Governor	A device designed to automatically limit engine speed.
Ground	An electrical conductor used as a common return for an electric circuit(s) and with a relative zero potential.
Idle	Rotational speed of an engine with vehicle at rest and accelerator pedal not depressed.
Ignition	System used to provide high voltage spark for internal combustion engines.
Indicator	A device which visually presents vehicle condition information transmitted or relayed from some other source.
Injector	A device for delivering metered pressurized fuel to the intake system or the cylinders.
Input Shaft	**A shaft in a device that is "driven" by the previous element in the powertrain.**
IIntake Air	Air drawn through a cleaner and distributed to each cylinder for use in combustion.
Knock (Engine)	The sharp, metallic sound produced when two pressure fronts collide in the combustion chamber of an engine.
Level	The magnitude of a quantity considered in relation to an arbitrary reference value.
Line	**A generic service term used to describe a system of pipes, tubes and hoses.**
Link (Electrical/Electronic)	General term used to indicate the existence of communication facilities between two points.
Manifold	A device designed to collect or distribute fluid, air or the like. Compare: Rail.
Memory	A device in which data can be stored and used when needed.
Mode	One of several alternative conditions or methods of operating a device or control module.
Module (Electrical/Electronic)	A self-contained group of electrical/electronic components, which is designed as a single replaceable unit.
Motor	A machine that converts kinetic energy, such as electricity, into mechanical energy. Compare: Actuator.
Open Loop	An operating condition or mode based on programmed instructions and not modified by a feedback system.
Output Shaft	**A shaft in a device that drives the next element in the powertrain.**
Park/Neutral	The selected non-drive modes of the transmission.
Power Steering	A system which provides additional force to the steering mechanism, reducing the driver's steering effort.
Powertrain	The elements of a vehicle by which motive power is generated and transmitted to the driven axles.
Pressure	Unless otherwise noted, is gage pressure.
Pressure (Absolute)	**The pressure referenced to a perfect vacuum.**
Pressure (Atmospheric)	The pressure of the surrounding air at any given temperature and altitude. Sometimes called Barometric Pressure.
Pressure (Barometric)	Pertaining to atmospheric pressure or the results obtained by using a barometer.
Pressure (Differential)	The pressure difference between two regions, such as between the intake manifold and the atmospheric pressures.
Pressure (Gage)	The amount by which the total absolute pressure exceeds the ambient atmospheric pressure.
Pump	A device used to raise, transfer, or compress fluids by suction, pressure or both.
Radiator	A radiator is a liquid to air heat transfer device having a tank(s) and core(s) specifically designed to reduce the temperature of the coolant in an internal combustion engine cooling system.
Rail	A manifold for fuel injection fuel. Compare: Manifold
Range	**The detent position of the transmission manual valve.**
Refrigerant	A substance used as a heat transfer agent in an air conditioning system.
Relay	A generally electromechanical device in which connections in one circuit are opened or closed by changes in another circuit. Compare: Actuator, Solenoid, and Switch.
Regulator (Voltage)	A device that automatically controls the functional output of another device by adjusting the voltage to meet a specified value.
Scan Tool	A device that interfaces with and communicates information on a data link.
Secondary Air	Air provided to the exhaust system.
Sensor	The generic name for a device that senses either the absolute value or a change in a physical quantity such as temperature, pressure or flow rate, and converts that change into an electrical quantity signal. Compare: Transducer.
Shift Solenoid	**A device that controls shifting in an automatic transmission.**
Signal (Electrical/Electronic)	A fluctuating electric quantity, such as voltage or current, whose variations represent information.
Solenoid	A device consisting of an electrical coil which when energized, produces a magnetic field in a plunger, which is pulled to a central position. A solenoid may be used as an actuator in a valve or switch. Compare: Actuator, Relay, and Switch.
Solid State	Crystalline circuit structures used to perform electronic functions. Examples of such structures include transistors, diodes, integrated circuits and other semiconductors.
Speed	The magnitude of velocity (regardless of direction).
Supercharger	A mechanically driven device that pressurizes the intake air, thereby increasing the density of charge air and the consequent power output from a given engine displacement.
Switch	A device for making, breaking, or changing the connections in an electrical circuit. Compare: Relay, Solenoid, and Valve.
System	A group of interacting mechanical or electrical components serving a common purpose.
Test	A procedure whereby the performance of a product is measured under various conditions.
Throttle	A valve for regulating the supply of a fluid, usually air or a fuel/air mix, to an engine.
Transaxle	A device consisting of a transmission and axle drive gears assembled in the same case. Compare: Transmission.
Transducer	A device that receives energy from one system and retransmits (transfers) it, often in a different form, to another system. For example, the cruise control transducer converts a vehicle speed signal to a modulated vacuum output to control a servo. Compare: Sensor.
Transmission	A device which selectively increases or decreases the ratio of relative rotation between its input and output shafts.

TABLE 3—GLOSSARY OF TERMS (CONTINUED)

Baseword/Single Word Modifier	Definition
	Compare: Transaxle.
Troubleshooting	See Diagnostics.
Turbine Shaft	**A shaft in a device that is driven by a turbine.**
Turbocharger	A centrifugal device driven by exhaust gases that pressurize the intake air, thereby increasing the density of charge air and the consequent power output from a given engine displacement.
Ultraviolet	The portion of the electromagnetic spectrum between violet visible light and X-Rays.
Vacuum	A circuit in which pressure has been reduced below the ambient atmospheric pressure.
Valve	A device by which the flow of liquid, gas, vacuum, or loose material in bulk may be started, stopped or regulated by a movable part that opens, shuts or partially obstructs one or more ports or passageways. A "Valve" is also the moveable part of such a device. Compare: Actuator and Switch.
Vapor	A substance in its gaseous state as distinguished from the liquid or solid state.
Volatile	(1) Vaporizable at normal temperatures. (2) Not permanent.
Wastegate	**A valve used to limit charge air pressure by allowing exhaust gases to bypass the turbocharger.**
Wheel	A circular frame of hard material that may be solid, partially solid, or spoked and that is capable of turning on an axle.

Bold indicates new/revised entry

(R)   *8. Alphanumeric Descriptor Table*—Table 4 is an alphabetical listing of alphanumeric descriptors to be used when required due to limited display sizes.

9. Revision Procedures—It will be appropriate to revise the published J1930 on an ongoing basis. Requested revisions and updates will be controlled by the SAE Vehicle E/E Systems Diagnostics Standards Committee using the normal Recommended Practice Ballot process. This will ensure proper distribution of the changes.

As required by SAE standards, the J1930 document will be formally updated and balloted at least once every five years. When warranted by the number of requested modifications, J1930 will be updated as often as every three months.

Use Appendix A for submission of new information.

TABLE 4— ALPHANUMERIC DESCRIPTOR TABLE

Recommended Term	Acceptable Acronized Usage	Alphanumeric Descriptor
Diagnostic Trouble Code Freeze Frame	**DTC Freeze Frame**	**DTC FRZF**
Freeze Frame	**Freeze Frame**	**FRZF**
Fuel Pressure	**Fuel Pressure**	**FUEL PRES**
Fuel System Status	**Fuel System Status**	**FUEL SYS**
Long Term Fuel Trim	**Long Term FT**	**LONG FT**
OBD Status	**OBD Status**	**OBD STAT**
Oxygen Sensor Location	**O2S Location**	**O2S LOC**
Parameter Identification Supported	**PID Supported**	**PID SUP**
Short Term Fuel Trim bp	**Short Term FT bp**	**SHRT FT bp**
Spark Advance	**Spark Advance**	**SPARK ADV**

b = bank
p = position
Bold indicates new/revised entry

APPENDIX A

REQUEST FOR REVISION to SAE J1930
ELECTRICAL / ELECTRONIC SYSTEMS
DIAGNOSTIC TERMS, DEFINITIONS, ABBREVIATIONS & ACRONYMS

To insure that your request is accepted for ballot and incorporation into J1930, please supply the following information consistent with the Methodology of Section 4:

Please send completed form to: *SAE J1930 Task Force, 3001 West Big Beaver Rd, Ste. 320, Troy MI 48084-3174 U.S.A.*

fax no.: (810) 649-0425

PURPOSE or RATIONALE FOR REQUEST: _____

_____

_____

SECTION 5.0
EXISTING USAGE(S) _____   **RECOMMENDED TERMS** _____

_____   _____

_____   _____

SECTION 6.0

		Add	Delete	Change
RECOMMENDED TERM				
EXISTING:_____				
SUGGESTED:_____		○	○	○
ACRONYM / ABBREVIATIONS				
EXISTING:_____				
SUGGESTED:_____		○	○	○
DEFINITION				
EXISTING:_____				
SUGGESTED:_____		○	○	○

EMISSION RELATED?   YES _____   NO _____

SECTION 7.0
GLOSSARY of TERMS _____

_____

_____

_____

(R) *SECTION 8.0*
ALPHANUMERIC DESCRIPTOR
DESIRED _____

REQUESTOR: _____   Phone:_____   Fax:_____

_____   _____
            Signature   Date
Address: _____

_____

COMMITTEE USE ONLY

RECOMMEND FOR BALLOT ?   YES _____   NO _____   BALLOT TARGET DATE _____
COMMENTS   _____

_____

J1930 CHAIRPERSON _____   DATE _____

FIGURE A1—REQUEST FOR REVISION FORM

Report of the Dual/Higher Voltage Vehicle Electrical Systems Committee approved June 1992. Rationale statement available.

Foreword—It is the opinion of the committee that a set of guidelines and standards related to higher voltage levels will ensure the safety, shorten the introduction time, and lower the cost of such systems. A primary area of concern has been the potential for an increase in electrical shock hazard. Of secondary importance has been the need for some standardization of higher voltage levels. The committee feels that settling these broad issues now will allow development efforts to be more focused, thus shortening the total development time for higher voltage systems. The committee's review of the available technical literature and the industry expertise of our members leads to the recommendations discussed as follows.

1. Scope—This SAE Information Report is a summary of the initial recommendations of the SAE committee on Dual/Higher Voltage Vehicle Electrical Systems regarding the application of higher voltages in vehicle systems. This document does not attempt to address the technical merits of specific voltages or electrical system architectures.

2. References

2.1 Applicable Documents—The following publications form a part of this specification to the extent specified herein.

"Effects of Current Passing Through the Human Body, Part 1: General Aspects," International Electrotechnical Commission Report IEC-479 Part 1, Second edition, 1984.

"Effects of Current Passing Through the Human Body, Part 2: Special Aspects," International Electrotechnical Commission Report IEC-479 Part 2, Second edition, 1987.

R. J. Sandel and J. V. Hellmann, "Activities of the SAE Committee on Dual/Higher Voltage Vehicle Electrical Systems," presented at the 1991 SAE Future Transportation Technology Conference, Portland, Oregon.

3. Technical Requirements

3.1 Protection From Contact—Protection against direct contact to electrical circuits shall not be necessary if the possible contact voltages do not exceed the permissible levels of 65 VDC, including periodic ripple, or 50 VAC, RMS. The application of voltages above these levels shall not be discouraged, but additional protection against direct contact shall be necessary.

A study of previous work in relation to human tolerance to electrical shock was conducted and the various information sources were examined and thoroughly discussed by the members of the committee. Based on this study, an understanding of present vehicle wiring practices, and the safety record of today's 12 and 24 V systems, the 65 VDC and 50 VAC levels are seen as appropriate from a practical standpoint. Particularly useful in the formation of this recommendation has been the International Electrotechnical Commission's (IEC) Publication 479, parts 1 and 2.

It is recognized that with a system of present architecture utilizing a higher system voltage, say 50 VDC, transient levels will exceed 65 V. The committee has deferred consideration of the shock hazard of non-periodic transient (less than 300 ms) voltages to a future time. Also, the committee has not addressed the protection against contact necessary for voltages above the recommended limits. However, other industries demonstrate daily that such contact can be appropriately prevented.

3.2 Standard Storage Voltages—Standard storage battery voltages shall be defined as those normally associated with 3, 6, 12, and 24 cell lead-acid storage batteries (6, 12, 24, and 50 VDC nominal, respectively). The application of battery systems other than lead-acid shall not be discouraged. Additionally, the number of distinct generation, supply, or storage voltages that may be present in a vehicle shall not be limited.

The lead-acid battery system is currently the only system used commercially in starting, lighting, and ignition (SLI) applications on internal combustion engine automobiles. The committee feels that lead-acid will continue to be the SLI system of choice for a significant period of time. Standard voltages higher than 50 V may be defined in the future but will require a yet undefined degree of contact protection as their charge voltage will likely exceed 65 V.

As vehicle electrical requirements continue to evolve, battery systems other than lead-acid may become a viable alternative and should be able to meet the same nominal storage voltages as lead-acid. We feel that this option should not be limited. Similarly, limiting the voltage levels in magnitude or count will only restrict system options that may otherwise be appropriate solutions.

4. Notes

4.1 Key Words—Human Shock Tolerance, Personnel Protection, Shock Tolerance, Standard Voltage, System Voltage, Admissible Contact Voltage, High Voltage, Electrical System

Technical Reports from Other SAE Technical Committees Referenced in SAE Lighting Reports

RECOMMENDED ENVIRONMENTAL PRACTICES FOR ELECTRONIC EQUIPMENT DESIGN—SAE J1211

SAE Recommended Practice

Report of the Electronic Systems Committee approved June 1978. Editorial change November 1978.

1. Purpose—This guideline is intended to aid the designer of automotive electronic systems and components by providing material that may be used to develop environmental design goals.

2. Scope—The climatic, dynamic, and electrical environments from natural and vehicle-induced sources that influence the performance and reliability of automotive electronic equipment are included. Test methods that can be used to simulate these environmental conditions are also included in this document.

The information is applicable to vehicles that meet all the following conditions and are operated on roadways:

2.1 Front engine rear wheel drive vehicles.

2.2 Vehicles with reciprocating gasoline engines.

2.3 Coupe, sedan, and hard top vehicles.

Part of the information contained herein is not affected by the above conditions and has more universal application. Careful analysis is necessary in these cases to determine applicability.

3. Application

3.1 Environmental Data and Test Method Validity—The information included in the following sections is based upon test results achieved by major North American automobile manufacturers and automobile original equipment suppliers. Operating extremes were measured at test installations normally used by manufacturers to simulate environmental extremes for vehicles and original equipment components. They are offered as a design starting point. Generally, they cannot be used directly as a set of operating specifications because some environmental conditions may change significantly with relatively minor physical location changes. This is particularly true of vibration, engine compartment temperature, and electromagnetic compatability. Actual measurements should be made as early as practical to verify these preliminary design baselines.

The proposed test methods are either currently used for laboratory simulation or are considered to be a realistic approach to environmental design validation. They are not intended to replace actual operational tests under adverse conditions. The recommended methods, however, describe standard cycles for each type of test. The designer must specify the number of cycles over which the equipment should be tested. The number of cycles will vary depending upon equipment, location, and function. While the standard test cycle is representative of an actual short term environmental cycle, no attempt has been made to equate this cycle to an acceleration factor for reliability or durability. These considerations are beyond the scope of this guideline.

3.2 Organization of Test Methods and Environment Extremes Information—The data presented in this document is contained in Sections 4 and 5. Section 4, Environmental Factors and Test Methods, describes the 11 major characteristics of the expected environment that have an impact on the performance and reliability of automotive electronic systems. These descriptions are titled:

3.2.1 Temperature.

3.2.2 Humidity.

3.2.3 Salt Spray Atmosphere.

3.2.4 Immersion and Splash (Water, Chemicals, and Oils).

3.2.5 Dust, Sand, and Gravel Bombardment.

3.2.6 Altitude.

3.2.7 Mechanical Vibration.

3.2.8 Mechanical Shock.

3.2.9 Factors Affecting the Automotive Electrical Environment.

3.2.10 Steady State Electrical Characteristics.

3.2.11 Transient, Noise, and Electrostatic Characteristics.

They are organized to cover three facets of each factor:

(a) Definition of the factor.

(b) Description of its effect on control, performance, and long term reliability.

(c) A review of proposed test methods for simulating environmental stress.

Section 5, Environmental Extremes by Location, summarizes the anticipated limit conditions at five general control sites:

(a) Underhood
  1. Engine
  2. Bulkhead—dash panel

(b) Chassis

(c) Exterior

(d) Interior
  1. Instrument Panel
  2. Floor
  3. Rear Deck

(e) Trunk

3.3 Combined Environments—The automotive environment consists of many natural and induced factors. Combinations of these factors are present simultaneously. In some cases, the effect of a combination of these factors is much more serious than the effect of exposing samples to each environmental factor in series. For example, the suggested test method for humidity includes both high and low temperature exposure. This combined environmental test is very important to compoments whose proper operation is dependent on seal integrity. Temperature and vibration is a second combined environmental test that can be significant to some components. During design analysis a careful study should be made to determine the possibility of design susceptibility to a combination of environmental factors that could occur at the planned mounting location. If the possibility of susceptibility exists, a combined environmental test should be considered.

3.4 Test Sequence—The optimum test sequence is a compromise between two considerations:

3.4.1 The order in which the environmental exposures will occur in operational use.

3.4.2 A sequence that will create a total stress on the sample that is representative of operation stress.

The first consideration is impossible to implement in the automotive case, since exposures occur in a random order. The second consideration prompts the test designer to place the more severe environments last. Many sequences that have been successful follow this general philosophy, except that temperature cycle is placed first in order to condition the sample mechanically.

4. Environmental Factors and Test Methods

4.1 Temperature

4.1.1 DEFINITION—Thermal factors are probably the most pervasive environmental hazard to automotive electronic equipment. Sources for temperature extremes and variations include:

4.1.1.1 The vehicle's climatic environment, including the diurnal and seasonal cycles. Additionally, variations in climate by geographical location must be considered. In the most adverse case, the vehicle that spends the winter in Canada may be driven in the summer in the Arizona desert. Temperature variations due to this source range from -40-85°C (-40-185°F).

4.1.1.2 Heat sources and sinks generated by the vehicle's operation. The major sources are the engine and drive train components, including the brake system. Very wide variations are to be found during operation. For instance, temperatures on the surface of the engine can range from the cooling system's 88-650°C (190-1200°F) on the surface of the exhaust system. This category also includes conduction, convection, and radiation of heat due to various modes of vehicle operation.

4.1.1.3 Self-heating of the equipment due to its own internal dissipation. A design review of the worst case combination of peak ambient temperature (due to 4.1.1.1 and 4.1.1.2 above), minimized heat flow away from the equipment and peak applied steady state voltage should be conducted.

4.1.1.4 Vehicle operational mode and actual mounting location. Measurements should be made at the actual mounting site during the following vehicular conditions while subjected to the maximum heat generated by adjacent equipment and at the maximum ambient environment:

4.1.1.4.1 Engine start.

4.1.1.4.2 Engine idle.

4.1.1.4.3 Engine high speed.

4.1.1.4.4 Engine turn off—prior history important.

4.1.1.4.5 Various engine/road load conditions.

4.1.1.5 Ambient conditions before installation due to storage and transportation extremes. Shipment in unheated aircraft cargo compartments may lower the minimum storage (non-operating) temperature to −50°C (−58°F).

The thermal environmental conditions that are a result of these conditions can be divided into three categories:

4.1.1.5.1 Extremes—The ultimate upper and lower temperatures the equipment is expected to experience.

4.1.1.5.2 Cycling—The cumulative effects of temperatures cycling within the limits of the extremes.

4.1.1.5.3 Shock—Rapid change of temperature. Fig. 1 illustrates one form

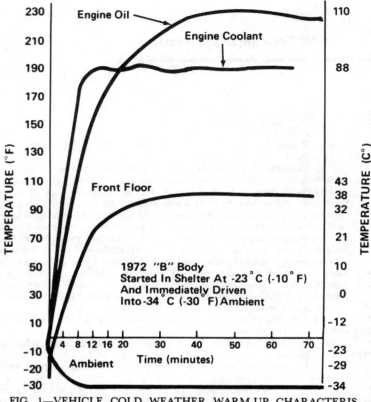

FIG. 1—VEHICLE COLD WEATHER WARM-UP CHARACTERISTICS

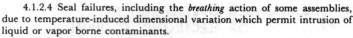

4.1.2.4 Seal failures, including the *breathing* action of some assemblies, due to temperature-induced dimensional variation which permit intrusion of liquid or vapor borne contaminants.

4.1.2.5 Failure of circuit components due to direct mechanical stress caused by differential thermal expansion.

4.1.2.6 The acceleration of chemical attack on interconnects, due to temperature rise, can result in progressive degradation of circuit components, printed circuit board conductors, and solder joints.

In addition to this, high temperature extremes can cause a malfunction by:

4.1.2.7 Exceeding the dissociation temperature of surrounding polymer or other packaging components.

4.1.2.8 Carbonization of packaging materials with eventual progressive failure of the associated passive or active components. This is possible in cases of extreme overtemperature. In addition, non-catastropic failure is possible due to electrical leakage in the resultant carbon paths.

4.1.2.9 Changes in active device characteristics with increased heat including changes in gain, impedance, collector-base leakage, peak blocking voltage, collector-base junction second breakdown voltage, etc. with temperature.

4.1.2.10 Changes in passive device characteristics such as permanent or temporary drift in resistor value and capacitor dielectric constants with increased temperature.

4.1.2.11 Changes in interconnect and relay coil performance due to the conductivity temperature coefficient of copper.

4.1.2.12 Changes in the properties of magnetic materials with increasing temperature, including Curie point effects and loss of *permanent* magnetism.

4.1.2.13 Dimensional changes in packages and components leading to separation of subassemblies.

4.1.2.14 Changes in the strength of soldered joints due to changes in mechanical characteristics of the solder.

Further, low temperature extremes can cause failure due to:

4.1.2.15 The severe mechanical stress caused by ice formation in moisture bearing voids or cracks.

4.1.2.16 The very rapid and extreme internal thermal stress caused by applying maximum power to semi-conductor or other components after extended cold soak under aberrant operating conditions such as 24-V battery jumper starts.

4.1.3 RECOMMENDED TEST METHODS

4.1.3.1 *Temperature Cycle Test*—A recommended thermal cycle profile is shown in Fig. 2 and recommended extreme temperatures in Table 1. The test method of Fig. 2A, a 24-h cycle, offers longer stabilization time and permits a convenient room ambient test period. Fig. 2B, and 8-h cycle, provides more temperature cycles for a given test duration. It is applicable only to modules whose temperatures will reach stabilization in a shorter cycle time. Stabilization should be verified by actual measurements. Thermocouples, etc.

Separate or single test chambers may be used to generate the temperature environment described by the thermal cycles. By means of circulation, the air temperature should be held to within ±2.8°C (±5°F) at each of the extreme temperatures. The test specimens should be placed in such a position, with respect to the air stream, that there is substantially no obstruction to the flow of air across the specimen. If two test specimens are used, care must be exercised to assure that the test samples are not subjected to temperature

of vehicle operation which induces thermal shock. Thermal shock is also induced when equipment at elevated temperature is exposed to sudden rain or road splash.

The automotive electronic equipment designer is urged to develop a systematic, analytic method for dealing with steady state and transient thermal analysis. The application of many devices containing semi-conductors will be temperature limited. For this reason, the potential extreme operating conditions for each application must be scrutinized to avoid later field failure.

4.1.2 EFFECT ON PERFORMANCE—The damaging effects of thermal shock and thermal cycling include:

4.1.2.1 Cracking of printed circuit board or ceramic substrates.

4.1.2.2 Thermal stress or fatigue failures of solder joints.

4.1.2.3 Delamination of printed circuit board and other interconnect system substrates.

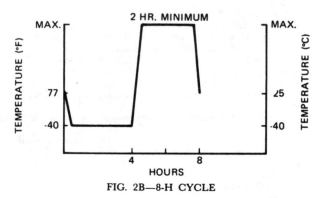

FIG. 2A—24-H CYCLE

FIG. 2B—8-H CYCLE

FIG. 2—RECOMMENDED THERMAL CYCLES

TABLE 1—RECOMMENDED TEMPERATURE EXTREMES

Location		Maximum Temperature
Chassis	—Isolated Areas	+ 85°C (+185°F)
	—Exposed to Heat Sources	+121°C (+250°F–1200°F)
	—Exposed to Oils	+177°C (+350°F)
Exterior		+121°C (+250°F)
Underhood	—Dash Panel	140°C (285°F)
	—Engine (Typical)	150°C (300°F)
	—Choke Housing	205°C (400°F)
	—Starter Cable Near Manifold	205°C (400°F)
	—Exhaust Manifold	650°C (1200°F)
Interior	—Floor	85°C (185°F)
	—Rear Deck	107°C (225°F)
	—Instrument Panel (Top)	113°C (236°F)
	—Instrument Panel (Other)	85°C (185°F)
Door Interior	—No data available	
Trunk		85°C (185°F)
Minimum Temperature		−40°C (−40°F)

transition rates greater than that defined in Fig. 2. Direct heat conduction from the temperature chamber heating element to the specimen should be minimized.

Electrical performance should be measured under the expected operational minimum and maximum extremes of excitation, input and output voltage and load at both the cold and hot temperature extremes. These measurements will provide insight into electrical variations with temperature.

Thermal shock normally expected in the automotive environment is simulated by the maximum rates of change shown on the recommended thermal cycle profile shown in Fig. 2. The proper thermal shock cycle should be determined by analysis of component power dissipation, expected rate of temperature change at its location in the system and the overall ambient operating temperature. In general, thermal shock is most severe when equipment is operated intermittently in low temperature environments. The effects of thermal shock include cracking and delamination of substrates, seal failures, wire bond breaks, and operating characteristic changes.

Thermal stress is caused by repeating cycling through the thermal profile of Fig. 2. The number of cycles required is a function of the equipment application. Functional electrical testing during temperature transitions or immediately after temperature transitions, is a means of detecting poor electrical connections. The effects of thermal stress are similar to thermal shock but are caused by fatigue.

NOTE: Although uniform oven temperatures are desirable, in some vehicle environments the only means of heat removal may be by special heat sinks or by free convection to surrounding air. It may be necessary to use conductive heat sinks with independent temperature controls in the former case and baffles or slow speed air stirring devices in the latter to simulate such conditions in the laboratory. (See Section 3.)

4.1.4 RELATED SPECIFICATIONS—A generally accepted method for small part testing is defined in MIL-STD-202E, Method 102A, Temperature Cycling. The short dwell periods at extreme temperature are satisfactory where temperature stabilization has been verified by actual measurements, thermocouples, etc.

4.2 Humidity

4.2.1, 4.2.2 DEFINITION AND EFFECTS ON PERFORMANCE—Both primary and secondary humidity sources exist in the vehicle. In addition to the primary source, externally applied ambient humidity, the cyclic thermal-mechanical stresses caused by operational heat sources, introduce a variable vapor pressure on the seals. Temperature gradients set up by these cycles can cause the dew point to travel from locations inside the equipment to the outside and back, resulting in additional stress on the seal.

The actual relative humidity in the vehicle depends on location due to operational heat sources, trapped vapors, air conditioning, and cool-down effects. Recorded data indicates an extreme condition of 98% relative humidity at 38°C (100°F).

Primary failure modes include corrosion of metal parts due to galvanic and electrolytic action, as well as corrosion due to interaction with water and due to adverse pH changes. Other failure modes include changes in electrical properties, surface bridging between circuits, and decomposition of organic matter.

4.2.3 RECOMMENDED TEST METHODS—The most common way to determine the effect of humidity on electronic equipment is to overtest and examine any failures for relevance to the more moderate actual operating conditions. Three general test methods are recommended. The most common is an active temperature humidity cycling under accelerated conditions. The second is a 10-day soak at 95% relative humidity and 38°C (100°F) temperature. A third method is an 8–24 h exposure at 103.4 kPa gauge pressure (15 psig) in a pressure vessel. This is a quick and effective method of uncovering defects in plastic encapsulated semi-conductors.

There are many acceptable accelerated humidity test cycles, including MIL-STD-202E, Method 103B; however, the test cycles in Fig. 3 are recommended as the most useful.

An optional frost condition may be incorporated during one of these humidity cycles (Fig. 3A). Electrical performance should be continuously monitored during these frost cycles to note erratic operation. Heat-producing and moving parts may require altering the frost condition portions of the cycle to allow a period of non-operation and induced frosting.

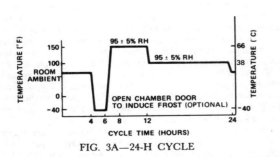

FIG. 3A—24-H CYCLE

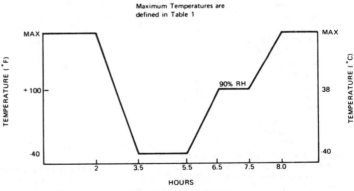

FIG. 3B—8-H CYCLE

FIG. 3—RECOMMENDED HUMIDITY CYCLES

The 10-day soak is normally conducted with equipment non-operating. Equipment that operates with standby voltage excitation and a low current drain when the ignition is off is a significant exception. Examples of this type include seat belt interlocks and electronic clocks. Samples of such equipment should be tested with normal standby conditions. Accelerated humidity effects should be expected under the conditions of high temperature, high humidity, and excitation voltage.

4.2.4 Related Specifications—A number of related humidity specifications are recommended for review and reference. The first: MIL-STD-810B, Method 507, Procedure 1, Humidity; is a system-oriented test method. The second; a modified version of MIL-STD-202E, Method 103B, Humidity (Steady State); is intended to evaluate materials. The third; MIL-STD-202E, Method 106D, Moisture Resistance; is a procedure for testing small parts.

4.3 Salt Atmosphere

4.3.1, 4.3.2 Definition and Effect on Performance—Electronic equipment mounted on the chassis, exterior, and underhood are often exposed to a salt spray environment. In coastal regions, the salt is derived from sea breezes and in colder climates, from road salt. Although salt spray is generally not found in the interior and trunk of the vehicle, it is advisable to evaluate the potential effects of saline solutions on the floor area as the result of transfer from the outside environment by vehicle operators, passengers, and transported equipment.

Failure modes due to salt spray are generally the same as those associated with water and water vapor. However, corrosion effects and alteration of conductivity are accelerated by the presence of saline solutions and adverse changes in pH.

4.3.3 Recommended Test Methods—The recommended test method for measuring susceptibility of electronic equipment to salt spray is the American Society for Testing and Materials (ASTM) Standard Method of Salt Spray (Fog) Testing-Number B 117-73.

The test consists of exposing the electronic equipment to a solution of 5 parts salt to 95 parts water atomized at a temperature of 35°C (95°F). The equipment being tested should be exposed to the salt spray for a period of from 24–96 h. The actual exposure time must be determined by analysis of the specific mounting location. When the tests have been concluded, the test specimens should be gently rinsed in clean running water, about 38°C (100°F) to remove salt deposits from their surface and then immediately dried. Drying should be done with a stream of clean, compressed dry air at about 241.3–275.8 kPa gauge pressure (35–40 psig). The equipment should then be tested under nominal conditions of voltage and load throughout the test.

Note: The Pascal (Pa) is the designated SI (metric) unit for pressure and stress. It is equivalent to 1 N/m^2.

Where leakage resistance values are critical, appropriate measurements in both the wet and dry states may be necessary.

4.3.4 Related Specifications—ASTM B 117-73, Salt Spray (Fog) Testing, is the recommended test method.

4.4 Immersion and Splash (Water, Chemicals, and Oils)

4.4.1 Definition—Electronic equipment mounted on or in the vehicle is exposed to varying amounts of water, chemicals, and oil. A list of potential environmental chemicals and oils includes:

Engine Oils and Additives
Transmission Oil
Rear Axle Oil
Power Steering Fluid
Brake Fluid
Axle Grease
Washer Solvent
Gasoline
Anti-Freeze Water Mixture
Degreasers
Soap and Detergents
Steam
Battery Acid
Water and Snow
Salt Water
Waxes
Freon
Spray Paint
Ether
Vinyl Plasticizers
Undercoating Material

The modified chemical characteristics of these materials when degraded or contaminated should also be considered.

4.4.2 Effect of Performance—Loss of the integrity of the container can result in corrosion or contamination of vulnerable internal components. The chemical compatibility can be determined by laboratory chemical analysis. Devices that may be immersed in fluids for a long period, such as sensors, should be subjected to laboratory life tests in these fluids.

4.4.3 Recommended Test Methods—The equipment designer should first determine whether the parts must withstand complete immersion or splash, and which fluids are likely to be present in the application. Immersion and splash tests are generally performed following other environmental tests because this sequence will tend to aggravate any incipient defects in seals, seams, and bushings which might otherwise escape notice.

Splash testing should be done with the equipment mounted in its normal operating position with all drain holes, if used, open. The sample is subjected to precipitation of 0.25 cm (0.1 in)/min delivered at an angle 45 deg below and above the sample with a nozzle having a solid cone spray.

During immersion testing, most commonly utilizing water as the fluid, the equipment ordinarily is not operated due to setup logistics and techniques of testing. Electrical tests should, therefore, be performed immediately before and after this test. In this test, the electronic equipment in its normal exterior package is immersed in tap water at about 18°C (65°F). The test sample should be completely covered by the wter. The sample is first positioned in its normal mounting orientation. It remains in this position for 5 min and then is rotated 180 deg. It should remain in that position for 5 min and then be rotated 90 deg about the other axis where it remains for 5 min. Immediately after removal, the sample should be exposed to some temperature below freezing until the entire mass is below freeezing. The sample is then returned to room temperature, air dried, functionally tested, and inspected for damage.

More severe tests such as combined temperature, pressure, and continuous fluid contact must be considered for equipment subjected to extreme environments as in the case of exposure to coolant water, brake fluid, and transmission oil. Caution must be used in specifying combined tests as they may be unrealistically severe for many applications.

4.5 Dust, Sand, and Gravel Bombardment

4.5.1 Definition—Dust is a significant environment for chassis, underhood, and exterior-mounted devices; and can be a long-term problem in interior locations, such as under the dash and seats. Sand, primarily windblown, is an important environmental consideration for chassis, exterior, and underhood. Bombardment by gravel is significant for chassis and exterior-mounted equipment.

4.5.2 Effect on Performance—Exposure to fine dust can cause problems with moving parts, form conductive bridges, and act as an absorbent material for the collection of water vapor. Some electromechanical components may be able to tolerate fine dust, but larger particles may affect or totally inhibit their mechanical action. While the exposure in desert areas is severe, exposure to a reasonable amount of road dust is common to all areas.

4.5.3 Recommended Test Methods—Dust, sand, and gravel bombardment tests should be at room temperature and the sample need not be operating, although functional tests should be performed prior to and after testing.

Dust conforming to that defined in SAE J726b (November, 1976), coarse grade should be used. If this dust packs or seals openings in the test sample or if the sample contains exposed mechanical elements, the following alternate dust mixture may be used:

J726b Coarse or Equivalent	70%
120 Grit Aluminum Oxide	30%

Components should be placed in a dust chamber with sufficient dry air movement to maintain a concentration of 0.88 g/m^3 (0.025 g/ft^3) for a period of 24 h.

An alternate method is to place the sample about 15 cm (6 in) from one wall in a 3-ft cubical box. The box should contain (10 lb) 4.54 Kgm of fine powdered cement in accordance with ASTM C150-56, specification for Portland Cement. At intervals of 15 min, the dust must be agitated by compressed air or fan blower. Blasts of air for a 2-s period in a downward direction assure that the dust is completely and uniformly diffused throughout the entire cube. The dust is then allowed to settle. The cycle is repeated for 5 h.

The recommended test for susceptibility of equipment to damage from gravel bombardment is SAE J400 (July, 1968), Recommended Practice Test for Chip Resistance of Surface Coatings. This document is intended to detect susceptibility of surface coatings to chipping, but the basic test equipment and procedures are useful for evaluation of the electronic equipment. The test consists of exposing the test sample to bombardment by gravel 0.96–1.6 cm ($\frac{3}{8}$–$\frac{5}{8}$ in) in diameter for a period of approximately 2 min. The sample is positioned about 35 cm ($13\frac{3}{4}$ in) from the muzzle of the gravel source. 470 cm³, (approximately 1 pt) of gravel (250–300 stones) is delivered under a pressure of 483 kPa gauge pressure (70 psig) over an approximate 10-s period. The process is repeated 12 times for a total exposure of 2 min. Judgment must be used in determining which sides should be exposed to the bombardment. Certainly all forward-facing surfaces not shielded by other parts are included. In many cases, the bottom and sides should also be exposed.

4.5.4 Related Specifications—Three specifications are referenced. The first: MIL-STD-202E, Method 110A, Sand and Dust, is a piece part test and is included for information and comparison. The second is SAE J726b (November, 1976), Air Cleaner Test Code, which defines the recommended dust. It also describes some test apparatus. The third specification is SAE J400 (July, 1968), Test for Chip Resistance for Surface Coatings, which is recommended in part for a gravel bombardment guide. Continued integrity at the conclusion of the exposure is the passing criteria.

4.6 Altitude

4.6.1 DEFINITION—With the exception of air shipment of unenergized controls, operation in the vehicle should follow the anticipated operating limits. Completed controls are expected to be stressed over these limits of absolute pressure:

Condition	Altitude	Atmospheric Pressure
Operating	3.7 km (12 000 ft)	62.1 kPa absolute pressure (9 psia)
Non-operating	12.2 km (40 000 ft)	18.6 kPa absolute pressure (2.7 psia)

4.6.2 EFFECT ON PERFORMANCE—With increased altitude the following effects are generally observed:

4.6.2.1 Reduction in convection heat transfer efficiency.

4.6.2.2 Change in mechanical stress on packages which have internal cavities. The reference cavity of an absolute pressure sensor is an example of this.

4.6.2.3 A very noticeable reduction in the high voltage breakdown characteristics of systems with electrically stressed insulator, conductor or air surfaces; this may result in setup of surface tracking with eventual component failure.

4.6.3 RECOMMENDED TEST METHODS—The recommended test method is to operate equipment during the thermal cycles described in the Temperature Test Section, but with the added parameter of 62.1 kPa absolute pressure (9 psia) pressure. The equipment should operate under maximum load. Failure effects will be similar to those experienced with thermal cycle and shock. Non-operating tests should be done at a minimum temperature of −51°C (−60°F) if possible.

4.7 Mechanical Vibration

4.7.1 DEFINITION—Vibration, which is prevalent whenever the vehicle engine or suspension system is in motion, is a key factor in the automotive environment. The intensity varies from low severity at smooth engine idle to extreme severity when traversing rough roads at high speed. Vibration also varies with location. Detailed data is included in Figs. 11–18.

4.7.2 EFFECT ON PERFORMANCE—A number of modes of degradation or failure are possible under applied vibration. A partial list includes:

4.7.2.1 Loss of wiring harness electrical connection due to improper connector design and/or assembly.

4.7.2.2 Excitation of tuned mass harmonic vibration within the equipment which eventually leads to failure due to metal fatigue at stress concentration points.

4.7.2.3 Failure of mounting structure due to the added acceleration forces acting on the mass of the equipment.

4.7.2.4 Mechanical flexure at seal and other interface areas which promotes the intrusion of other environmental factors, such as moisture, in a manner similar to the phenomena described under temperature cycling effects.

4.7.2.5 Temporary abberation of equipment performance due to acceleration forces on control component masses. Two examples illustrate this:

4.7.2.5.1 Sensor measurement error due to motion of the sense element. An example of this is a pressure sensor which gives incorrect information under some applied frequencies due to the mass of a diaphragm-spring mechanism.

4.7.2.5.2 False operation of electromechanical components—e.g., a relay whose contacts close or open, due to vibratory movement of its armature's mass.

The designer should be particularly alert to failures which are intermittent or which cause faulty operation during applied vibration. Many malfunctions of this type revert to normal operation after the vibration excitation is removed. It is, therefore, recommended that electronic performance tests be conducted during vibration tests for those functions which must perform under this condition. In most cases this is only practical under laboratory simulation of the road test situation.

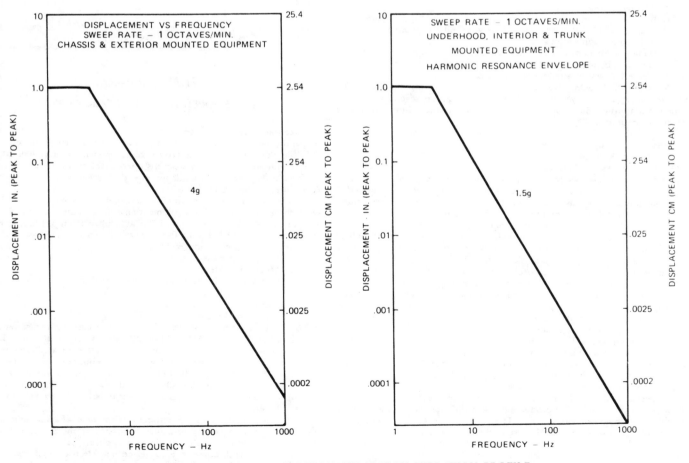

FIG. 4—RECOMMENDED RESONANT SEARCH VIBRATION PROFILE

4.7.3 Recommended Test Methods—A typical test for this environmental factor has been operation of a test vehicle over a group of severe road test track conditions. These include surfaces described as the Belgium Block Road, the Hop, the Tramp, the Square Block Test Course, and other complex surfaces. These courses are excellent test beds for complete transportation packages installed in the vehicle. Unfortunately, they are relatively inconvenient for electronic control evaluation during the design phase. In many cases electronic equipment exhibit intermittent or degraded performance during vibration and returns to normal operation when the excitation is removed.

Failure of electronic equipment in a vibratory environment may be the result of fixed frequency or random vibrations. Current practice within the industry is to conduct a resonant search up to 1000 Hz and then dwell at the major resonances if they are applicable to the operating environment spectrum.

Fig. 4 shows the recommended amplitude and sweep rate for this search. This profile is primarily gravity unit-oriented. A second recommended procedure is to sweep from 10–55 Hz and return in 1 min at an amplitude determined by measurements taken at the proposed mounting location. The test is conducted in each of three mutually perpendicular planes.

Experience has shown that in some cases random vibration may be a valuable approach in uncovering electronic equipment failure modes. While random testing is more difficult and costly, consideration should be given to this approach where required.

In the time sweep and resonant dwell, vibration must be conducted in each of three mutually perpendicular axes. Test duration must be determined by the equipment designer.

4.7.4 Related Specifications—Three specifications are referenced. The first, MIL-STD-202E, Method 201A. Vibration, and the second, MIL-STD-202E, Method 204C, Vibration, High Frequency, are concerned with sine vibration and offer procedural details and information on resonant dwell periods. The third, MIL-STD-202E, Method 214, Random Vibration, offers similar information on the random vibration approach.

4.8 Mechanical Shock

4.8.1, 4.8.2 Definition and Effect on Performance—The automotive shock environment is logically divided into four classes:

Shipping and handling shock.

Installation shock.

Operational shock.

Crash shock.

Shipping and Handling Shocks—These are similar to those encountered in non-automotive applications.

Installation Shock—It is common production-line practice to lift and carry equipment by its harness. Therefore, it is recommended that the harness design assure for secure fastening and suitable strain relief.

Operational Shocks—The shocks encountered during the life of the vehicle that are caused by curbs, pot holes, etc. can be very severe. These vary widely in amplitude, duration and number, and the test condition can only be generally simulated.

Crash Shock—This is included as an operating environment for safety systems. The operational requirements of these systems are limited to longitudinal shock at the present time.

4.8.3 Recommended Test Methods

Bench Handling Shock—The component shall be placed on a solid wooden bench top at least 3.4 cm (1⅜ in) thick. The test shall be performed as follows: using one edge as a pivot, lift the opposite edge of the component until one of the following conditions shall first occur:

(a) The component forms a 45 deg angle with bench top.

(b) The lifted edge is just below the balance point. The component shall be allowed to drop to the bench top. Repeat using other practical edges of the same face as pivot points. The procedure is then repeated with the component resting on other faces until it has been dropped on each face that the component might normally be placed when bench handling or servicing.

Transit Drop Test—The drop shall be from a height of 122 cm (48 in) onto a solid 5 cm (2 in) thick plywood base backed by concrete or a rigid steel frame with the test sample properly installed in its shipping container. The drop shall be performed on each face, edge, and corner.

Installation Shock Test—A recommended test is to support the device and the far end of the harness at the same elevation, then release the device. Care should be taken to prevent the equipment from striking another object during this test. The drop should be repeated and the harness terminals or strain relief area inspected for damage.

Operation Shock—With the possible exception of collision, the most severe shock anticipated after production line installation is encountered when driving over complex road surfaces. The complex profile that was used to derive this test profile consists of a rise in the roadway followed by a depression or dip. Upon leaving the dip at 48 km/h (30 mph), the vehicle will often become airborne. The severe shock is experienced when the vehicle returns to the roadway. Fig. 5 shows the shock measured on a steering column just below

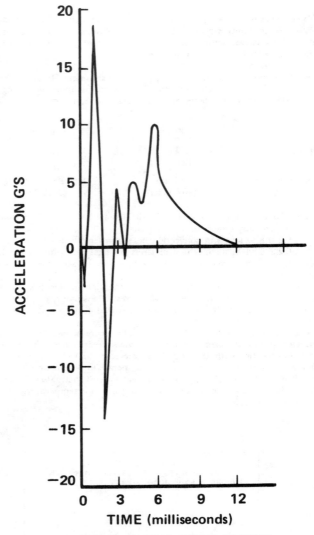

FIG. 5—OPERATIONAL SHOCK PROFILE

the steering wheel. The accelerometer was mounted with its sensitive axis perpendicular to the axis of the column and in the vertical plane.

While this location is not typical of component mounting locations, it probably represents the most severe operational shock environment. This information is provided for guidance only; there are no generally accepted test procedures at the present time.

Crash Shock Test—Only limited and preliminary data on the effects of crash shock on the electronic equipment environment are available. However, a representative deceleration profile for a 48 km/h (30 mph) barrier crash is shown in Fig. 6. The following factors vary with each installation and should be considered in pretest analysis:

(a) Equipment mass.

(b) Mounting system.

(c) Structure of the associated vehicle (crush distance, rate of collapse, etc.)

(d) Particular engine package.

(e) Direction of crash.

4.8.4 Related Specifications—Two specifications are recommended for consideration. The first, MIL-STD-202E, Method 203B, Random Drop, is designed to uncover failures that may result from the repeated random shocks that occur in shipping and handling. It is an endurance test. The second, MIL-STD-202E, Method 213B, Shock (Specified Pulse), is intended to measure the effect of known or generally accepted shock pulse shapes. It is intended that operational shock be reduced into a standard pulse shape to achieve a repeatable test method.

4.9 General Automotive Electrical Environment—Factors unique to the automobile that make the vehicular environment more severe than that encountered in most electrical equipment applications are:

Interaction with other vehicular electronic/electrical systems.

Voltage variations.

346

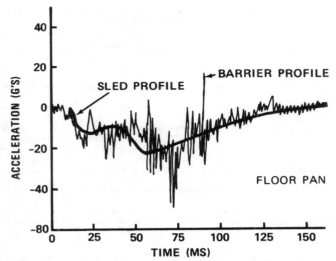

FIG. 6—48 KM/H (30 MPH) BARRIER AND SLED SHOCK PRO-
FILES

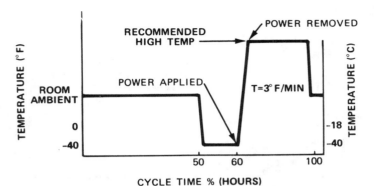

FIG. 7—COMBINED THERMAL AND ELECTRICAL STRESS PRO-
FILE

Customer added equipment.

Lack of maintenance.

Complex external electromagnetic fields.

Discussion of the electrical environment falls into two categories:

(a) Electrical, Steady-State—Including variations in applied vehicle DC voltages with a characteristic frequency of below 1 Hz.

(b) Electrical, Transient, and Noise—Including all noise and high voltage transient with characteristic frequencies above 1 Hz.

These conditions are discussed in Sections 4.10 and 4.11 respectively.

4.10 Steady State Electrical Characteristics

4.10.1 DEFINITION—A normally operating vehicle will maintain supply voltages ranging from +11–+16 VDC. However, under certain conditions, the voltage may fall to approximately 9 VDC. This might happen in an idling vehicle which has a heavy electrical load (lights and air conditioning) and a partially depleted battery. Therefore, depending upon the application, the designer/user may wish to specify the +9–+16 VDC range. For specific equipment such as those that must be functioning during engine start, voltage may be specified as appropriate. Cold starting with a partially depleted battery charge at −40°C (−40°F) can reduce the nominal 12 V voltage to between 4.5 and 6.0 VDC.

Another condition affecting the DC voltage supply is developed when the vehicle voltage regulator fails, causing the alternator to drive the system 18 V. Extended 18 V operation will eventually cause boil-off of the battery electrolyte resulting in voltages as high as 75–130 V. Other charging system failures could result in lower than normal battery voltages. The general steady state voltage regulation characteristics are shown in Table 2.

Emergency starts by garages and emergency road services sometimes utilize 24 V sources, and there have been reports of 36 V being used for this purpose. High voltages such as these are applied for up to 5 min and sometimes even with reverse polarity. The use of voltages which are above the vehicle system voltage can damage components in a vehicular electrical system, and the higher the voltage, the greater the likelihood of damage. A designer cannot cope with ever-increasing excitation potentials, and the above values usually are not a part of his design criteria. The possibility of the use of voltages above system voltage is included here for information only.

4.10.2 EFFECT ON PERFORMANCE—Equipment that must operate during the starting conditon is generally designed to perform with slight degradation over a wide range of voltage. The designer is alerted to the possibility of failure from a combination of voltage and temperature variation. Over-voltage and high temperature, both from the external environment and internal dissipation, may cause excessive heat and result in failure. Under-voltage will probably result in degraded or non-performance. Conditions must be carefully examined to determine the true temperature and excitation voltage of the equiment.

4.10.3 RECOMMENDED TEST METHODS—Critical automotive equipment is performance-tested for operation within predetermined limits. Samples are also subjected to combinations of temperatures and supply voltage variation which are designed to represent the worst case stresses on control components. A typical cycle for this form of test is shown in Fig. 7.

The voltage applied and removed at the two points shown in Fig. 7 is generally 16 V, the maximum normal voltage. If the test is performed for the high voltage *booster battery* start condition of 24 V, a narrower temperature range is used. This is a destructive test which is often used as an indication of basic design environmental capability. The number of cycles expected before failure, the actual limit values for temperature and voltage, and the period of each cycle are dependent on the design goals for the equipment being considered.

Samples of finished units are generally tested for extended operation at the peak voltage/temperature combination expected at the equipment's location. In the absence of actual temperature measurements, the values in Table 1 are recommended. These tests often run for extended periods and are particularly stringent for equipment in the underhood environment.

4.11 Transient Noise and Electrostatic Characteristics

4.11.1, 4.11.2 DEFINITION AND EFFECT ON PERFORMANCE—Four principal types of transients are encountered on automobile wire harnesses. These are load dump, inductive switching transients, alternator field decay, and mutual coupling. Generally, they occur singly, but there are cases where the latter two could occur simultaneously. EMC characteristics vary considerably with type of vehicle and wiring harness. The equipment user and/or designer should determine the actual values of peak voltages, peak current, source impedance, repetition rate, frequency of occurrence at the interface between his equipment and the electrical distribution system, then design and test the electronic equipment to withstand values consistent with the expected use. Table 3 summarizes typical transient characteristics.

TABLE 2—AUTOMOTIVE VOLTAGE REGULATION CHARACTERISTICS

Condition	Voltage
Normal operating vehicle	16 V max 14.2 V nominal 9 V min[a]
Cold Cranking at −40°C (−40°F)	4.5–6.0 V
Jumper Starts	+24 V
Reverse Polarity	−12 V
Charging System Failure	<9–18 V
Battery Electrolyte Boil-Off	75–130 V

[a] See Section 4.10.1 for a definition of normal voltage.

TABLE 3—AUTOMOTIVE TRANSIENT VOLTAGE CHARACTERISTICS

Type	Max Amplitude (V)	Characteristic	Remarks
Load Dump	120	$106\epsilon^{-t/0.188} + 14$	Damage potential
Inductive Load Switching	−286	$-300\epsilon^{-t/0.001} + 14$ followed by +80 Volt excursion	Logic Errors
Alternator Field Decay	−90	$-90\epsilon^{-t/0.038}$	Occurs at Shutdown Only
Mutual Coupling	214	$+200\epsilon^{-t/0.001} + 14$	Logic Errors

347

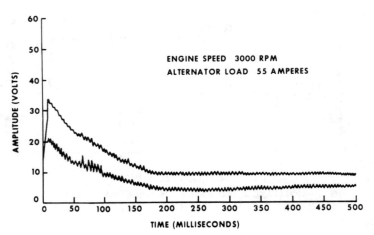

FIG. 8—LOAD DUMP TRANSIENT

TABLE 4—SUMMARY OF AUTOMOTIVE ELECTRICAL CONTINUOUS NOISE CHARACTERISTICS

Type	Max Amplitude	Duration	Repetition Rate	Remarks
Normal Accessory Noise	1.5 V Peak	Frequency	50 Hz–10 kHz	Total Pulse Height is 3 V-PP
Normal Ignition Pulses	3 V Peak	10–15 μs	Dependent on engine speed	Total Pulse Height is 6 V-PP
Abnormal Ignition Pulses	75 V Peak	~90 μs	Dependent on engine speed	
Transceiver Feedback	15–20 mV	Carrier	Frequency	Sinusoid

Load Dump Transient—Load dump occurs when the alternator load is abruptly reduced. This sudden reduction in current causes the alternator to generate a positive voltage spike. The worst case load dump is caused by disconnecting a discharged battery when the alternator is operated at rated load. Using the discharged battery load to create the load dump creates the worst situation for two reasons:

(a) The battery normally acts like a capacitor and absorbs transient energy when it is in the circuit.

(b) The partially discharged battery forms the single greatest load on the alternator and, therefore, disconnecting it creates the greatest possible step load change.

This transient may be the most severe encountered in the automobile and can result in component damage. In the practical case, it is most often initiated by defective battery terminal connections. Transient voltages of as high as 125 V or more have been reported with rise times of approximately 100 μs. Reports of decay time vary from 100 μs–4.5 s. The long duration decay occurs during vehicle turn off with a disconnected or dry vehicle battery. However, even the shortest time (100 ms) is relatively long, requiring that significant energy must be dissipated. Fig. 8 shows oscillograms of more typical load dump transients.

The load dump transient contains considerable electrical energy which must be safely dissipated to prevent damage to electronic equipment. This transient occurs randomly in time appearing as individual or repetitive pulses at random unknown rates due to vibration.

Inductive Load Switching Transient—Inductive transients are caused by solenoid, motor field, air conditioning clutch, and ignition system switching. These occur during vehicle operation whenever an inductive accessory is turned off. The severity is dependent on the magnitude of switched inductive load and line impedance. Unfortunately, measurements to date have not been taken with standardized procedures and were most probably observed with different loads.

These transients generally take the form of a large negative peak, followed by the smaller damped positive excursion. The highest reported by the data acquisition task force is −300/+80 V with an effective duration of 320 ms. Transients of this nature may cause component damage or introduce logic or functional computational errors.

Alternator Field Decay Transient—This is a special case of the inductive load switching transient. It is a negative pulse caused by alternator field decay and may occur when the field is disconnected from the battery as the ignition switch is turned to the *off* position. The amplitude is dependent on the voltage regulator cycle and load at the time of shutdown, varying from −40 to −100V and a duration of 200 ms.

Coupling—Coupling is not, strictly speaking, a generator of transients, but a mechanism which is capable of introducing transients into circuits not directly connected to the transient source. There are three general coupling modes in the automobile: magnetic, capacitive, and conducted. Briefly, the automobile coupling problems are caused by long harnesses, nonshielded conductors, and common ground return impedances. Long harnesses are one of the principal coupling media that distribute transients throughout the automobile (Ref. 2). When a number of wires are bundled into a harness and a step change in current or voltage occurs, inductive or capacitive coupling, between the conductor experiencing the change and the other wires, can result.

Other Effects—It is possible that inductive switching of certain solenoids and the alternator decay transient condition occur simultaneously. This hy-

pothesis would account for the higher voltage transients that have been reported, but not explained. Measurement of 600 V transients on engine shutdown have been reported. Also to be considered are noise suppression capacitors that are sometimes placed on the fuse block, and some accessories that are applied to quiet interference on the entertainment radio. In some cases, these capacitors may form tuned circuits with automotive inductive loads, causing high voltage transient conditions.

Certain devices, with high levels of stored energy, such as coasting permanent magnetic motors, may maintain line voltage for a finite interval of time after the ignition is shut off. Some equipment may perform in an unsatisfactory mode of operation under such conditions.

NOTE: Direct conduction through common circuits constitutes the most frequent path by which transients are introduced into electronic equipment.

Electrical Noise—Noise will normally have a repetition rate which is dependent on the characteristics of the interfering device or engine speed. There are four general types as summarized in Table 4. A typical oscillogram of automotive electrical noise is shown in Fig. 9.

Normal Accessory Noise—Generally, the normal compliment of accessories contributes less than 1.5 V peak over a frequency range of 50 Hz–10 kHz.

Normal Ignition Pulses—Normal ignition pulses can cause 3 V peak pulses of 10–15 μs duration at a repetition rate dependent on engine speed.

Abnormal Ignition Pulses—Normally, the battery acts as a low impedance path to ground for the voltage pulse caused by the primary and secondary windings of the ignition coil. If the battery is disconnected, the repetitive voltage pulses will increase to a significant amplitude. Under this condition, there have been reports of voltages as high as 75 V peak and 90 ms duration with the repetition rate dependent on engine speed. The energy level is substantial and component damage is possible.

Since this condition can occur simultaneously with load dump, consideration should be given to testing both conditions together.

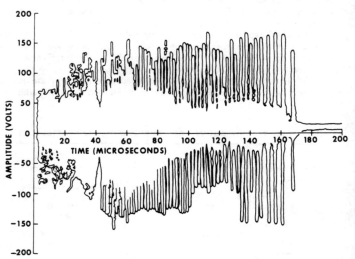

FIG. 9—POWER LINE ELECTRICAL NOISE

Transceiver Feedback—Some automotive transceivers feedback energy to the power line at carrier frequency when the transmitter is keyed. These potentials are small, 15–20 mV peak, and are mentioned here only because they are at a predictable frequency.

Electrostatic Discharge—The electrostatic charge stored by the human body and then discharged into a device may cause operating anomalies. Recent investigations indicate that discharging a 300 pF capacitor that has been charged to a potential of 15 kV through a 5 kΩ resistor is adequate to simulate this effect.

External Sources of Radiated Energy—The vehicle is exposed to radiated energy from a multitude of sources which have the potential to disrupt normal system operation.

A more detailed discussion of these transient and noise effects is available in Ref. 3 and 4.

NOTE: The mechanisms governing the introduction of transients into an electronic assembly or its interrelated components are very complex. The equipment designer/packager must, therefore, be familiar with the configuration of the total vehicle electrical system, e.g., wire routing, shielding, grounding, filtering and decoupling practices and equipment locations.

5. Environmental Extremes by Location—This section quantifies guidelines for the extreme operating conditions for five major in-vehicle equipment mounting sites:

(a) Underhood
    1. Engine Compartment
    2. Bulkhead—dash panel
(b) Chassis
(c) Exterior
(d) Interior
    1. Instrument Panel
    2. Floor
    3. Rear Deck
(e) Trunk

The physical locations of these sites are given in Fig. 10. Each site (denoted by shaded section) is individually discussed together with the following detail:

(a) A table listing extremes of temperature; humidity; salt spray; sand, dust, and gravel; oil and chemical; mechanical shock and vibration and electrical steady and transient; operating conditions.

(b) Comments germane to other operating conditions of interest.

(c) Charts and other information pertaining to the vibration environment.

This section contains data from environmental measurements made by North American vehicle manufacturers or automotive original equipment suppliers. Decisions concerning each environmental factor and the test methods used to determine equipment performance and durability, should only be arrived at after examining the information in Section 4 of this report. In addition, the designer should be satisfied, by referring to pertinent test data, that the particular application falls within the described operating extremes. See Section 3.

5.1 Underhood—Engine—Caution should be exercised in applying electronics equipment in the underhood region because of the wide range of environments. Data is summarized in Table 5.

5.1.1 TEMPERATURE—Equipment in the vicinity of the exhaust system may experience temperature peaks that are beyond the survival limits of many insulation materials and electronic components.

Investigators have found that the lowest peak temperature areas are often forward in the lower compartment, near the interior or exterior radiator support hardware. The exterior has the disadvantage of being subject to more splash with resultant potential for moisture intrusion, corrosion, or thermal shock.

The heat flow temperature control mechanism for typical engine-mounted equipment relies heavily on the conduction of heat via the engine mass rather than convection via fins projecting into the airflow. Equipment thermally interlocked by conduction with the engine, has two advantages during normal operation:

1. During engine operation, the upper temperature limit is set by the coolant peak temperature, which is in turn controlled by the thermostat.

2. The time rate of change of temperature is limited by the combined engine and coolant system thermal mass.

5.1.2 PEAK TEMPERATURE (HEAT SOAK) TEST—The temperature profile varies widely with individual engine/body combinations. Therefore, it is impossible to specify all possible operating conditions. Generally, worst case temperature operating conditions should be obtained by instrumenting a proposed location for the following operating conditions:

5.1.2.1 The largest engine installation expected in that body style.
5.1.2.2 Peak ambient temperature.
5.1.2.3 Air condition *ON*.

The vehicle is driven at highway speed for about 20 min and then parked. Underhood temperatures are monitored for the *heat soak* conditions as the thermal energy stored in the engine system is released in the absence of underhood airflow. Design modifications which contribute thermal energy to the underhood area, such as secondary air thermal reactors or catalytic reactors, should be in place and operating for this test.

Test procedures of this type have revealed that the region to the rear of the engine compartment, and the locations near radiated and conducted heat from the exhaust/reactor manifold tend to be much higher in temperature.

Present control practice has limited the location of electronic equipment to temperature situations similar to those shown for the intake manifold, although operation in the vicinity of the alternator heat source will probably add about 10°C (18°F) to the peak 121°C (250°F) shown for the intake manifold. Some experimenters expect the temperature near the radiator support structure to be no higher than 100°C (212°F).

Consideration should also be given to heat flow into the engine compartment from the front wheel suspension/brake and tire combination. Some consideration has been given to electronic equipment thermally interlocked with the engine cooling system, although the high pressure-temperature combination experienced during coolant boil-off may cause unacceptable catastrophic failure.

Rate of temperature change with time is also a consideration in this area, since cold starts will result in very rapid changes, as shown in Fig. 1.

5.1.3 VIBRATION—Vibration profiles recorded on the intake manifold are shown in Fig. 11, together with the equivalent power spectral density profiles.

5.2 Underhood—Dash Panel—Data is summarized in Table 6.

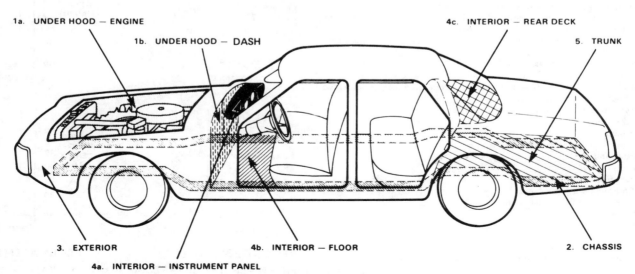

1a. UNDER HOOD — ENGINE
1b. UNDER HOOD — DASH
4c. INTERIOR — REAR DECK
5. TRUNK
3. EXTERIOR
4b. INTERIOR — FLOOR
2. CHASSIS
4a. INTERIOR — INSTRUMENT PANEL

FIG. 10—VEHICLE ENVIRONMENTAL ZONES

UNDERHOOD-ENGINE ENVIRONMENTAL EXTREME DATA

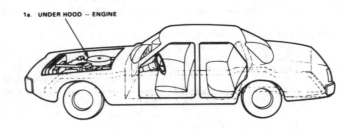

1a. UNDER HOOD — ENGINE

	TEMPERATURE			HUMIDITY (%RH)			SALT SPRAY	IMMERSION	SAND, DUST & GRAVEL	OIL & CHEMICAL	MECHANICAL SHOCK & VIBRATION	ELECTRICAL	
	LOW	HIGH	SLEW RATE	HIGH	LOW	FROST						STEADY-STATE	TRANSIENT
Choke Housing	-40°C (-40°F)	204°C (400°F)		95% at 38°C (100°F)									
Exhaust Manifold	-40°C (-40°F)	649°C (1200°F)	-7°C/Min. (20°F/Min.)		0	yes	Sect. 4.3	Splash present	Sect. 4.5	Sect. 4.4	Figure 11	Table 2 & Table 4	Table 3
Intake Manifold	-40°C (-40°F)	121°C (250°F)											

TABLE 5

5.2.1 TEMPERATURE—Temperature conditions are similar to the Underhood-Engine intake manifold, except that the primary method of heat flow is convection rather than conduction, and the resultant temperature slew rate is less. Equipment in this area generally relies heavily on convection due to the relatively low thermal conduction characteristics and unpredictable thermal interface between the equipment and the dash panel sheet metal. The rate of change in temperature is therefore set by the thermal mass of the equipment itself, and heat flow due to air movement in its vicinity rather than conduction via the mounting surface. Thermal shock due to the impact of cold mud, slush, etc., is not likely in the upper dash panel location. However, consideration should be given to melted snow and ice leakage from the hood/windshield area.

The majority of investigators have experienced peak temperatures of 121°C (250°F), although one data source expects this to be 140°C (285°F). Of course, locations on the dash panel near or just above the exhaust manifold(s) which is at 649°C (1200°F), will experience higher temperatures. The effects of underhood exhaust processing components (catalytic reactors, etc.) will also raise the peak temperatures.

5.2.2 HUMIDITY—This condition is similar to the associated engine condition, with the peak value shown in Table 6. The possibility of snow and ice intrusion, with hot ethylene glycol and water mixtures, due to cooling system failure, should also be considered.

5.2.3 SALT SPRAY—This condition is often a factor, particularly on the lower outboard portions where the dash panel joins the forward floor pan. Driving through salt slush can cause the entrance of salt spray through the radiator. The spray is then delivered to the engine compartment at high velocity by the fan. Spray due to this source is impacted on the dash panel, except for areas shielded by the engine or other underhood components.

5.2.4 IMMERSION—Not generally required.

5.2.5 SAND, DUST, AND GRAVEL—Gravel is not generally a problem, except at the lower dash panel near the transition into the forward floor pan.

5.2.6 OILS AND CHEMICALS—Commonly encountered components (with and without contaminants) are:

  Engine oils and additives (hot and cold)
  Brake fluid
  Gasoline
  Ethylene glycol and water (hot and cold)
  Water and snow
  Waxes
  Transmission oil
  Windshield washer solvent
  Degreasers and cleaning compounds
  Detergents
  Battery acid
  Steam
  Freon

5.2.7 MECHANICAL SHOCK AND VIBRATION—Vibration profiles are shown in Fig. 12.

5.3 Chassis—Data is summarized in Table 7.

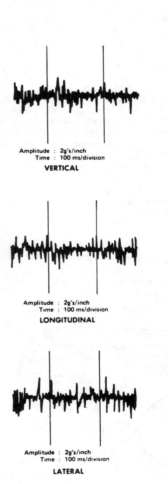

Amplitude : 2g's/inch
Time : 100 ms/division

VERTICAL

Amplitude : 2g's/inch
Time : 100 ms/division

LONGITUDINAL

Amplitude : 2g's/inch
Time : 100 ms/division

LATERAL

RECORDED DATA

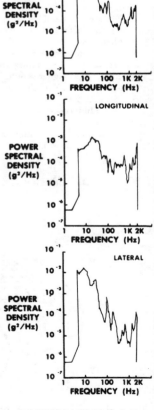

VERTICAL

POWER SPECTRAL DENSITY (g^2/Hz)

FREQUENCY (Hz)

LONGITUDINAL

POWER SPECTRAL DENSITY (g^2/Hz)

FREQUENCY (Hz)

LATERAL

POWER SPECTRAL DENSITY (g^2/Hz)

FREQUENCY (Hz)

EQUIVALENT P.S.D.

FIG. 11—ENGINE INTAKE MANIFOLD VIBRATION MEASUREMENTS

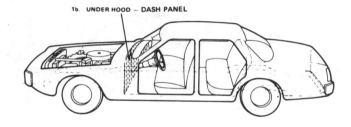

1b. UNDER HOOD — DASH PANEL

	TEMPERATURE			HUMIDITY (%RH)			SALT SPRAY	IMMERSION	SAND, DUST & GRAVEL	OIL & CHEMICAL	MECHANICAL SHOCK & VIBRATION	ELECTRICAL	
	LOW	HIGH	SLEW RATE	HIGH	LOW	FROST						STEADY-STATE	TRANSIENT
Normal	-40°C (-40°F)	121°C (250°F)	open	95% at 38°C (100°F)			Sect. 4.3	no	Sect. 4.5	Sect. 4.4	Figure 12	Tables 2 & 4	Table 3
Extreme	-40°C (-40°F)	141°C (285°F)	open	80% at 66°C (150°F)				no					

TABLE 6

5.3.1 TEMPERATURE—The heat sources encountered in the chassis area include (in rank of decreasing surface temperature):

Source	Peak Temperature
a. Exhaust/catalytic reactor system	649°C (1200°F)
b. Brake system/tires and transmission/differential drivetrain components	177°C (350°F)
c. Engine	121°C (250°F)
d. Vehicle ambient peak temperature	85°C (185°F)

The practical limitations of equipment components (with the possible exception of sensors) will restrict the designer to locations with the peak temperatures given in *c* and *d* above. Again, the designer is urged to check his particular installation for the actual peak temperatures experienced under operating conditions.

5.3.2 HUMIDITY—As shown in Table 7.

5.3.3 SALT SPRAY—With the exception of a few shielded locations, all chassis components are subject to heavy salt spray.

5.3.4 IMMERSION—Typical chassis components are subject to immersion.

5.3.5 DUST, SAND, AND GRAVEL—All chassis components in line with the wheel track that are not shielded are subject to continuous bombardment during vehicle operation on gravel roads. In nontrack aligned portions of the chassis, some bombardment will be experienced by equipment mounted on forward-facing chassis surfaces. All chassis components are subject to heavy dust and sand environments.

5.3.6 OILS AND CHEMICALS—The chassis is subject to all of the oils and chemicals listed in Section 4.4.

5.3.7 MECHANICAL, SHOCK, AND VIBRATION—Vibration data collected on the frame bumper attachment, frame transmission mount, frame crossmember and wheel backplate with equivalent power spectral density profiles are shown in Figs. 13–15.

5.3.8 ELECTRICAL—STEADY STATE (Refer to Section 4.10.1 for further information—Three operating conditions are recognized:

    a. Normal starting and running   9–16 V[1]
    b. Cold starting   4.5–6 V
    c. Booster battery starting   24 V

5.3.9 ELECTRICAL—TRANSIENT—This condition varies, depending upon the electrical distance of the equipment from the battery and the nearness of transient sources (e.g., inductive motors, solenoids, the alternator). Typical data is shown in Table 7. (Refer to Section 4.11 for further information.)

5.4 Exterior—The exterior consists of all outward and external vehicle surfaces above the chassis. This includes the forward grille area and potential mounting areas just above the bumpers. Data is summarized in Table 8.

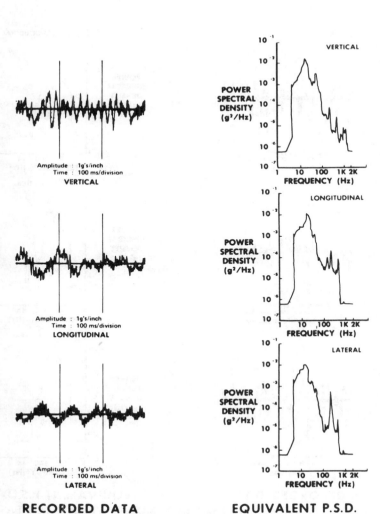

RECORDED DATA

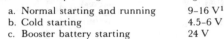

EQUIVALENT P.S.D.

FIG. 12—PLENUM VIBRATION MEASUREMENTS

[1] See Section 4.10.1 for a definition of normal voltage.

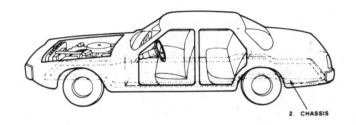

2. CHASSIS

| | TEMPERATURE | | | HUMIDITY (%RH) | | | SALT SPRAY | IMMERSION | SAND, DUST & GRAVEL | OIL & CHEMICAL | MECHANICAL SHOCK & VIBRATION | ELECTRICAL | |
	LOW	HIGH	SLEW RATE	HIGH	LOW	FROST						STEADY-STATE	TRANSIENT
Isolated	-40°C (-40°F)	85°C (185°F)	NA	98% at 38°C (100°F)	0	yes	Sect. 4.3	Sect. 4.4	Sect. 4.5	Sect. 4.4	Figures 13, 14 & 15	Table 2 & 4	Table 3
Near Heat Source	-40°C (-40°F)	121°C (250°F)	NA	66°C (150°F)	0	yes							
At Drive Train High Temp Location	-40°C (-40°F)	177°C (350°F)	NA	80%	0	yes							

TABLE 7

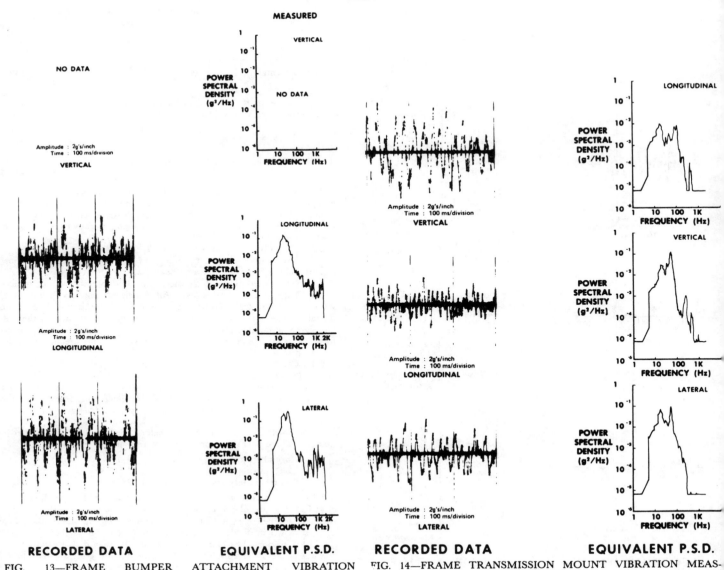

FIG. 13—FRAME BUMPER ATTACHMENT VIBRATION MEASUREMENTS

FIG. 14—FRAME TRANSMISSION MOUNT VIBRATION MEASUREMENTS

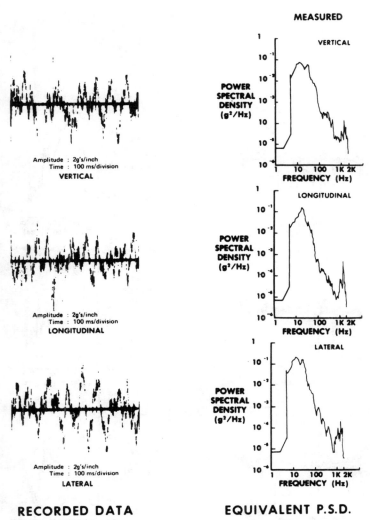

MEASURED

VERTICAL

POWER SPECTRAL DENSITY (g²/Hz)

FREQUENCY (Hz)

LONGITUDINAL

POWER SPECTRAL DENSITY (g²/Hz)

FREQUENCY (Hz)

LATERAL

POWER SPECTRAL DENSITY (g²/Hz)

FREQUENCY (Hz)

Amplitude : 2g's/inch
Time : 100 ms/division
VERTICAL

Amplitude : 2g's/inch
Time : 100 ms/division
LONGITUDINAL

Amplitude : 2g's/inch
Time : 100 ms/division
LATERAL

RECORDED DATA　　　　**EQUIVALENT P.S.D.**

FIG. 15—FRAME CROSS MEMBER VIBRATION MEASURE-MENTS

5.4.1 TEMPERATURE—Since all surfaces are away from internal vehicle heat sources, the temperature is primarily controlled by the climatic ambient conditions. These are discussed in Section 4.1 and shown in Table 8. Thermal shock due to splash or immersion, particularly on the front of the vehicle, should be anticipated.

5.4.2 HUMIDITY—Shown in Table 8.

5.4.3 SALT SPRAY—Most exterior surfaces are subject to heavy salt spray, with the possibility of crystalline salt buildup in some grill areas.

5.4.4 IMMERSION—Equipment mounted approximately below the vehicle axle line are possibly subject to occasional immersion. Components above this line experience splash.

5.4.5 GRAVEL, DUST, AND SAND—Components on the front of the vehicle are subject to bombardment from the vehicle ahead. Sand and dust impinges on all surfaces.

5.4.6 OILS AND CHEMICALS—Environmental chemicals include:
Road tar
Anti-freeze/water mixture
Soaps and detergents
Steam
Salt spray
Washer solvent
Degreasers
Waxes
Water and snow

5.4.7 MECHANICAL SHOCK AND VIBRATION—Data collected at the wheel back plate is shown in Fig. 16, and center pillar data is shown in Fig. 17.

5.4.8 ELECTRICAL—STEADY STATE—Three operating conditions are recognized:

a. Normal starting and running　　9–16 V[1]
b. Cold starting　　　　　　　　　4.5–6 V
c. Booster battery starting　　　　24 V

5.4.9 ELECTRICAL—TRANSIENT—This condition appears to vary widely, depending upon the electrical distance of the equipment from the battery and the nearness of transient sources (e.g., inductive motors, solenoids, the alternator). Typical values are shown in Table 8.

5.5 Interior—Instrument Panel—This includes the top of the dashboard and the near vertical section carrying the instruments and steering wheel. Data is shown in Table 9.

5.5.1 TEMPERATURE—Two temperature conditions are traceable to the climatic vehicle environment. Components not in direct sunlight experience temperatures from −40–85°C (−40–185°F). Components on the top surface of the instrument panel experience a greater heat buildup when closed vehicles are parked in the bright sun. Heat radiated incident sunlight and re-radiated energy from the windshield cause the temperature to build to 113°C (235°F) in this region. Heat due to underdash components, such as radio or heater, is also a contributing factor.

5.5.2 HUMIDITY—As shown in Table 9. A tightly closed vehicle with wet upholstery experiences very high internal humidity at high temperature.

5.5.3 SALT SPRAY—Not generally a problem at the instrument panel.

5.5.4 IMMERSION—Not anticipated, although liquid spills are possible on the upper dash surface.

[1]See Section 4.10.1 for a definition of normal voltage.

EXTERIOR ENVIRONMENTAL DATA

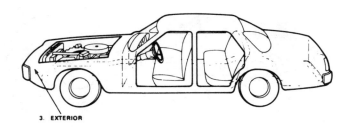

3. EXTERIOR

| | TEMPERATURE | | | HUMIDITY (%RH) | | | SALT SPRAY | IMMERSION | SAND, DUST & GRAVEL | OIL & CHEMICAL | MECHANICAL SHOCK & VIBRATION | ELECTRICAL | |
	LOW	HIGH	SLEW RATE	HIGH	LOW	FROST						STEADY-STATE	TRANSIENT
Normal	−40°C (−40°F)	85°C (185°F)	NA	95% at 38°C (100°F)	0	yes	Sect. 4.3	Sect. 4.4	Sect. 4.5	Sect. 4.4	Figure 16 & 17	Table 2 & 4	Table 3

TABLE 8

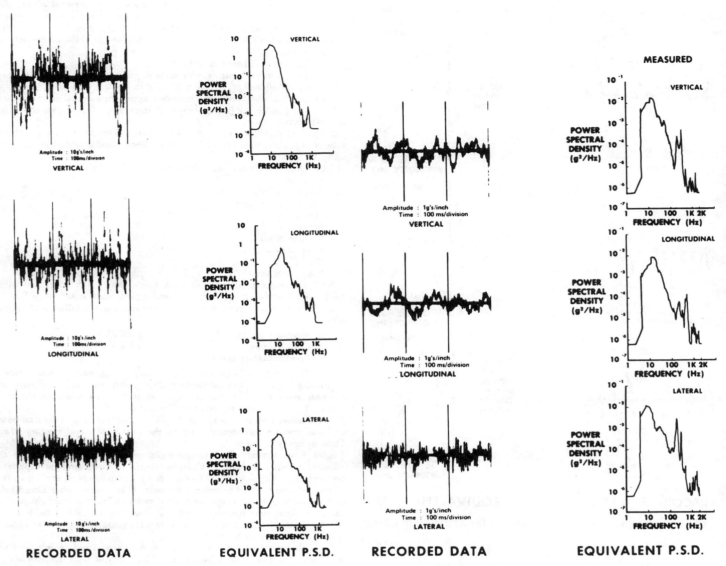

FIG. 16—WHEEL BACK PLATE VIBRATION MEASUREMENTS   FIG. 17—CENTER PILLAR VIBRATION MEASUREMENTS

INTERIOR - INSTRUMENTAL PANEL ENVIRONMENTAL DATA

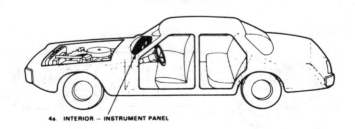

4a. INTERIOR — INSTRUMENT PANEL

	TEMPERATURE			HUMIDITY (%RH)			SALT SPRAY	IMMERSION	SAND, DUST & GRAVEL	OIL & CHEMICAL	MECHANICAL SHOCK & VIBRATION	ELECTRICAL	
	LOW	HIGH	SLEW RATE	HIGH	LOW	FROST						STEADY-STATE	TRANSIENT
Nominal	-40°C (-40°F)	85°C (185°F)	NA	98%at 38°C (100°F)	0	yes	no	Partial	Dust only	Sect. 4.4	Figure 18	Table 2 & 4	Table 3
Top Surface	-40°C (-40°F)	113°C (235°F)	NA	80%at 66°C (150°F)									

TABLE 9

5.5.5 GRAVEL, SAND, AND DUST—Gravel not anticipated. Coatings of sand and dust are expected on all horizontal surfaces.

5.5.6 OILS AND CHEMICALS—Mainly cleaning agents: waxes, soaps, and detergents.

5.5.7 MECHANICAL VIBRATION—As shown in Fig. 18.

5.5.8 ELECTRICAL—STEADY STATE—Three operating conditions are recognized:

    a. Normal starting and running   9–16 V[1]
    b. Cold starting   4.5–6 V
    c. Booster battery starting   24 V

5.5.9 ELECTRICAL—TRANSIENT—This condition appears to vary widely, depending upon the electrical distance of the equipment from the battery and the nearness of transient sources (e.g., inductive motors, solenoids, the alternator). Typical data is shown in Table 9.

5.6 Interior—Floor—This covers all approximately horizontal surfaces, including the floor beneath the front seat(s), the footrest areas in front of the seat(s) and beneath the dashboard, and the interior surfaces of the drive tunnel. Data is shown in Table 10.

5.6.1 TEMPERATURE—As shown in Table 10. Higher temperatures may be experienced directly over drivetrain components (transmission, etc.) and the exhaust system (including catalytic converters) although data is not available at this time.

5.6.2 HUMIDITY—As shown in Table 10, standing water is possible in depressions due to rain entry through open windows or leaking body seals. Also, water is carried into the vehicle by wet garments or packages.

5.6.3 SALT SPRAY—The water entry discussed in humidity section may also be a saturated salt solution.

5.6.4 IMMERSION—Immersion is possible as discussed in humidity section.

5.6.5 GRAVEL, DUST, AND SAND—Gravel bombardment is not a condition, although a buildup of dust and sand is common.

5.6.6 OILS AND CHEMICALS—Contaminants include the following:
    Engine oils and additives (tracked in on occupant's shoes)
    Cleaning solvents
    Water and snow
    Gasoline
    Salt water

5.6.7 MECHANICAL SHOCK AND VIBRATION—No data available at this time. Similar to conditions shown for the transmission mounts in the chassis section.

5.6.8 ELECTRICAL—STEADY STATE—Three operating conditions are recognized:

    a. Normal starting and running   9–16 V[1]
    b. Cold starting   4.5–6 V
    c. Booster battery starting   24 V

5.6.9 ELECTRICAL—TRANSIENT—This condition appears to vary widely, depending upon the electrical distance of the control site from the battery and the nearness of transient sources (e.g., inductive motors, solenoids, the alternator).

5.7 Interior—Rear Deck—This area includes horizontal surface extending from the top of the rear seat to the body work just below the bottom edge of the backlight. Data is shown in Table 11.

5.7.1 TEMPERATURE—The major heat source is climatic incident radiant energy from direct sunlight and sunlight reflected from the backlight. The peak temperature of 104°C (220°F) is slightly less than that given for the upper dashboard surface because of the absence of heat sources beneath the panel.

[1]See Section 4.10.1 for a definition of normal voltage.

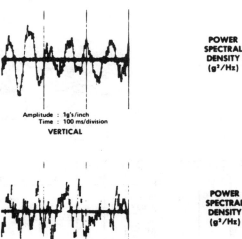

Amplitude : 1g's/inch
Time : 100 ms/division
VERTICAL

Amplitude : 1g's/inch
Time : 100 ms/division
LONGITUDINAL

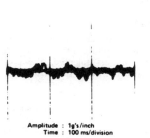

Amplitude : 1g's/inch
Time : 100 ms/division
LATERAL

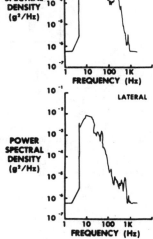

RECORDED DATA   **EQUIVALENT P.S.D.**

FIG. 18—INSTRUMENT PANEL VIBRATION MEASUREMENTS

5.7.2 HUMIDITY—As shown in Table 11.

5.7.3 SALT SPRAY—Not expected.

5.7.4 IMMERSION—Not present.

5.7.5 SAND AND DUST—Light coatings of sand and dust are present.

5.7.6 OILS AND CHEMICALS—Only cleaning agents expected.

5.7.7 MECHANICAL SHOCK AND VIBRATION—No data available at this time. The condition is similar to conditions shown for the dashboard, with the exception that vibration at the vehicle's rear is a function of high variable trunk, rear seat, and bumper loading conditions.

5.7.8 ELECTRICAL—STEADY STATE—Three operating conditions are recognized:

INTERIOR - FLOOR ENVIRONMENTAL DATA

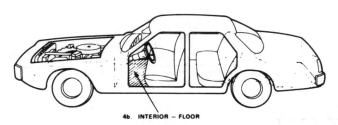

4b. INTERIOR – FLOOR

TEMPERATURE			HUMIDITY (%RH)			SALT SPRAY	IMMERSION	SAND, DUST & GRAVEL	OIL & CHEMICAL	MECHANICAL SHOCK & VIBRATION	ELECTRICAL	
LOW	HIGH	SLEW RATE	HIGH	LOW	FROST						STEADY STATE	TRANSIENT
-40°C (-40°F)	85°C (185°F)	NA	98% RH 38°C (100°F)	0	-	NO	NO	Sect. 4.5	Sect. 4.4	Not measured	Table 2 & 4	Table 3

TABLE 10

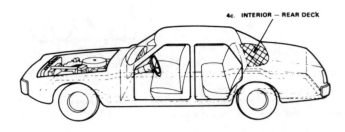

4c. INTERIOR — REAR DECK

TEMPERATURE			HUMIDITY (%RH)			SALT SPRAY	IMMERSION	SAND, DUST & GRAVEL	OIL & CHEMICAL	MECHANICAL SHOCK & VIBRATION	ELECTRICAL	
LOW	HIGH	SLEW RATE	HIGH	LOW	FROST						STEADY-STATE	TRANSIENT
-40°C (-40°F)	104°C (220°F)	NA	98%at 38°C (100°F) ---- 80%at 66°C (150°F)	0	no	no	no	Sect. 4.5	Sect. 4.4	Not Measured	Table 2 & 4	Table 3

TABLE 11

a. Normal starting and running   9–16 V[1]
b. Cold starting   4.5–6 V
c. Booster battery starting   24 V

5.7.9 ELECTRICAL—TRANSIENT—This condition appears to vary widely, depending upon the electrical distance of the equipment from the battery and the nearness of transient sources (e.g., inductive motors, solenoids, the alternator). Care should be taken to measure transients due to electrical rear window lifts, if present.

5.8 Trunk—Environmental data is defined in Table 12.

5.8.1 TEMPERATURE—The anticipated temperature limits are fairly similar to those expected for the interior. However, the thinner insulation may increase temperatures in some areas of the trunk floor due to radiated and conducted exhaust system heat. The inside of the trunk lid may also experience higher temperatures than those given due to direct sunlight heating.

5.8.2 HUMIDITY—The presence of stored liquids or wet clothing, etc., makes this the highest humidity enclosed volume in the car. Condensation is possible on all surfaces.

5.8.3 SALT SPRAY—A standing saturated salt solution is possible on the compartment floor.

5.8.4 IMMERSION—Standing liquid on the floor is anticipated unless the area is equipped with drains.

5.8.5 SAND AND DUST—A heavy buildup of sand and dust is anticipated.

5.8.6 OILS AND CHEMICALS—Spillage of all of the chemicals listed in Section 4.4 is possible.

5.8.7 MECHANICAL SHOCK AND VIBRATION—No data available at this time. Conditions are similar to those shown for the dashboard, with the exception

[1]See Section 4.10.1 for a definition of normal voltage.

that vibration at the vehicle's rear is a function of highly variable trunk, rear seat, and rear bumper loading conditions.

5.8.8 ELECTRICAL—STEADY STATE—This condition appears to vary widely, depending upon the electrical distance of the equipment from the battery and the nearness of transient sources (e.g., inductive motors, solenoids, the alternator). Typical values are shown in Table 12.

5.9 Environmental Extremes Summary—Table 13 summarizes the information provided in Sections 5.1–5.8.

ACKNOWLEDGMENTS

The subcommittee acknowledges the contribution of Mr. J. R. Morgan. Mr. Morgan provided oscillograms of the load dump transient and electrical noise, and critiqued the electrical section of this document.

REFERENCES

1. O. T. McCarter, "Environmental Guidelines for the Designer of Automotive Electronic Components." Paper 740017 presented at SAE Automotive Engineering Congress, Detroit, March 1974.

2. J. R. Morgan, "Transients in the Automotive Electrical System." Motorola CER-114, 1973.

3. G. B. Andrews, "Control of the Automotive Electrical Environment." Paper 730045 presented at SAE Automotive Engineering Congress, Detroit, January 1973.

4. SAE J1113a, Electromagnetic Susceptibility Procedures for Vehicle Components (Except Aircraft) (June, 1978).

TRUNK & ENVIRONMENTAL DATA

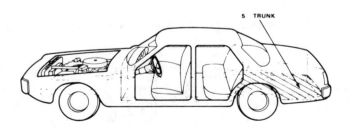

5. TRUNK

TEMPERATURE			HUMIDITY (%RH)			SALT SPRAY	IMMERSION	SAND, DUST & GRAVEL	OIL & CHEMICAL	MECHANICAL SHOCK & VIBRATION	ELECTRICAL	
LOW	HIGH	SLEW RATE	HIGH	LOW	FROST						STEADY-STATE	TRANSIENT
-40°C (-40°F)	85°C (185°F)	NA	98% at 38°C (100°F) ---- 80% at 66°F	0	yes	no	no	Sect. 4.5	Sect. 4.4	Not Measured	Tables 2 & 4	Table 3

TABLE 12

TABLE 13—ENVIRONMENTAL EXTREME SUMMARY

Location	Temperature			Humidity (%RH)			Salt Spray	Immersion	Sand, Dust, and Gravel	Oil and Chemical	Mechanical Shock and Vibration	Electrical	
	Low	High	Slew Rate	High	Low	Frost						Steady-State	Transient
1. Underhood—Engine Choke Housing	−40°F −40°C	400°F 204°C	20°F/min	95% at 100°F 38°C	0	yes	Section 4.3	splash present	sand and dust		Fig. 11	−0	
Exhaust Manifold	−40°F −40°C	1200°F 649°C	−7°C/min										
Intake Manifold	−40°F −40°C	250°F 121°C											
Underhood—Firewall Normal	−40°F −40°C	250°F 121°C	open	95% at 100°F 38°C	0		Section 4.3	no	sand and dust		Fig. 12		
Extreme	−40°F −40°C	285°F 141°C	open	80% at 150°F 66°C	0			no					
2. Chassis Isolated	−40°F −40°C	185°F 84°C	NA	98% at 100°F 38°C	0	yes	yes	yes	yes			See Section 4.10 and Tables 2 and 4	
Near Heat Source	−40°F −40°C	250°F 121°C	NA	80% at 150°F 66°C	0	yes		yes	yes		Figs. 13, 14, and 15		See Section 4 and Table 3
At Drivetrain High Temp Locations	−40°F −40°C	350°F 177°C	NA						yes				
3. Exterior Normal	−40°F −40°C	235°F 113°C	NA	95% at 100°F 38°C	0	yes	yes	yes	yes	See Section 4.4	Figs. 16 and 17		
4. Interior Instrument Panel	−40°F −40°C	185°F 84°C	NA	98% at 100°F 38°C	0	yes	no	no	dust only		Fig. 18		
Top		225°F 113°C											
Floor	−40°F −40°C	185°F 84°C		98% at 100°F 38°C									
			NA	80% at 150°F 66°C	0	no	no		dust and sand		Not measured		
Rear Deck	−40°F −40°C	220°F 104°C	NA	98% at 100°F 38°C	0	no	no	no	dust and sand		Not measured		
5. Trunk	−40°F −40°C	185°F 84°C	NA	98% at 100°F 38°C	0	yes	no	no	sand and dust		Not measured		

Cancelled SAE Technical Reports
on Motor Vehicle Lighting Subjects

This list of cancelled SAE Technical Reports on motor vehicle lighting subjects is intended to assist users in reference and research. Copies of these documents can be ordered from the SAE Publications Division.

J-Number	Title	Year Cancelled
SAE J29	Plastic Material for Use in Housings of Motor Vehicle Lighting Devices	1983
SAE J32	Service Performance Requirements for Sealed Beam Headlamp Units for Motor Vehicles	1988
SAE J94	Combination Tail and Floodlamp for Industrial Equipment	1988
SAE J186	Supplemental High Mounted Stop and Rear Turn Signal Lamps for Use on Vehicles Less than 2032 mm in overall Width	1996
SAE J210	Wiring Identification System for Industrial and Construction Equipment	1987
SAE J353	Replaceable Bulbs for Headlamps	1992
SAE J566	Headlamp Mountings	1971
SAE J568	Sockets Receiving Prefocus Base Lamps	1978
SAE J569	Lamp Bulbs and Bases	1970
SAE J570	Wedge Base Bulbs	
SAE J571	Dimensional Specifications for Sealed Headlamp Units	1988
SAE J574	12-Volt Lamp Bulbs and Sealed Units for Heavy Duty Vehicles	1964
SAE J577	Vibration Test Machine	1980
SAE J579	Sealed Beam Headlamp Units for Motor	1992
SAE J580	Sealed Beam Headlamp Assembly	1992
SAE J591	Spot Lamps	1994
SAE J601	Light Output Meter	1965
SAE J603	Incandescent Lamp Impact Test	1981
SAE J774	Emergency Warning Device (Triangular Shape)	1994
SAE J816	Supplemental High Mounted Stop and Rear Turn Signal Lamps for Use on Vehicles Less than 2032 mm in overall Width	1996
SAE J822	Wedge Base Type Socket	1972
SAE J908	Lighting and Marking of Farm and Light Industrial Equipment on Public Roads	1971
SAE J976	Combination Tail and Floodlamp for Agricultural Equipment	1986
SAE J1049	Service Performance Requirements and Test Procedures for Motor Vehicle Lamp Bulbs	1990
SAE J1055	Service Performance Requirements for Turn Signal Flashers	1987
SAE J1056	Service Performance Requirements for Vehicular Hazard Warning Flashers	1987
SAE J1104	Service Performance Requirements for Warning Lamp Alternating Flashers	1989
SAE J1221	Headlamp-Turn Signal Spacing	1988
SAE J1395	Front and Rear Turn Signal Lamps for use on Motor Vehicles 2032 mm or More in Overall Width	1996
SAE J1398	Stop Lamps for Use on Motor Vehicles 2032 mm or More in Overall Width	1996
SAE J2068	Combination Turn Signal Hazard Warning Signal Flashers	1994

Key Word Index

This Key Word Index is based on words and phrases found in the titles of reports listed in the current SAE Ground Vehicle Lighting Manual. It is intended to assist users in locating information by providing a simplified alphabetic listing of basic terms.

<u>Term</u>   <u>Report</u>

- A -

Abbreviations	J1930
Agricultural Equipment	
Flashing Warning Lamps	J974
Headlamps	J975
Lighting and Marking	J137
Mounting Brackets, Warning Lamps and Emblems	J725
Slow Moving Vehicle Identification	J943
All-Terrain Vehicle Headlamps	J1623
Alternating Flashers, Warning Lamp	J1054
Accuracy Guidelines, Photometry Laboratory	J1330
Aim Test Machines, Headlamp	J600
Aiming Device, Headlamp	J602
Arm, School Bus Stop	J1133
Automobile Wiring	J1292
Auxiliary	
Driving Lamps	J581
Low Beam Lamps	J582
Front Lamps, Motorcycle	J1306

- B -

Backup Lamps	J593
Switches	J1076
Beam	
Headlamp, Switching	J564
Low, Auxiliary Lamps	J582
Bulb	
Lamp, Retention System	J567
Miniature Lamp	J573
Motorcycle Lamp, Replaceable	J1577

- C -

Cable	
Low Tension Primary	J1128
High Voltage Primary	J1654
Cargo Lamps	J1424
Castings J1647	
Clearance Lamps	J592
Vehicles more than 2032 mm in Width	J204
Code	
Identification	J759
Inspection	J599
Color Specification	J576
Components, Tests for	J575, J2039, J1113/41
Jacketed Cable	J1067

Bibliography of Related International Documents

International Electrotechnical Commission

IEC 61 - Lamp Caps and Holders Together with Gauges for Control of Interchangeability and Safety
IEC 809 - Lamps for Road Vehicles - Dimensional, Electrical and Luminous Requirements
IEC 810 - Lamps for Road Vehicles - Performance Requirements

International Organization for Standardization

ISO 303:1986 - Lighting and Signalling for Motor Vehicles and Trailers
ISO 1185 - Road Vehicles - Electrical Connections Between Towing Vehicles and Towed Vehicles with 24 V Electrical Equipment - Type 24 N (normal)
ISO 1724 - Road Vehicles - Electrical Connections Between Towing Vehicles and Towed Vehicles with 6 or 12 V Electrical Equipment - Type 12 N (normal)
ISO 3267:1991 - Road Vehicles - Headlamp Cleaners
ISO 3559:1976 - Road Vehicles - Working Voltages for Lights Fitted to Motor Vehicles and Their Trailers
ISO 3731 - Road Vehicles - Electrical Connections Between Towing Vehicles and Trailers with 24 V Electrical Equipment - Type 24 S (supplementary)
ISO 3732 - Road Vehicles - Electrical Connections Between Towing Vehicles and Trailers with 6 or 12 V Electrical Equipment - Type 12 S (supplementary)
ISO 4082:1981 - Road Vehicles - Motor Vehicles - Flasher Units
ISO 4092:1988 (B) - Road Vehicles - Electrical Connections Between Towing Vehicles and Trailers - Test Methods and Requirements
ISO 4141 - Road Vehicles - Seven Core Connecting Cable
ISO 4148-1988 - Road Vehicles - Special Warning Lights - Dimensions
ISO 4165:1979 - Road Vehicles - Electrical Connections - Double Pole Connector
ISO 4182:1986 - Road Vehicles - Motor Vehicles - Measurement of Variation of Passing Beam Inclination as a Function of Load
ISO 6742-1:1987 - Cycles - Lighting and Retro-Reflective Devices - Photometric and Physical Requirements - Part 1:Lighting Equipment
ISO 6742-2:1985 - Cycles - Lighting and Retroreflective Devices - Photometric and Physical Requirements - Part 2 - Retroreflective Devices
ISO 6797:1982 - Road Vehicles - Motor Vehicles - Production Conformity Requirements for Flasher Units
ISO 7227-1987 - Road - Lighting and Signalling Devices - Vocabulary (ISO 7227 is needed for definitions in ISO 303)
ISO 7398-1990 - Road Vehicles - Motorcycles - D.C. Flasher Units
ISO 7399-1990 - Road Vehicles - Motorcycles - A.C. Flasher Units
ISO 7400-1990 - Road Vehicles - Mopeds - A.C. Flasher Units
ISO 7588-1983 - Road Vehicles - Relays and Flashers - Mounting and Positioning Dimensions of Male Tabs and Socket Apertures for Relays and Flashers
ISO 7591 - Road Vehicles - Retro-Reflective Registration Plates for Motor Vehicles and Trailers - Specification
ISO 8052-1990 - Road Vehicles - Mopeds - D.C. Flasher Units
ISO 8218-1989 - Road Vehicles - Leveling Devices for Headlamp Dipped Beam
ISO TR8857:1986 - Road Vehicles - Flashers - Functional Allocation of Terminals
ISO TR9819:1991 - Road Vehicles - Comparison Tables of Regulations on Photometric Requirements of Light Signalling Devices
ISO 9987:1990 - Motorcycles - Measurement of Variation of Dipped Beam Inclination as a Function of Load

ISO 10603:1992 - Road Vehicles - Legal Situation Concerning Lighting and Light Signalling Devices
ISO 11460:1993 - Two-Wheeled Motorcycles - Positioning of Lighting and Light Signalling Devices

Bibliography of Related SAE Papers, Books and Manuals

Recent SAE Papers on Lighting

The papers listed below, which relate to motor vehicle lighting subjects, were presented in recent years at SAE National or Section Meetings. For information on or copies of these papers, or those from previous years, contact the SAE Publications Group.

940511 940512 940636 940637* 940638* 940639* 940640 940641* 940643* 941046 941047
* *Included in SP-1033*

950511 950591 950592 950594 950595 950596 950597 950598 950599 950606 950607
950904 950905 950906 950907 950908 950909 950910 950911 950912 950913 950914

960488 960489 960490 960491 960492 960493 960788* 960789* 960790*
* *Included in SP-1155*

Books and Manuals on Lighting Available from SAE

PT-60 Motor Vehicle Lighting
R-164 Automobile Electrical and Electronic Systems
SP-692 Vehicle Lighting Trends
SP-786 Lighting Systems for Motor Vehicles
SP-813 Vehicle Lighting and Driver Visibility for the 80's
SP-857 Vehicle Lighting for Optimal Visibility and Performance
SP-1033 Human Factors - Lighting, Mirrors and User Needs
SP-1081 Fibreoptics for Automotive Lighting
SP-1088 Human Factors in Vehicle Design
SP-1139 Topics in Vehicle Safety Technology
SP-1155 Automotive Design Advancements in Human Factors

Bibliography of Related SAE Aerospace Lighting Documents
(Alphabetic Listing)

Number	Title
	SAE Aircraft Lighting Handbook
ARP 694A	Aerial Refueling Lights - Design Criteria
AS 827	Aircraft Anti-Collision Lights
AIR 512B	Aircraft Cabin Illumination
AS486B	Aircraft Circuit Breaker and Fuse Arrangement
ARP4404	Aircraft Electrical Installations
AIR 1276A	Aircraft Flashtube Anti-Collision Lighting Systems
ARP 1283A	Cargo Compartment Lighting for Transport Category Aircraft and Rotorcraft
AS 4156	Color-Coded Incandescent Flange Base T1 and T1-3/4 Lamps for Voltage Identification
ARP1161	Crew Station Lighting - Commercial Aircraft
AIR1329A	Compatibility of Electrical Connectors
ARP498A	Design, Layout, Criteria - Plastic Integrally Lighted Panels
ARP922	Electroluminescence, Design Criteria and Recommendations for Use in Aerospace Vehicle Crew Station Areas
ARP503E	Emergency Evacuation Illumination
AIR1151	Flight Compartment Glare
ARP4103	Flight Deck Lighting for Commercial Transport Aircraft
ARP712A	Galley Lighting
ARP914A	Glossary of Electrical Connection Terms
ARP711	Illuminated Signs
ARP1048	Instrument and Cockpit Illumination for General Aviation Aircraft
AS264D	Instrument and Cockpit Lighting for Commercial Transport Aircraft
ARP881C	Lamps for Aircraft Lighting
ARP693B	Landing and Taxiing Lights - Design Criteria for Installation
ARP4392	Lighting, Aircraft Exterior, Night Vision Imaging System (NVIS) Compatible
ARP582A	Lighting, Integral, for Aircraft Instruments: Criteria for Design of Red Lighted Instruments
AS8037	Minimum Performance Standard for Aircraft Position Lights
AS8017A	Minimum Performance Standard for Anticollision Light Systems
AIR4168	Night Vision Goggle (NVG) Compatible Light Sources
AIR4169	Night Vision Goggle (NVG) Filters
ARP378A	Passenger Reading Lights
ARP991A	Position and Anti-Collision Lights - Transport Category Airplanes
ARP4102/5	Primary Flight Controls by Electrical Signalling
AIR1106A	Some Factors Affecting Visibility of Aircraft Navigation Lights
AIR1336	Vehicle Electrical Systems
ARP4087	Wing Inspection Lights

(Check with SAE aerospace staff engineers for other new, revised and deleted reports. The above list was derived from the 1996 SAE Aerospace Standards Index.)